LUMINESCENCE
of Organic and
Inorganic Materials

Sponsored by:

Air Force Aeronautical Research Laboratory
Army Research Office, Durham
Office of Naval Research
New York University

New York • London • JOHN WILEY & SONS, INC.

International Conference
New York University
Washington Square

𝔚 𝔭 𝔥

edited by HARTMUT P. KALLMANN
GRACE MARMOR SPRUCH

Wm. Philip Helman

LUMINESCENCE
of Organic and
Inorganic Materials

PREFACE

The purpose of the Luminescence Conference held at New York University was to bring together for the first time on a large scale, workers in the field of inorganics and those in organics. Accordingly, half day sessions were devoted alternately to invited papers on inorganics and organics, and at the end of the conference there was a half day each for general discussion of organic and inorganic systems at which short communications were presented from the floor. In setting forth the proceedings, however, it seemed advisable not to follow the order of the conference program, but rather to divide the book into two categories, organic and inorganic. For a discussion of the fact that this is an unnatural division see the comments of H. Kallmann at the end of the General Discussion of Inorganic Systems. The humorous remarks of N. Riehl which follow those of Kallmann are not to be taken seriously. Photographs exist which prove that participation in organic sessions was not limited to workers in organics; the same holds for inorganics.

Since the deaths of both Georges Destriau and Michael Schön had occurred during the previous year, it was thought appropriate to open the conference with a memorial session to these two outstanding workers in the field. Those talks open this volume.

We were fortunate to have the aid of the Air Force Aeronautical Research Laboratory, the Army Research Office, Durham, and the Office of Naval Research, as well as New York University, in the undertaking. This permitted the extension of invitations to some of the heads of foreign laboratories to bring with them some of their younger coworkers, in the belief that these younger people do not ordinarily get to attend international conferences and might very well stand to profit most from them.

The editors wish to extend their sincere gratitude to Waltraud Wess for her dedicated and more-than-able assistance in the preparation of both the conference and the proceedings, and to F. Brown for his extensive aid in editing. We wish also to thank M. Pope for editorial help.

TABLE OF CONTENTS _____

IN MEMORIAM

ORGANIC SYSTEMS

General Discussion of Organic Systems

Short Communications

INORGANIC SYSTEMS

General Discussion of Inorganic Systems

INTRODUCTORY REMARKS ─────────

I wish to introduce the Proceedings of this Conference on Luminescence with the same words with which I opened the conference itself, "It is only with deep sadness that I stand before you without my good friend Michael Schön at my side. It was in the summer of 1960 that, following an invitation from Schön, several members of my group met with his for a week of seminars on luminescence in organic as well as inorganic materials. Schön and I both felt that the discussions were so fruitful that it would be worthwhile to organize another such seminar the following year, but on a broader scale perhaps. After some discussion we thought the best way to proceed would be to organize an actual conference on luminescence which would be held at New York University.

During the early stages of preparation for the conference, the news reached me that Schön had died suddenly. This tragic event almost put an end to all plans and decisions. But then, after some thought, I decided to go on with the organization of the conference. I decided to go on because Schön and I both had felt so strongly that a meeting on organics and inorganics would be of significant value. So I tried to organize the meeting in the spirit of Schön." The wide response to the conference, the spirited atmosphere which prevailed, and the interesting communications in this volume, allow me to feel that it was right to have done so.

H. K.

Conference Chairman: Hartmut P. Kallmann
Conference Secretary: Grace Marmor Spruch

CHAIRMEN OF THE SESSIONS:

E. J. Bowen - General Discussion of Organic Systems
W. Brandt   - General Discussion of Inorganic Systems
N. Arpiarian
Th. Förster
M. Furst
N. Riehl
M. Shamos
H. Sponer
F. Williams

PARTICIPANTS

ABERS, ELLIOTT L., Admiral Corp., Chicago, Illinois
ABRAHAMSOHN, ILSE, Itek Laboratories, Lexington, Mass.
ADAMS, IRVING, U.S. Army Signal Research & Development
    Labs, Fort Monmouth, N. J.
AFTERGUT, S., General Electric Co., Schenectady, N. Y.
APPLE, E. F., General Electric Co., Cleveland, Ohio
ARPIARIAN, NOUBAR M., Université de Paris, Paris, France
AZUMI, TOHRU, Louisiana State University, Baton Rouge, La.
BALKIN, PAUL, New York University, New York, New York
BANCIE-GRILLOT, MARGUERITE, Université de Paris,
    Paris, France
BANKS, E., Polytechnic Institute of Brooklyn, Brooklyn, N. Y.
BARR, NATHANIEL F., U.S. Atomic Energy Commission,
    Washington, D.C.
BASILE, LOUIS J., Argonne National Laboratory, Argonne,
    Illinois
BASSEIN, LEONA, New York University, New York, New York
BENNETT, RICHARD G., E. I. du Pont de Nemours and Co.,
    Wilmington, Delaware
BERLMAN, ISADORE, Argonne National Laboratory, Argonne, Ill.
BERNSTEIN, B., Loral Electronics Corp., Bronx, New York
BERTHIER, G., Université de Paris, Paris, France
BIRKS, J. B., The University, Manchester, England
BIRMAN, JOSEPH, General Telephone Labs, Bayside, L. I., N.Y.
BLASE, ERNEST F., Edgerton, Germeshausen and Grier, Inc.,
    Goleta, California
BÖER, KARL W., New York University, New York, New York
BOWEN, E. J., Oxford University, Oxford, England
BRANDT, WERNER, New York University, New York, New York
BREITSCHWERDT, KURT G., Remington Rand, Norwalk, Conn.
BRIL, A., Philips Research Labs, Eindhoven, The Netherlands
BRODY, FREDERICK, American Cyanamid Co., Bound Brook,
    N. J.

BRODY, S. S., IBM, New York, New York
BROSER, I., Max Planck Institut, Berlin, Germany
BROSER-WARMINSKY, R., Max Planck Institut, Berlin,
    Germany
BROWN, FELIX H., New York University, New York, N. Y.
BROWN, G. P., General Electric Co., Schenectady, N. Y.
BROYDE, B., New York University, New York, N. Y.
BROYDE, SUSE E., Polytechnic Institute of Brooklyn,
    Brooklyn, N. Y.
BUCK, WARREN L., Argonne National Laboratory, Argonne,
    Illinois
BURGOS, JOSE DEL C., New York University, New York, N.Y.
BUTLER, CHARLES L., Oak Ridge National Laboratory, Oak
    Ridge, Tenn.
BYLER, WILLIAM H., U.S. Radium Corp., Morristown, N. J.
CARLSTON, R., Grumman Aircraft Engineering Corp.,
    Bethpage, L. I., N. Y.
CASAVANT, DOMINIQUE, New York University, New York, N.Y.
CEVA-SEBASTIA, TOMAS, New York University, New York,
    N. Y.
CHERNOW, FRED, M.I.T., Cambridge, Mass.
CHIAO, HENRY, New York University, New York, N. Y.
CIVIT-BREU, ANTON, La Laguna University, Canary Islands,
    Spain
COHEN, ERWIN V., New York University, New York, N. Y.
CONN, JOHN B., Merck and Co., Rahway, N. J.
CONNER, WILLARD P., Hercules Powder Co., Wilmington,
    Delaware
CSAVINSZKY, PETER, General Dynamics/Electronics,
    Rochester, N. Y.
CURIE, DANIEL, Université de Paris, Paris, France
CURIE, GERMAINE, Université de Paris, Paris, France
CUSANO, DOMINIC A., General Electric Co., Schenectady, N.Y.
DARNELL, FREDERICK, E. I. du Pont de Nemours & Co., Inc.,
    Wilmington, Delaware
DEHOUST, OSKAR, Technische Hochschule, München, Germany
DeLAP, JAMES H., Chemstrand Research Center, Inc.,
    Durham, North Carolina
DEL RE, G., RIAS 7212, Baltimore, Md.
DÖLLER, EDITH, Technische Hochschule, Stuttgart, Germany
DONOGHUE, JAMES J., Tektronix, Inc., Beaverton, Oregon
DROPKIN, JOHN J., Polytechnic Institute of Brooklyn,
    Brooklyn, N. Y.
DUBIN, DANIEL, New York University, New York, N. Y.

DUBOIS, JEAN T., Aeronautical Research Laboratory, Wright-
Patterson Air Force Base, Dayton, Ohio
DYMON, JOSEPH J., General Telephone and Electronics Labs,
Flushing, N. Y.
EL-BAYOUMI, M.ASHRAF, M.I.T., Cambridge, Mass.
ENGELMANN, REINHART, CBS Laboratories, Stamford, Conn.
ETTMAN, HENRY L., A. S. Aloe Co., Clayton, Missouri
FARIA. SIXDENIEL, Sylvania Electric Products Co.,Towanda,Pa.
FARRAN, GEORGE, Sylvania Elec. Prod.,Inc., Seneca Falls,N.Y.
FELDMAN, HERBERT, New York University, New York, N.Y.
FERGUSON, JAMES L., Westinghouse Electric Research Labs,
Pittsburgh, Pa.
FERNANDEZ, MANUEL, Ingénieur École Supérieure
d'Électricité, Paris, France
FEUER, IRVING, Canrad Precision Industries, New York, N.Y.
FÖRSTER, TH., Technische Hochschule, Stuttgart, Germany
FOWLER, ALAN B., IBM Research Labs, Yorktown, N. Y.
FRANCK, JAMES, University of Chicago, Chicago, Illinois and
Durham, N. C.
FRIED, ALVIN P., Hughes Research Corp., Santa Monica, Calif.
FROELICH, HERMAN C., General Electric Co., Cleveland, Ohio
FRONK, JOHANN, G. E. Space Science Lab., Philadelphia, Pa.
FRYSHMAN, BERNARD, New York University, New York, N.Y.
FUJIMORI, EIJI, Cambridge Research Center, Cambridge, Mass.
FURST, MILTON, Department d'Électronique, C.E.N. Saclay,
France
GAGLIANO, ANTOINE, Université de Paris, Paris, France
GALATI, DENNIS ERIC, Heart Disease Research Foundation,
Lawrence, L. I., N. Y.
GANS, F., École Normale Supérieure, Paris, France
GAULÉ, GERHART K., U.S. Army Signal Research and Develop-
ment Agency, Fort Monmouth, N. J.
GILL, JAMES E., Stanford University, Stanford, Calif.
GILMAN, PAUL, Eastman Kodak Co., Rochester, N. Y.
GOLDBERG, PAUL, General Telephone and Electronics Labs,
Bayside, L. I., N. Y.
GOLDMAN, WERNER, New York University, New York, N. Y.
GOODMAN, JEROME, Nuclear Research Assoc., Inc., Hunters
Point, L. I., N. Y.
GRABNER, L., IBM Research Labs, Yorktown Heights, N. Y.
GRAJCAR, LYDIE, Université de Paris, Paris, France
GREEN, MICHAEL E., Yale University, New Haven, Conn.
GREENBERG, ARTHUR, New York University, New York, N.Y.

GREENBERG, IRVING N., U.S. Army Signal Research and
    Development Agency, Fort Monmouth, N. J.
GRILLOT, EDMOND, Université de Paris, Paris, France
GRONER, WARREN, New York University, New York, N. Y.
GROSS, GORDON E., Midwest Research Institute, Kansas City,
    Missouri
GROSS, RICHARD A., New York University, New York, N. Y.
HAAK, F. A., Hughes Research Labs, Malibu, Calif.
HALON, BERNARD, New York University, New York, N. Y.
HALPERIN, A., Mellon Institute, Pittsburgh, Pa.
HALSTED, RICHARD E., General Electric Co., Schenectady,
    N. Y.
HALVERSON, FREDERICK, American Cyanamid Co.,
    Stamford, Conn.
HAMMOND, DAVID A., Harshaw Chemical Co., Cleveland,
    Ohio
HANSEN, P. ARNE, University of Maryland, College Park, Md.
HANSON, V. F., E. I. du Pont de Nemours and Co., Wilmington,
    Delaware
HAUPTMAN, M., Grumman Aircraft Eng. Corp., Bethpage,
    N. Y.
HAYAKAWA, SOHACHIRO, New York University, New York,
    N. Y.
HEIN, D. W., American Cyanamid Co., Bound Brook, N. J.
HERTZBERG, MARTIN, Republic Aviation Corp., Farming-
    dale, L. I., N. Y.
HIRAYAMA, FUMIO, Argonne National Laboratory, Argonne,
    Illinois
HOCHSTRASSER, ROBIN M., Florida State University,
    Tallahassee, Fla.
HORANI, MARCEL, Université de Paris, Paris, France
HORIKIRI, S., New York University, New York, N. Y.
HORNIG, A. W., Baird-Atomic, Inc., Cambridge, Mass.
HOSLER, JOHN F., American Cyanamid Co., Bound Brook, N.J.
HOWERTON, H. K., American Instrument Co., Inc., Silver
    Spring, Md.
HUBBARD, CHARLES J., Airborne Instruments Lab.,
    Huntington, N. Y.
IBUKI, S., Mitsubishi Electric Corp., Amagasaki, Japan
ISAKSON, FRANK B., Office of Naval Research, Washington, D.C.
IVEY, H.F., Westinghouse Electric Corp., Bloomfield, N. J.
JAFFE, SHERMAN, New York University, New York, N. Y.
JAFFE, P. M., Westinghouse Electric Corp., Nutley, N. J.

JOHNSON, PETER D., General Electric Co., Schenectady, N.Y.
KALLMANN, HARTMUT P., New York University, New York,
    N. Y.
KAINER, SELIG, New York University, New York, N. Y.
KAZAN, B., Hughes Research Labs, Malibu, California
KEARNS, DAVID, M.I.T., Cambridge, Mass.
KECK, PAUL H., General Telephone and Electronics
    Laboratories, Inc., Bayside, L. I., N. Y.
KEDESDY, H.H., U.S. Army Signal Research and Development
    Labs, Fort Monmouth, N. J.
KEPLER, R. GLEN, E. I. du Pont de Nemours and Co.,
    Wilmington, Delaware
KHAN, AHSAN ULLAH, Polytechnic Institute of Brooklyn,
    Brooklyn, N. Y.
KLEINERMAN, MARCOS, Louisiana State University, Baton
    Rouge, La.
KORSAKOFF, LEONARD, RCA Research Labs, Princeton, N.J.
KOURY, FREDERIC, Sylvania Lighting Products Co., Salem,
    Mass.
KRAMER, BERNARD, New York University, New York, N. Y.
KRASNANSKY, VICTOR J., New York University, New York,
    N. Y.
KRESCH, ALAN J., National Cash Register Co., Dayton, Ohio
KRISTIANPOLLER, N.N., Hebrew University, Jerusalem, Israel
KROPP, JOHN L., University of Notre Dame, Notre Dame, Ind.
KRYSZEWSKI, MARIAN, Polytechnic Institute of Brooklyn,
    Brooklyn, N. Y.
KUPFERBERG, CLARISSA, New York University, New York,
    N. Y.
KURTZ, RAYMOND J., General Instrument Corp., Newark, N.J.
LAFKAS, CONSTANTINE, New York University, New York, N.Y.
LAMBE, JOHN, Ford Motor Co., Dearborn, Michigan
LaPAGLIA, S. R., Aeronautical Research Laboratory, Wright-
    Patterson Air Force Base, Dayton, Ohio
LEACH, SYDNEY, Université de Paris, Paris, France
LEE, J. W., Johns Hopkins University, Baltimore, Maryland
LEFEBVRE, ROLAND, Centre de Mecanique Ondulatoire
    Appliquée, Paris, France
LEGOWSKI, STANISLAW, Brandeis University, Waltham, Mass.
LELL, EBERHARD, Bausch and Lomb, Inc., Oak Ridge, Tenn.
LEMPICKI, A., General Telephone Laboratory, Bayside, L.I.,
    N. Y.
LEVENTHAL, EDWIN, New York University, New York, N. Y.

LIEBSON, WILBUR, U.S. Army Engineer Research and
    Development Labs, Ft. Belvoir, Virginia
LIM, EDWARD C., Loyola University, Chicago, Illinois
LINSCHITZ, HENRY, Brandeis University, Waltham, Mass.
LIPPERT, ERNST, Technische Hochschule, Stuttgart, Germany
LIPSETT, F. R., National Research Council, Ottawa, Canada
LIPSKY, SANFORD, University of Minnesota, Minneapolis, Minn.
LIU, DAVID C., NASA Lewis Research Center, Cleveland, Ohio
LIVINGSTON, ROBERT, University of Minnesota, Minneapolis,
    Minn.
LOEBNER, EGON E., RCA Laboratories, Princeton, N. J.
LOHMANN, WILLI, Westinghouse Electric Corp., Livingston,
    N. J.
LOHMANN, WOLFGANG, University of Arkansas Medical
    Center, Little Rock, Arkansas
LUCHNER, KARL M., Technische Hochschule, München,
    Germany
McALLISTER, W. A., Westinghouse Electric Corp., Morris-
    town, N. J.
McCLAINE, LESLIE A., Arthur D. Little, Inc., San Francisco,
    California
McCLURE, DONALD S., RCA Laboratories, Princeton, N. J.
McGLYNN, SEAN P., Louisiana State University, Baton
    Rouge, La.
MAGNANTE, PETER, New York University, New York, N. Y.
MARK, PETER, Polaroid Corp., Cambridge, Mass.
MARKO, ALBERT, Loral Electric Corp., Bronx, N. Y.
MARSHALL, WILLIAM J., E. I. du Pont de Nemours and Co.,
    Wilmington, Delaware
MATTLER, JOSEPH, Université de Paris, Paris, France
MELAMED, NATHAN T., Westinghouse Electric Corp.,
    Pittsburgh, Pa.
METLAY, MAX, General Electric Co., Schenectady, N. Y.
MEYER, AXEL, Oak Ridge National Laboratory, Oak Ridge,
    Tenn.
MICHAELSON, STUART, New York University, New York, N.Y.
MIKUS, F. F., Sylvania Electric Products Co., Towanda, Pa.
MOCHEL, VIRGIL D., Corning Glass Works, Corning, N. Y.
MOOMAW, WILLIAM R., M.I.T., Cambridge, Mass.
MORGAN, DANIEL, New York University, New York, N. Y.
MURRAY, R. B., Oak Ridge National Laboratory, Oak Ridge,
    Tenn.

MURTY, N. R. University of Notre Dame, Notre Dame, Indiana
NEUMARK, GERTRUDE F., Philips Laboratories, Irvington,
    N. J.
NICKERSON, JOHN W., General Telephone and Electronics
    Laboratories, Bayside, L. I., N. Y.
NISHIJIMA, YASUNORI, Kyoto University, Kyoto, Japan
NORTHROP, JOHN A., Los Alamos Scientific Laboratory,
    Los Alamos, N. Mex.
O'DWYER, MICHAEL, Florida State University, Tallahassee,
    Florida
OHLMANN, ROBERT C., Westinghouse Research Laboratories,
    Pittsburgh, Pa.
ORENSTEIN, ALBERT, New York University, New York, N. Y.
OSTER, GERALD, Polytechnic Institute of Brooklyn, Brooklyn,
    N. Y.
OSTER, GISELA KALLMANN, Polytechnic Institute of Brooklyn,
    Brooklyn, N. Y.
PALILLA, FRANK, General Telephone and Electronics Labor-
    atories, Maspeth, L. I., N. Y.
PARIS, JEAN P., E. I. du Pont de Nemours and Co., Wilmington,
    Delaware
PARISER, RUDOLPH, E. I. du Pont de Nemours and Co.,
    Wilmington, Delaware
PETERS, ROBERT R., Heart Disease Research Foundation,
    New York, N. Y.
POLLAK, PETER I., Merck and Co., Rahway, N. J.
POPE, MARTIN, New York University, New York, N. Y.
PORTER, GERALD, University of British Columbia, Vancouver,
    British Columbia
POTTER, RALPH M., General Electric Corp., Cleveland, Ohio
PRESENT, GERALD, New York University, New York, N. Y.
RANBY, P. W., Thorn Electrical Industries Ltd., Wembley,
    England
RAUHUT, MICHAEL M., American Cyanamid Co., Stamford,
    Conn.
RAVICH, LEONARD E., Itek Laboratories, Lexington, Mass.
REINTJES, JOHN W., U. S. Biological Laboratory, Beaufort,
    N. C.
REISFELD, MARTIN J., Los Alamos Scientific Laboratory,
    Los Alamos, N. Mex.
RENEKER, D. H., E. I. du Pont de Nemours and Co.,
    Wilmington, Delaware
RENNERT, JOSEPH, New York University, New York, N. Y.

RHODES, WILLIAM, Florida State University, Tallahassee,
    Florida
RIEHL, NIKOLAUS, Technische Hochschule, München, Germany
ROBEY, RICHARD F., Esso Research Center, Linden, N. J.
ROPP, R. C., Sylvania Electric Products, Towanda, Pa.
ROSENTHAL, A. H., Kollsman Instrument Corp., Elmhurst,
    L. I., N. Y.
ROSOFF, MORTON, IBM - Watson Labs, New York, N. Y.
RUMP, BJÖRN S., American Cyanamid Co., Stamford, Conn.
SCHAUFELE, ROBERT F., Sylvania Electric Products Co.,
    Towanda, Pa.
SCHMILLEN, ALBERT, Giessen University, Giessen, Germany
SCHNEIDER, W. G., National Research Council, Ottawa, Ontario
SCOTT, JOHN M. W., American Cyanamid Co., Stamford, Conn.
SEAMAN, DAVID, Oxford University, Oxford, England
SEGAL, ALVAN, New York University, New York, N. Y.
SEARLE, NORMA ZIZMER, American Cyanamid Co.,
    Stamford, Conn.
SELIGER, H. H., Johns Hopkins University, Baltimore, Md.
SERRE, JOSIANE, École Normale Supérieure, Paris, France
SHAMOS, MORRIS H., New York University, New York, N. Y.
SHARMA, J., Princeton University, Princeton, N. J.
SHIONOYA, SHIGEO, University of Tokyo, Tokyo, Japan
SHRADER, ROSS E., RCA Laboratories, Princeton, N. J.
SHORTT, BRIAN, CBS Laboratories, Inc., Stamford, Conn.
SHURGAN, JOEL, Duro Test Corp., North Bergen, N. J.
SIDRAN, MIRIAM, Grumman Aircraft Engineering Corp.,
    Bethpage, L. I., N. Y.
SILVER, MARVIN, Army Research Office, Durham, N. C.
SIZMANN, RUDOLF, Technische Hochschule, München, Germany
SMITH, M., American Cyanamid Co., Stamford, Conn.
SOXMAN, E. J., Servomechanisms, Inc., Goleta, Calif.
SPONER, HERTHA, Duke University, Durham, N. C.
SPORER, ALFRED H., IBM Research Labs, San Jose, Calif.
SPRUCH, GRACE MARMOR, New York University, New York,
    N. Y.
STAMM, ROBERT F., American Cyanamid Co., Stamford, Conn.
STOCKMAN, DAVID, General Electric Co., Syracuse, N. Y.
STROBL, ALEXANDER, Stroblite Co., New York, N. Y.
STROCK, LESTER W., Sylvania Electric Co., Towanda, Pa.
STUPP, EDWARD H., IBM Research Center, Peekskill, N. Y.
SUCHOW, LAWRENCE, IBM Research Labs, Yorktown
    Heights, N. Y.

SUNDHEIM, BENSON R., New York University, New York, N.Y.
SUSSMAN, ALAN, RCA Laboratories, Princeton, N. J.
SWINEHART, C. F., Harshaw Chemical Company, Cleveland,
  Ohio
TAVLA, MARIA, AF Cambridge Research Labs, Cambridge,
  Mass.
TAYLOR, ROBERT C., CBS Laboratories, Stamford, Conn.
THIELENS, EMIL H., CBS Laboratories, Stamford, Conn.
THOMAS, JOSEPHUS Jr., E. I. du Pont de Nemours and Co.,
  Wilmington, Delaware
THOMAS, MARTHA J. B., Sylvania Electric Products Co.,
  Salem, Mass.
THORINGTON, LUKE, Duro-Test Corp., North Bergen, N. J.
THORNTON, W. A., Westinghouse Electric Corp., Bloomfield,
  N. J.
TITLE, R. S., IBM Research Center, Yorktown Heights, N. Y.
TOBIN, MARVIN, American Cyanamid Co., Stamford, Conn.
TRESTER, SEYMOUR, New York University, New York, N. Y.
TSOU, K. C., Borden Chemical Co., Philadelphia, Pa.
VAN BROEKHOVEN, JACOB, Westinghouse Electric Corp.,
  Bloomfield, N. J.
VAN GOOL, W., Philips Labs, Eindhoven, The Netherlands
VAN SCIVER, WESLEY, University of Puerto Rico, Rio
  Piedras, Puerto Rico
VOGEL, H., Technische Hochschule, München, Germany
VOGEL, MARCEL J., IBM, San Jose, Calif.
WACHTEL, ANSELM, Westinghouse Electric Corp., Bloom-
  field, N. J.
WACHTER, PETER, New York University, New York, N. Y.
WAKFER, DAGNY, New York University, New York, N. Y.
WALLACE, HENRY S., The Martin Company, Orlando, Fla.
WALY, A., Stamford, Connecticut
WANG, SHIH-PING, National Radiac, Inc., Newark, N. J.
WATSON, ROBERT B., Army Research Office, Washington, D.C.
WEINREB, ARYE, Hebrew University, Jerusalem, Israel
WEISS, RONALD D., New York University, New York, N. Y.
WELLER, ALBERT, Technische Hochschule, Stuttgart,
  Germany
WHITE, CHARLES E., University of Maryland, College Park,
  Md.
WHITE, RAYMOND J., New York University, New York, N. Y.
WILKINSON, FRANCIS, Oxford University, Oxford, England

WILLIAMS, FERD E., University of Delaware, Newark, Del.
WINTERS, EARL D., M.I.T., Cambridge, Mass.
WINSBERG, SUZANNE, Kollsman Instrument Corp., Elm-
    hurst, L. I., N. Y.
WIRTH, H., University of Mainz, Mainz, Germany
WITTERHOLT, V. G., E. I. du Pont de Nemours and Co., Inc.,
    Wilmington, Delaware
WOTHERSPOON, NEIL, New York University, New York, N. Y.
WYATT, SAMUEL B., U. S. Radium Corp., Whippany, N. J.
WYMAN, GEORGE M., Army Research Office, Durham, N. C.
YGUERABIDE, JUAN, University of Notre Dame, Notre Dame,
    Indiana
ZWICK, MARTIN, Office of Naval Research, Washington, D.C.

IN MEMORIAM: MICHAEL SCHÖN
(1903 - 1960)

N. Riehl

Technische Hochschule München

It is about one year ago that we lost Michael Schön, a physicist of eminence in luminescence research and a man whose death was deplored by very many colleagues and friends.

At the beginning of his adult life, Michael Schön wanted to devote himself not to physics, but to philosophy and theology. Born in 1903 at Wiesbaden, he finished his education there in a humanist school and then went on to study at the Seminary of the Universitas Gregoriana in Rome. However, he then went to Munich and began his studies in physics. It was the period when Willy Wien and Arnold Sommerfeld taught there. Schön finished his university studies and received his doctorate for a dissertation on the total reflection of long wavelength X-rays. The time he spent in Munich was, in two respects, of decided importance for his later life. Scientifically, his interest in the processes of light emission was awakened by Sommerfeld. In the personal and private sphere, it was the joyful friendly atmosphere of Munich which complemented Schön's own character so very well. Schön became an apologist for the town. His love for Munich later, in the post-war years, exerted some influence on his own professional decisions as well as on those of some of his friends.

After having finished his university studies, Schön remained in Munich for two more years in the private laboratory of Baron Hirsch in his castle *Planegg* and worked on the light emission of canal rays. Then, he worked for about two years in the

Physikalisch-Technische Reichsanstalt, the German "Bureau of Standards", and in 1935 joined the Osram research laboratory in Berlin. After some investigations on gas discharge he became interested in the luminescence of crystal phosphors, which was to become the main subject of his scientific research.

I believe it is not necessary to describe to this audience Schön's extremely important work in luminescence. But I should like to say a few words to characterize his work. I was witness to his first endeavors in the field of luminescence. Even his earliest proposals for a theory of crystal phosphor luminescence were in excellent accordance, at least qualitatively, with our experimental findings, especially those on ZnS. Our first discussion convinced me that we had met each other at just the right moment. The one could complete to some degree the work of the other. That day saw the birth of our scientific friendship, which led later on to a personal friendship which lasted for the rest of his life. One might say that that moment was also the end of the Lenard period of luminescence. Lenard's old conceptions and pictures could be replaced by new considerations which were in accord with modern physics. These first attempts led immediately to a qualitative explanation of almost all the common effects in crystal phosphors: the transfer of energy; the difference between excitation of the host-lattice and excitation of the luminescence centers; the dependence of the efficiency upon the density of excitation and temperature; the influence of these factors on the relative intensities of different emission bands in the "two-band phosphors" and so on. Later, Schön attempted to work out a quantitative theory of these effects, and obtained important new results. During this period he maintained contact with other groups outside Germany. Among these groups the Dutch group in Eindhoven must be mentioned in particular because of the similarity in the direction of their work. In spite of the fact that the behavior of zinc sulfide could be quite well understood, qualitatively, the quantitative theory was less successful, probably because of the complicated character of the lattice anomalies in these phosphors. Schön often said: "Zinc sulfide has not yet learned the electron-kinetic theory of luminescence." Thus, zinc sulfide became something like an 'unhappy love'. It must be confessed, however, that this substance is an unhappy love not of Schön alone.

One of these unsolved problems which occupied Schön's mind in the last years may be mentioned briefly. It is the theory of glow curves in zinc sulfide. The simple zone theory of crystal phosphors leads to the conclusion that thermal equilibrium between the different traps can be established if the electrons are not frozen in. If the traps are not completely filled, one must expect the appearance of only one glow peak, because the electron set free from the shallow traps will be retrapped by the deeper traps. If the population of electrons in the traps is extremely low (extremely weak excitation), one observes only one glow peak, which corresponds to the deepest traps. Thus far, the effects are understandable, and they indicate the possibility of retrapping. But at stronger excitation one observes the three glow peaks of the common ZnS:Cu phosphor, even when the traps are far from being completely filled. Schön suggested tentatively that the spatial distribution of different traps in an actual ZnS crystal is not homogeneous, so that the retrapping of electrons is somewhat hindered. Judging from our last observations on the physico-chemical nature of centers and traps, which I shall discuss later in another communication, such an assumption is conceivable.

Let us return to the life of Michael Schön. During the first post-war years he lived in Mosbach, in Southwest Germany, as the head of one of the Osram laboratories. In 1947 he became Professor at the University of Heidelberg, and in 1955 he moved to Munich. There, at the Technical University of Munich, he built up a large luminescence group. He enjoyed once again his beloved Munich. But he enjoyed his numerous scientific and personal contacts with his friends in other countries no less. Many of the members of this audience remember the successful conference in Garmisch-Partenkirchen, which was arranged mainly by Michael Schön. I believe everybody enjoyed his hospitality there; it was always extremely friendly, but never obtrusive. In his last years he maintained a very close contact with the Physics Department of New York University, our host today. I am sure that the friendship, founded by Michael Schön and our host, between the solid state people in this institution and those in Munich, will survive our Michael Schön for a long time.

It is impossible to characterize the life of Michael Schön without mentioning the specific conditions in Germany during the last three decades. Schön was not only a decided opponent of Nazism, but of all the other varieties of dictatorship as well. It was typical of him not only to like and enjoy the liberal way of life, but to believe in the inner power of liberalism, in spite of all the temporary defeats of the liberal system. Let us hope that the future will verify this belief of our friend Michael Schön.

IN MEMORIAM: GEORGES DESTRIAU
(1903 - 1960)

J. Mattler

Faculté des Sciences de Paris

For more than fifteen years, I worked in direct collaboration with Professor Destriau at the Laboratoire de Luminescence in Paris. Through almost daily contact with him, I had the opportunity to appreciate his human qualities as much as the richness and the originality of his scientific work. It is a great honor for me today to pay homage to his memory.

Georges Destriau was born in Bordeaux on August 1, 1903.

In 1926, he received his degree in Engineering from the Ecole Centrale des Arts et Manufactures and then worked in an industrial concern, where he dealt with X-ray installations. He published a technical book entitled "Applied Physics of X-Ray Plants"; in this book he incorporated his own contribution to the field of radiological techniques and X-ray equipment.

Attracted by scientific research, he left industry in 1932 and entered the Laboratory of Marie Curie at the Institut du Radium to prepare a Doctor's thesis.

He carried out research work on the distribution of the trajectories of α particles in air by means of scintillations. The fluctuations obtained by this method were greater than those determined by other methods of observation, for example, the Wilson cloud chamber. Destriau showed that this difference was due to the fact that in addition to their own path fluctuations

there were, in addition, fluctuations in the number of luminescence centers excited by the α particles.

In this context, he carried out research on sulfides sensitive
to α particles. He attempted to establish correlations between
the mechanism for scintillation and other modes of luminescence in zinc sulfides. It was during these experiments, when
he tried to compare the ionization of the crystal lattice by
α particles with that by electric fields, that, in 1936, he observed the emission of light from zinc sulfide under the single
action of varying electric fields.

This was the discovery of a fundamental phenomenon, uni-
versally called today electroluminescence or the Destriau
effect.

He realized the importance of his discovery, and, encouraged
by the physicists Aimé Cotton, Maurice Curie and Jean Perrin,
he immediately oriented his research towards the study of this
new phenomenon.

Having tested systematically a large number of luminescent samples of different origin, he showed that the effect exists
in zinc sulfides, in zinc oxides and weakly in some silicates.
Among these different specimens there was a zinc sulfide activated by copper and prepared by Güntz, bearing the number 13,
which was strongly sensitive to electric fields. This product,
which could not be reproduced, as it was the result of a calcina-
tion accident during its preparation, was the one mainly employed
by Destriau for his first investigations on electroluminescence.

As early as 1937 his first electroluminescent cells were
realized. They were a kind of condenser, first cylindrical and
then plane, in which one of the electrodes was transparent, and
where a sensitive sulfide was incorporated in the dielectric.
The transparent electrode was a mica sheet covered with a mixture of salt water and glycerine, while the phosphor was embedded in oil and later on in a solid insulator.

Certainly, as far as appearance, convenience and luminous efficiency were concerned, these early cells were far from
the present types, but they permitted him to establish the principal laws of electroluminescence.

First of all he showed that the emission L increases exponentially with the field intensity according to a relationship of the
form $L \sim \exp(-b/E)$. This experimental law he interpreted
theoretically by assuming that in the crystal the electric field
accelerates the conduction electrons until they acquire enough
energy to excite the luminescence centers.

Taking into account the conductivity ρ and the dielectric
constant K of the luminescent material, Destriau also calculated

the variations of the internal active field E as a function of the
applied voltage V. This mathematical analysis permitted him
to foresee the form of the brightness waves. He found that they
were out of phase with the potential waves, leading them by an
angle ϕ given by the expression $\tan \phi = 4\pi/K\rho\omega$. This was confirmed in 1944 when he observed the brightness waves for the
first time.

To plot these brightness waves, he conceived of a mechanical device, particularly ingenious, because at that time he had
no double beam cathode ray oscillograph or electronic com-
mutator at his disposal: a metallic disc, with a hole near its
edge, was rotated by a synchronous electric motor and unmasked
the E. L. cell always at the same point of the corresponding
sinusoïdal curve of the applied voltage. By turning the stator of
the motor, it was possible to obtain, point by point, the brightness wave. The measurements of luminosity were exclusively
visual and to plot one curve took nearly a complete day. However the waves established in this way were as good as those
obtained later by more perfect devices. They already showed
the existence of a secondary peak, the inequality of the consecutive principal peaks corresponding to the change in direction of
the applied field, the dephasing of the internal field with respect
to the external field, the distortion of the waves by the action of
the applied voltage and their complexities in the case of some
electroluminescent substances (See J. Physique et le Radium,
Vol. 6, p. 227, 1945).

Again in the field of electroluminescence, G. Destriau carried out his fruitful researches on the preparation of more
sensitive powders, on the activator distribution in the mass of
the crystal, on the emission spectra and their modification with
the intensity and frequency of the electric field, on the mean
life of centers in excited states in correlation with the continuous
and periodic components of brightness waves, etc.

During the first ten years, the investigations in electroluminescence were performed exclusively in France, by Destriau
and his coworkers. Partly due to the poor diffusion of French
scientific publications during the war and partly to the fact that
the new effect met with much scepticism, all the tenacity and
faith of the author were necessary to convince the incredulous.

In 1947 Professor N. F. Mott saw various demonstrations in
the Laboratoire de Luminescence in Paris. He suggested to
Destriau that he publish a review article in the Philosophical
Magazine (Vol. 38, p. 700, 774 and 880, 1947). This paper immediately stimulated great interest in electroluminescence in
various countries, the U.S.A. in particular. This interest was

due to the fact that this phenomenon offered new possibilities of research in solid state physics and also because of the practical applications expected from it, especially in lighting, since there is a direct conversion of electrical energy into light, without intermediate energy transformations. At present, according to a recent paper by H. F. Ivey, about 1300 articles and patents have been published on electroluminescence and related topics (Journ. Electrochem. Soc., Vol. 108, p. 590, 1961).

Georges Destriau, the father of pure electroluminescence, also discovered or studied other effects of electric fields on luminescence:

(1) The momentary illumination, or Gudden and Pohl effect, in which the field liberates electrons trapped during previous excitation, resulting in a temporary enhancement of phosphorescence or photoluminescence under the action of electric fields.

(2) The electro-extinction effect, that he mentioned for the first time in 1943, in which the field favors the non-radiative transitions and consequently reduces more or less the photoluminescence of these phosphors.

(3) In 1954, in collaboration with his son Michel Destriau, he discovered the electro-enhancement effect which consists in a permanent increase of X-ray photoluminescence of certain Mn-activated sulfides, when they are subjected to electric fields during X-ray irradiation. In this case, quite weak fields are sufficient to obtain an appreciable light gain and it does not seem possible to interpret it by a mechanism based on electron acceleration. G. Destriau devoted his last years exclusively to the study of this new phenomenon because he visualized the possibility of making light amplifiers of great simplicity which would allow one to reduce the X-ray doses in radiological examination and also to increase contrast in images. Almost at the same time, another type of enhancement effect was discovered, independently, by F. E. Williams and D. A. Cusano.

Thus the main scientific activity of G. Destriau was concerned with electroluminescence and the action of electric fields on photoluminescence. By its remarkable unity, his work is a model of harmony and perseverance. However, he was always against extreme specialization and it must be pointed out that he made original contributions in many other fields of physics, in relation to the teaching work of which he was in charge: the propagation of electric charges in weakly conducting thin films; the realization of quasi-monochromatic quarter-wave plates and the study of achromatic interference fringes; the investigation of electric fields with the help of the Kerr effect;

the metal-solution potential difference through thin metallic films; the viscosity of mercury under the action of magnetic fields; the study of eagres, etc.

Side by side with his career as a researcher, Destriau was a remarkable teacher. He started as an Assistant at the University of Bordeaux, then was nominated Chef de Travaux at Caen, then Professor at Poitiers, and finally was appointed as Professor at the Faculté des Sciences de Paris. His lectures on general physics were attended by a large number of students, who highly appreciated the qualities of his teaching and had profound regard for his personality.

He was also a great traveller and took frequent trips in France and to foreign countries. He often visited the U.S.A., on the occasion of scientific conferences or for a stay at the research laboratory of Westinghouse Electric Corporation at Bloomfield, N. J., where he had been a consultant for several years.

I had the pleasure of accompanying him on his last trip in May, 1959. He had the feeling that it was to be his last visit to the United States and he was deeply moved in seeing the first practical realization of electroluminescence, an expression of his long and patient researches.

When his work was well recognized, he became a member of many French and foreign scientific societies, Doctor honoris causa of the University of Louvain, and received the scientific grand prix of the City of Paris. However these honors never changed his great modesty, because he never looked for honors. He found in the fulfilment of his task as a scientist and professor and in the affection of his family all the necessary encouragement to support the cruelty of his illness, which he knew was incurable.

Georges DESTRIAU died on January 21, 1960, in his native city where he always liked to live among his large family. His premature death, in perfect intellectual vigor, was received with consternation by the scientific world, where he was well known for the originality and importance of his work. His death was still more deeply felt by all those who were associated with him, friends, students or collaborators, who will always cherish the memory of his acute intelligence, his kindness and the nobility of his character.

ORGANIC SYSTEMS

THE PRIMARY PHOTOCHEMICAL STEP IN PHOTOSYNTHESIS:
A COMPARISON OF TWO THEORIES

James Franck, Department of Chemistry (Fels Fund),

University of Chicago, J. L. Rosenberg, Department of Chemistry,

University of Pittsburgh*, and

C. Weiss, Jr., Conant Chemical Laboratory, Harvard University‡

ABSTRACT

Observations of fluorescence, afterglow and absorption spectra of chlorophyll *in vivo* and *vitro,* together with chemical kinetic data on photosynthesis rates under a variety of external conditions, have led the authors to a theory of the primary photochemical steps of photosynthesis.

Another theory, based on evidence of photoionization of chlorophyll in the chloroplasts, has been proposed several times and recently has been presented in more detailed form by Calvin *et al.*

This paper contains a survey of the status of both theories, and a comparison of their conclusions with the available experimental evidence.

This paper contains a very condensed comparison of two theories for the photochemical steps of photosynthesis. The one held by the present authors assumes that light absorbed by the chloroplast pigments is utilized according to the usual rules of photochemistry while the second is based on the assumption that a photo-induced ionization of chlorophyll molecules and the migration of charges play an essential role in photosynthesis. We discuss our theory first.

---

*These studies were aided by a contract between the Office of Naval Research, Department of the Navy, and the University of Pittsburgh, NR304-416.

‡C. Weiss is indebted to the National Institutes of Health for a summer research fellowship which supported this work.

11

Every theory of the photochemical step of photosynthesis must be based on the biochemical progress made with the help of C^{14} as tagging agent. It furthermore must take into account our knowledge of the structure of the chloroplasts. An important result of the experiments with tagged CO_2 is the proof that a 5-carbon sugar, ribulose diphosphate, acts as the acceptor for the CO_2 that is to be reduced.[1] The compound or compounds which result from the carboxylation of the 5-carbon sugar are ultimately reduced. The 6-carbon sugar made in this way reproduces ribulose diphosphate by the Calvin-Benson cycle. Thus the CO_2-acceptor utilized in photosynthesis is also produced by it. During a dark pause the concentration of the 5-carbon sugar is lowered practically to zero. It is consumed by a dark reaction of CO_2 with ribulose diphosphate in which the resulting substance decays quickly into two phosphoglyceric acid molecules. Thus at the beginning of irradiation the ribulose diphosphate concentration has to be raised autocatalytically to the level needed for photosynthesis. This is the principal reason for the occurrence of induction periods at the onset of irradiation or even at a sudden increase of the light intensity corresponding to a higher steady-state photosynthetic rate. Whether the 6-carbon compound made by the addition of CO_2 is reduced by the light directly or only after splitting into two phosphoglyceric acid molecules is still an open question.[2] Calvin and Bassham propose that both processes might happen.

The importance of the structural relations within the chloroplast is acknowledged by all workers in the field of photosynthesis. Electron microscopy shows a lamellar structure which develops with the formation of the chlorophyll.[3] Freshly formed chlorophyll, not yet attached to a phytol tail, is adsorbed in the relatively structureless chloroplasts at the surface of lipoproteins. As soon as the tail is attached the layers are formed and the chlorophylls are supposed to migrate into position best described as an ordered monomolecular adsorption layer at the interface of two lipoprotein layers having lipid sides in juxtaposition.[4] Both chlorophylls *a* and *b* might be contained in this layer in the green plants. A third pigment, β-carotene or some other carotenoid of lipophilic character, will also be contained in the neighborhood of this chlorophyll layer. As fluorescence measurements indicate, the energy absorbed by chlorophyll *b* and by carotene are transferred to chlorophyll a by the usual method of energy transfer, sensitized fluorescence

or exciton movement.[5] It seems improbable that the bulk of
all these dyestuffs can take part in photochemical acts because
they could not be in contact with water and its solutes. It is
more likely that excitation energy acquired directly or indirectly by chlorophyll a can be used by transfer to a few chlorophyll molecules in a key position exposed to water. These few
molecules do all the photochemistry and also are responsible
for the fluorescence observed during photosynthesis, while
the protected chlorophyll molecules within the layer are responsible for most of the light absorption. This picture for
the photosynthetic unit is an old one.[6] It originated from observations by Emerson and Arnold on flash saturation.[7]

Much other evidence not discussed here permitted the deduction that the exposed chlorophyll a molecules are in direct
contact with the prosthetic group of a cytochrome.[8-10] The role
ascribed to the cytochrome is to act as an $-OH$ acceptor in the
photosynthetic splitting of water while the H atom is given to
the primary photosynthetic oxidant. Four such acts are involved in photosynthesis. Since quantum yield measurements
together with energy considerations indicate that eight quanta
are needed for the reduction of one CO_2, two quanta must be
used to effect one water-splitting act.[11] A picture thus emerges
in which one photochemical preparatory step might be needed
followed by a second act in which the actual water splitting and
the transfer of H and $-OH$ to their respective acceptors occur.

The question arises as to which excited states of the exposed
chlorophyll a are involved in its direct participation in photochemistry. As is always the case in dyes, only the first excited
singlet or the lowest long-living metastable triplet state can be
utilized. If only the singlet state were involved in the two reactions the ratio of the fluorescence intensity in absence of photochemistry to that observed during optimal use of the energy for
photosynthesis should be a high one. If only the metastable state
could be used in photosynthesis the above fluorescence ratio
should be unity. In this case fluorescence emission of the chlorophyll from the singlet state should be competitive only with the
radiationless transition into the metastable state and would be
independent of the use of the latter, be it phosphorescent emission in the near infrared or photochemistry. The actual observations under suitable conditions show a fluorescence ratio of two.
That is an indication that half of the photochemical acts require
excited singlet energy directly and half metastable state energy.[12]

The concentration of any substances likely to be primary oxidants of photosynthesis is too small to quench the singlet energy by collisions to half its value. We conclude, therefore, that the preparatory step makes use of the energy of the metastable state for collecting the reactants, bringing them together, and performing a photochemical act. This step might store some of the energy chemically but has as its major function the bringing together of the reaction partners into such positions that the next step, the splitting of water and the transfer of H and $-OH$ to the acceptors, could be done by the excited singlet with the least energy of activation.

Without needing so far any special assumption about the nature of the oxidant it seems to us that substances like TPN, present in exceedingly low concentration, cannot well be regarded as the primary oxidant because other substances present in higher concentration would compete successfully with the TPN for the use of metastable state energy. Oxygen, always present during normal photosynthesis and known to be a very efficient user of metastable state energy, would be one of these competing substances.[13] Tentatively we have come to a proposal which involves the formation of an enol complex between the chlorophyll and the oxidant. That enol formation of the chlorophyll itself could be of importance in photosynthesis has been maintained by one of us for a long time.[14] The scheme in Fig. 1 summarizes this proposal. Its merit is that it will fit very well into observations to be discussed further on; its disadvantage is that it contains the assumption that the primary oxidants must be able to possess both keto and enol forms.* Our photochemical scheme leads to the production of a semiquinone-reduction product, XH, from the oxidant X. We assume that two semi-quinone molecules subsequently undergo a dark dismutation reaction of the type, $2XH \rightarrow XH_2 + X$. Such a dismutation is exothermic. Since it is presumably an enzymatic reaction, the energy released might very well be used for the phosphorylations known to be required in the Calvin-Benson cycle.

This picture contains an explanation of the intensity ratio, 2, of the fluorescence. Actually observations do not give this

---

*Footnote added in proof. In the meantime Franck and Rosenberg have formulated a better chemical model for the two reactions which avoids this difficulty and fits even better certain recently found peculiar transient phenomena. This change has very little influence on the conclusions of this paper.

value of the ratio under all conditions. In green plants the factor 2 is observed between idle and fully occupied states of the photosynthetic apparatus if the latter is emptied for the measurement of the fluorescence under idle conditions by: (1) prolonged irradiation in the absence of all CO_2 and O_2, the safest way to empty the photosynthetic unit without disturbing its structure; (2) irradiation with medium intensity after incubation with a poison which completely inactivates an enzyme involved in the photosynthetic CO_2 uptake; (3) emptying the apparatus quickly and temporarily by irradiating after a preceding dark period, i.e., in the absence of ribulose diphosphate. Fig. 2 illustrates an example of case (2). It shows the chlorophyll fluorescence as a function of light intensity for Chlorella algae during optimal photosynthesis and also during complete cyanide inhibition of the photosynthetic carboxylation reaction of ribulose diphosphate. We must keep in mind that the photosynthetic rate in the presence of cyanide is practically normal at low intensities until the compensation of respiration is reached but never rises beyond this value. Correspondingly the fluorescence becomes abnormally high only at intensities surpassing the compensation point. This indicates that below

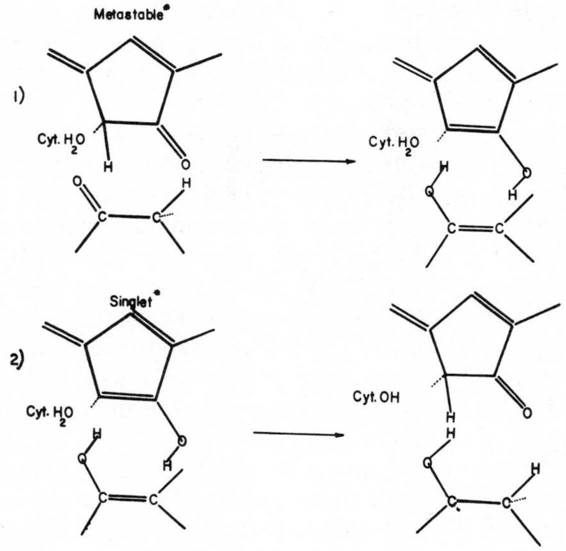

Fig. 1 — Proposed Scheme for the Two Photochemical Steps in Photosynthesis. The upper reaction represents the preparatory step. The lower reaction represents the water-splitting.

compensation substitute oxidants, which are respiratory intermediates, replace the normal photosynthetic oxidant. The
same substitution occurs as a
transient phenomenon at the early
part of the induction period. In
this particular case more information is available about the nature of the substitute oxidants.
At high concentration of CO_2 it
is oxalacetic acid; at low CO_2 it
is probably pyruvic acid.[16] Both
these acids are known to exist
in keto and enol forms.

Deviations from the value 2
for the ratio occur. It can go up
to values as high as 5 under conditions which prevent the excitation energy transfer to the exposed chlorophyll.[17] In such a
case fluorescence of the protected chlorophylls is observed.
Its yield is nearly as high as that
of chlorophyll in organic solvents.
The optimal yield of the exposed
chlorophyll is lowered considerably by contact with the heavy
iron atom of the cytochrome.

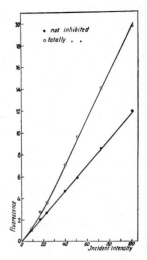

Fig. 2 — Chlorella Fluorescence.
The lower curve is for uninhibited
Chlorella. The upper curve is for
Chlorella under complete cyanide
inhibition. The figure is taken
from Wassink's paper (15).

This point and the influence which oxygen has on the enclosure
of excitation energy will be discussed elsewhere. Of more
direct interest for our present discussion are cases of reversible lowering of fluorescence and photosynthesis rates by external factors, such as reducing the humidity of the air surrounding certain algae living on the bark of trees.[18] Another
way to reduce considerably the quantum yields of both rates and
fluorescence is to irradiate the green cells with light absorbed
by chlorophyll at the long wave-length side of the main red absorption band of chlorophyll *a*.

These phenomena become understandable if we compare the excitation levels of chlorophyll dissolved in polar or non-polar organic solvents and relate them to positions indicated by the absorption spectra of chlorophyll *in vivo*. Fig. 3 gives the positions of the
excitation levels of chlorophyll *a* in polar and non-polar solvents
as indicated by observations of both absorption and emission
spectra. Absolute correctness of these energy level diagrams is

not claimed because the exact values of the levels depend not only on the polarity of the solvents but to some minor degree on the exact nature of the solvent. This set of electronic levels owes its complexity to the fact that chlorophyll has two different systems of electronic transitions which lie very near together, the π-π transitions and the n-π transitions. The former are the normal transitions within the π-electron system of the conjugated rings; the n-π transitions in chlorophyll a are caused by the oxygen bonded to C-9 in the keto form of ring V[21]. One of the non-bonding electrons of

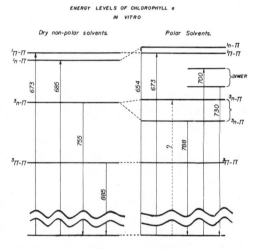

Fig. 3 — Energy Levels of Chlorophyll *in vitro*. The direction of the arrows indicates whether the transition was observed in absorption (↑) or in emission (↓). Transitions are labelled by the wave-lengths, in mμ, of the band maxima. The data for the dimer and for the n-π absorption in polar solvents are taken from Stensby and Rosenberg (20). Other data are from Becker and co-workers (19).

this oxygen atom can be promoted into the π-electron system of the conjugated rings. Though π-π and n-π excitations are not much different energetically they behave differently. The π-π levels experience only a small red shift, not indicated in the diagram, when the non-polar medium is replaced by a polar one. The n-π levels, on the other hand, experience a greater shift toward the blue as far as the absorption spectra are concerned, while the emission spectra show a red shift.[22] The latter fact, related to the Franck-Condon Principle, is often overlooked in the literature. Of particular interest for our present problem is the reversal of the relative positions of the π-π and n-π first excited singlet levels in polar and non-polar solvents. In non-polar solvents free of any trace of moisture the n-π

level lies below the π-π singlet level; quick radiationless transitions from the π-π to n-π occur; and normal π-π fluorescence is not observed at room temperature.[23] Spectroscopy has shown that the n-π level has a greater admixture of triplet character than the π-π levels; thus internal transitions from n-π singlet to n-π triplet are quick and fluorescence emitted from n-π is also not visible at room temperature. At very low temperature n-π fluorescence is expected because a type of energy of activation is necessary for the internal transition into the n-π triplet state. A small activation energy is also necessary to make possible the transition from the π-π singlet to the n-π singlet when the latter lies at a lower level. In polar solvents or in non-polar solvents containing small amounts of polar additives the π-π level is the lower one and its fluorescence occurs.

If we compare the positions of the levels observed *in vivo* with those in Fig. 3 we find that the bulk of light absorption by chlorophyll corresponds to that observed in dry non-polar solvents *in vitro*. French's derivative spectroscopy indicates clearly the presence of an n-π companion to the π-π transition on the long wave-length side of chlorophyll's red absorption band.[24] Its position relative to the π-π level is exactly the same as has been found in non-polar solvents. Also, a weak absorption observed by Rabinowitch *et al.* at about 750 mμ corresponds to the n-π triplet transition observed in emission in dry non-polar solvents.[25] Another weak absorption level found by French at about 695 mμ might not belong to the chlorophyll. Holt found such a peak for chlorophyll oxidized at its vinyl group.[26]

Postponing the discussion of the 700 mμ absorption *in vivo* and *in vitro* first reported by Brody,[27] we want to discuss first an apparent difficulty which results from our conclusion that the protected chlorophylls of the layer are in a dry non-polar surrounding so that the n-π level lies below the π-π level. How, then, can the excitation energy migrate to the exposed chlorophyll undisturbed by the supposedly quick radiationless transitions from the π-π singlet to the n-π singlet and from there to the n-π triplet? Our answer is that the adsorption of the chlorophylls lying flat at the interface of the lipoprotein delays these internal conversions considerably, as is well known from the influence of adsorption on the lifetime of excited states.[28] This, however, need not exclude a process of sensitization of the n-π transition in one molecule by a π-π level of higher energy in a

neighboring molecule. Here the co-planarity of all the chlorophyll molecules in the layer prevents this sensitization. The
transition moments of the π-π states lie in the plane, those of
the n-π state perpendicular to the plane.[21] So long as the surface layer retains its planar orientation the coupling necessary
for the sensitized transition is absent. Also the internal conversion of singlet energy into triplet energy is delayed by the
adsorption. Thus, if n-π states are directly populated by long
wave-length absorption, the n-π singlet energy can move to the
exposed chlorophyll, but will be transferred to it only if the
exposed chlorophyll possesses a suitable acceptor.

The absorption at about 700 mμ indicates a transition which
can be excited by the arriving n-π energy in the exposed chlorophyll. Indeed we regard it as excitation of an n-π singlet lowered
by the immediate neighborhood of reduced cytochrome. Each
n-π excitation involves a transfer of a localized non-bonding
electron into the ring system where the charge is smeared out.
Since the non-bonding electron in chlorophyll comes from the
oxygen of C-9 in the keto state of ring V, this oxygen atom will
acquire a positive charge and thus become a good electron acceptor during the lifetime of its excited state. On the other hand
the reduced state of cytochrome is a good electron donor. Consequently during the excited state this pair acquires a charge-
transfer stabilization with respect to an isolated chlorophyll
molecule because of the flow of negative charge to the positive
oxygen.[29] The absorption in the same spectral region occurring
in concentrated chlorophyll solutions in polar solvents at low
temperature might be a similar charge-transfer transition between two chlorophyll molecules that have face-to-face contact.[27]
Such dimers would not form *in vivo,* where neighboring molecules are alongside each other, not on top of each other. Our
conclusion is, then, that absorption of n-π by the protected
chlorophylls populates a special n-π state of the exposed chlorophyll, which will then quickly go over to its metastable state.
Thus this energy can be used only for the first act of photosynthesis. This interpretation of the 700 mμ absorption band fits
very well the observations of Kok, who found that this band
vanishes if cytochrome is oxidized by exogenous oxidants.[10]
He also observed that in living cells irradiation with 700 mμ
eliminates this absorption for a short time, while irradiation
with light of shorter wave-length restores this absorption band.
If our proposal about the chemistry of the preparatory and second photochemical steps is correct, the 700 mμ absorption

produces an enol complex, which no longer has n-π transitions, while the second photochemical act restores chlorophyll to its keto form as a by-product. We leave out many other observations on the behavior of the 700 mμ level. They seem to be in accord with our view. We must mention, however, the occurrence of a strong emission caused by the 700 mμ absorption if *Chlorella* cells are cooled down to liquid nitrogen temperature. The consiaerable shift of this emission to longer wave-lengths than the absorption is the rule for n-π transitions. That the emission occurs at low temperature is understandable in view of the energy of activation needed for radiationless conversion to the triplet state. That this fluorescence is much stronger than the π-π fluorescence, as shown by different authors, indicates sensitization of this n-π fluorescence by light absorbed by other chlorophyll molecules and accessory pigments.[27],[30] This indicates that at low temperature the co-planarity is disturbed to a great extent. Indeed cells once cooled down to liquid nitrogen temperature never regain their ability to photosynthesize.

Finally we come to Emerson's last important discovery, which bears his name. Emerson *et al.* found that the very low photosynthetic quantum yield observed on irradiating green plants with light on the long wave-length side of the red chlorophyll band can be improved considerably by simultaneous irradiation with light of shorter wave-lengths.[31] In other words the rate of photosynthesis of the combined irradiations is greater than the sum of the rates observed with the separate irradiations. [In fact, the possibility of cooperation exists even if a delay of several seconds separates the two irradiations.[32]]

Our interpretation of the Emerson effect is evident from the previous discussions. Irradiation with wave-lengths which promote transfer of n-π excitation to the exposed chlorophyll produces only the first photochemical step, and the small observed yield of photosynthesis in far-red light is possible only by some overlapping of light absorbed and transmitted at the π-π level. Addition of short wave-length irradiation permits utilization of the surplus of the product of the first photochemical step by the light which promotes the second step. In other words, the two light sources divide to some degree the chores of promoting the first and the second photochemical steps. A variant of this effect occurs in red and blue-green algae. Blinks had observed that in these algae the light absorbed directly by the chlorophyll is inefficient in promoting photosyn-

thesis and chlorophyll fluorescence.[5,33] Light absorbed by the
accessory pigments, whose hydrophilic character places them
in the protein region in contact with water, is very efficiently
utilized for photosynthesis and for excitation of chlorophyll
fluorescence. Obviously the conditions in the layer of protected
chlorophyll favor in this case the excitation and migration of
n-π singlets. It may be that the surface of the lamella is not
planar as in green algae. Then the same effect which in green
algae is caused by the addition of short wave-length to long
wave-length absorption is expected here to occur when light
absorption by the accessory pigments is added to that absorbed
by the chlorophyll. Indeed this effect has been found and studied
extensively.[34,35] More details of transient effects connected with
this problem are omitted from this paper, but it may be said
in passing that such observations are in agreement with our
view.

The following discussion of the afterglow of chlorophyll,
which has the same spectrum as fluorescence, belongs as much
to the discussion of our own theory as of those theories which
are based on the photoionization of chlorophyll in its monomolecular layer. Arnold has presented very convincing evidence that
the afterglow is indeed caused by a recombination process of
positive chlorophyll ions with electrons.[36] Photoionization produces both these charge carriers during irradiation, some of
the electrons are trapped, and the delayed recombination connected with light emission can be seen. The decay curve indicates the presence of traps of different depths so that the tail
of this luminescence can be observed nearly an hour after the
irradiation has stopped.[37] The whole kinetics of this process is
exactly the one observed in inorganic salts which become phosphors on addition of impurities. Indeed all observations of the
afterglow observed by a number of authors under a variety of
conditions confirm Arnold's interpretation. The afterglow,
though weak under all conditions, is 10 to 20 times higher when
photosynthesis is absent or hindered by suitable poisons then
it is during normal photosynthesis.[38] Arnold, who prefers the
explanation that electron movement to certain reaction centers
is the essence of the photosynthetic process, concludes that the
non-use of the electrons at these centers quite naturally will
enhance the recombination process and thus the afterglow. We,
on the other hand, believing that migration of light energy to
the centers of photochemical activity is the important process,
regard photoionization in the chlorophyll layer as an alternative

process which occurs only if excitation energy is prevented
from reaching the exposed chlorophyll. Most inhibitors of
photosynthesis will not completely prevent π-π singlet excitation energy from reaching the exposed chlorophyll, even if it
cannot make use of the energy for photochemistry. However
the n-π singlet cannot be transferred to the exposed chlorophyll if for one or another reason the cytochrome is oxidized.
Under such conditions n-π singlet energy thus remains within
the layer of the protected chlorophyll and quickly produces
n-π triplet states which by use of excitation energy absorbed
by another chlorophyll will be sensitized to a transition into a
higher-lying quantum state. The doubly-excited chlorophyll
may contain enough excitation energy for photoionization. Were
it not for this possibility of using two quanta for such ionization
acts, it would be not understandable why red light, whose quanta
can by no means suffice to cause photo-ionization in one act,
indeed produces afterglow. The very emission of fluorescence
light upon recombination would not be expected if the ionization
potential were lower than the π-π singlet excitation energy.

Calvin and co-workers used their observations of electron
spin resonance signals which occur on illumination of dried
leaves and chloroplasts as a proof for photo-ionization.[39] With
their apparatus the resolution of the signal was not good enough
to distinguish between charge separation and radical formation.
In the meantime Commoner made measurements with Town-
send's more sensitive apparatus, studying wet algae under conditions where they are able to photosynthesize.[40] In such samples he observed signals typical for radical formation. This
experiment on the other hand does not exclude the possibility
that the signals observed with dried out preparations might be
caused by photo-ionization occurring in the absence of photosynthesis. In such a case the action spectrum of the EPR is of
interest. The curve is taken with a thick layer of dried material.
It shows a maximum in the long wave-length region at 720 mμ,
where chlorophyll absorbs weakly and a minimum where chlorophyll absorbs strongly. In the dried material very little energy-
migration is expected. Thus the excitation energy will remain
in the layer. It is then used for production of metastable states
and with the help of a second quantum for photo-ionization acts.
As Calvin rightly pointed out in his last paper [43] the lifetime of
products of photo-ionization will be the longer, the smaller the
number is of photo-ionization acts occurring in the same layer
because the recombination rate becomes low. Thus the steady

state number of separated charges produced by an equal number of absorption acts is the highest where the absorption is weak.

Summarizing, we believe that Arnold's observations on after-glow (and certain other optical phenomena not discussed here) give definite proof that photo-ionization occurs in the chlorophyll layer in the absence or practical absence of photochemical use of the energy.[41] They do not prove that it occurs also when excitation energy is used efficiently for photosynthesis. Furthermore, hole migration and mobility of negative charges by electron exchange must be exceedingly small in a monomolecular layer where the chlorophylls lie flat on the protein surface. Absence of stacking like that in a crystal is also indicated by the absorption spectra. Therefore the chlorophyll molecules are very little coupled as compared with the much stronger coupling in face to face positions which can exist to some degree even in amorphous three-dimensional solids. Thus conduction of the products of ionization is expected to be quite inefficient in the layer. A brief survey of results on photoconductivity in crystals might be helpful to show that the type of photoconductivity Calvin has studied and used as a model for his latest theory[43] differs from that observed by Arnold *et al.*

Many measurements on dark and light conductivity have been carried out with crystals of anthracene. Genuine photo-ionization occurs in anthracene crystals but depends on the presence of an impurity and has a small yield.[42a] Electrons freed by this process are quickly trapped in such a way that they cannot contribute much to the conductivity. Only a small fraction of the free electrons are captured by the anthracene molecules to form negative ions. Their charge can migrate with about the same mobility as the positive holes.[42b]

A much more efficient way of promoting photoconductivity or even thermally induced conductivity can be achieved by interactions between metal electrodes and the crystal molecules. In anthracene the photoconductivity is so much stronger than the dark conductivity that it is sufficient to discuss only the former. Kallmann and his school have shown that this photoconductivity is much greater if the irradiation is at the crystal-anode boundary than at the cathodic boundary.[44] Many experiments have convinced these authors that this photoconductivity is caused by injection of electrons from excited anthracene molecules into the anode, leaving positive holes behind in the crystal. The holes can diffuse to the cathode where they are discharged by electrons extracted from the electrode. Of interest is the fact that the positive holes can easily move away from the anode and follow the electric field, although a small activation energy is required. The explanation lies in the fact that the electron injected into the anode does not remain localized, but belongs to the whole piece of metal. Still a small attraction of the positive hole for the anode metal exists as the so-called mirror-image force, which is weak in the case of a relatively big ion and is the origin of the energy of activation for the process.

Of special interest in connection with the hypothesis that hole migration in the chlorophyll layer may play a role in photosynthesis are recent observations by Kallmann and Pope.[45] The authors found that something similar to electrolysis of water can be achieved by irradiating one side of an anthracene crystal placed between two electrolytic solutions. Under these conditions, light absorption occurs only near the irradiated surface of the crystal and all excitation energy can move back to the surface by exciton movement. There it is used for the transfer of electrons to individual cations in the solution. Thus positive holes are produced at the surface of the crystal and are driven by the resulting space charge at the illuminated surface to the dark side of the crystal, where they oxidize negative ions in the solution. Although direct observation of hydrogen and oxygen is still lacking, the over-all reaction should be the splitting of water. Since in this process the charge transfers take place from neutral molecules to monovalent positive ions, or from positive ions in the crystals to negative electrolytic ions, the products of charge transfer do not attract each other electrically. That organic compounds exist however, which are genuine semi-conductors with a small gap between the conductivity layer and the ground state has been shown by Kepler *et al.*[46] They found that tetracyanoquinodimethane (TCNQ), a strong electron acceptor, forms salts of the form $M^+T^{\circ}T^-$ where M^+ is any of several substituted ammonium cations, T° a neutral TCNQ molecule, and T^- a TCNQ negative radical ion. Such salts are very efficient semiconductors with a gap of 0.01 to 0.14 volts. Deviation of the ratio of acceptors to donors from 2:1 results in a reduction of the conductivity. In a theoretical discussion, Menefee and Pao ascribe this conductivity to the fact that there are twice as many acceptors as donors, so that the highest bonding group orbital of the TCNQ is only partly filled.[47] The electric ("crystal") field of the cations splits this orbital by an energy that could account for the observed gap between the localized ground state and a narrow conduction band of the triethylammonium salt, and electrons delocalized over a small group of molecules could easily move from one such group to the next.

Calvin and co-workers have used for a model of chloroplasts a donor-acceptor system which has a similarity to Kepler's semiconducting organic salt.[48] The dye phthalocyanine (or in some experiments violanthrene) is the electron donor and chloranil (or iodine or tetracyanoethylene) is the electron acceptor. This system has been studied by Calvin and co-workers for several years and has lately been reinterpreted in the light of recent work. Since no discussion of the elementary processes has been given in that paper, we might briefly discuss similarities and dissimilarities with Kepler's work. The donor-acceptor cell of Calvin *et al.* contained a layer of phthalocyanine, 10^{-4} to 10^{-3} cm. thick, sublimed onto Aquadag electrodes arranged atop a glass plate in such a way that cathode and anode interlace. A thin layer of chloranil is sublimed on top of this amorphous or microcrystalline layer. Kearns and Calvin found a considerable dark current when they applied a potential difference across the electrodes.[48] Irradiation of the boundary by light penetrating the electron acceptor gave a smaller additional photocurrent. The quantum yield was not measured directly, but according to their deductions from other observations should be near unity. It should be noted that this yield was calculated on the basis of observations made at a field strength of about 10^4 volts/cm., a necessary condition, in our opinion, for separation of the charges.

Calvin and Kearns' donor-acceptor layers differ from Kepler's salts in two ways. Instead of using two acceptor molecules per monovalent donor, they use a donor-acceptor interface and assume that the acceptor can accept either one or two electrons. Secondly, Calvin's cell has only a thin layer of conducting material that may be roughly compared to a strip of metal (actually, to a good semiconductor) atop the phthalocyanine. Kallmann's work, as well as that of Le Blanc and Kepler on the conductivity of aromatic crystals suggests that the phthalocyanine would inject electrons into such a "metal" with a small energy of activation supplied either thermally or by absorption of light.[49] This injection demands a corresponding transfer of electrons to phthalocyanine, presumably at points opposite the anodes where injected electrons accumulate. Electrons must then migrate to the anode by electron exchange from phthalo-

cyanine-negative ions to adjacent neutral molecules. Kearns
and Calvin found that the thermal and light-induced currents
have the same activation energy. Electron spin resonance observations were made and discussed.

The model system leads Calvin to the following assumptions
about the photosynthetic apparatus: it contains electron-donors
and acceptors. The order of the two-dimensional lamella corresponds to the order in the three-dimensional array of phthalocyanine. Light energy absorbed by the chlorophyll layer migrates (as in other theories which make use of a photosynthetic
unit) to the rim where it is used for a reaction. The reaction
visualized in his theory is the transfer of an electron from the
chlorophyll to the acceptor regarded to be plastoquinone. The
charge transfer complex separates into the negatively charged
plastoquinone which acts as reducing agent, while the positive
hole of the chlorophyll migrates to the ferrocytochrome oxidizing it to ferricytochrome. The oxidized cytochrome is supposed
to revert to the reduced state by discharging a negative ion
(probably OH^-) in the first step of the reactions leading to
photosynthetic oxygen evolution. The problem is how the separation of charges occurs. The concentration of plastoquinone,
about $1/8$ of the chlorophyll concentration, suffices to form a
ring or a part of a ring around the chlorophyll layer; thus the
two-dimensional charge transfer layer of the model becomes
a one-dimensional curve in the chloroplast. However, this
borderline is not ionized by thermal population of the narrow
conductivity band. The charge transfer occurs only in the light
and so the conductivity band must be energetically much higher
than that of the pair phthalocyanine-chloranil. If enough resonance overlap exists between the chlorophyll molecules and between the plastoquinones so that the positive and the negative
charges are both smeared out over a number of molecules the
separation of the charges will not demand much energy. Thermal fluctuations together with a strong external field will easily
carry the positive hole or the negative charge to the respective
electrodes. If no external field is present, however, as in the
chloroplast, it is difficult to see that the positive hole of chlorophyll should diffuse away from the negative plastoquinone to the
cytochrome. An even greater difficulty exists if one combines
Kamen's proposal, formation of a charge complex of excited
chlorophyll and cytochrome, with Calvin's theory of separation
of charges.[50] In this case the chlorophyll is the negative partner
and the electron must move away by charge exchange with

neighbors. The energy to separate the negative charge from the cytochrome must be greater because the increased positive charge is localized on the only cytochrome molecule of the unit and no smearing out of charge can occur on the positive side.

Calvin's picture, if viewed as a four-quantum process, has all the difficulties of any other four-quantum process summarized in the first part of this paper. We therefore tried combining a photo-ionization process requiring two quanta per electron with a number of considerations discussed in our theory to get a result which might be free of these difficulties. Such a two-quantum process could occur in the following way: the first quantum produces a charge-transfer chlorophyll-plastoquinone complex, $Chl^+ - Qu^-$; the second quantum takes the electron away from the plastoquinone and uses it for a partial reduction of the photosynthetic oxidant. After that has been done the positive chlorophyll is no longer attracted and is free to diffuse through the layer until it arrives at the cytochrome. This picture implies the assumption that the transfer of charge to the oxidant can be done only by excitation energy of a long life-time in order to allow diffusion of the oxidant to the excitation site. π-π and n-π triplet states could possibly fulfill this condition. The outlined process would avoid the difficulties of the quantum yield and would also give the right dependence of fluorescence intensity upon presence or absence of photosynthetic oxidants under those conditions in which π-π singlet energy migrates by exciton movement to the chlorophyll adjacent to the plastoquinones. No difficulty would exist for the positive hole to diffuse to the cytochrome after the second act has restored the plastoquinone to its uncharged state. If, however, under the same conditions discussed in the first part of the paper only n-π singlet energy arrives at the exposed chlorophyll in contact with plastoquinone, one might assume that only charge-transfer complex formation can occur and not the second step, the transfer of the electron to the oxidant. One even might make use of our deduction that the 700 mμ absorption is an n-π excitation of the chlorophyll-plastoquinone complex and thus come to an explanation of the Emerson effect quite similar to the one given in the first part of this paper. Great difficulties would still remain. It becomes impossible to explain the observation of French and Myers that the Emerson effect can be observed even if the irradiation with short-wave light comes a few seconds after the long-wave. This is a time so much longer than the life-times of metastable states that the first act must be a chemical reaction whose product lives several seconds. The life-time of the charge-transfer complex itself becomes identical with the life-time of an n-π excitation if, as in this picture, the complex does not dissociate spontaneously into oppositely charged components. Furthermore, Kok's observations and all the connected phenomena point in the direction that charge-transfer complexes are made only at the cytochrome, and there only by n-π excitation of the chlorophyll. Also certain transient phenomena which we have not discussed can be explained by our theory, but so far as we see not by the merger of our picture with Calvin's basic idea. Thus we conclude that at least for the time being no theory exists which is based on charge separation under the influence of light and at the same time is in accordance with all the experimental evidence.

REFERENCES

[1] J.A. Bassham and M. Calvin,"The Path of Carbon in Photosynthesis," Prentice-Hall, Englewood Cliffs (1957).

[2] M.Gibbs and O. Kandler, Proc.Nat.Acad.Sci. U.S., 43,446 (1957).

[3] J.J.Wolken, in "The Photochemical Apparatus," Brookhaven Sym. in Biol. #11, p. 87 (1959).

[4] W.L. Butler, Arch. Biochem. and Biophys., 92, 287 (1961).

[5] L. N. M. Duysens, Dissertation, Univ. of Utrecht (1952).

[6] H. Gaffron and K. Wohl, Naturwissenschaften, 24, 81 (1936).

[7] R. Emerson and W. Arnold, J. Gen.Physiol., 15, 391 (1932).

[8] H.E.Davenport and R.Hill, Proc.Roy.Soc.London,B139,327(1952).

[9] M.D.Kamen, in "Enzymes: Units of Biological Structure and Function," (O.H.Gaebler, ed.), Academic Press, N.Y., p. 483 (1956).

[10] B. Kok, Biochim. et Biophys. Acta, 48, 527 (1961).

[11] J. Franck, Daedalus, 86, 17 (1955).

[12] J. Franck, Proc. Nat. Acad. Sci. U.S., 44 941 (1958).

[13] E. Fujimori and R. Livingston, Nature, 180, 1036 (1957).

[14] J. Franck, in "Research in Photosynthesis," (H. Gaffron, Ed.), Interscience Publishers, New York, p. 142 (1957).

[15] E. C. Wassink and E. Katz, Enzymologia, 6, 145 (1938).

[16] H. Gaffron, in "Research in Photosynthesis," (H. Gaffron, ed.), Interscience Publishers, New York, p. 430 (1957); J. Franck, Handbuch der Pflanzen Physiologie, Vol. V, Springer, Berlin, p. 689 (1960).

[17] R. Lumry, B. Mayne, and J.D. Spikes, Far. Soc.Discussions,#27, 149 (1959); J.L. Rosenberg and S. DeJaegere, unpublished.

[18] A. Seybold and K. Egle, Bot. Arch., 41, 578 (1940).

[19] J. Fernandez and R. S. Becker, J. Chem. Phys., 31, 467 (1959); I.S. Singh and R.S. Becker, J. Am. Chem. Soc., 82, 2083 (1960)

[20] P.S. Stensby and J.L. Rosenberg, J.Phys.Chem., 65, 906 (1961).

[21] J. R. Platt, in "Radiation Biology," (A. Hollaender, ed.,), Vol. III, McGraw-Hill, New York, p. 71 (1956).

[22] V. G. Krishna and L. Goodman, J. Chem. Phys.,33, 381 (1960).

[23] R. Livingston, W.F. Watson, and J. McArdle, J.Am.Chem.Soc., 71,1542 (1949); V.B. Evstigneev, V.A. Gavrilova, and A.A. Krasnovskii, Doklady Akad. Nauk. S.S.S.R., 66,1133 (1949).

[24] J. S. Brown and C. S. French, Plant Physiol., 34, 305 (1959).

[25] Govindjee, E. Rabinowitch, and J. B. Thomas, Biophys.J., 1, 91 (1960).

[26] A. S. Holt, Can. J. Botany, 39, 327 (1961).

[27] S. S. Brody, Science, 128, 838 (1958).

[28] P. Pringsheim, "Fluorescence and Phosphorescence," Interscience Publishers, New York, p. 434 (1949).

[29] R. S. Mulliken, J. Am. Chem. Soc., 74, 811 (1952).

[30] W. L. Butler, Arch. Biochem. and Biophys., 93, 413 (1961).

[31] R. Emerson, R. Chalmers, and C. Cederstrand, Proc. Nat. Acad. Sci. U.S., 43, 133 (1957).

[32] J. Myers and C. S. French, Plant Physiol., 35, 963 (1960).

[33] F. T. Haxo and L. R. Blinks, J. Gen. Physiol., 33, 389 (1950).

[34] R. Emerson and E. Rabinowitch, Plant Physiol. 35, 477 (1960).

[35] L. R. Blinks, Proc. Nat. Acad. Sci. U.S., 46, 327 (1960).

[36] W. A. Arnold and H. K. Sherwood, Proc. Nat. Acad. Sci. U.S., 43, 105 (1957).

[37] W. Arnold, in "Research in Photosynthesis," (H. Gaffron, ed.) Interscience Publishers, New York, p. 128 (1957).

[38] B. L. Strehler and W. Arnold, J.Gen.Physiol.,34,809(1951); J. Brugger and J. Franck, Arch. Biochem. and Biophys.,75, 465 (1958).

[39] P. B. Sogo, L. A. Carter, and M. Calvin, Proc. Nat. Acad. Sci. U.S., 43, 387 (1957).

[40] B. Commoner, in "Light and Life," (W. D. McElroy and B. Glass, ed.), Johns Hopkins Press, Baltimore, p. 356 (1961).

[41] W. Arnold and R. K. Clayton, Proc. Nat. Acad. Sci. U.S., 46, 769 (1960).

[42a] W. Moore and M. Silver, J. Chem. Phys., 33, 1671 (1960).

[42b] O. H. LeBlanc, Jr., J. Chem. Phys., 33, 626 (1960).

[43] M. Calvin, J. Theoret. Biol., 1, 258 (1961).

[44] H. Kallmann and M. Pope, J. Chem. Phys., 30, 585 (1959).

[45] H. Kallmann and M. Pope, Nature, 188, 935 (1960).

[46] R. G. Kepler, P. E. Bierstadt, and P. E. Merrifield, Phys. Rev. Letters, 5, 503 (1960).

[47] E. Menefee and Y. H. Pao, in press.

[48] D. R. Kearns, G. Tollin, and M. Calvin, J. Chem., Phys., 32, 1020 (1958); D. R. Kearns and M. Calvin, J. Am. Chem. Soc., 83, 2110 (1961).

[49] R. G. Kepler, Phys. Rev., 119, 1226 (1960).

[50] M. D. Kamen, in "Light and Life," (W. D. McElroy and B. Glass, ed.), Johns Hopkins Press, Baltimore, p. 483 (1961).

FLUORESCENCE DECAY TIMES OF ORGANIC CRYSTALS

A. Schmillen
Physics Institute
Giessen University, Giessen, Germany

ABSTRACT

Fluorescence decay time measurements of several solid hydrocrabons and related compounds under α particle, electron impact, and UV excitation are reported. Different methods of decay measurements are used for different excitations. Under α excitation the decay time τ was determined from the Fourier spectrum of scintillations, under UV excitation by a phase-fluorometer. For electron impact excitation, a sampling method permitted the determination of the fluorescence intensity versus time relation.

The samples investigated (polycrystalline powders) were carefully purified and freed from all fluorescing contaminants. Whereas the fluorometer reveals only one decay time, the Fourier analysis of α excited luminescence gives several decay times for all purified samples. Especially for anthracene three components were determined with τ values (and relative intensities) of 18.8 (74%), 160 (17%), and 2100 (9%) nanosec. The same fluorescence spectrum is emitted by all three components. On the other hand, most samples examined containing fluorescing host molecules, as for instance tetracene in chrysene, showed only one nearly exponential decay time.

The significance of the above for the excitation and energy transfer mechanism is discussed.

A well known phenomenon in the luminescence of organic molecules or molecular systems is the energy transfer between different partners. One of the first discussions of this subject may be found in the papers of Bowen and Mikiewicz[1,2] and Ganguly,[3] who observed this phenomenon in anthracene crystals with impurities of tetracene. Since that time, numerous papers have been published on this subject.

Starting with measurements of short decay times, we ex-
perimented in particular on crystalline aromatic hydrocarbons
and related compounds, expecting to obtain information about
the mechanism of energy transfer by observation of the decay
processes. The following is a brief report of our results and
conclusions are discussed as well.

Methods of Preparation and Measurement:

In general, measurements were made on polycrystalline
powders of pure substances or of binary systems. The latter
were obtained by adding known concentrations (between 10^{-6} –
10^{-1} mol p. mol) of molecules having fluorescence at longer
wave lengths to the melt of the pure substance.

A typical fluorescence spectrum of such a binary sustem at
different concentrations is shown in Fig. 1a, b. The system
chrysene-perylene, when excited by light of 3665 Å (27500 cm^{-1})
shows the emission of the host substance (chrysene) at 26000–
22000 cm^{-1}, and the emission of the guest molecules (perylene)
at 22000–18000 cm^{-1}.

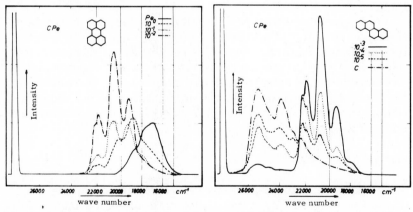

Fig. 1 a, b — Fluorescence spectrum of chrysene with different perylene concentrations
excited with the 3650 Å Hg line.

The host fluorescence decreases with growing guest concentration while the guest fluorescence increases. In general, the
guest fluorescence intensity reaches a maximum at concentrations between 10^{-4} – 10^{-2} mol p. mol and then drops again.
Only direct excitation of perylene fluorescence is obtained when
excitation is by light of 4300 Å. This is characteristic of the
other binary systems investigated as well. There are, however,
quantitative differences. Further details, such as the changes

in the spectrum of guest molecules with concentration, shall not be considered at present.

We have tried to measure the decay times of several systems of this kind under different excitation conditions, separating the host fluorescence from the guest fluorescence by filters. A complete separation is almost impossible, since the two emission regions generally overlap.

The luminescence decay was measured by three methods:

a) In the case of excitation with UV or visible light, we employ a phase fluorometer. The determination of the decay times τ from the phase angles ϕ with the relation $\tan \phi = \omega\tau$ is only possible for single exponential processes. In binary systems, phase angles exceeding 90° were occasionally observed; in these cases the supposition of a single exponential decay is certainly not possible. Thus, the information which can be revealed by a phase fluorometer is limited.

b) Under excitation with α particles a Fourier analysis of the scintillations is made with the aid of a selective valve voltmeter.[4] This method is quite troublesome and takes much time; however, it is relatively exact and furnishes more detailed information.

c) When excited with periodically repeated electron pulses (1 Mcps rep. rate) of a very steep rise and decay ($<$1 n sec), the light pulses emitted are oscillographed by a sampling method.[5] The equipment used is similar to that reported by Dreeskamp and Burton[6] for X-ray excitation. Unfortunately, the precision of the method does not as yet meet our expectations. Therefore, only brief references will be made to the results of this method.

A) UV Excitation

We have reported repeatedly on measurements using the phase fluorometer. As a typical example of such a measurement we may mention the system chrysene with perylene. Figure 2 shows the phase angle of the luminescence of this system as a function of perylene concentration.

The phase angle of the host-(chrysene-) fluorescence decreases with growing guest-(perylene-) concentration (Curve a). The scale on the right gives the decay time obtained from the tangent relationship. It is therefore concluded that there is a competing process which transfers the energy of the excited host state to the guest molecules. Curve b shows the phase of

the directly excited guest molecule fluorescence and its decay
time (7-10 n sec) respectively. By excitation of the host lattice,

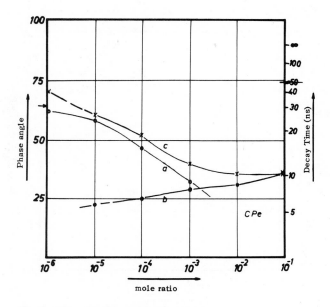

Fig. 2 — Phase angles and decay times of the fluorescence of
chrysene with different concentrations of perylene. Curve (a)
chrysene emission and curve (c) perylene emission, both excited
with Hg 3650 Å radiation, curve (b) perylene emission, excited
with Hg 4300 Å radiation.

however, phase angles of the guest fluorescence are obtained
which in general are greater than the phase angles of the host
fluorescence. They also exceed considerably the phase angles
of the directly excited guest fluorescence in the region of low
concentration. A determination of the decay time from the phase
angle applying the tangent relationship to this curve is of no
avail, since in this case there is apparently no single exponential process. The growing phase angle of the guest fluorescence
only allows the conclusion that energy transfer from host to
guest takes increasing time with decreasing concentration. This
diagram (2) is also typical of the other samples investigated.

However, we have found several systems in which there is only a small decrease of the decay times in spite of a comparable energy transfer efficiency. Figure 3, as an example, shows the system fluorene-pyrene, which is also interesting from a different point of view.

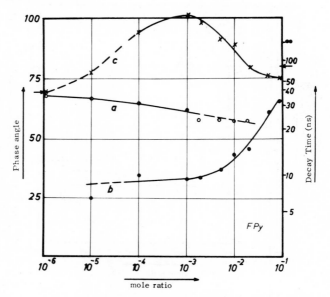

Fig. 3 — Phase angle and decay times of the fluorescence of fluorene with different concentrations of pyrene. Curve (a) fluorene emission and curve (c) pyrene emission, both excited with Hg 3131 Å radiation, curve (b) pyrene emission excited with Hg 3650 Å radiation.

The large phase angle of the indirectly excited guest fluorescence in comparison with the small angle by direct excitation in the region of not too large concentrations demonstrates energy transfer. On the other hand, the phase angle of the host fluorescence shows, in this case, only a small decrease. Moreover, when excited directly, the decay time of the guest molecules rises steeply at higher concentrations. In a recent paper[7] we have pointed out that this is caused by two different pyrene emissions, one with a short, the other with a long decay time.

Without going into quantitative details, we conclude from these measurements the existence of two different transfer mechanisms, only one of which influences the decay constant of the host fluorescence, or of two different emission processes of the host.

B) α Particle Excitation

The square of the frequency dependent Fourier amplitude $G^2(\omega^2)$ of a single exponential scintillation pulse obeys the relation

$$G^2(\omega^2) = \frac{C}{\omega^2 + \alpha^2}$$

or

$$\frac{1}{G^2(\omega^2)} = \frac{1}{C}(\omega^2 + \alpha^2)$$

The values determined for $1/G^2$ in the frequency range from 20 Kcps to 180 Mcps plotted against ω^2 do not always lie on a single straight line. The curves can only be approximated by several straight lines of different slopes and intersepts in succeeding frequency ranges. This can be interpreted by assuming several exponentially decaying components. Whether or not this is physically reasonable is an open question. Moreover, at very high frequencies the rise of the scintillations can be seen in the Fourier spectrum and the rise time can be evaluated, but at present the accuracy is still poor.

In Figure 4, the square of the Fourier amplitude G^2 of several pure polycrystalline substances is plotted versus $(\omega\tau)^2$. In such a plot all single exponential decay processes, which by definition contain only one decay time, are represented by the same curve, independent of the value of the decay constant.

If there are several decay components, we insert for τ the shortest value determined from the straight line of the $1/G^2$ diagram at the highest frequencies. The comparison of our measurements with the single exponential curve reveals that all the pure substances investigated have several decay components.

In the case of anthracene, we have made a detailed analysis assuming three decay components

$$\tau = \tau_0(a_1 e^{-\tau/\tau_1} + a_2 e^{-\tau/\tau_2} + a_3 e^{-\tau/\tau_3})$$

and have obtained the following values

$$a_1 = 1, a_2 = 0.027, a_3 = 0.0011$$

$$\tau_1 = 18.8; \tau_2 = 160; \tau_3 = 2100 \text{ (n sec)}$$

and for the fractions E_1, E_2, E_3 of the total of emitted energy of the three components the relation

$$E_1 : E_2 : E_3 \ = 1 : 0.23 : 0.12$$

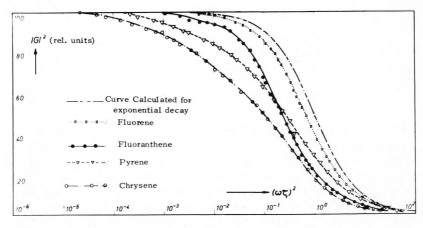

Fig. 4 — Fourier spectrum (G^2) of exponential decay scintillations —— · —— and of several pure materials.

Table I contains the shortest decay times of some pure substances. They all show longer components which we have not yet analyzed in detail.

Table I

Substance	Decay Time (nsec)	Rise Time (nsec)
Anthracene	18.8	–
Brasan	9.6	1.6
Chrysene	24.5	1.3
Naphthalene	52.0	–
Pyrene	19.8	1.3
Fluorene	37.8	4.6
Fluoranthene	23.8	

In contrast to the pure samples, the fluorescence of the guest molecules in binary systems is, in most cases, of single exponential nature. Several examples are shown in Figure 5. To our knowledge, these systems form mixed crystals if the guest concentration is not too high. The guest fluorescence of the system naphthalene-tetracene, however, contains longer decay components as well; at higher tetracene concentrations, this system is known to form an eutectic. Based on experience with some other binary systems we suppose that the different decay in mixed crystals or eutectics is a more general behavior.

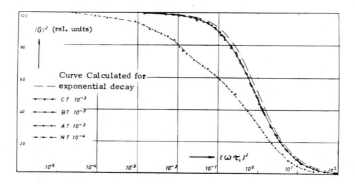

Fig. 5 — Fourier spectrum of the scintillations of the binary systems chrysene-tetracene (CT), brasan-tetracene (BT), anthracene-tetracene (AT) and naphthalene-tetracene (NT).

For the two binary systems brasan (= 2.3 benzodiphenylene-oxide) – tetracene and fluorene – tetracene, the decay times and some of the rise times of host and guest fluorescence under α excitation are tabulated in Table II.

The decay time of the host fluorescence decreases with growing guest molecule concentration as was found under UV excitation. The rise time of the pyrene fluorescence in fluorene is particularly long. Furthermore, the very long decay time of pyrene (120 nsec) contradicts the value of 8 nsec measured under UV excitation. At highest pyrene concentrations a second fluorescence component of the pyrene at longer wave lengths with even longer rise and decay times is observed.

C) Electron Excitation

The results received from excitation by electrons agree passably with those from α particle excitation. However, components with relatively small amplitudes and longer decay times are not measurable, because they sink below the noise level. A plot showing the results obtained from excitation by electrons is given in Figure 6 and a number of decay values of binary systems in Table III. But these are only to be taken as

Table II

System	Guest Concentr. mol p. mol	Host Fluorescence		Guest Fluorescence	
		Decay Time nsec	Rise Time nsec	Decay Time nsec	Rise Time nsec
Brasan-tetracene	0	9.6	1.6	–	–
	10^{-6}	9.7	2.0	–	–
	3.10^{-5}	9.0	1.5	18.0	–
	10^{-4}	8.7	–	16.1	–
	10^{-3}	7.8	–	19.1	1.2
	3.10^{-3}			14.7	–
	10^{-2}			14.5	–
	3.10^{-2}			12.0	–
Fluorene-pyrene	0	37.8	–	–	–
	10^{-6}	37.2	–	–	–
	10^{-5}	37.0	–	119	12
	10^{-4}	36.0	–	118	24
	10^{-3}	–		113	22
	10^{-2}	–		116	9
Short } wavelength-	10^{-1}	–		112	9
Long } component	10^{-1}			141	40

Table III

Fluorescence Decay Times by Electron Pulse Excitation

System	Guest Concentr. mol p. mol	Host Fluorescence Decay Time n sec	Rise Time n sec	Guest Fluorescence Decay Time n sec	Rise Time n sec
Brasan-tetracene	10^{-5}	15	3	25	4
	10^{-4}	13	3	25	3
	10^{-3}	10	2	20	3,5
	10^{-2}	–	–	17	3
(the decay time of direct UV excited tetracene is 15 n sec.)					
Chrysene-perylene	10^{-6}	24	5	–	–
	10^{-5}	20	5	21	4
	10^{-4}	15	5	18	3,5
	10^{-3}	12	5	13	3
	10^{-2}	9	4	9	3
(the decay time of direct UV excited perylene is 8 n sec.)					
Naphthalene-pyrene	10^{-6}	78	6	–	–
	10^{-5}	72	7	(150)	10
	10^{-4}	65	6	160	10
	10^{-3}	55	6	155	10
	10^{-2}	–	–	130	11
	10^{-1}	–	–	120	16,5
(the decay time of direct UV excited pyrene is 8 n sec.)					
Fluorene-pyrene	10^{-6}	39	7	–	–
	10^{-5}	33	8	–	–
	10^{-4}	28	9	133	11
	10^{-3}	25	7	125	10
	10^{-2}	–	–	100	9
	10^{-1}	–	–	128	10

provisional data. In the system fluorene-pyrene, the exceptionally long rise and decay times of the guest fluorescence are
also obtained under excitation by electrons.

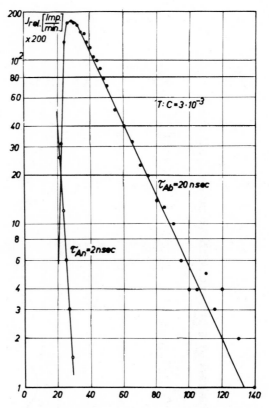

Fig. 6 — Fluorescence rise and decay under electron
pulse excitation. The intensity of the tetracene fluorescence in the system chrysene-tetracene with tet-
racene-concentration of 10^{-5} is plotted against time.

DISCUSSION

In a former paper,[8] we interpreted the concentration dependence of the phase angles or decay times in binary systems with
a transition scheme as shown in Fig. 7.

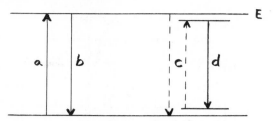

Fig. 7 — Transition scheme for energy transfer in a binary system by exciton capture.

a) is the transition to the exciton state E due to the absorption of ultraviolet light, b) the exciton emission (host fluorescence), c) the exciton capture by a guest molecule, and d) the succeeding emission from the guest molecule. The probability of exciton capture by guest molecules increases with their concentration and causes the decrease in decay time of the exciton emission. From this point of view, the intensity B should increase in the same manner as the decay time τ. The relation $B/B_0 = \tau/\tau_0$ should hold. But in fact, it does not. As can be seen in two examples given in Figure 8, the relative intensity B/B_0 decreases more rapidly with guest concentration than the relative decay time τ/τ_0.

This means that an energy transfer process which does not influence the transition probability of the host emission mentioned above should be possible. The most simple explanation for this would be absorption of host fluorescence by guest molecules.

But the results from α particle excitation contradict such an assumption. The long and the short components of the host fluorescence, having the same spectral distribution, should then be absorbed by the guest molecules according to their relative intensities and therefore should be seen in the guest fluorescence as well. Thus another explanation of the decrease of intensity without decrease of the decay time must be found.

In a recent paper by V. M. Agranovich[9] on the effect of defects on exciton processes in molecular crystals, the following concept is developed: disordered molecules or molecules at defect sites are capable of capturing excitons and of emitting their energy as eigenluminescence as well as of inducing a transformation of the energy of excitons of too great momentum into electromagnetic radiation (exciton-luminescence) without localization of the exciton.

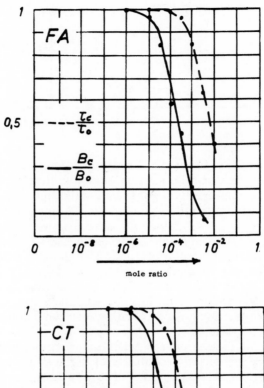

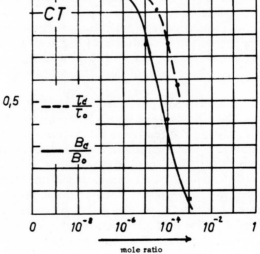

Fig. 8 — Relative Intensity $\frac{\beta}{\beta^0}$ and decay time $\frac{\tau}{\tau_0}$ of the host fluorescence of the binary systems fluorene-anthracene and chrysene-tetracene.

The two emission mechanisms for the host fluorescence contained in this concept start from the exciton state and therefore are influenced by the guest molecules; however, the decay process is likely to be different. Possibly, the explanation for the discrepancy between B/B_o and τ/τ_o under UV excitation can be given on this basis.

As to the nature of the slow components, we argue as follows: All transitions following the α particle energy absorption, which finally end at the exciton state, influence the guest molecule fluorescence. Therefore, the long components of the host fluorescence are of another origin, for they do not prolong the decay of guest fluorescence.

The exceptionally long rise and decay time of pyrene in fluorene under α particle excitation can only be understood with the assumption of an additional level between the exciton state and the level from which the guest fluorescence starts. The decay time of emptying this additional level must be in the order of 120 nsec. The short decay time ($\sim$ 9 nsec) measured under ultraviolet excitation corresponds to the emission transition in guest molecules. For indirect excitation via the exciton band this short time constant plays the role of the rise time in agreement with the experiment.

We consider these interpretations only as working hypotheses for further experiments. By this we actually admit that we do not yet know precisely the mechanisms involved in the luminescence of our crystals.

LITERATURE

[1] E. J. Bowen, (Journal of Chem. Phys.) 13, 306 (1945)
[2] E. J. Bowen, E. Mikiewicz, Nature 159, 706, (1947)
[3] S. C. Ganguly, (Journal of Chem. Phys.) 13, 128 (1945)
[4] A. Schmillen and K. Kramer, will be published in Naturforsch
[5] H. Schulz, Physik, 156, 27 (1954)
[6] H. Dreeskamp, Mr. Burton, Phys. Rev. Letters 2, 45 (1959)
[7] A. Schmillen, Naturforsch 16a, 5 (1961)
[8] A. Schmillen, Physik 150, 123 (1958)
[9] V. M. Agranovich, Uspekhi Fiz. Nauk 71, 141 (1960)
   Sovj. Phys. USPEKHI 3, 427 (1960)

EFFECTS OF TEMPERATURE AND VISCOSITY ON SCINTILLATION DECAY TIMES OF SOLUTIONS*

A. Weinreb

Department of Physics, The Hebrew University, Jerusalem, Israel

and

Argonne National Laboratory, Argonne, Illinois

ABSTRACT

The efficiency of energy transfer (ϵ) from toluene to diphenyloxazole (PPO) is determined for solutions of PPO in (1) toluene, (2) in a mixture of toluene and cyclohexane and (3) in a mixture of toluene and paraffin oil. It is found that ϵ is similar in systems (1) and (2) but considerably lower in system (3). For this last system ϵ is further examined as a function of temperature and viscosity. The main part of the work deals with the fluorescence decay times of these systems when excited by electrons. The decay time is measured as a function of temperature in the presence and absence of PPO. In the latter case the measured decay time is that of toluene. In no case is the decay of the PPO solutions strictly exponential. Strong deviations from exponential decay are found in viscous solutions at low temperature. The transfer probabilities are determined from the results. The transfer probability in the viscous systems at low temperatures decreases remarkably with time. This effect becomes smaller with increasing temperature. The transfer efficiencies are computed and compared with the results obtained from intensity measurements of optically excited solutions. The decay of solutions of PPO in paraffin oil (without toluene) is studied. An explanation of the results is attempted.

---

*All the experimental work described in this article has been performed at Argonne National Laboratory under the auspices of the U.S. Atomic Energy Commission, during a leave from the Hebrew University.

A. INTRODUCTION

The influence of diffusion on the process of energy transfer in solution has been questioned by several authors.[1,2,3] An attempt to clarify this question has been made by the author in a recent publication.[4] The transfer efficiency of several solutions was measured as a function of temperature and viscosity and it was found that the transfer efficiency increases considerably with T/η (T = absolute temperature, η = viscosity) which is proportional to the diffusion coefficient. These results were tentatively interpreted as an indication of the rather important contribution of Brownian motion to the observed transfer efficiencies. The present work is a continuation of these investigations. The transfer efficiency is again investigated as a function of temperature and viscosity. Particular emphasis was placed, however, on the determination of the decay times of the solutions as a function of these parameters. The decay time is of interest for several reasons. In this study, it was primarily the important role of the decay time in the elucidation of the transfer process which motivated the measurements. The decay time data essentially supplement the results obtained from intensity measurements and the form of the decay provides information on those details of the mechanism which practically cannot be obtained from intensity measurements.

The systems investigated are solutions in which diphenyloxazole (PPO) is the acceptor and toluene the transferring agent. The viscosity of the system was changed by changing the solvent and the temperature. Most of the information was obtained from solutions of 0.5 g/liter PPO in toluene, in a mixture of 1 part toluene and 9 parts cyclohexane, and in a mixture of 1 part toluene and 9 parts paraffin oil. Since the absolute concentration of the acceptor (PPO) is the same in all three cases, the rate constants for energy transfer in these systems are directly proportional to the resulting transfer probabilities. The combination toluene-PPO is widely used in liquid scintillation counting.

B. EXPERIMENTAL

The transfer efficiencies were measured according to a method previously described.[5]

2650Å radiation was used to excite toluene.

3130Å radiation was used to excite PPO directly.

The decay times of the solutions were measured by an apparatus constructed by Swank *et al.*[6,7] The experimental arrangement is shown in Figure 1. The solution is introduced

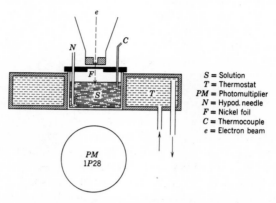

S = Solution
T = Thermostat
PM = Photomultiplier
N = Hypod. needle
F = Nickel foil
C = Thermocouple
e = Electron beam

Fig. 1 — Experimental arrangement for measuring decay time as function of temperature.

into a quartz cell. The center opening on the top of the cell is covered with a nickel foil of 0.002 inch thickness. The solution is constantly deoxygenated by a flow of nitrogen which is introduced into the solution through a hypodermic needle and leaves the cell by a small opening at the top. The cell is placed in a double-walled cylindrical metal container. The cell closely fits the inner wall of the container and good thermal conduction is obtained. The temperature of the system is adjusted by flooding the container with a liquid (water, cooled alcohol) the temperature of which is regulated by a thermistor device and which is circulated at a controlled speed. The temperature of the solution is measured by a thermocouple which is dipped into the solution. The solutions are excited by a pulsed beam of electrons of about 75 kev and the resulting light pulse is detected and recorded.

C. RESULTS AND DISCUSSION

a. Transfer Efficiencies Obtained by Excitation by U.V.

Figure 2 shows the viscosity as a function of temperature of a solution of 0.5 g/liter PPO in a mixture of 1 part toluene and 9 parts paraffin oil. Figure 3 shows the transfer efficiency of this system as a function of temperature. Interpolated values of the transfer efficiencies are given in column 8 of Table 1A.

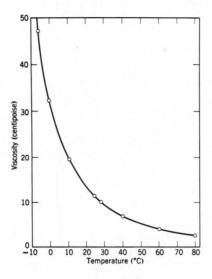

Fig. 2 — Variation of viscosity with temperature of a solution of 0.5 g/liter PPO in a mixture of 1 part toluene and 9 parts paraffin oil.

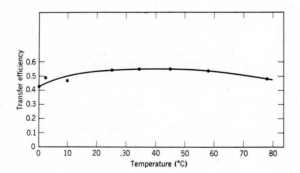

Fig. 3 — Variation of efficiency of energy transfer from toluene to PPO with temperature for 0.5 g/liter PPO in a mixture of 1 part toluene and 9 parts paraffin oil.

TABLE 1

Decay times and transfer efficiencies

A: 0.5 g/liter PPO in a mixture of toluene and paraffin oil (1:9)

1	2		3	4	5	6	7	8
t	τ_0		τ_1	τ_2	$1/\tau_{T_1}$	$1/\tau_{T_2}$	ϵ	ϵ_0
°C	nsec		nsec	nsec	$10^7 \sec^{-1}$	$10^7 \sec^{-1}$		
0	32	u.	14.1	26.9	4.0	0.6	0.40	
		c.	13.1	26.9	4.6	0.6	0.43	0.42
20	28	u.	13.2	19.0	4.0	1.7	0.45	
		c.	11.8	19.0	4.9	1.7	0.48	0.53
40	23	u.	11.5	13.6	4.3	3.0	0.47	
		c.	9.8	13.6	5.8	3.0	0.51	0.53
60	16.5	u.	9.2	10.0	4.8	3.9	0.43	
		c.	7.6	9.8	7.1	4.1	0.49	0.52
70	13.7	u.	7.9	8.8	5.4	4.1	0.40	
		c.	6.3	8.4	8.6	4.6	0.47	0.50

B: 0.5 g/liter PPO in a mixture of toluene and cyclohexane (1:9)

(6	35.9	u.	10.0	11.3	7.2	6.1	0.71	
		c.	8.0	11.2	9.7	6.1	0.74	....)
28	30.3	u.	7.4	8.2	10.2	8.9	0.75	
		c.	5.8	7.8	14.0	9.5	0.78	0.76
43	23.5	u.	6.6	7.2	10.9	9.6	0.71	
		c.	5.5	7.0	13.9	10.0	0.74	....
60	16.5	u.	5.8	6.3	11.1	9.8	0.64	
		c.	4.3	4.9	17.1	14.3	0.73	....

C: 0.5 g/liter PPO in toluene

28	17.0	u.	4.6	4.9	15.9	14.5	0.72	
		c.	3.4	3.8	23.5	20.5	0.79	0.74

t	=	temperature
τ_0	=	decay time of solvent
τ_1	=	decay time of PPO solution - first period
τ_2	=	decay time of PPO solution - second period
$1/\tau_{T_1}$	=	transfer probability computed from decay time of first period
$1/\tau_{T_2}$	=	transfer probability computed from decay time of second period
ϵ	=	computed transfer efficiency
ϵ_0	=	transfer efficiency obtained from intensity measurements
u.	=	uncorrected values (decay time of PPO assumed to be very short)
c.	=	corrected values (decay time of PPO assumed to be 2.7 nsec)

Columns 8 of Tables 1B and 1C give the transfer efficiencies of solutions of 0.5 g/liter PPO in a mixture of toluene and cyclohexane and in toluene alone, respectively.

DISCUSSION. A comparison of the transfer efficiencies of the three systems at room temperature shows that whereas the transfer efficiency in a solution of PPO in a mixture of toluene and cyclohexane is very similar to that of a solution in pure toluene, the efficiency in a solution of which the major constituent is paraffin oil is considerably smaller. This corresponds well with the results obtained for solutions of anthracene in toluene and in a mixture of toluene and paraffin oil which have been reported previously.[4] The fact that the viscous solution has a much lower transfer efficiency than the two non-viscous solutions suggests again that a considerable part of the observed transfer efficiency in scintillator solutions is due to mutual diffusion of the accepting and transferring molecules during the lifetime of the latter.

On this basis one would also expect a great change in the transfer efficiency with a change in the diffusion parameter, T/η, of the system as the temperature is changed. It is, however, seen that within the indicated limits of temperature the changes in transfer efficiency are small when compared with the great difference between these values and the values in the non-viscous systems. One reason for this is that we have not yet considered the considerable changes which occur in the transferring agent, toluene, with changing temperature and which manifest themselves in a great decrease in its fluorescent yield. By taking account of this change one can correct the results relative to an arbitrary point, as was done in reference 4. Instead of doing so we now compute the transfer efficiencies and transfer probabilities from the decay times of the solutions.

b. Decay Time Measurements.

1. PPO in a mixture of toluene and paraffin oil. Figure 4 shows a semilogarithmic representation of scintillation pulse shapes. Curves (a) show the pulse shape of a deoxygenated mixture of 1 part toluene and 9 parts paraffin oil, curves (b) show the pulse shape of a deoxygenated solution of 0.5 g/liter PPO in this mixture. Figure 4A shows the pulse shapes at low temperatures [curve (a): $-7°C$, curve (b): $-8°C$]. Fig. 4B shows the pulse shapes at higher temperature (both curves $77°C$). The curves in each figure were made to coincide at their

peaks. The units of the abscissa (time scale) for curves (a) and
(b) are slightly different; for the sake of clearness the differences are not indicated in the figures. Omitted also are all the

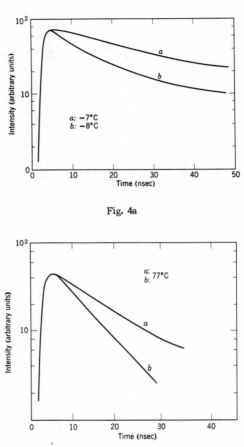

Fig. 4a

Fig. 4b

Fig. 4 — Shapes of scintillation light pulses. Curves
a - 1 part toluene and 9 parts paraffin oil. Curves b -
0.5 g/liter in the mixture of toluene and paraffin oil.

fine details of the actual tracings which are due to statistical
fluctuations of the light intensity. These curves are representative of a series of tracings carried out for these systems at
various temperatures.

DISCUSSION. In explaining the results we make the following assumptions: The greatest part of the incident energy is
absorbed by paraffin oil. A fraction of the excited paraffin
molecules transfer their excitation energy to toluene. Since
the molar concentration of toluene is about 450 times greater
than that of PPO energy transfer from paraffin oil to PPO is
negligible when compared with the transfer to toluene. A part
of the excited toluene molecules transfer their excitation
energy to PPO. The observed light pulse in the absence of PPO
is the fluorescence of toluene, whereas in the presence of PPO
the observed fluorescence is exclusively that of PPO. Energy
transfer from paraffin oil to toluene is so much faster than the
radiative decay of toluene and the transfer of energy from
toluene to PPO that it is irrelevant for the resulting pulse shape
whether a toluene molecule has been excited directly by the
incident radiation or via energy transfer from paraffin oil.

It is seen from the figure that the decay of toluene is practically exponential over the greatest part of the decay shown.
At longer times the decay constant becomes appreciably longer.
The tail of long lived fluorescence has been observed by many
investigators of the scintillation process and various explanations have been given for this phenomenon. Whatever the detailed explanation, however, we believe that this effect is of
only little influence on the observed transfer efficiencies when
the solutions are optically excited. It is also seen that the relative intensity of the long lived component decreases considerably with temperature. The variation of the decay time of
toluene in paraffin oil with temperature is shown in Figure 5.

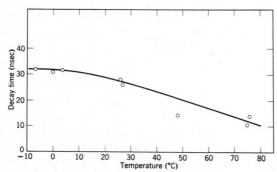

Fig. 5 – Variation of the fluorescent decay time of toluene
with temperature in a mixture of 1 part toluene and 9 parts
paraffin oil.

Interpolated values (τ_0) are given in Table 1A, Column 2.

From Figure 4 it is seen that the decay constant of the solution of PPO in toluene-paraffin oil (1:9) is rather constant over the greatest part of the observed time range at high temperatures. It changes strikingly, however, at low temperatures. The decay is initially fast and becomes gradually slower.

Quantitatively an increase in the decay constant with time would be expected if diffusion is small and hence the distribution of acceptor and donor molecules does not change with time. According to the theory developed by Förster[8] and by Galanin[9] local fluctuations in concentration will cause a non-exponential decay of the fluorescence of the solution.

It can be shown that in this case the intensity I at any given time θ will be given by the expression:

$$I(\theta) = \alpha\eta \, \frac{1}{\tau_f} \, \frac{q n_0}{\sqrt{\tau_0}} \int_0^\theta \frac{\exp\left(-t/\tau_0 - 2q\sqrt{t}/\tau_0 + t/\tau_f - \theta/\tau_f\right)}{\sqrt{t}} \, dt \tag{1}$$

where α is a constant which depends on the experimental arrangement, η is the quantum yield of PPO, n_0 is the number of initially excited toluene molecules, q is the transfer parameter assuming that the main mechanism is a dipole-dipole interaction, τ_0 is the decay time of toluene in the absence of PPO and τ_f is the fluorescence decay time of PPO. A computer program was initiated to determine the parameters τ_0, q and τ_f from the obtained decay curves. The results for a series of curves analyzed by this program were not promising. The present interpretation of the decay curves is based on the simple approximation of two successive average decay times of toluene in the presence of PPO, as a consequence of the changing transfer probability with time. In each of these regions the curve is assumed to represent a cascade of two exponential functions of the form:

$$I = A(e^{-t/\tau_t} - e^{-t/\tau_f}) \tag{2}$$

where τ_t is the decay time of toluene in the presence of PPO and τ_f is the fluorescence decay time of PPO. As a first approximation the decay time of PPO is assumed to be very short in comparison with the decay time of the transferring toluene even in the case where τ_t is short as a consequence of high transfer efficiency and/or high temperatures. The two average decay times τ_t of toluene for every temperature are then given by the successive time intervals during each of which the intensity of the pulse decreases by a factor of e. They are designated by τ_1 and τ_2, respectively. This is the crudest possible approximation to the actual shape of the decay which is of course much more complicated since, in many cases the decay constant changes continuously.

The values τ_1 and τ_2 which result from this analysis are given in Figure 6. Interpolated values (designated by "u") are

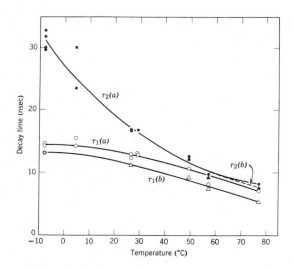

Fig. 6 — Variation of decay times [τ_1 and τ_2] with temperature for a 0.5 g/liter PPO in a mixture of 1 part toluene and 9 parts paraffin oil. Curves a - uncorrected values. Curves b - corrected values.

given in columns 3 and 4 of Table 1A. It is seen that at low temperatures and high viscosities the difference between τ_1 and τ_2 is very great. At higher temperatures and low viscosities the differences become successively smaller. From these decay times the transfer probabilities $1/\tau_t$ are computed according to the relation:

$$1/\tau_{T1} = 1/\tau_1 - 1/\tau_0$$

$$1/\tau_{T2} = 1/\tau_2 - 1/\tau_0$$

(3)

($1/\tau_t$ is the sum of the probabilities for spontaneous decay and other competing processes all expressed together as $(1/\tau_0)$ and of the probability for energy transfer $(1/\tau_T)$). The results are given in columns 5 and 6 of Table 1A. Finally the transfer efficiencies ϵ are computed from the decay times by the relations:

$$\epsilon_1 = \frac{\tau_0 - \tau_1}{\tau_0}$$

$$\epsilon_2 = \frac{\tau_0 - \tau_2}{\tau_0}$$

$$(4)$$

The transfer process and hence the efficiency is assumed to be composed of two parts: a transfer process of high efficiency ϵ_1 during which the number of initially excited toluene molecules is reduced by a factor of $1/e$, followed by a transfer process of relatively low efficiency ϵ_2 during which the remaining excited toluene molecules are entirely deactivated. The numerical value of ϵ is then obtained by the relation:

$$\epsilon = 0.63 \; \epsilon_1 + 0.37 \; \epsilon_2 \qquad (5)$$

This is a consequence of the above crude approximation with the additional assumption that the transfer process after the second period remains constant.* A comparison of the resulting values of ϵ with the transfer efficiencies ϵ_0 which are obtained from intensity measurements and which are given in column 8 of Table 1A shows that even for these very crude approximations the results obtained by both methods correspond to a degree which indicates that the basic assumptions are justified.

The decay time τ_f of PPO under the given conditions can be evaluated only by direct excitation of PPO by light of a wavelength to which the solvent is transparent. Since we did not have the necessary equipment we could only assume approximate values. The decay time of PPO in toluene is 2.6 nsec.[11] The decay time of 0.5 g/liter PPO in cyclohexane was found by us to

---

*The inaccuracy in this assumption is of no decisive influence on the quantitative results for two reasons: 1. the number of still excited toluene molecules after the second period is small and an error in the transfer efficiency is of relatively small influence on the final sum. 2. Actually n decreases more slowly than I, hence the error in the assumed greater transfer probability in the final part of the pulse is counterbalanced by the implicit assumption of a faster decrease of n.

be 2.7 nsec. If the decay time of PPO in the present system is similar to the above value, it is easily seen that the assumption which was made in the evaluation of the values of τ_1 and τ_2, namely that the decay time of PPO is so short that the second exponential in equation (2) can be neglected, results in serious errors. The finite decay time of PPO must be taken into account not only for the values of high temperatures but even for the greatest values of τ_1 and τ_2 and a minimum of curve analysis becomes unavoidable. The corrected values of τ_1 and τ_2 (designated by "c") which have been obtained by assuming $\tau_f = 2.7$ nsec are given beneath the respective uncorrected values in columns 3 and 4 of Table 1A. It is seen that they are considerably shorter than the corresponding uncorrected values, particularly at higher temperatures. The corrected transfer probabilities and transfer efficiencies are given beneath the uncorrected values in columns 5, 6 and 7, respectively. It is seen that the resulting transfer efficiencies are similar to the values obtained from intensity measurements (ϵ_0) In view of the inherent experimental inaccuracies and the approximative character of the analysis this fit seems rather satisfactory.

The most significant quantities in this investigation are the transfer probabilities ($1/\tau_{T1}$, $1/\tau_{T2}$). Their dependence on the various parameters indicates best the influence of these parameters on the transfer process. In Figure 7 the transfer

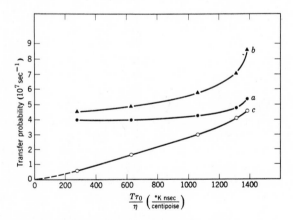

Fig. 7 — Variation of the transfer probabilities $1/\tau_{T1}$ and $1/\tau_{T2}$ with the diffusion parameter $\frac{T\tau_0}{\eta}$. a - uncorrected values of $1/\tau_{T1}$ b - corrected values of $1/\tau_{T1}$ c - corrected values of $1/\tau_{T2}$

probability is plotted as a function of the parameter

$$\frac{T\,\tau_0}{\eta}$$

(T = absolute temperature; η = viscosity; τ_0 = decay time of
toluene at temperature T in the absence of PPO.) This parameter is proportional to the diffusion coefficient. Curve (a)
gives the uncorrected values of $1/\tau_{T1}$, curve (b) the corrected
value and curve (c) the corrected values of $1/\tau_{T2}$ which are
similar to the uncorrected values. Curves (a) and (b) show both
that at higher viscosities the transfer process changes slowly
with the changing diffusion parameter. This confirms the assumption that the transfer mechanism is basically a long range
interaction. At low viscosities, however, the rate of increase
of the transfer probability increases rather fast with the diffusion parameter. In view of the apparently complicated nature
of the system it is certainly premature to expect a close fit
of the results with any existing theory. It may, however, be
pointed out that the described behavior of $1/\tau_{T1}$ as a function of
the diffusion parameter does not correspond even qualitatively
with Vavilov's theory on diffusion controlled quenching processes.[13] According to Vavilov's formula the slope of $1/\tau_{T1}$ as
a function of the diffusion parameter should decrease with the
argument, whereas our results show a clear increase.

A possible explanation of the results is that the measured
macroscopic viscosity is different from the microscopic viscosity experienced by the interacting molecules. It is possible
that although the viscous interaction between molecular clusters
of the solution is weakened with increasing temperature, the
viscous interaction within the individual clusters is still strong
and diffusion within the cluster is slow. There arises, however,
a question of much more general character, namely: is the observed increase in transfer probability due only to increased
diffusion or do other effects contribute to these changes? In
the works of Bowen[14] and Porter[15] it has been shown that first
order effects may be dependent on viscosity. If the probability
of certain intramolecular processes increases with their vibrational freedom, why should not a similar vibrational freedom
be necessary for the process of energy transfer to be efficient?
In this case the differences between macroscopic and microscopic viscosity would be even more important. We believe this
point should be further investigated.

The dependence of $1/\tau_{T2}$ on the diffusion parameter (curve c) is approximately linear. (The accuracy of the initial part of the graph is rather poor, since in this region the difference between τ_0 and τ_2 is relatively small and a slight error in the determination of one of them causes a considerable error in the computed value of $1/\tau_{T2}$). These results indicate that at the given acceptor concentration the transfer process at longer times becomes essentially diffusion controlled. This seems reasonable. After the initial stages of the transfer process which involve mainly the acceptor molecules which are closest to the donor, the transfer time is determined by the rate of diffusion of the acceptor molecules which are further away.

For $(T\tau_0)/(\eta) \to 0$, $i.\,e.$ in the absence of diffusion $1/\tau_{T2}$ will vanish. The extrapolated value of ϵ is about 0.32 ± 0.04. Computation of the critical interaction distance R_0 for the dipole-dipole interaction between toluene and PPO according to Förster's theory yields a value of $27\mathring{A}$ for R_0. The corresponding theoretical value of the necessary acceptor concentration is about 2.5 times greater than the actual concentration of 0.5 g/liter employed in the experiment.

From the preceding discussion it is seen that although the transfer efficiency of the present system does not change very much with temperature and viscosity each of the individual processes which determine the transfer efficiency changes rather drastically with these parameters. Thus the transfer efficiency itself does not give sufficient information for a detailed elucidation of the transfer process.

2. PPO in a mixture of toluene and cyclohexane. Curve (a) of Figure 8 presents the shape of the scintillation light pulse of a deoxygenated mixture of 1 part toluene and 9 parts cyclohexane. Curve (b) shows the pulse shape of a deoxygenated solution of 0.5 g/liter PPO in this mixture. These pulse shapes which are obtained at room temperature are representative of a series of tracings carried out at various temperatures.

DISCUSSION: For the interpretation of these results we maintain the same basic assumptions which were made for solutions in paraffin oil. The interpolated value of the decay time of the mixture of 1 part toluene and 9 parts cyclohexane at various temperatures is given in column 2 of Table 1B. In columns 3 and 4 the decay times of solutions of 0.5 g/liter PPO in this mixture are given. The transfer probabilities and transfer efficiencies are given in columns 5, 6 and 7. Again the

uncorrected (u.) and corrected (c.) values are both given.
The method used in evaluating these results from the tracings
of the pulse shapes is the same as that employed for the solutions in paraffin oil.

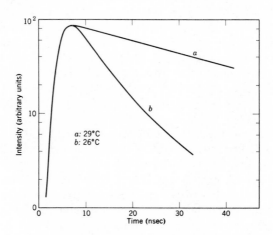

Fig. 8 — Shapes of scintillation light pulses. a -
mixture of 1 part toluene and 9 parts cyclohexane.
b - solution of 0.5 g/liter PPO in the mixture of
toluene and cyclohexane.

Self quenching of toluene is appreciable even at room temperature. This is well known from intensity measurements and
can also be seen by comparing the decay times of diluted and
undiluted toluene (Tables 1B and 1C, respectively). From the
table it is seen, however, that the decay times of toluene when
dissolved in cyclohexane are similar to the values for toluene
in paraffin oil. This indicates that the process of self quenching in toluene is not viscosity dependent. The decrease of the
fluorescent intensity and decay time of toluene with concentration suggests a process of energy transfer between toluene
molecules which causes a partial deactivation of the excited
molecules. The decrease of intensity and decay time with temperature may be due exclusively to an intramolecular deactivation mechanism. It is possible that the quenching interaction
between toluene molecules is facilitated by an increase in temperature, although in that case one would expect a broadening of
the absorption and/or emission spectrum of toluene. The observed spectral changes with temperature are, however, very

slight and can hardly account for an appreciable increase of the interaction between toluene molecules.

Comparison of the decay times and transfer probabilities of this system with the corresponding values for the solution in a mixture of toluene and paraffin oil shows the following differences: the decay times τ_1 and τ_2 are appreciably shorter in the non viscous system and the resulting transfer probabilities are correspondingly higher. The ratios τ_1/τ_2 and the corresponding ratios of the transfer probabilities in the non-viscous solution with cyclohexane are considerably smaller than those in the solution with paraffin oil. The changes in transfer probability with temperature in the non-viscous system are appreciably smaller than in the viscous system.* The transfer efficiency from intensity measurements was determined at room temperature only. The correspondence with the results obtained from decay times seems again to justify the basic assumptions and approximations made in the interpretation.

The differences between the two systems are most probably a consequence of the differences in their viscosities. Again the question whether the considerably higher transfer probabilities in the non-viscous system are due exclusively to the much increased mutual diffusion of acceptor and donor molecules or whether some additional not yet elucidated effect of viscosity causes a decrease in the transfer process needs further investigation. The smaller changes in transfer probability with temperature in the non-viscous system are expected since diffusion may contribute significantly to the transfer process at all temperatures. Also the change in transfer probability with time in the non-viscous system is much smaller than in the viscous system since diffusion diminishes the fluctuations in concentration and since the acceptor molecules diffuse into the region of interaction with the donor much faster in the non-viscous system.

3. <u>PPO in toluene</u>. Figure 9 shows the shape of the scintillation pulse of deoxygenated toluene (curve a), and of a deoxygenated solution of 0.5 g/liter PPO in toluene (curve b).

---

*One should be careful in interpreting the results for the solution in cyclohexane at 6°C. This is the freezing point of cyclohexane and though the addition of toluene probably lowers the freezing point, certain structural changes may take place which influence the transfer process. The accuracy of the corrected values at 60°C is also rather low, since at these short decay times a slight error in the correction causes an appreciable variation in the result.

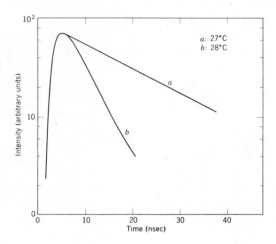

Fig. 9 — Shapes of scintillation light pulses: a - toluene. b. - 0.5 g/liter PPO in toluene.

DISCUSSION: The shorter decay time of pure toluene as compared to that of toluene dissolved in cyclohexane shows the effect of self quenching discussed in the preceding section. The transfer efficiency computed from the corrected decay time is seen to be similar to that obtained from intensity measurements, although the correspondence is not very good. Again this may be due to an error in the correction, which at these short times is of low accuracy. Comparison of the transfer efficiency of this solution with the efficiency of the system in cyclohexane shows that they are very similar. From this fact it has been previously concluded that the transfer process in both systems is the same.[16] Comparison of the transfer probabilities, however, shows that the probability in the undiluted system is higher than in the system diluted with cyclohexane. This implies that in the undiluted system an additional transfer mechanism may be acting such as energy migration between neighboring toluene molecules.

The discussion of the system PPO in paraffin oil (without toluene) will have to be deferred. It should be pointed out that contrary to the systems discussed in the preceding sections, the decay time increases with increasing temperature. A tentative explanation of these results is that the viscous interaction between the transferring paraffin oil molecules is reduced and hence their lifetime increased. The importance of a possible connection between viscosity and decay time for an understanding of the liquid state should be considered.

The author wishes to express his gratitude to Mr. J. Brichta for his most cooperative and valuable assistance throughout this work, to Mr. E. A. Mroz for his very kind help and instruction in the decay time measurements and to Dr. I. B. Berlman for much valuable information and for the fluorescence spectrum of PPO in the viscous solutions.

REFERENCES

[1] H. Knau, Z. Naturforsch. 12a, 881 (1957).
[2] R. Hardwick, J. Chem. Phys., 26, 323 (1957).
[3] G. Laustriat, Thesis, Strasbourg 1960.
[4] A. Weinreb, J. Chem. Phys., 35, 91 (1961).
[5] S. G. Cohen and A. Weinreb, Proc. Phys. Soc. (London) B69, 593 (1956).
[6] R. K. Swank, H. B. Phillips, W. L. Buck and L. J. Basile, IRE Transactions on Nuclear Science, NS-5, 183 (1958).
[7] R. K. Swank and E. A. Mroz, Rev. Sci. Instr. 30, 10, 880 (1959).
[8] Th. Förster, Ann. Physik 2, 55 (1948).
[9] M. D. Galanin, Soviet Phys. JETP 1, 2, 317.
[10] H. Kallmann and G. J. Brucker, Phys. Rev. 108, 5, 1122 (1957).
[11] I. B. Berlman, J. Chem. Phys. 33, 4, 1124 (1960).
[12] A. Weinreb, J. Chem. Phys. (to appear).
[13] S. I. Vavilov, Acta physica polonia 5, 417 (1936).
[14] E. J. Bowen, Discussions of the Faraday Soc. No. 27, 40 (1959).
[15] G. Porter and M. R. Wright, Discussions of the Faraday Soc. No. 27, 18 (1959).
[16] V. Bar and A. Weinreb, J. Chem. Phys. 29, 6, 1412 (1958).

ULTRAVIOLET AND LIFETIME STUDIES OF MECHANISMS IN THE SCINTILLATION PROCESS

I. B. Berlman

Argonne National Laboratory, Argonne, Illinois

ABSTRACT

The technique of using a pulsed beam of electrons to excite an organic scintillation solution and the recording of the resultant pulse of emitted radiation is described. Sample pulse profiles are shown and the values of the measured decay time of several solvents and solutes are presented. For specific solutions this technique is used to advantage to study the mechanism of non-radiative energy transfer from solvent to solute as a function of the solute concentration. Energy transfer values are determined which agree favorably with those obtained from other coordinated methods. One such method, involving the static excitation of the solution by monochromatic UV radiation and the recording of the fluorescence spectrum, is described. The anomalous changes in the measured value of the decay time and in the shape of the emission spectrum as the solute concentration is increased to a large value are investigated by the above methods.

I. INTRODUCTION

Two coordinated experiments are described which were used in the study of energy transfer and related phenomena occurring in an organic liquid scintillator.[1] In the first the solution is excited by a pulsed beam of electrons and the mean fluorescence decay time measured; in the second the solution is excited statically by a uv source and the fluorescence emission spectrum recorded. This presentation deals first with the results from solutions containing a low solute concentration ($\leqslant 10^{-2}$ M) and then with the anomalous behavior of similar solutions containing a high solute concentration ($\geqslant 10^{-1}$ M).

II. DECAY-TIME MEASUREMENTS FOR LOW SOLUTE CONCENTRATIONS

The apparatus for measuring the fluorescence decay times can be found in references 2 and 3.

The solutions are contained in thin (1/12 in.) wafer-like quartz cells which have a 3/16 in. hole in the center of the top surface. The electron beam impinges on the solution through this hole. To minimize absorption and reemission of the fluorescence radiation, the volume of the solution was reduced by inserting a teflon tube with an inner diameter of 1/16 in. through the hole and the thickness of the samples was reduced by only partially filling this insert. Only the solution inside the hole was excited by the electron beam and was involved in the subsequent fluorescence process. To avoid quenching by oxygen, two overlapping layers of 0.00025 in. aluminum or aluminum coated mylar were placed over the cell opening. These coverings were visually inspected with an 8 power eyepiece for possible pinholes.

The solvents were purified by distillation in which the first and last 20% of the distillate were discarded. The solute was usually used without additional purification. Nitrogen was bubbled through the liquids to obviate oxygen quenching. Oxygen-free conditions were maintained by storing and handling the solutions in a nitrogen-filled glove box, through which nitrogen was passed continuously. The solutions were kept in the dark and used within 48 hours after preparation in order to avoid possible photochemical effects.

Fig. 1 presents two sample pulse contours and some of the values of the mean decay times are listed in Table I. The accuracy of these values is approximately ± 10%.

A simple theory expresses the decay time of the solvent in terms of several independent probabilities.[4] The decay time of a solvent without solute is expressed as $\tau_o = (p_e + p_q)^{-1}$ where τ_o is the mean decay time of the first excited electronic state of the solvent, where p_e is the probability per second that an excited solvent molecule will emit its excess energy as fluorescence radiation and p_q is the probability per second for inter- and intra-molecular quenching of the excitation energy. On adding a solute to the solvent the decay time becomes $\tau_c = (p_e + p_q + p_t)^{-1}$ where p_t is the probability per second for nonradiative transfer. By definition $\epsilon = p_t / (p_e + p_q + p_t)$, so that a $\epsilon = 1 - (\tau_c / \tau_o)$. It is assumed that p_q and p_e are independent of solute concentration.

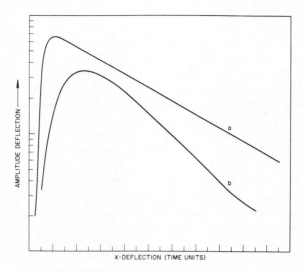

Fig. 1 — Sample decay contours. Curve *a* is a semilog plot of
pure p-xylene and curve *b* is a semilog plot of 1 g/liter of PPO
in xylene. The calibration of the time base is different for the
two curves.

Table I

Solvent	τ (nsec)	Solute in Cyclohexane	τ (nsec)
Benzene	17.7	PPO (1 g/l)	2.7
Toluene	19.0	POPOP (~1/10 g/l)	2.6
Benzotrifluoride	8.6	αNPO (1 g/l)	2.6
p-Xylene	20.2	p-Terphenyl (1 g/l)	2.7
1,4-bis (trifluoromethyl) Benzene	5.5	m-Terphenyl*(1 g/l)	21.4
		Diphenyl(1 g/l)	19.3
		Naphthalene (1 g/l)	75.0
		Pyrene**(0.5 g/l)	80.0

* Also has a faster component.
**Blue component of the fluorescence.

Legend: αNPO is 2-(1-Naphthyl) -5-Phenyloxazole
         POPOP is p-Bis [2-(5-Phenyloxazolyl)]-Benzene.

In studying energy transfer either from solvent to solute or from solute (S_1) to solute (S_2) it is advantageous among other considerations to have the transferring molecule long lived and the acceptor molecule comparatively short lived. Decay-time measurements and energy transfer studies were made using solutions of 2,5-diphenyloxazole (PPO) in p-Xylene.

As solute is added to the solvent the measured decay time decreases. At low concentrations ($\leqslant$ 0.1 g/liter) the transfer time is much larger than the solute decay time so that the measured decay time is exponential and is essentially that of the solvent. In a higher concentration range ($\geqslant$ 0.1 to 2 g/liter) the transfer time becomes comparable to the decay time of the solute and the pulse contour assumes a convex shape. The value of the decay time of the solvent is obtained by approximating the pulse shape by means of a formula which includes the difference of two exponentials. Curve fitting is a trial and error method and as is generally the case with these methods, it is tedious and not trouble-free.

The use of nitrogen-bubbled solutions has the significant advantage that the longer decay time of the solvent permits the use of higher solute concentrations before it becomes necessary to use the laborious curve-fitting technique involving the difference of two exponentials.

III. UV MEASUREMENTS FOR LOW SOLUTE CONCENTRA-
   TIONS

The second method records the fluorescence spectrum emitted under static uv excitation. Monochromatic radiation from a Bausch and Lomb monochromator was used to excite the solutions and a Beckman DK-2 spectrophotometer was used to record the emission spectrum. The solutions are contained in standard 1-cm quartz absorption cells containing quartz insert to reduce the light path through the solution. The thickness of the sample was chosen to be as thin as possible consistent with total absorption of the exciting light. The sample cell is positioned at the entrance slit of the recording instrument. With this arrangement, it was possible to record the emission from either solvent, or solute, or both. The spectrophotometer was calibrated with respect to relative wavelength response[5] and the corrected spectra are presented.

This experiment was performed within as short a time interval as possible after the decay-time experiments to eliminate possible photochemical effects.

Figure 2 is a spectrogram of a dilute PPO-xylene solution.

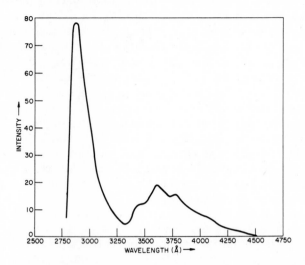

Fig. 2 — Spectrogram of PPO-xylene solution; concentration of 0.02 g/liter, exciting radiation of $\lambda = 2650$ Å, sample thickness of 0.05 mm.

As the concentration of PPO is increased the xylene emission yield decreases and the PPO emission yield increases. The shape of each component does not change in the low concentration region. Since the fluorescence spectra of the solvent and solute do not overlap, the intensity near the peak of each spectrum was taken as the best measure of the fluorescence yield. For p-xylene this is 2920 Å and for PPO, 3820 Å. However, the absorbance of PPO in the region of 2920 Å is strong but measurable, so that a correction must necessarily be made in this case.

From the change in yield of either one of these components as a function of concentration, the energy-transfer parameter, ϵ, may be computed. The xylene emission, L_o, is proportional to the quantum yield which is equal to $p_e/(p_e + p_q)$. When the concentration of the solute is increased from O to c, the intensity of the xylene emission decreases because of the added probability term in the denominator; $i.e.$, L_c is proportional to

$p_e/(p_e + p_q + p_t)$. Hence the efficiency of energy transfer is
$\epsilon = 1 - L_c/L_o$, since by definition $\epsilon = p_t/(p_e + p_q + p_t)$.

ϵ was also determined by studying the hyperchromic change
in the fluorescence intensity of PPO as a function of PPO concentration. The solution was excited with 2650 Å radiation to
excite the solute indirectly by means of energy transfer. Radiation of this wavelength is almost completely absorbed by the
solvent in the concentration range of PPO under consideration
so that no correction for direct solute excitation was deemed
necessary. Then the solution was excited with 3130 Å radiation
to excite the solute directly. By exciting the solute directly it
is possible to determine what the intensity of the PPO emission
would be at 100% energy transfer. To calibrate the relative
incident radiation flux at 2650 and 3130 Å, a PPO-cyclohexane
solution was excited by each of these two wavelengths; cyclohexane being transparent at these two wavelengths.

The assumptions made in this type of computation are:
(1) the quantum yield of PPO is the same at both wave-
    lengths. In an ancillary experiment this has been
    shown to be true.
(2) the quantum yield remains constant over the concentra-
    tion range of the experiment; this is true within experi-
    mental limits.
(3) No correction has been applied to account for radiative
    transfer. Because of the precautions taken it is assumed
    that ϵ would be at most 5% too large because of radiation
    transfer.

The results of the three methods of measuring ϵ are shown
in Table II. The close agreement between the energy transfer
efficiencies obtained by electron excitation and those by uv excitation suggests that ϵ is independent of these two modes of excitation. This inference agrees with the conclusion of Lipsky and
Burton[6] and of Brown, Furst and Kallmann.[7] Also since the
parametric values of ϵ in columns two and three are in good
comparative agreement, it is reasonable to assume that for this
solution the excited state of the solvent which gives rise to
emission is the one involved in energy transfer

From a Stern-Volmer plot of the parameters used in determining ϵ as a function of the concentration the value of the rate
constant for transfer, k_t may be obtained. The value of k_t thus
obtained is approximately 7×10^{10} liter/mol/sec.

Table II

Efficiency of Energy Transfer (%)
as a Function of the Solute Concentration

Conc. PPO	Method I (Lifetime)	Method II (Xylene emission)	Method II (PPO Emission)
0.02	14 ± 3	12 ± 2	14 ± 2
0.04	26 ± 3	25 ± 2	23 ± 2
0.1	40 ± 3	39 ± 2	41 ± 2
0.2	55 ± 3	59 ± 2	56 ± 2
0.25	59 ± 3	62 ± 2	62 ± 2
0.5	75 ± 3	80 ± 2	77 ± 2
1.0	84 ± 3	88 ± 2	85 ± 2
2.0	90 ± 3		92 ± 2

IV. HIGH SOLUTE CONCENTRATIONS AND RESULTING ANOMALIES

In studying more concentrated solutions of PPO in xylene it was noted that a very high solute concentrations a change in the fluorescence spectrum and in the decay time takes place. A long wavelength component appears in the emission spectrum and simultaneously a long component of approximately 14 nsec appears in the decay-time curve. These results are interpreted by assuming the possible existence of an excited, transient dimer state.

In 1955 Förster and Kasper [8] studied the very striking change in the spectrum of pyrene in benzene as a function of the solute concentration. They noted that as the solute concentration is increased the violet emission decreases and a new component, in the blue-green region, becomes prominent. They concluded that the violet emission is produced by monomolecular pyrene whereas the long wavelength blue emission comes from excited transient dimers. Brown, Furst, and Kallmann [9] in 1959 postulated that self-quenching in most cases could be explained by transient dimer formation. In the case of pyrene the transient dimers emit. It has been postulated by the author [10] that transient excited dimers are formed in PPO solutions at large solute concentrations. The evidence for this assumption is as follows:

1) The shape of the emission spectrum from xylene-PPO

solutions excited with 3130 Å radiation changes progressively
with increasing PPO concentration (Fig. 3). That these observations are not the result of aborption and reemission processes

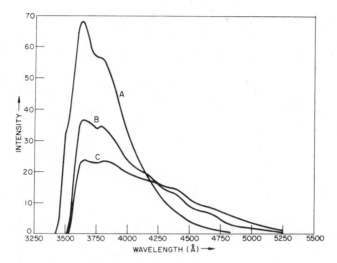

Fig. 3 — Relative spectrograms of PPO-xylene solutions. Concentration values are per liter of solution. Curve A: − 1 g/liter, 1 mm
sample. Curve B: 100 g/liter, 0.2 mm sample. Curve C−: 200 g/liter,
0.05 mm sample. Exciting radiation of λ = 3130 Å. Concentration
values are per liter of solution.

can be easily demonstrated by varying the thickness of the
solution sample at a constant concentration.

2) Absorption measurements were made using a variable
light-path cell,[11] and the results indicate that the shape of
absorption spectrum does not change with concentration. These
observations negate the possibility of permanent dimers.

3) Measuring the decay-time of a concentration solution indicates a fast component of less than 2.5 nsec and one of approximately 14 nsec. In Fig. 4 it is seen that the long component
in the decay curve becomes more prominent at higher concentrations. Interposing a Wratten 2B series VI filter between the
solution and the detecting equipment to eliminate the shorter
wavelengths results in eliminating the short component in the
decay curves leaving only the longer, 14.0 ± 2 nsec component.
However interposing a 7-39 Corning filter to eliminate the
longer emission wavelengths results in reducing, but not eliminating the longer decay components.

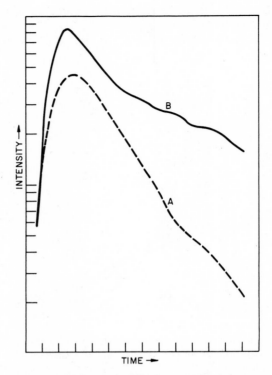

Fig. 4 — Semilog plots of the fluorescence decay
time of a PPO-xylene solution at concentrations of
4 g/liter, curve A, and 100 g/liter, curve B. Intensities are arbitrary.

4) Cooling enhances dimerization whereas heating inhibits
aggregate formation.[12] This is true for the present solution.
Heating a solution of 100 g/litter PPO in xylene by approximately 20°C dramatically affects the emission spectrum as
shown in Fig. 5; whereas heating a 1 g/liter of PPO-xylene
solution to the same temperature does not change the magnitude
or shape of the emission spectrum. Cooling the concentrated
solution below room temperature increases the long wavelength
portion of the spectrum at the expense of the shorter wavelengths.

5) For the same concentration of PPO and for relatively
similar values of viscosity the anomalies occur less readily in
aromatics than in aliphatics and in alcohols. Fig. 6 shows the
emission spectrogram of 50 g/l PPO in methylcyclohexane.

This observation negates the possibility of impurities causing the new portion of the spectrum.

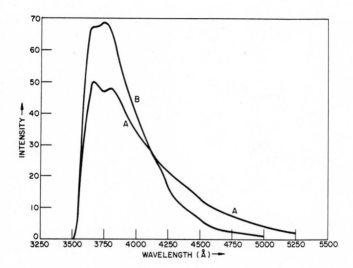

Fig. 5 — Effect of temperature on modified spectrum of PPO-xylene solutions. Curve A: 100 g/1, 0.2 mm sample, exciting radiation λ = 3130 Å, room temperature; Curve B: same solution but warmed slightly.

7) Aerating a concentrated PPO-cyclohexane solution reduces the fluorescence yield of the long wavelength portion of the spectrum approximately in the same ratio as the short wavelength region.

Therefore the following mechanisms are postulated:

$$A^* \rightarrow A + h\nu \tag{1}$$

$$A^* + A \rightleftharpoons (AA)^*, \tag{2}$$

$$(AA)^* + S \rightleftharpoons (AA)^{**} + S, \tag{3}$$

$$(AA)^{**} \rightarrow (AA) + h\nu', \tag{4}$$

where A^* is an excited solute monomer, $(AA)^*$ is an excited dimer, S is a solvent molecule, $(AA)^{**}$ is an excited dimer which has lost its excess vibrational energy, and (AA) is the dimer in the ground state.

The back reactions of Equations 2 and 3 indicate that in PPO

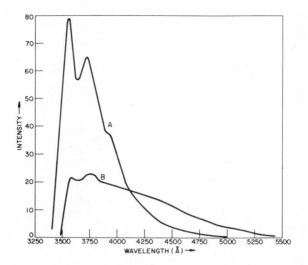

Fig. 6 — Fluorescence spectrograms of PPO in methylcy-clohexane. Curve A: 1 g/liter, 1 mm sample. Curve B: 50 g/liter, 1 mm sample. Exciting radiation λ = 3130 Å. Concentration values are per liter of solution.

the first excited singlet of the transient dimers lies lower but close to the first excited singlet level of the monomer. In the case of pyrene the emission change is large thus indicating that the first singlet excited level of the dimer is significantly lower than that of the monomer. Therefore at room temperature the back reaction is not favored. In the case of m-terphenyl where there is a minimal fluorescence change at high solute concentrations but where there is a decay anomoly (a long component in the decay time) the levels of the dimer and monomer must be either very close or must essentially coincide.

ACKNOWLEDGMENTS

The author wishes to thank Melvin Zarr for his assistance during the summer months of 1958 and 1959, and Warren L. Buck, Eugene Mroz, and Robert K. Swank for their cooperation in allowing me the frequent use of the accelerator.

REFERENCES

[1] I. B. Berlman, J. Chem. Phys. 33, 1124 (1960).
[2] R. K. Swank, H. B. Phillips, W. L. Buck, and L. J. Basile, I.R.E. Trans. on Nuclear Sci. NS-5, 183 (1958).
[3] R. K. Swank and E. A. Mroz, R.S.I. 30, 880 (1959).
[4] G. Brucker and H. Kallmann, Phys. Rev. 108, 1122 (1957).
[5] Performed by W. R. Anderson.
[6] S. Lipsky and M. Burton, J. Chem. Phys. 31, 1221 (1959).
[7] F. H. Brown, M. Furst, and H. Kallmann, Discussion Faraday Soc. 27, 43 (1959).
[8] T. Förster and K. Kasper, Z. Electrochem. 59, 976 (1955).
[9] F. H. Brown, M. Furst, and H. Kallmann, International Symposium on Nuclear Electronics 1, 15 (1959).
[10] I. B. Berlman, J. Chem. Phys. 34, 1083 (1961).
[11] Research and Industrial Instrument Company, England
[12] P. Pringsheim "Fluorescence and Phosphorescence" (Interscience Publishers, Inc., New York, 1949), p. 359.

FLUORESCENCE QUENCHING STUDIED
by FLASH SPECTROSCOPY

Horst Leonhardt and Albert Weller

(Laboratorium für physikalische Chemie der Technischen
Hochschule Stuttgart)

ABSTRACT

Studies of fluorescence quenching by amines in solution
have shown that, generally, an amine is the more efficient a
quencher the smaller its ionization potential. This leads to the
assumption that in these cases quenching occurs by univalent
reduction of the excited molecules. A flash photolysis investigation carried out with solutions of perylene has confirmed
this assumption. In the presence of strongly quenching amines,
these solutions exhibit a transient absorption with a maximum
at 580mµ when irradiated under the conditions such that only perylene absorbs light. The transient substance has been identified
as the perylene monoanion radical. In addition to this radical
spectrum which is very pronounced in polar solvents like acetonitrile or dimethylformamide, a weaker absorption around
490mµ is observed which is due to a triplet-triplet transition of
perylene. This absorption is very much enhanced in nonpolar
solvents (benzene, methylcyclohexane), where no 580mµ absorption has been found. These results indicate (i) that stabilization by solvation of ionic radicals is strongly favored in polar
solvents, (ii) that additional triplet state population may take
place by electron exchange.

INTRODUCTION

It is well known that the intensity of fluorescence emitted from
the solution of a fluorescent compound can be reversibly diminished by addition of so-called quenching substances. The
molecular process on which this phenomenon is based consists
in a radiationless deactivation by quencher molecules (Q) of
exited molecules ($\overset{*}{F}$) of the fluorescent compound. The thermal

74

energy dissipated in this process is equivalent to the energy of excitation which for compounds fluorescing in the visible or ultraviolet region amounts to 50–100 kcal/mole. It has been postulated[1,2] on theoretical grounds that <u>direct</u> transfer of electronic excitation energy into vibrational or translational degrees of freedom of the two molecules is too unlikely a process to compete effectively with emission of fluorescence and, therefore, it has been assumed that intermediate states of chemical and/or electronic nature are involved.

There are, essentially, two types of processes which have been suggested in order to explain this <u>inner</u> mechanism[2,3] of quenching. They can be represented in the following manner:

$$\overset{*}{F} + Q \rightarrow F^{(\mp)} \cdot Q^{(\pm)} \rightarrow F + Q \tag{I}$$

$$^1\overset{*}{F} + Q \rightarrow {}^3F \cdot Q \rightarrow F + Q \tag{II}$$

In both cases, of course, the two reactants are required to form an encounter complex† $(F \cdot Q)$, <i>i.e.</i>, they must approach to a distance where chemical interaction may become significant. Mechanism (I) which has been proposed by Baur[4] and by Weiss[5] involves the intermediate formation of radicals by one-electron-transfer between excited molecule and quencher molecule. So far, no <u>direct</u> experimental proof of this mechanism exists, but the results of some fluorescence quenching investigations carried out with acridine (Table 1) and with perylene (Table 2) using amines as quenching substances are in favor of an electron-transfer mechanism.

The quenching constants, $k\tau_0$, were obtained from the concentration dependence of the relative fluorescence intensity, ϕ/ϕ_0, with the aid of equation (1) which has been derived earlier[6]:

$$\frac{\phi}{\phi_0} = \frac{\exp\left(-V_D\sqrt{\frac{\phi}{\phi_0}} \cdot c_Q\right)}{1 + k\tau_0 \, c_Q} \tag{1}$$

---

†The two possible modes of formation of this complex which lead to the distinction between dynamic and static quenching are irrelevant to the scope of this paper and shall, therefore not be considered here. Cf.3)

Table 1

Quenching of Acridine Fluorescence
in Aqueous Solution (0.03 M NaOH) at 25°

Quencher	I^a (eV)	$(D_F + D_Q)\cdot 10^5$ (cm^2 . sec^{-1})	(l.mole^{-1})	γ_o^a (Å)
NH_3	10.16	3.10	0.38	0.012
$CH_3.NH_2$	8.97	2.35	2.45	0.10
$i-C_3H_7.NH_2$	8.72	1.80	2.4	0.13
$n-C_4H_9.NH_2$	8.71	1.65	6.5	0.39
$(CH_3)_2.NH$	8.24	2.00	21.5	1.07
$(CH_3)_3.N$	7.82	1.80	25.2	1.40
$(C_2H_5)_3.N$	7.56	1.45	40.1	2.75

Here c_Q is the quencher concentration in moles/l and τ_o the mean lifetime of the excited molecules. V_D, the molar volume of diffusion and k, the bimolecular rate constant of the quenching process are given by:

$$V_D = 4\pi (\gamma a)^2 \cdot \sqrt{D\tau_o} \cdot N' \frac{\sqrt{D\tau_o}}{(1-\gamma)a + \sqrt{D\tau_o}} \qquad (2)$$

and

$$k = 4\pi \gamma a \cdot D \cdot N' \qquad (3)$$

respectively, with γa = effective encounter distance, D = sum of the respective diffusion coefficients $(D_F + D_Q)$, N' = Avogadro's number per millimole (which corrects for the dimensions l.mole^{-1}). Using equations (1) - (3), a constant value of γa can be obtained by successive approximation.

Obviously, γa is a suitable measure for the efficiency of the inner mechanism. Therefore, the close correlation between γa and the ionization potential of the quencher, I, given in the second column, is highly suggestive of an electron-transfer taking place from the amine to the excited molecule. The results of similar experiments which have been carried out with perylene using different solvents are summarized in Table 2.

These data, again, indicate that quenching by amines very

a) Ionization potential from work of K. WATANABE and co-workers (J. Chem. Phys. 26 (1957) 542; 1773)

probably occurs by electron-transfer to the excited perylene molecules. Moreover, there is a remarkable influence of the solvent on γa which shows that the efficiency of the inner mechanism is reduced, not only when the ionization potential of the amine is high, but also when solvents of low polarity are used. This solvent effect is consistent with a lower rate of ion-pair formation (first step in reaction (I) in solvents of lower dielectric constant.

Mechanism (II) has been suggested by Kasha[6] to take place with quenchers containing heavy atoms through the agency of a spin-orbital perturbation. In this case quenching is explained by an increase of the $^1\overset{*}{F} \to {}^3\overset{*}{F}$ radiationless intercombination. $^3\overset{*}{F}$ denotes molecules in the triplet state which do not radiate in fluid media. The efficiency of this inner mechanism depends, essentially, on the degree of penetration of the π - electron

Table 2

Quenching of Perylene Fluorescence in Different Solvents
(air-free)

Quencher	Solvent	$(D_s+D_s)\times 10^6$ $(cm^2\cdot sec)$	$k\tau_s$ $(l/mole)$	$k\cdot 10^{-9}$ $(l/mole\cdot sec)$	γa $(Å)$
N(C$_2$H$_5$)$_2$ $I = 7.2\ eV$	Acetonitrile	3.20	102.0	16.7	6.9
	Dimethyl-formamide	1.32	49.0	7.9	7.9
	Benzene	1.77	7.5	1.2	0.9
N(CH$_3$)$_2$ $I = 7.3\ eV$	Acetonitrile	3.35	106.0	17.4	6.9
	Methanol	2.05	70.9	11.5	7.4
	Dimethyl-formamide	1.39	49.7	8.0	7.6
	Formamide	0.32	11.5	1.8$_5$	7.6
	Benzene	1.85	8.8	1.4	1.0
	Me-cyclohexane	1.65	2.0	0.32	0.26
NH$_2$ $I = 7.7\ eV$	Acetonitrile	3.80	47.0	7.7	2.7
	Benzene	2.10	0.1	0.01$_6$	0.001
N(C$_2$H$_5$)$_3$ $I = 7.6\ eV$	Acetonitrile	3.60	23.5	3.8	1.4
	Dimethyl-formamide	1.50	10.3	1.7	1.5
I$^-$	Acetonitrile	6.30	73.2	12.0	2.5
	Methanol	3.85	1.4	0.23	0.08
	Dimethyl-formamide	2.60	49.5	8.0	4.0

of the excited molecule into the electric field of the nucleus of the heavy atom. Therefore, close proximity of the species

without interfering solvent molecules is required, so that so-
lute-solvent interaction may be expected to play an important
role in this mechanism. Indeed, this seems to be borne out by
the peculiar solvent effect which is observed with quenching by
iodide ions (last rows of Table 2). Here the efficiency of the
inner mechanism decreases in the series: dimethyl-formamide,
acetonitrile, methanol, and it is in this same series that the
solubility of sodium iodide increases.

In order to establish the inner mechanism of fluorescence
quenching directly and unequivocally, a flash photolysis invest-
gation was carried out with the systems given in Table 3. It
was hoped to obtain by this method transient absorption spectra
which could be used to identify intermediate states possibly involved in fluorescence quenching.

EXPERIMENTAL METHOD

The general procedure, which has been applied earlier,[7]
consists in irradiating with an intense light flash the air-free
solutions in fused silica cells and, at the same time, taking the
optical absorption spectrum with a part of the irradiation flash
lamp as the source. In this way the absorption spectra of very
short-lived ($\geq 10^{-6}$ sec) photochemical products can be obtained.

The flash lamp used in these experiments consists of two
U-shaped quartz tubes ($i.d.$ 1.2 cm) which are connected at the
ends. (Total length 100 cm; filling:xenon 250 Torr). 100 Joule
of electrical energy stored at 20 kV in a 0.5 μF condensor yield
a flash of 9 μsec duration with an effective light output of 1.10^{17}
quanta, from 350 to 450mμ (the region of the long wave-length
absorption band of perylene), into a 12-cc sample, in a 10-cm-
long cell.

Two such sample cells, placed above each other and filled
with the same solution, were used. One of them was covered
with brass tubing and served as a reference. A small part of
the flash light passing axially through the two cells yielded two
adjacent spectra on Perutz Peromnia plates in a Hilger medium
spectrograph. The spectra were evaluated using a recording
microdensitometer (Mark III, Joyce, Loebl, and Co.). Two filter cuvettes were placed between flash tube and sample cells.
They were filled with highly concentrated quencher solution,

to prevent the quencher in the sample cell from becoming excited.

In the solution investigated the concentration of perylene
was 10^{-4} M throughout. The quencher concentration varied between 0.05 and 0.8 M and was chosen to give, at least, 80%
quenching. The solutions were carefully freed from oxygen by
repeated evacuation at low temperatures.

RESULTS AND DISCUSSION

Flash irradiation of perylene in air-free acetonitrile and
dimethyl-formamide containing amines as quenching substances
gives, in each case, a characteristic transient absorption spectrum showing a distinct narrow band at 580mμ and two diffuse
overlapping bands with maximum near 490mμ (Fig. 1).

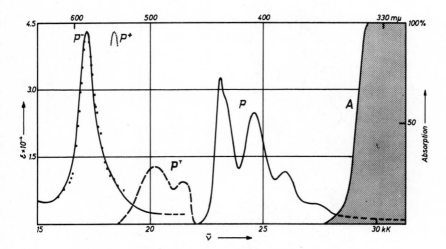

Fig. 1 — Perylene + 0.15 moles/1 dimethylaniline in acetonitrile.
P^-: absorption spectrum of perylene-mononegative ion.
P: absorption spectrum of perylene
P^T: absorption of perylene in the triplet state (rhs. ordinate)
A: absorption of filter solution (rhs. ordinate)

The 490mμ bands alone are found when benzene and methyl-
cyclohexane are used as solvents or when sodium iodide is the
quenching substance in solvents like acetonitrile or dimethyl-

formamide. In the absence of quencher, no transient absorption
has been found. A small permanent decomposition of perylene
with a quantum yield of ~ 0.015 has been observed to occur in
acetonitrile with dimethylaniline.

From densitometer analysis of the spectrum plates the difference in plate-blackening, ΔS, of unirradiated and irradiated
solution has been obtained. Values of ΔS at 580 and 490mμ are
given in Table 3.

Table 3

Difference of Plate-Blackening, ΔS

Fluorescing Substance	Quencher	Solvent	ΔS	
			at 580 mμ	at 490 mμ
	$N(C_2H_5)_2$	Acetonitrile	0.63 D	0.13 D
		Dimethyl-formamide	0.62 D	0.13 D
		Benzene	<0.04 D	0.26 D
	$N(CH_3)_2$	Acetonitrile	0.48 D	0.14 D
		Dimethyl-formamide	0.48 D	0.15 D
		Benzene	<0.04 D	0.28 D
		Me-cyclohexane	<0.04 D	0.24 D
	NH_2	Acetonitrile	0.29 D	0.06 D
	$N(C_2H_5)_3$	Acetonitrile	0.14 D	
	I^-	Acetonitrile	<0.04 D	0.31 D
		Dimethyl-formamide	<0.04 D	0.40 D

In the assignment of the 580mμ band the findings of Hoijtink
et. al. are very helpful. These authors have measured the absorption spectrum of perylene reduced by metallic sodium in
tetrahydrofuran and other etheral solvents and were able to
assign it unequivocally to the perylene-mononegative ion. The
absorption spectrum has a very prominent band at 580mμ which
is shown in Fig. 1 by the fully drawn curve denoted by P^-. The
filled circles are obtained from ΔS-values assuming a gradation
of unity and a maximum optical density of 0.05 cm^{-1}. The latter

corresponds to an average concentration of perylene-mononegative ion of about 1.10^{-6} M. This means that roughly 20%
of the perylene molecules which have been excited and quenched
during one flash appear as mononegative ions. Similar results
have been obtained in dimethyl-formamide solution and when
diethylaniline (26%), aniline (12%) and triethylamine (6%) are
used as quencher. There is, however, no indication, within the
precision of the measurements, of perylene-mononegative ion
in benzene and methyl-cyclohexane solutions. On the other
hand, the transient absorption bands around 490mμ are about two
times more intense in these solutions than in the more polar
solvents. These bands can be ascribed to the triplet-triplet absorption of perylene. A transient spectrum to which these bands
bear a very close resemblance has been found by Porter and
Windsor [9] on flash irradiation of perylene solution and has been
assigned to perylene in the triplet state. No extinction coefficients are given by these authors, so that no triplet concentration can be obtained from the ΔS-values of Table 3.

The results of this investigation are in accord with a mechanism for quenching of perylene fluorescence by amines which
can be presented by the following reaction scheme:

$$^{1}\overset{*}{F} + Q \xrightarrow{(1)}$$
$$^{3}\overset{*}{F} + Q \xrightarrow{(2')} F^{-} \cdot Q^{+} \xrightarrow{(3)} F^{-}_{solv} + Q^{+}_{solv} \qquad \text{(III)}$$
$$\xrightarrow{(2)}$$
$$F + Q$$

According to this scheme, the primary product of quenching
is a very short-lived ($< 10^{-7}$ sec) charge-transfer complex
($F^{-} \cdot Q^{+}$) (It should be noted that no indication of a charge-
transfer absorption has been found.) This charge-transfer complex can disappear in two ways—

(a) by back transfer of an electron which, according to steps
(2) and (2'), leads to formation of perylene in the ground state
and in the triplet state, respectively, and

(b) by (simultaneous) separation and solvation of the two
radical ions (step (3)). Obviously, the rate of this latter process
is smaller in solvents of lower dielectric constant. This explains both, the absence of perylene-monoanion absorption in
solvents like benzene or methyl-cyclohexane and the appearance
of more triplet state perylene in these solvents.

The results obtained when iodide is used as a quencher can

certainly not be explained by the above reaction scheme (III). The high intensity of the transient triplet absorption which is found with these systems strongly suggests that quenching of perylene (and probably other aromatics too) by iodide ion occurs according to the "heavy-atom" mechanism (II) as has been anticipated on account of the peculiar solvent effect on the efficiency of the inner mechanism of quenching.

ACKNOWLEDGMENT

We are indebted to the Research Corporation, New York for the support of this research and to the Deutsche Forschungs-gemeinschaft for placing to our disposal the recording micro-densitometer and for the fellowship given to one of us (H. L.).

REFERENCES

[1] J. Franck and H. Levi, Z. Phys. Chem. B27, (1935) 409
[2] Th. Förster, Fluoreszenz organischer Verbindungen, Vanden-hoeck und Ruprecht, Göttingen (1951), Chapter 47
[3] A. Weller, Disc. Far. Soc. 27, (1959) 28
[4] E. Baur, Z. phys. Chem. B16, (1932) 465
[5] J. Weiss and H. Fischgold, Z.phys. Chem. B32, (1936) 135
[6] M. Kasha, J. Chem. Phys. 20, (1952) 71
[7] K. Breitschwerdt, Th. Förster and A. Weller, Naturwiss. 43, (1956) 443
K. Breitschwerdt and A. Weller, Z. phys. Chem. N.F. 20, (1959) 353
[8] P. Balk, G. J. Hoijtink and J. W. H. Schreurs, Rec. trav. chim. P.-B. 76, (1957) 813
[9] G. Porter and M. W. Windsor, Proc. Roy. Soc. A 245, (1958) 238

QUENCHING OF ELECTRONIC ENERGY TRANSFER IN ORGANIC LIQUIDS*

S. Lipsky, W. P. Helman† and J. F. Merklin
Department of Chemistry, The University of Minnesota
Minneapolis, Minnesota

ABSTRACT

In a previous publication[1] bromobenzene was shown to quench the luminescence of a dilute air-equilibrated benzene-p-terphenyl solution when the system was excited either with 2537 Å light or with Co^{60} gamma rays. The quantitative results of this study indicated that:
1. The quenching by bromobenzene involves an interaction with the benzene solvent prior to the benzene-terphenyl transfer process.
2. The quenching efficiency is greater than would be expected on the basis of a diffusion-limited process with geometric cross-sections for solvent and quencher.
3. The quenching is about 25% more efficient under high energy irradiation conditions.

These studies have been repeated now in the absence of molecular oxygen and have been extended to a benzene-cyclohexane mixture solvent and to a dibromomethane quencher. The mechanism of the energy transport process both under UV and high energy excitation conditions is discussed.

*Supported in part by Air-Research and Development Command, USAF Contract No. AF19(604)-8356 and in part by a University of Minnesota Graduate School Grant (1959-1960).

†E. I. du Pont de Nemours and Company, Predoctorate Summer Fellowship.

INTRODUCTION

The non-radiative transfer of electronic energy in organic solutions at high concentrations of the energy donor has been studied both under high energy and UV excitation conditions.[1-5] The system most extensively characterized to date has been dilute solutions of p-terphenyl in a benzene or toluene solvent. If the solvent is excited either with $Co^{60}\gamma$ rays or with 2537 Å radiation, a luminescence characteristic of the emission spectrum of p-terphenyl is observed. The dependence of the intensity of this luminescence both on terphenyl concentration and on the concentration of an added quencher (e.g. bromobenzene) has been shown to be consistent with the following kinetic sequence:[1,6]

$$
\begin{array}{rcll}
C & \rightsquigarrow & C* & (0)\dagger \\
C* & \rightarrow & C & (1)\dagger \\
C* + T & \rightarrow & C + T* & (3) \\
T* + T & \rightarrow & 2T & (4) \\
T* & \rightarrow & T & (5) \\
T* & \rightarrow & T + h\nu & (6) \\
D + C* & \rightarrow & D + C & (7)
\end{array}
$$

where C, T and D refer, respectively, to solvent, solute and quencher. Assuming a stationary state is obtained, it follows that the luminescence intensity in the absence of quencher is given by

$$
I_0 = \frac{\{k_0 k_3 k_6 / k_1 (k_5 + k_6)\}[T]}{(1 + k_3[T]/k_1)(1 + k_4[T]/(k_5 + k_6))}
\qquad \underline{1}
$$

and that the ratio of I_0 to the luminescence intensity in the presence of quencher will be given by

$$
I_0/I = 1 + \gamma[D]
\qquad \underline{2}
$$

where

$$
\gamma = k_7/(k_1 + k_3[T])
\qquad \underline{3}
$$

But studying the dependence of the quenching constant, γ, on $[T]$ it is possible to determine the ratios k_7/k_1 and k_3/k_1 and,

---

†Similar reactions in reference 1 were erroneously labeled (1) and (2). To be consistent with some of the expressions derived from the kinetics, these reactions should be relabeled, as shown here, (0) and (1).

from these, some indication of the mechanism of the energy transport process. Using air-equilibrated solutions of benzene-p-terphenyl and bromobenzene as quencher, lower limits for these ratios

$$k_7/k_1 \geqslant 220 \text{ liter/mole}$$

$$k_3/k_1 \geqslant 300 \text{ liter/mole}$$

have been previously established.[1]

On the basis of a value for $k_1 = 2 \times 10^8 \text{ sec}^{-1}$, it was argued that k_3 and k_7 were at least four times larger than would be expected if the energy transfer and energy quenching reactions were diffusion controlled with geometric cross-sections. Arguments were also advanced against either of these reactions involving a long-range dipole-dipole interaction. It seemed that both the energy transfer and quenching processes somehow involved the intermediate participation of neighboring solvent molecules. The diffusion of the excitation away from an initially excited benzene molecule via randomly oriented neighboring benzene molecules was shown theoretically to be too slow, largely because of the large Stokes Shift and low oscillator strength for the 2600 Å transition. It was therefore postulated that a degree of short-range order existed in liquid benzene, extending over perhaps 10-15 molecules. The initial energy absorption act was assumed now to excite an exciton state of the ordered region resulting in delocalization of the energy over the dimensions of the region. According to this view, the rate-determining step in the energy transfer and quenching reactions would be the molecular diffusion of terphenyl and bromobenzene to the excited region. The specific rates k_7 and k_3 should therefore be approximately the same and equal to the encounter frequency of the molecule with any point of this region.

The present investigation was undertaken in order to more precisely establish the ratios k_7/k_1 and k_3/k_1 by repeating previous measurements in the absence of molecular oxygen. In addition, optical studies have been made of the quenching process at 1/10 and 1/100 dilutions of benzene with cyclohexane. If the suggested mechanism for these processes is correct, one expects, on dilution, a lowering of the quenching constant. If neighboring benzene molecules do not participate in the quenching process, increasing dilution should tend, rather, to increase the quenching constant due to decreased self-quenching of the benzene and therefore decrease in the magnitude of k_1.

In the previous work,[1] the only difference noted between the gamma and optical excitation experiments was a slightly greater quenching efficiency in the case of high energy excitation. In order to determine how general is this phenomenon, a few initial investigations have been performed with bromobenzene in a phenylcyclohexane solvent, and dibromomethane in a benzene solvent.

2. EXPERIMENTAL

Mallinckrodt A. R. benzene was purified by three successive crystallizations from the melt (with rejection of about 15 per cent of the liquid after each crystallization) and then distilled. A middle fraction of about 40 per cent was retained having a boiling point of 79°C. The benzene was accepted for use as a solvent if its optical density in a 1 cm. cell at 2800 Å and 2880 Å did not exceed 0.5 and 0.05 respectively.

Eastman White Label cyclohexane was purified by chromatography through a one meter silica gel column followed by distillation in a 20 theoretical plate column. A middle fraction of about 40 per cent was retained having a boiling point of 80°C. The cyclohexane was accepted for use as a solvent if its optical density in a 1 cm. cell at 2100 Å and 2260 Å did not exceed 0.7 and 0.15 respectively.

Eastman White Label phenylcyclohexane was purified by chromatography through a one meter silica gel column followed by distillation at ca 58 mm Hg. A middle fraction of about 40 per cent was retained having a boiling point range of 142.5-143°C. The phenylcyclohexane was accepted for use as a solvent if its optical density in a 1 cm. cell at 2910Å and 3000Å did not exceed 0.8 and 0.2 respectively.*

Eastman White Label bromobenzene and dibromomethane and Pilot Scintillation Grade p-terphenyl were used without further purification.

Cells for degassing the solutions were sealed to a high vacuum line and baked during evacuation. The cells were then filled

---

*At the conclusion of the work herein reported, it was found that re-crystallization of the phenylcyclohexane prior to the above treatment considerably improved the UV spectrum of the liquid with optical densities at 2910Å and 3000Å of 0.17 and 0.07 respectively.

with He, broken open, the solutions introduced, cooled to liquid nitrogen temperature and sealed under a He atmosphere. The solutions were degassed by at least four freeze-thaw cycles.

In the gamma excitation experiments, 25 ml. of each solution were degassed in this fashion and then attached via a break seal to the vacuum line shown in Figure 1. Each cell was successively opened and the fluorescence cell filled. After each filling air or helium was admitted and the fluorescence cell removed from the line, capped with a 6/20 joint, and a second fluorescence cell attached to the line and evacuated. The luminescence was excited with a 10 mc. Cs^{137} source placed about one cm. above the front surface of the cell. The emission was taken from the back surface of the cell which was placed about 1 cm. above the end window of a Dumont 6292 photomultiplier. The tube was operated at 1200 volts and the anode current measured with a Keithley Model 410 micro-microammeter. The cell was repeatedly rinsed with solvent prior to reuse.

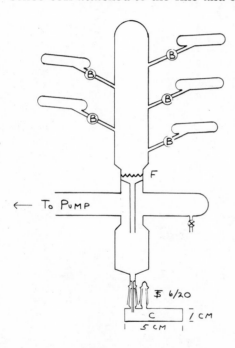

Fig. 1 — Vacuum line for Cs^{137} excitation experiments B-break seals; C-fluorescence; F-fritted glass disc.

For the optical excitation experiments, 100 ml. of two stock solutions, one with, the other without quencher added, were separately degassed and then attached via a break seal to the vacuum line shown in Figure 2. This entire line was evacuated until a leak rate of less than 10^{-6} mm. Hg/min. was established. Valve H was then closed and the cells opened. Aliquot portions of each stock solution were measured out in the calibrated volume G admitted to and magnetically stirred in chamber M, and then passed into the fluorescence cell C. The cell was constructed with suprasil quartz windows one cm. apart. All valves "S" shown in Figure 2 are greaseless ground glass seat valves, magnetically operated.

Light of the desired frequency from an Hanovia Sc 5030
mercury arc was isolated with a Baush and Lomb 250 mm.
grating monochromator and focused on the front face of the
fluorescence cell by means
of a front surface-alumi-
nized parabolic mirror operating about 30° off axis.
The emission was taken
from the back face of the
cell which was placed im-
mediately in front of the
entrance slit of a Beckman
DU monochromator. Two
front surface aluminized
plane mirrors reflected
the beam from the exit port
of the DU onto the window
of a 1P21 photomultiplier.
The tube was operated at
800 volts and the signal
monitored by a Keithley
Model 410 micro-microam-
meter.

After a run it was found
possible to efficiently clean
the vacuum line by reflux-
ing pure solvent through it
under vacuum.

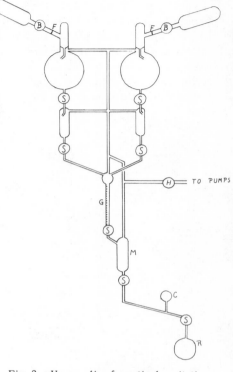

Fig. 2 — Vacuum line for optical excitation
excitation experiments B - break scale; C-
fluorescence cell; F - fritted glass discs;
G - calibrated volume; H - metal valve; M-
mixing chamber; R - resevoir; S - ground
glass seat valves.

3. RESULTS

3.1. Bromobenzene Quenching of Benzene-p-Terphenyl Solutions

The effect of bromobenzene was studied at three concentrations of p-terphenyl under Cs^{137} irradiation. The nonquenchable
contribution to the observed luminescence from cell wall fluorescence, gamma rays interacting directly with the photomultiplier,
Cerenkov radiation, etc., was corrected for by plotting $(I_1 - I)^{-1}$
vs [bromobenzene]$^{-1}$ where I_1 is the observed luminescence
intensity at [bromobenzene] = 0. As predicted, such plots are
linear (see Figure 3) and from the ratio of intercept to slope,

the quenching constant γ can be obtained. The values presented in Table I are least square estimates of γ and its standard deviation.

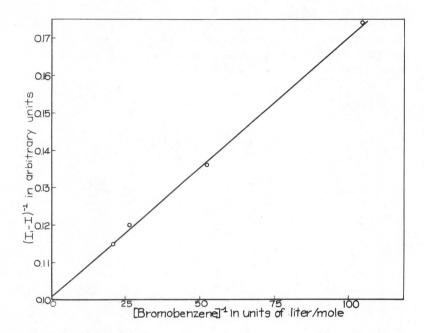

Fig. 3 — Bromobenzene quenching of benzene — p-terphenyl solution; [p-terphenyl] = 1.74×10^{-3} M; Cs^{137} excitation.

In Figure 4 a straight line has been fitted to the quenching data of Table I, and the least square estimates of the reciprocal intercept (k_7/k_1), ratio of slope to intercept (k_3/k_1) and their standard deviations obtained. These are given in Table I.

For the case of excitation with light, four p-terphenyl concentrations were studied. Measurements of the emission at 3440 Å were made both with 2537 Å and 2900 Å exciting light. The solvent, benzene, is essentially transparent at 2900 Å and the observed emission is attributable to primarily excited p-terphenyl. Only very slight quenching was observed at this wavelength up to bromobenzene concentrations of $ca.$ .05M. We estimate an upper limit of about 4 liter/mole for direct quenching of p-terphenyl.

The 2537 Å line is essentially completely absorbed by the solution with over 99% of this attributable to solvent absorption over the entire range of bromobenzene and p-terphenyl concentrations. For the purposes of this study, it was deemed unnecessary to correct our results either for these small effects or that of the direct p-terphenyl quenching. Plots of $(I_1 - I)^{-1}$ vs. [bromobenzene]$^{-1}$ were found to be linear with intercept at infinite quencher concentration equal to $(I_1)^{-1}$. Least square analysis was therefore performed by fitting the data to the more statistically favorable equation

$$I^{-1} = I_1^{-1} (1 + \gamma [D]),$$

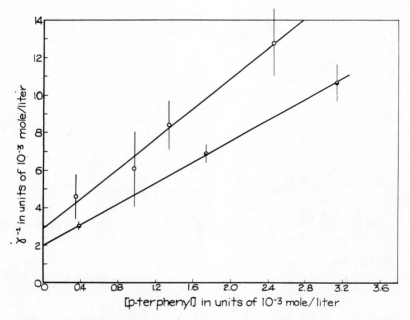

Fig. 4 — Dependence of reciprocal quenching constant on p-terphenyl concentration
● - Cs^{137} excitation O - 2537Å excitation.

as shown in Figure 5. The least square estimates of γ and standard deviations are presented in Table I. In Figure 4 a straight line has been fitted to the equation

$$\frac{1}{\gamma} = \frac{k_1 + k_3 [T]}{k_7}$$

and least square estimates of the rate constant ratios are presented in Table I.

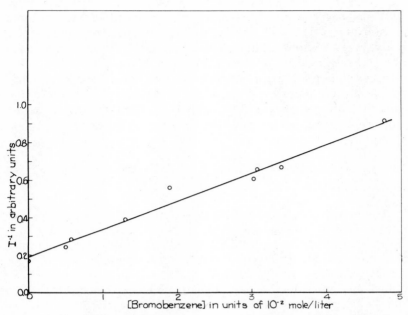

Fig. 5 — Bromobenzene quenching benzene - p-terphenyl solution [p-terphenyl] = 2.46 × 10⁻³ M; 2537 Å excitation.

Table I.

Values of γ (liter mole^{-1}) for Bromobenzene Quenching
of the System P-Terphenyl-Benzene

[Terphenyl]	Cs^{137}	2537 Å
0.351 × 10⁻³	–	262 ± 60
0.385 × 10⁻³	333 ± 20	–
0.967 × 10⁻³	–	164 ± 51
1.34 × 10⁻³	–	119 ± 20
1.74 × 10⁻³	145 ± 8	–
2.46 × 10⁻³	–	78 ± 11
3.14 × 10⁻³	94 ± 8	–

$$\frac{k_7}{k_1} = 508 \pm 57 \text{ liter/mole} \qquad \frac{k_7}{k_1} = 350 \pm 120 \text{ liter/mole}$$

$$\frac{k_3}{k_1} = 1410 \pm 160 \text{ liter/mole} \qquad \frac{k_3}{k_1} = 1400 \pm 380 \text{ liter/mole}$$

A plot of I_0^{-1} vs. [p-terphenyl]$^{-1}$ was also found to be linear in the case of the Cs[137] excitation studies and from least square analysis the ratio of intercept to slope and its standard deviation was determined as 1070 ± 170 l/mole.

Since the optics were changed slightly before and after each run, a similar determination in the case of 2537 Å excitation experiments was not possible. However, the linearity of such a plot in air-equilibrated solutions has been previously demonstrated.[1]

3.2. Bromobenzene Quenching of Benzene-Cyclohexane-p-terphenyl Solutions.

The effect of bromobenzene on solutions of cyclohexane containing 1.13 M benzene and 0.113 M benzene was studied with optical excitation at several terphenyl concentrations. Bromobenzene concentration was varied from 0 to 0.0476 M in the 1.13 M benzene solutions and from 0 to 0.00952 M in the 0.113 M benzene solutions. At both benzene concentrations the 2537 Å line is again essentially completely absorbed within the solution. Bromobenzene, at its highest concentration, accounts for about 3% and 6% of this absorption in the 1.13 M and 0.113 M solutions respectively. Because of this effect, plots of I^{-1} vs. [bromobenzene] should become concave upward. This, however, was not noted within the experimental scatter of our points, and no correction was attempted.

The direct absorption of the 2537 Å line by p-terphenyl becomes appreciable in these solutions accounting for about 24% at [p-terphenyl] $= 1.82 \times 10^{-3}$ M and about 50% at [p-terphenyl] $= 0.613 \times 10^{-3}$ M in the 1.13 M and 0.113 M benzene solutions respectively. Assuming the validity of our kinetic sequence, it can be shown that

$$I = \frac{I_1}{(1 + \delta)(1 + \gamma_t [D])} \left(1 + \frac{\delta}{1 + \gamma [D]} \right)$$

and therefore

$$[I_1 - I(1 + \gamma_t D)]^{-1} = \left(\frac{1 + \delta}{I_1 \delta} \right) \left(\frac{1 + \gamma D}{\gamma D} \right)$$

where δ is proportional to the ratio of optical densities of benzene to p-terphenyl at 2537 Å and γ_t is the p-terphenyl quenching constant.

With a value of γ_t = 4 liter/mole, we noted no significant improvement in linearity as compared with the case γ_t = 0. Increasing γ_t to greater than 4 liter/mole reduced the quality of the fit to a straight line in several cases. In view of the uncertainty in γ_t, the values for γ presented in Table II were obtained assuming γ_t = 0. The values may therefore be too low by as much as perhaps 10-20 l/mole. The uncertainties shown in Table II are again least square estimates of the standard deviation. However, these are now undoubtedly underestimated and are not to be taken too seriously.

Table II

Values of γ (liter mole^{-1}) for Bromobenzene Quenching of the System p-Terphenyl-Benzené-Cyclohexane

[terphenyl],M	[$C_6 H_6$],M	γ (liter mole^{-1})
0.299×10^{-3}	0.113	42 ± 2
0.333×10^{-3}	1.13	230 ± 11
0.613×10^{-3}	0.113	43 ± 3
1.24×10^{-3}	1.13	151 ± 5
1.82×10^{-3}	1.13	169 ± 2

3.3 Dibromomethane Quenching of Benzene p-Terphenyl Solutions

The results of dibromomethane quenching are shown for the case of Cs[137] and 2537 Å excitation in Figures 6 and 7 respectively. At the highest dibromomethane concentrations employed in the optical experiments ($ca.$ 0.07 M), the benzene accounts for more than 99% of the total absorbed light at 2537 Å. With excitation by 2900 A, again only very slight quenching was observed not exceeding about 4 liter/mole. Mixtures of dibromomethane and p-terphenyl in cyclohexane were examined spectrophotometrically for evidence of complex formation, but none was found.

3.4 Bromobenzene Quenching Phenylcyclohexane-p-Terphenyl Solutions

A few experiments were performed with phenylcyclohexane as solvent. Experimental difficulties precluded our investigating this system extensively. However, the quenching behavior

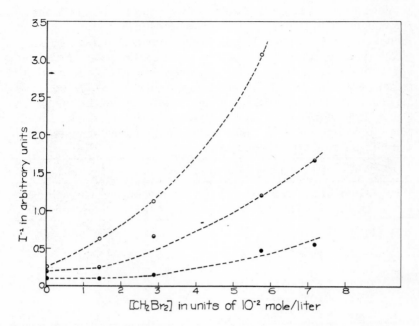

Fig. 6 — Dibromomethane quenching benzene - p-terphenyl solutions; Cs^{137} excitation

● - [p-terphenyl] = 2.87 × 10^{-3}M

◕ - [p-terphenyl] = 0.765 × 10^{-3}M

○ - [p-terphenyl] = 0.356 × 10^{-3}M

does not seem to be greatly different from that exhibited by benzene. Some preliminary results are as follows:

2540 Å excitation; [p-terphenyl] = 1.38 × 10^{-3} M,
$$\gamma = 90 \pm 20 \ l/m$$

Cs^{137} excitation; [p-terphenyl] = 1.65 × 10^{-3} M,
$$\gamma = 180 \pm 80 \ l/m$$

Again slight quenching of the emission was noted with 2900 Å excitation, not exceeding 4 l/m.

DISCUSSION

The values of k_7/k_1 and k_3/k_1 are consistent with the lower limits reported from work on the air-equilibrated solutions. In the case of p-terphenyl, the self quenching constant, $k_4/(k_5 + k_6)$ has been shown to be about 3 liter/mole.[6],[7] For concentrations of p-terphenyl less than .10^{-2} M, plots of reciprocal I_o vs. re-

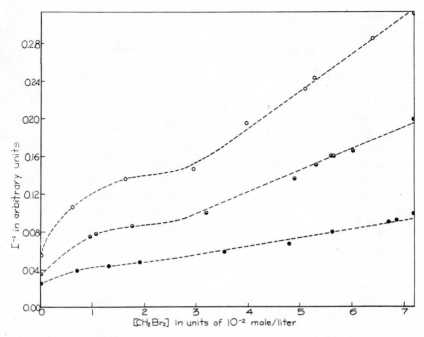

Fig. 7 — Dibromomethane quenching benzene - p-terphenyl solutions; 2537 Å excitation
O - [p-terphenyl] $= 1.65 \times 10^{-3}$ M
◐ - [p-terphenyl] $= 0.660 \times 10^{-3}$ M
● - [p.terphenyl] $= 0.350 \times 10^{-3}$ M

ciprocal terphenyl concentration should therefore be linear with ratio of intercept to slope equal to k_3/k_1. The value obtained in this fashion for Cs[137] excitation, 1070 ± 170 liter/mole (see Section 3.1), is in reasonable agreement with the value shown in Table I. For air-equilibrated solutions, a value of 330 l/m was found[1] for the ratio $k_3/(k_1 + k_{7a} [O_2]_s)$, where k_{7a} is the specific rate for oxygen quenching and $[O_2]_s$ the concentration of oxygen in the solution (1.4×10^{-3} M). With the value of k_3/k_1 ~ 1400 liter/mole reported in this work, we obtain

$$\frac{k_{7a}}{k_1} = 2300 \; l/\text{mole}$$

The ratios, k_7/k_1, k_3/k_1, k_{7a}/k_1 all seem to be about five times larger than the lower limits reported earlier.

Burton[8] has recently reported a value of about 3.3×10^{-8} sec. for the lifetime of benzene in the pure deaerated liquid using

X-ray excitation. Since k_1 is interpreted as the reciprocal of this lifetime, we can now estimate the specific rates k_7, k_3 and k_{7a}. These become respectively 1.1×10^{10}, 4.2×10^{10} and 7.0×10^{10} liter/mole sec. Both energy transfer (k_3) and oxygen quenching (k_{7a}) specific rates are clearly larger than would be expected on the basis of diffusion controlled reactions with normal (*i. e.* approximately kinetic) cross-sections.

The results presented in Table II for quenching constants in more dilute benzene solutions also are consistent with the view that the transfer and quenching mechanisms somehow involve the participation of neighboring benzene molecules. If the processes involved only the initially excited benzene molecule it would be difficult to explain, on the basis of changes in diffusion constants, the large differences noted between quenching constants in liquid benzene and 0.1 M benzene in cyclohexane. The quenching constants in the 1 M benzene solutions seem to be not too different from those in pure benzene. Assuming the existence of the postulated short range ordering in liquid benzene, it is, perhaps, not unreasonable to further postulate that such regions would not become too statistically unfavorable until one reaches dilutions greater than 1/10.

It is to be noted that the dependence of the quenching constant on terphenyl concentration in the 0.1 M solutions is essentially absent. Of course, as mentioned earlier, the uncertainties shown in Table II are probably underestimated. Nevertheless, it seems possible to conclude that the energy transfer constant, k_3/k_1, is also reduced in these solutions.

It is still possible, of course, to interpret these results with an energy transport mechanism involving the diffusion of excitation via neighboring benzene molecules with a mean free path of the order of a molecular diameter. However, if such were the case, one might expect the measured lifetime of the transferring species to be about the same as that estimated on the basis of a simple calculation involving the oscillator strength of the 2600 Å band, the emission quantum yield at infinite dilution and the benzene self-quenching constant. Dammers-de Klerk[9] has recently measured a self-quenching constant for benzene of 57.5 liter/mole. This value was measured for benzene concentrations as large as 0.15 M and seems capable of extrapolation to even greater concentrations. Using Bowen's[10] value of 0.11 *

---

*This value could be as low as 0.025. E. J. Bowen, private communication. The lifetime we calculate with the 0.11 value will, therefore, be an upper limit.

for the fluorescence quantum yield at infinite dilution and an oscillator strength of 0.002 [11] (radiative lifetime $\sim 5 \times 10^{-7}$ sec.), we calculate that for a 0.15 M benzene solution, the lifetime of the emitting species should be approximately 5×10^{-9} sec. For the pure liquid we would expect the lifetime to be even shorter. However, the values obtained both by Burton [8] and by Berlman † for the lifetimes of the transferring and emitting species respectively are considerably larger than this calculated upper limit. A reasonable conclusion, we feel, is that the species responsible both for energy transport and for emission in pure liquid benzene is not the same as the species responsible for these processes in dilute solutions. In particular, we feel that the transferring species in the pure liquid not only lives longer but has also a larger cross-section for energy transport and quenching processes.

In these experiments, we have again observed somewhat higher quenching constants for bromobenzene under gamma ray excitation. The transfer constant, k_3/k_1, seems not to be effected. This conclusion was also established in the earlier work. [1] For the phenomena of gamma ray induced luminescence, the only important distinction to be made with the optically excited systems is the mode of production of the electronically excited solvent species. Ions seem not to play a role in the transfer mechanism. However, processes of the type

$$C \rightsquigarrow C^+ + e^- \tag{8}$$

$$C^+ + e^- \rightarrow C^* \tag{9}$$

certainly contribute to the production of the electronically excited species C^*. If we postulate that bromobenzene not only is capable of quenching C^* but may also interfere with the ionic route to the production of C^* by electron capture or charge transfer processes, i.e.,

$$C^+ + e^- + D \rightarrow C + D \tag{10}$$

then it follows that the intensity of terphenyl luminescence will be given by:

$$I = \frac{\alpha}{1 + \gamma D} \left(1 + \frac{\epsilon}{1 + \beta D} \right) \tag{6}$$

---

†For deaerated benzene, 1.77×10^{-8} sec. I. Berlman, private communication.

where

$$\alpha = \frac{k_6 k_3 k_0 [T]}{(k_5 + k_6 + k_4 [T])(k_1 + k_3 [T])}$$

$$\beta = k_{10}/k_9$$

and

$$\epsilon = k_8/k_0.$$

From this it follows that

$$(I_0 - I)^{-1} = \frac{(1 + \gamma D)(1 + \beta D)}{\alpha \gamma D [1 + \epsilon + \beta \epsilon/\gamma + \beta(1 + \epsilon)D]} \qquad \underline{7}$$

Therefore if

$$\gamma \beta D \ll \gamma + \beta$$

and measurements are made for concentrations of quencher not exceeding $1/\beta$, then a plot of $(I_0 - I)^{-1}$ vs. $[D]^{-1}$ will seem to be linear with ratio of intercept to slope equal to $\gamma + \beta$. It is not unreasonable then to attribute the difference between the quenching constants to step 10. If this does eventually prove to be true, the luminescence technique may prove fruitful in estimating the ratio $\epsilon = k_8/k_0$.

The quenching by dibromomethane in the case of Cs^{137} excitation is not inconsistent with the views expressed above. Equation $\underline{6}$ predicts that a plot of $1/I$ vs. $[D]$ will appear concave upward if reaction (10) is efficient. However, the behavior with 2537 Å radiation is puzzling and we have no explanation for the effect. It should be mentioned that we have found dibromomethane to enhance the $^1A_{1g} \rightarrow \,^3B_{1u}$ transition in benzene but with considerably lower efficiency than that exhibited by molecular oxygen.[12] If the recent theoretical explanations[13,14] for the oxygen effect are correct, then it is not unlikely that dibromomethane is also associated with benzene in a charge transfer complex.

REFERENCES

[1] S. Lipsky and M. Burton, J. Chem. Phys. 31, 1221 (1959)

[2] H. Kallmann and M. Furst, Phys. Rev. 79, 857 (1950)

[3] F. H. Brown, M. Furst and H. Kallmann, Disc. Far. Soc. 27, 43 (1959)

[4] J. B. Birks and K. N. Kuchela, Disc. Far. Soc. 27, 57 (1959)

[5] S. G. Cohen and A. Weinreb, Proc. Phys. Soc. (London) B69, 593 (1956)

[6] P. J. Berry, S. Lipsky and M. Burton, Trans. Far. Soc., 52, 311 (1956)

[7] M. Furst and H. Kallmann, Phys. Rev. 86, 816 (1952)

[8] M. Burton, Z. Elektrochem. 64, 975 (1960)

[9] A. Dammers-de Klerk, Mol. Phys. 1, 141 (1958)

[10] E. J. Bowen and A. H. Williams, Trans. Far. Soc. 35, 765 (1939)

[11] Almsay and Laemmel, Helv. chim. Acta. 34, 462 (1951)

[12] D. F. Evans, J. Chem. Soc. 1351, 3885 (1957)

[13] G. J. Hoijtink, Mol. Phys. 3, 67 (1960)

[14] J. N. Murrell, Mol. Phys. 3, 319 (1960)

A SUMMARY OF
QUENCHING STUDIES OF ENERGY TRANSFER IN ORGANIC SYSTEMS*

F. H. Brown, M. Furst** and H. P. Kallmann

Department of Physics, New York University

ABSTRACT

Quenching studies afford a convenient method for discriminating between the possible processes of non-radiative energy transfer. The similarities of the concentration dependence of energy transfer from solvent to solute to that of solvent quenching within the solvent system, and of the concentration dependence of energy transfer in liquids to that in rigid systems, show the importance of energy transport by migration in both liquid and rigid systems.

Further support for migration is found in the reduction of quenching rate obtained upon dilution with a non-transferring liquid. The connection of energy transfer and quenching by the energy transport process is demonstrated by the use of o-terphenyl as a quencher in liquid systems. It is found that this compound acts both as a quencher and as an energy transferring agent.

INTRODUCTION

Three processes of non-radiative energy transfer from solvent to solute have been described.[1] These are:

---

*Grateful acknowledgment is made of the support of this work by the U.S. Army Signal Corps under Contract DA 36-039 SC-85126 and by the U.S. Air Force, Wright Air Development Command, under Contracts AF 33(616)-6119 and AF 33(616)-8317.

**Also with Department of Physics, Hunter College, New York. At present on leave at CEN Saclay, France.

1. Single step transfer over a relatively large distance directly from a primarily excited solvent molecule to a solute molecule, bypassing any transport (Förster Mechanism);

2. Energy transport by migration from solvent to solvent molecule terminating in a transfer as in 1 but over shorter distances;

3. Energy transport by material diffusion of the primary excited solvent molecule terminating in a transfer as in 2.

The relative importance of the three processes in a given system depends in the main on the nature of the solvent. Process 3, for example, can be ruled out in plastics.

Process 1 must be excluded in most cases of quenching because it would require the existence of an energy state in the quencher which can take over the excitation energy of the solvent. Therefore quenching studies offer a convenient method for discriminating between the possible processes. A comparison of the kinetics of energy transfer to a·fluorescent solute and of solvent quenching in the same system can give information about the relative importance of the various processes. In dilute liquid systems solute quenching must occur chiefly via process 3, the diffusion of an excited solute molecule within the interaction distance of a quencher molecule, because the solute molecules are too far apart for solute-solute migration to play a significant role. This is also shown by the almost total absence of solute quenching in plastic systems.[2] Since process 3 is excluded in plastics, a comparison of the kinetics of solvent quenching in liquid and plastic systems at low quencher concentrations makes it possible to estimate the extent to which process 3 is responsible for energy transfer in liquid systems.

CONCENTRATION DEPENDENCE OF QUENCHING AND
ENERGY TRANSFER

Table 1 presents the molar half value concentrations for energy transfer from solvent to solute and for solvent quenching respectively in various scintillator systems.

The two rates show such similar concentration dependence in polystyrene and in polyvinylnaphthalene, that it seems highly probable that, though the final step may very well be different in the two cases, the transport process is identical. That the rates are not identical in the two systems can be ascribed to the difference in the final transfer of energy to solute or quencher.

Table 1

Energy Transfer and Quenching

Solvent	Molar Half Value Conc. Energy Transfer $\neq$ $C_A^{1/2}$	Molar Half Value Conc. Quenching* $\neq$ $C_D^{1/2}$	M
Polystyrene	0.02	0.06	
PS/naphthalene (0.2 M)	0.004	0.07	
PVN	0.005	0.007	
Xylene	0.002	0.015	

* Quencher: diphenylmercury
$\neq$ Solute: PPO

The half value concentration for energy transfer in liquids and in plastic systems are not very different, demonstrating the importance of the migration process in liquids as well. The somewhat lower value for xylene compared to that for PVN, a rigid material in which the migration transport process occurs with extreme efficiency, may be ascribed to the additional influence of mass diffusion, process 3, which occurs in xylene but not in the plastic. The higher half value concentration for quenching in xylene compared to energy transfer is not yet understood.

It is of interest to compare quenching in PS/naphthalene to that in PVN systems. A comparison of lines 1 and 2 of the table shows the well known effect of added naphthalene in increasing the rate of energy transfer to the solute and decreasing the rate of quenching in polystyrene systems. Figure 1 presents the effect of increasing the naphthalene concentration in PS/PPO on quenching by diphenylmercury. It can be seen that increasing the naphthalene concentration beyond 0.2M causes a further decrease of the quenching rate. It has been shown that 0.2 M naphthalene in unquenched polystyrene is the maximum effective concentration for increasing the rate of energy transfer.[3] Increasing the naphthalene concentration still further shows an effect in quenched polystyrene because the solvent lifetime is decreased by the quencher, requiring more naphthalene to extract the same energy.

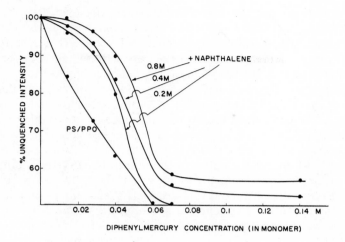

Fig. 1 — Effect of Naphythalene on the γ-ray Induced Fluorescence of PS/PPO Quenched by Diphenylmercury

Based on these results it was thought that polyvinylnaph-thalene systems should be quenched very little by diphenyl-mercury due to the large concentration of naphthalene nuclei. As can be seen from Table 1, however, the opposite is true. Figure 2, presenting the quenching of PVN/PPO as a function

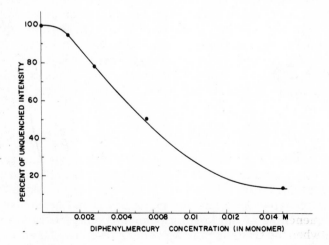

Fig. 2 — Quenching of the γ-ray Induced Fluorescence of PVN/PPO (0.045M) by Diphenylmercury

of diphenylmercury concentration shows this even more strikingly. A comparison with Figure 1 shows that the rate with which diphenylmercury quenches PVN/PPO is greater by an order of magnitude than the rate with which it quenches PS/PPO even in the absence of any naphthalene.

This behavior may, however, be understood by considering the action of naphthalene as an intermediate solvent in polystyrene. In unquenched systems, the energy is transferred to naphthalene and transport by naphthalene-naphthalene migration occurs efficiently at 0.2 M naphthalene. This results in more rapid energy transfer to the solute because of the longer lifetime of naphthalene, the greater efficiency of transfer from naphthalene to solute and the more efficient energy migration in naphthalene.[4,5] In quenched systems the process is the same, except that larger naphthalene concentrations are required to extract the energy. The absence, previously mentioned, of an energy state in the quencher which can readily accept the solvent excitation energy results in a smaller cross-section for quenching than for energy transfer. This may, in part, account for the result in the liquid case in Table 1, which shows the molar half value for quenching to be more than five times as great as that of energy transfer in the liquid. Since, in rigid media, the distance between naphthalene and solute or quencher molecules remains fixed, it is to be expected that the addition of naphthalene would result in a more rapid increase of energy transfer than of quenching. When the migration process becomes extremely effective throughout a rigid system, as is the case in polyvinylnaphthalene, and essentially involves every transferring molecule no matter how close to solute or quencher it may be, it is to be expected that the rate of energy transfer be comparable to that of quenching as seen in Table 1 and Figure 2.

EFFECT OF DILUTION ON QUENCHING

The similarity of the half values for quenching and energy transfer in liquid and rigid systems indicates the importance of energy transport by migration in the liquid case. More insight into the transport process can be gained from the investigation of the quenching of liquid solutions under energy transfer conditions when the transferring solvent is diluted with an inactive (non-transferring) liquid.

It is often stated that the solvent is quenched to a greater

extent that the solute by the addition of quenchers.[5] For example, xylene is quenched much more than anthracene by the
addition of CCl_4 to the solution. This is a somewhat mislead-
ing statement, however, because when the system is diluted so
that the concentration of xylene becomes as small as the solute
concentrations usually employed, it is found that xylene quenching is reduced to such an extent that it becomes comparable to
that of anthracene. This effect is independent of the nature of
the diluent so long as it does not transfer energy.[6]

Figure 3 presents the effect of $\alpha,\alpha,\alpha,\alpha',\alpha',\alpha'$ -hexachloro-
p-xylene as quencher on the γ-ray induced fluorescence of solutions of 3 g/1 of 2-(1-naphthyl)5-phenyloxazole in xylene diluted with tri-n-butylphosphate. The solute emission is
measured, but the solute is so little quenched that its fluorescence is a good indication of the extent of energy transfer
from o-xylene. The diluent acts as an inert material with
respect to transfer to the small concentration of solute employed. $[(I_0/I) - 1]$ is plotted against the concentration of quencher and the expected straight lines are obtained.

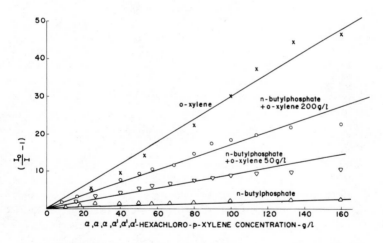

Fig. 3 — Effect of Dilution on Fluorescence Quenching by $\alpha,\alpha,\alpha,\alpha',\alpha',\alpha'$-
hexachloro-p-xylene in o-xylene/2-(1-naphthyl)-5-phenyloxazole Solutions

Figure 4 presents the results of similar experiments using
1-methylnaphthalene as the transferring solvent and CCl_4 as
quencher. Once again the effect of dilution in separating the
molecules of 1-methylnaphthalene results in sharply decreased
quenching. In both cases, the decrease of solvent quenching

brought about by increasing dilution is too great to be accounted for by the small extent of quenching in tri-n-butylphosphate (lowest curve). It can be ascribed in great part to the increasing distance between the transferring o-xylene molecules which

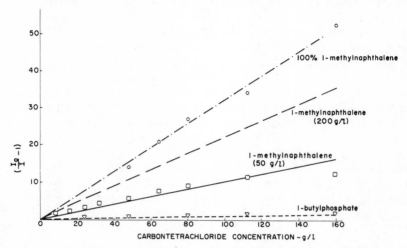

Fig. 4 —Effect of Dilution on Fluorescence Quenching by CCl$_4$ in 1-methylnaphthalene/2-(1-naphthyl)-5-phenyloxazole Solutions

increasingly inhibits energy transport by migration to the quencher. There is no doubt, however, that particularly in the diluted systems, process 3, material diffusion of the excited solvent, plays a role.

ENERGY TRANSFER AND QUENCHING BY THE SAME COMPOUND

That energy transfer and quenching are connected by the transport process is shown by a study of quenching by o-terphenyl. o-terphenyl quenches the gamma ray induced fluorescence of 9,10-diphenylanthracene o-xylene solutions. While the quenching is not as great as that by CCl$_4$ shown in the previous section, it is nevertheless clearly evident. The quenching behavior of o-terphenyl is, however, quite different from that of CCl$_4$.

Figure 5 is an $[(I_0/I) - 1]$ plot of quenching versus o-terphenyl concentration in solutions of 3 g/l and 10 g/l of 9,10-diphenylanthracene in o-xylene. The usual straight line is not found, but instead, the curves show a definite saturation of quenching as high quencher concentrations are reached. At higher o-terphenyl concentration the quenching rate is much lower than would be expected. As is generally the case, the higher solute concentration results in reduced quenching.

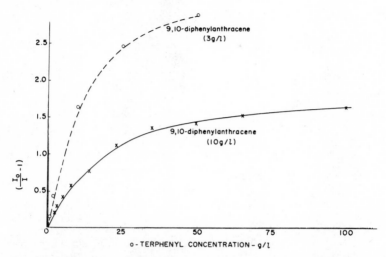

Fig. 5 — Fluorescence Quenching by o-terphenyl of o-xylene/9,10-diphenylanthracene Solutions

Figure 6 shows a similar curve using 10 g/l of 9,10-diphenylanthracene, but the solvent has been changed to 1-methyl-naphthalene. In this case the quenching is reduced by a factor of twenty and does not set in until a concentration of approximately 10 g/l of o-terphenyl is reached.

These results are interpreted as the occurence of both quenching by and energy transfer from o-terphenyl. o-xylene transfers energy to both o-terphenyl and 9,10-diphenylanthracene. The energy is degraded more rapidly in o-terphenyl than in o-xylene, but still has a finite lifetime in o-terphenyl. Thus a small fraction of o-terphenyl molecules transfer their energy to 9,10-diphenylanthracene before it is degraded. As the o-terphenyl concentration is increased, more and more of the energy of the excited o-xylene is transferred to o-terphenyl until the amount transferred to 9,10-diphenylanthracene via o-terphenyl becomes significant compared to that transferred directly from o-xylene. Finally, essentially all the excitation energy reaching the fluorescent solute reaches it by way of o-terphenyl. Thus the curves reach a maximum of quenching which corresponds to the fraction of the energy degraded in o-terphenyl compared to that transferred.

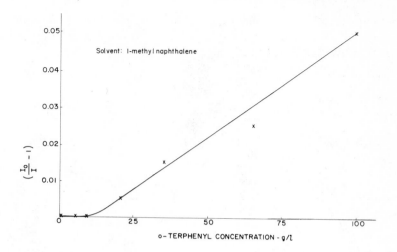

Fig. 6 — Fluorescence Quenching by o-terphenyl of 1-methylnaphthalene/9,10-diphenylanthracene Solutions

It seems probable that this fraction does not remain completely constant as the concentration of o-terphenyl is increased because it is expected that transport by migration in o-terphenyl becomes significant at high concentrations and leads to a more rapid rate of energy transfer.

The excitation energy in 1-methylnaphthalene is at about the same level as that of o-terphenyl so that it can be assumed that energy transfer to o-terphenyl is quite small. This is similar to the earlier finding that naphthalene as intermediate solvent does not enhance energy transfer to p-terphenyl.[7] Thus, as seen in Figure 6, o-terphenyl is less effective as a quencher in 1-methylnaphthalene than in o-xylene, since its quenching action depends on energy transfer to it from the solvent.

If the above interpretation is correct, o-terphenyl should enhance energy transfer to a solute when the bulk solvent has a still shorter lifetime than o-terphenyl. This is the case when tri-n-butylphosphate is used as the bulk solvent. Figure 7 shows the fluorescence intensity as a function of solute concentration under γ-ray excitation of 1-naphthylphenyloxazole in tri-n-butylphosphate containing 20 and 200 g/l of o-terphenyl. It is seen that the higher o-terphenyl concentration results in enhanced energy transfer to the solute. Thus the decreased quenching rate at higher concentrations of o-terphenyl, shown

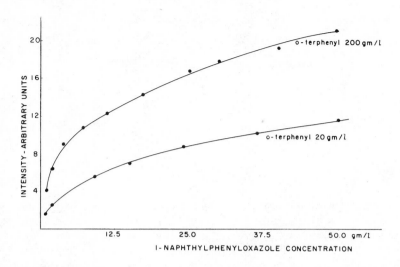

Fig. 7 — Enhancement by o-terphenyl of the γ-ray Induced Fluorescence of n-butylphosphate/1-naphthylphenyloxazole Solutions

in Figure 5, is due to energy transfer from the "quencher" to the solute.

REFERENCES

[1] M. Furst and H. Kallmann in Liquid Scintillation Counting, Pergamon Press, New York (1958), p. 237.
[2] Brown, Furst and Kallmann in Nuclear Electronics, International Atomic Energy Agency, Vienna (1959), p. 15.
[3] Brown, Furst and Kallmann, J. de Chim. Physique, 1958, 688.
[4] M. Furst and K. Kallmann, Phys. Rev. 97, 583 (1955).
[5] Furst, Kallmann and Brown in Semiconductors and Phosphors, Interscience Publishers, New York (1958), p. 269.
[6] Brown, Furst and Kallmann in Organic Scintillation Detectors, U. S. Atomic Energy Commission, T. I. D. 7612 (1961), p. 37.
[7] M. Furst and H. Kallmann, Phys. Rev. 96, 902 (1954).

DECAY AND POLARIZATION OF FLUORESCENCE OF SOLUTIONS

A. Jablonski

Nicholas Copernicus University
Toruń, Poland

ABSTRACT

It is shown that measurements of the polarization of fluorescence of an isotropic luminophor together with measurements of the mean durations $\tau^{\parallel}$ and $\tau^{\perp}$ of the components $I^{\parallel}$ and $I^{\perp}$ of the fluorescence parallel and perpendicular to the electric vector of plane polarized exciting light permit one, in the simplest cases, to obtain some new information on the processes causing depolarization of fluorescence. If the total fluorescence intensity I (emitted in all directions) decays according to $I(t) = I_0 \exp(-t/\tau)$ and its emission anisotropy $r = (I^{\parallel} - I^{\perp}) / (I^{\parallel} + 2I^{\perp})$ according to $r(t) = r_0 \exp(-\phi t)$, such measurements permit the evaluation of both r_0 and ϕ (t is the decay time and τ the mean duration of total fluorescence, ϕ is a constant). It follows from the theory given by F. Perrin that in the case of fluorescent solutions, in which depolarization is caused by thermal rotations of luminescent molecules $\phi = kT/v\eta$ (v is the volume of the luminescent molecule together with its solvation shell, η the viscosity coefficient of the solvent and k and T have the usual meanings), provided that the rotations of the molecules are governed by the laws of Brownian rotation of spherical particles. Thus, in addition to r_0, v can also be evaluated. Appropriate experiments were performed by R. Bauer (to be published shortly).

As was shown in several papers[1], processes causing depolarization of fluorescence of luminophors in general influence the course of decay of particular components of fluorescence. It appears that, if in addition to polarization, the mean durations $\tau^{\parallel}$ and $\tau^{\perp}$ of components of fluorescence $I^{\parallel}$ and $I^{\perp}$ parallel and perpendicular respectively to the electric vector of the plane polarized exciting light are measured, new information concerning the properties of fluorescent solutions can be gained. As an example let us consider the case of an isotropic fluorescent solution excited with plane polarized primary light. It is convenient to describe polarization in terms of emission anisotropy

$$r = (I^{\parallel} - I^{\perp})/(I^{\parallel} + 2I^{\perp}), \tag{1}$$

instead of the familiar degree of polarization $p = (I^{\parallel} - I^{\perp}) / (I^{\parallel} + I^{\perp})$.

It follows from Eq. (1) that

$$I^{\parallel} = I/3\,(1 + 2r) \text{ and } I^{\perp} = I/3\,(1 - r), \tag{2}$$

where $I = I^{\parallel} + 2I^{\perp}$.

Now, if the decay of total (emitted in all directions) fluorescence intensity, I, follows the simple exponential law

$$I(t) = I_0 \exp(-t/\tau), \tag{3}$$

and $r(t)$ is a function of the decay time, t, the decay of $I^{\parallel}$ and $I^{\perp}$ is given by

$$I^{\parallel}(t) = I_0/3\,[1 + 2r(t)]\,\exp(-t/\tau)$$

and $\tag{4}$

$$I^{\perp}(t) = I_0/3\,[1 - r(t)]\exp(-t/\tau),$$

where τ denotes the mean duration of $I(t)$. Thus the decay of components depends on the course of $r(t)$, and does not in general follow the simple exponential law.

If the explicit form of $r(t)$ is known, expressions for $\tau^{\parallel}$ and $\tau^{\perp}$, as well as for the mean value of emission anisotropy $\bar{r}$ over the decay time can be obtained. So far, not the instantaneous value $r(t)$, but rather $\bar{r}$ is accessible to observation.

One of the processes causing depolarization of fluorescence is the thermal rotation of luminescent molecules. It follows from the theory given by F. Perrin[2] that in this case

$$r(t) = r_0 \exp(-\phi t), \tag{5}$$

provided the rotation of luminescent molecules is governed by the laws of Brownian rotation of spherical particles. r_0 denotes the value of $r(t)$ for $t = 0$, and $\phi = kT/v\eta$, v being the volume of the luminescent molecule together with its solvation shell,

η the viscosity coefficient of the solvent, and k and T having
their usual meanings. Since the shape of luminescent molecules is in general not spherical, the course of $r(t)$ may differ
somewhat from that of Eq. (5), but the deviations (according to
F. Perrin) are not very marked. The question of whether the
laws of Brownian rotation apply to molecules in solutions raises
some doubts (*cf. e.g.* Frenkel[3]), but it will be provisionally
assumed that they apply.

Using Eqs. (3) and (5) one obtains

$$\bar{r} = r_0/(1 + \phi \tau). \tag{6}$$

Eqs. (4) and (5) lead to

$$I^{\parallel}(t) = I_0/3 \,(1 + 2 r_0 \, e^{-\phi t}) \, e^{-t/\tau}$$

and $\tag{7}$

$$I^{\perp}(t) = I_0/3 \,(1 - r_0 e^{-\phi t}) \, e^{-t/\tau}$$

The mean durations of $I^{\parallel}(t)$ and $I^{\perp}(t)$ resulting from Eqs. (7)
by using Eq. (6) are

$$\tau^{\parallel} = \tau \, \frac{r_0 + 2\bar{r}^2}{r_0 + 2 r_0 \bar{r}}$$

and $\tag{8}$

$$\tau^{\perp} = \tau \, \frac{r_0 - \bar{r}^2}{r_0 - r_0 \bar{r}} \,,$$

and hence (*cf.* ZS. Naturf.[1])

$$r_0 = \frac{2\bar{r}^2 \, \tau}{\tau^{\parallel}(1 + 2\bar{r}) - \tau} = \frac{\bar{r}^2 \, \tau}{\tau - \tau^{\perp}(1 - \bar{r})} \tag{9}$$

All the quantities appearing on the right side of Eq. (9) can be
measured directly.

It may be noted that in order to evaluate τ it suffices to
measure $\tau^{\parallel}$ and $\tau^{\perp}$. τ can also be measured directly. After
the value of r_0 is thus obtained, ϕ can be calculated by means
of Eq. (6). Since $\phi = kT/v\eta$, the volume, v, of the luminescent
molecule together with its solvation shell can be evaluated.
Thus information concerning solvation shells in different solvents can be acquired. The appropriate experiments were performed by my collaborator, R. Bauer, (to be published shortly).
As an example his results on uranine in glycerol + water may
be quoted. Fig. 1 shows that r_0 first increases very slightly
with increasing water content, and then decreases very abruptly.

v, however, increases steadily, but especially markedly when the content of water reaches about 85 per cent mol/mol.

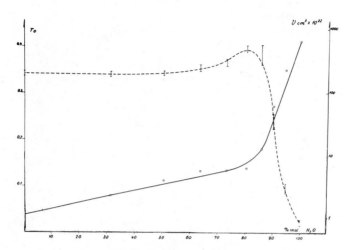

Fig. 1. r_0 and v for uranine in glycerol + water as functions of water content (according to R. Bauer).

In many solvents, however, r_0 and v remain constant when the relative concentration of components of the solvent is varied. It may be noted that the experimental value of r_0 appears to be smaller than that expected on theoretical considerations. This fact can be explained by the assumption that, apart from depolarization of fluorescence by thermal rotations of luminescent molecules, there also occurs depolarization by (irregular) torsional vibrations of luminescent molecules. They reduce r_0 but do not influence ϕ. Their effect depends on the constitution of the solvation shell (on the average value of the torsion moment acting on the molecule). If the constitution of the solvation shell does not change when the relative concentration of the components of the solvent is varied, r_0 and v remain constant. In this case $1/\bar{r}$ is *ceteris paribus* a linear function of $1/\eta$ (it follows from Eq. (6) that $1/\bar{r} = (1 + \phi\tau)/r_0 = (1 + kT\tau/v\eta)/r_0$) in agreement with the observations of Pringsheim and Vogels.[4] If, however, the constitution of the solvation shell does vary when the relative concentration of the components of the solvent is varied, both r_0 and v vary, and thus $1/\bar{r}$ ceases to be a linear function of $1/\eta$, a fact also observed by the authors quoted above.[5]

REFERENCES

[1] A. Jabloński, Z. Phys. 95, 53 (1935); 103, 526 (1936); Z. Naturf. 16a, 1 (1961).

[2] F. Perrin, Ann. Phys., Paris 12, 169 (1929); J. de Phys., 5, 497 (1934); 7, 1 (1936); Acta Phys. Polon, 5, 335 (1936).

[3] J. Frenkel, Kinetic Theory of Liquids, Oxford, 1946.

[4] P. Pringsheim and H. Vogels, J. de Phys. 7, 121 (1937)

[5] In a recent paper (Bull. Acad. Polon. Sci., Sér. Sci. Math., Astr. et Phys., 8, 655 (1960)) I have proposed an explanation of these deviations by assuming that only r_0 varies. The results of experiments of Bauer show that both r_0 and v vary.

THE SENSITIZATION OF BIACETYL FLUORESCENCE IN FLUID SOLUTIONS

J. T. Dubois

Aeronautical Research Laboratory, Wright–Patterson
Air Force Base, Ohio

and

B. Stevens*

Department of Chemistry, The University, Sheffield, England

ABSTRACT

The sensitization of biacetyl fluorescence in aerated cyclohexane solutions was studied at 25°C, using napthalene, benzene and acetone as donors. The simultaneous quenching of donor fluorescence by biacetyl was also investigated and it is concluded that the energy transfer process involves the lowest excited singlet states of donor and acceptor in each case, and proceeds at a rate consistent with a diffusion-controlled process.

INTRODUCTION

The transfer of electronic energy from an exicted donor $D*$ to an acceptor molecule A has been the subject of numerous investigations[1-7] from which it appears that the transfer process 1 is diffusion controlled in solution

$$D* + A \rightarrow D + A* \qquad (1)$$

if (a) the energy of the excited acceptor $A*$ is less than that of the donor and (b) the overall spin angular momentum is conserved during transfer. In certain cases where the fluorescence spectrum of $D*$ exhibits considerable overlap with the

*Visiting Research Associate, Aeronautical Research Laboratory, Wright-Patterson Air Force Base, Ohio, July - September 1961.

absorption spectrum of A, the observed transfer over a distance
of several molecular diameters[4,5,6] is attributed to the strong
dipole-dipole interaction of the transferring species of which
the extent of overlap is a measure[5].

If either the donor or acceptor is luminescent under the conditions of observation, process 1 is conveniently followed by
measuring either the quenching[1] of donor luminescence by the
acceptor or the intensity of acceptor emission[2] as a function
of donor concentration; the quantitative treatment is simplified
if measurements are made at low optical density[8,9] such that
the extent of light absorption is a linear function of concentration to a first approximation. A complete description of process 1 however requires that the identity of the electronic states
involved be established together with a demonstration that donor quenching and acceptor sensitization proceed at the same
rate; the electronic states may be identified from luminescent
spectra, but since the emission spectrum of the donor almost
inevitably lies in a region of strong absorption by the acceptor
(unless the donor is excited indirectly), a complementary investigation of donor quenching by acceptor is complicated by
effects due to reabsorption.

This communication describes the sensitized fluorescence
of dissolved biacetyl which has a region of weak absorption
extending from 320 - 360 mμ as shown in Fig. 1; this permits the

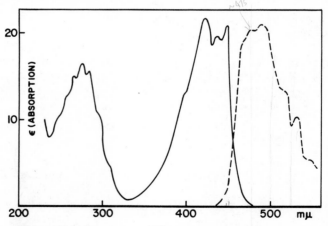

Fig. – Absorption ——— and Fluorescence – – – – Spectra of
Biacetyl in Cyclohexane at 25°C.

use of relatively concentrated solutions of low optical density
so that donor emission in this region is not appreciably absorbed. Moreover the fluorescence of biacetyl extending from

450μ to longer wavelengths is well isolated from that of suitable donors, and is conveniently investigated in aerated solutions in which the phosphorescence is completely quenched[2]. Naphthalene is used as the principal donor since the fluorescence of this compound in the region of 320 - 360mμ is not appreciably reabsorbed by biacetyl, and its weak absorption at 320mμ allows the use of relatively concentrated solutions of low optical density when light of this wavelength is used for excitation. Data are also presented in which acetone and benzene are used as donors at excitation wavelengths of 320 and 265mμ respectively since the acetone- and benzene-sensitized luminescence of biacetyl have been investigated[20,21] in the vapor phase; moreover, acetone represents a donor of the n, π^* type which might be expected to sensitize the n, π^* transition of biacetyl[10] more efficiently than donors of the π, π^* type like benzene and naphthalene. Unfortunately the fluorescence spectra of both acetone and benzene coincide with regions of relatively strong absorption by biacetyl which leads to complications due to reabsorption, while the necessity of using 265mμ excitation for benzene severely limits the useful upper concentration of biacetyl which absorbs appreciably in this region.

The very low fluorescence yields of acetone[11], benzene[12] and biacetyl[2] require the use of a sensitive detector and consequently a non-luminescent solvent; cyclohexane fulfilled this condition under the experimental conditions employed and was available in sufficient quantity to allow dilute solutions to be prepared with the desired accuracy.

EXPERIMENTAL

Materials

Biacetyl supplied by Matheson, Coleman and Bell was distilled at reduced pressure until the vapor phase chromatogram of a collected sample showed less than 1% impurity and stored in the absence of light. Cyclohexane (spectroquality) and benzene (A.C.S. analyzed) from the same source exhibited no impurity fluorescence under the experimental conditions and were used without further treatment; Eastman's acetone (spectrograde) and naphthalene (recrystallized from alcohol) passed the same test.

Instrumental

An Aminco-Bowman spectrophotofluorimeter was used to record the fluorescence spectra of the prepared solutions; with the recommended slit arrangement No. 3, it was unnecessary to work at the highest sensitivity and the noise was thereby considerably reduced. The wider slits led to no appreciable loss in resolution of the recorded spectra but undoubtedly led to an increase in the half-peak width of the exciting radiation. Since this instrument records the emission along a direction at 90° to that of the incident radiation, the vertical cylindrical quartz cell of 7 mm internal diameter was used to contain the solutions; this reduced the effective absorption depth to $\leqslant 4$ mm. The scan speed control was set to scan as slowly as possible consistent with an even traversal of the pen arm of the X-Y recorder after which the scanning was controlled only by the off-on switch. Each spectrum was recorded twice and showed no change during the time of tracing. In order to convert the recorded signal to relative quantum output for the purpose of spectral identification, the wavelength sensitivity of the detector assembly was determined by recording the signal from a 5×10^{-3} M solution of quinine bisulphate in 1.0 M H_2SO_4 and compared with the quantum output reported by Melhuish[13]. Absorption measurements were made on a Carey recording spectrophotometer and extinction coefficients obtained from plots of optical density as a function of concentration.

Procedure

Solutions of acceptor and donor at the required concentrations were prepared volumetrically (gravimetrically in the case of naphthalene) in tightly-stoppered flasks and stored in a cool dark cupboard until their fluorescence spectra were recorded, usually within one hour. The solutions were well shaken to saturate them with air at atmospheric pressure and the spectra of a given series, with either the acceptor or donor concentration constant, recorded on the same chart under the same experimental conditions; sample charts are reproduced in Figures 2 and 3. The height of the trace at a given wavelength (usually the peak height) measured from the base line obtained with pure solvent in the cell, was taken as the measured fluorescence intensity F; in the case of acetone-biacetyl mixtures a correction was applied for the contribution

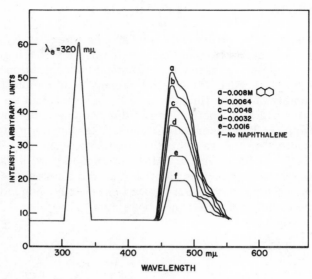

Fig. 2 — Typical Experimental Tracing of the Naphthalene Sensitized Fluorescence of Biacetyl (0.04 M) in Cyclohexane at 25°C λ_e = 320 mμ.

of acetone luminescence to that of biacetyl which it overlaps to a certain extent. All recordings were made at 25°C.

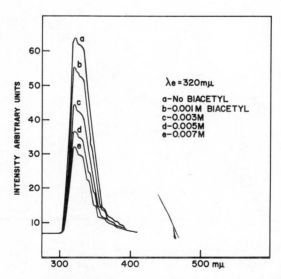

Fig. 3 — Typical Experimental Tracing of the Quenching of Naphthalene Fluorescence (0.01 M) by Biacetyl in Cyclohexane at 25°C. λ_e = 320 mμ.

RESULTS

The ratio of measured fluorescence intensity F_A of biacetyl in the presence of donor to the intensity F_A° in the absence of donor is shown as a function of donor concentration in Figures 4, 5 and 6. Figure 7 shows the Stern-Volmer plots for the quenching of donor fluorescence by biacetyl, and the decadic molar extinction coefficients of donors and acceptor are given in Table 1. The recorded luminescence spectrum of biacetyl corrected for the wavelength sensitivity of the detector assembly is shown in Figure 1 and, by comparison with the previously reported spectrum[2], is identified as the fluorescence. The quenched donor emission in each case corresponded with the corresponding fluorescence spectrum.

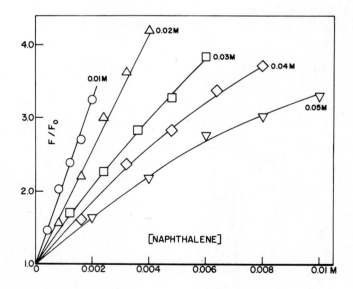

Fig. 4 — Naphthalene Sensitization of Biacetyl Fluorescence in Cyclohexane at 320 mμ and 25°C, at Different Concentrations of Biacetyl.

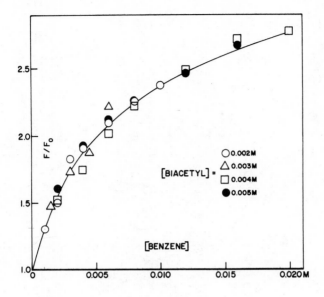

Fig. 5 — Benzene Sensitization of Biacetyl Fluorescence in Cyclohexane at 265 mμ and 25°C.

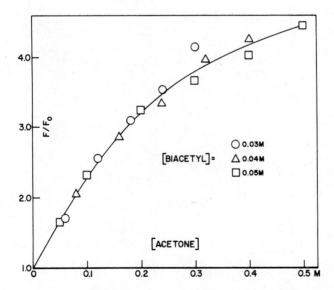

Fig. 6 — Acetone Sensitization of Biacetyl Fluorescence in Cyclohexane at 320 mμ and 25°C.

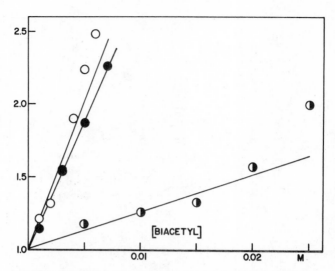

Fig. 7 – Fluorescence Quenching of Various Donors by Biacetyl in Cyclohexane at 25°C. 0 – Benzene 0.008 M at 265 mμ; ● – Naphthalene 0.01 M at 320 mμ; ◑ – Acetone 0.08 M at 320 mμ.

DISCUSSION

In an aerated solution containing both acceptor A and donor D the following processes are the most probable and provide the basis for a quantitative interpretation of the results:

$$D + h\nu \rightarrow D* \tag{2}$$

$$D* \rightarrow D + h\nu_D \tag{3}$$

$$D* \rightarrow D \text{ or } {}^3D \tag{4}$$

$$*D + O_2 \rightarrow \left.\begin{array}{c} \\ \end{array}\right\} \text{ Quenching} \tag{5}$$

$$*D + D \rightarrow \tag{6}$$

$$D* + A \rightarrow D + A* \tag{1}$$

$$A + h\nu \rightarrow A* \tag{7}$$

$$A* \rightarrow A + h\nu_A \tag{8}$$

$$A* \rightarrow A \text{ or } {}^3A \tag{9}$$

$$A* + O_2 \rightarrow \left.\begin{array}{c} \\ \end{array}\right\} \text{ Quenching} \tag{10}$$

$$A* + A \rightarrow \tag{11}$$

The asterisk denotes an electronically-excited singlet state and the triplet states ^3A and ^3D are assumed to be rapidly removed by internal conversion, oxygen quenching, or solvent interaction.

Under photostationary conditions the intensity of acceptor fluorescence f_A in the presence of donor is given by

$$f_A = k_8 \, (A^*) \; = k_8 \left\{ \frac{I_A + k_1 \, (D^*) \, (A)}{k_8 + k_9 + k_{10} \, (O_2) + k_{11} \, (A)} \right\}$$

and in the absence of donor by

$$f_A^{\circ} = \frac{k_8 \, I_A^{\circ}}{k_8 + k_9 + k_{10} \, (O_2) + k_{11} \, (A)}$$

where I_A and I_A° are the intensities of light absorbed by the acceptor with and without added donor respectively. The recorded fluorescence signal F at wavelength λ is related to the total intensity of fluorescence f at λ by

$$F(\lambda) = \underline{k} \, Q(\lambda) \, f(\lambda)$$

where $\underline{k}$ is an instrumental constant determining the fraction of the emitted radiation intercepted by the detector and $Q(\lambda)$ is the signal intensity per quantum at λ. The ratio of signals recorded in the presence and absence of donor at the same wavelength is therefore given as

$$\frac{F_A}{F_A^{\circ}} = \frac{f_A}{f_A^{\circ}} = \frac{I_A}{I_A^{\circ}} + \frac{k_1 \, (D^*) \, (A)}{I_A^{\circ}}$$

or since

$$(D^*) = \frac{I_D}{k_3 + k_4 + k_5 \, (O_2) + k_6 \, (D) + k_1 \, (A)}$$

we have

$$\frac{F_A}{F_A^{\circ}} = \frac{I_A}{I_A^{\circ}} + \frac{I_D}{I_A^{\circ}} \left\{ \frac{k_1 \, (A)}{k_3 + k_4 + k_5 \, (O_2) + k_6 \, (D) + k_1 \, (A)} \right\} \tag{I}$$

where I_D is the intensity of light absorbed by the donor in the presence of acceptor.

Equation (I) is considerably simplified if the exponentials in the Beer-Lambert expression for I_A, I_A° and I_D are expanded

Table 1

Decadic Molar Extinction Coefficients

Molecule	$\lambda m\mu$	ϵ l. mole^{-1} cm^{-1}
Acetone	320	1.18
Benzene	265	25
Naphthalene	320	22
Biacetyl	320	1.25
Biacetyl	265	15

and second and higher order terms neglected; if the conditions are such that

$$[\epsilon_A(A) + \epsilon_D(D)]d < 0.043$$

where ϵ_A and ϵ_D are the decadic molar extinction coefficients of acceptor and donor and d is the absorption path ($\not> 0.4$ cm), this approximation leads to an error of $\not> 5\%$ and equation (I) becomes

$$\frac{F_A}{F_A^\circ} \simeq 1 + \frac{\epsilon_D(D)}{\epsilon_A(A)} \left\{ \frac{k_1(A)}{k_3 + k_4 + k_5(O_2) + k_6(D) + k_1(A)} \right\} \quad \text{(II)}$$

The initial slope of the sensitization curves in Figures 4, 5 and 6 is consequently given by

$$\left\{ \frac{d(F_A/F_A^\circ)}{d(D)} \right\}_{(D)\to 0} = \frac{\epsilon_D}{\epsilon_A} \left\{ \frac{k_1}{k_3 + k_4 + k_5(O_2) + k_1(A)} \right\}$$

$$= \frac{\epsilon_D}{\epsilon_A} \left\{ \frac{k_1 \tau_D}{1 + k_1 \tau_D(A)} \right\} \quad \text{(III)}$$

where τ_D, the actual lifetime of the donor in the absence of acceptor at limiting donor concentrations is

$$\tau_D = \frac{1}{k_3 + k_4 + k_5(O_2)} \quad \text{(IV)}$$

The validity of equation (III) simply requires that

$$\epsilon_A(A) < 0.043$$

since

$$\epsilon_D(D)d \to 0 \text{ as } (D) \to 0$$

In the same way it may be shown that the ratio of donor fluorescence signals F_D and F_D° in the presence and absence of acceptor at concentration (A) is given by

$$\frac{F_D{}^\circ}{F_D} = \frac{I_D{}^\circ}{I_D} + \frac{I_D{}^\circ}{I_D} \left\{ \frac{k_1 \tau_D (A)}{1 + k_6 \tau_D (D)} \right\}$$

which, under the condition $[\epsilon_A(A) + \epsilon_D(D)] d < 0.043$ gives

$$\frac{F_D{}^\circ}{F_D} = \left\{ 1 + \frac{k_1 \tau_D (A)}{1 + k_6 \tau_D (D)} \right\}$$

whence the slope of the curves in Figure 7

$$\frac{d (F_D{}^\circ/F_D)}{d(A)} = \frac{k_1 \tau_D}{1 + k_6 \tau_D(D)} \tag{V}$$

THE NAPHTHALENE-BIACETYL SYSTEM AT $320 m\mu$

From Figure 4 it is seen that the slope of the tangent to the sensitization curves at the origin decreases as the concentration of biacetyl is increased as would be expected from equation (III). Inversion of equation (III) provides

$$\left\{ \frac{d (D)}{d(F_A/F_A{}^\circ)} \right\}_{(D) \to 0} = \frac{\epsilon_A}{\epsilon_D} \left\{ (A) + \frac{1}{k_1 \tau_D} \right\}$$

so that a plot of the reciprocal initial slope of the sensitization curves against biacetyl concentration (A) should be linear with

slope $= \epsilon_A / \epsilon_D$

and intercept $= \epsilon_A / \epsilon_D k_1 \tau_D$

This is verified in Figure 8 from which

$\epsilon_D / \epsilon_A = 20 \pm 1$
and slope/intercept $= k_1 \tau_D = 175 \pm 20 \, \text{l./mole}$

The ratio of extinction coefficients is within 10% of that obtained from measured optical densities at $320 m\mu$ (Table 1) which is satisfactory in view of the fact that the slit system used for fluorescence measurements permits a comparatively wide range of wavelengths to fall on the cell.

From the Stern-Volmer plot shown in Figure 7

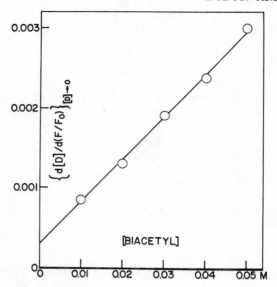

Fig. 8 — Naphthalene Sensitization of Biacetyl Fluorescence. Reciprocal of the Initial Slopes in Figure 4
Versus Biacetyl Concentration.

$$\frac{d\left(F_D{}^\circ/F_D\right)}{d\left(A\right)} = \frac{k_1\,\tau_D}{1 + k_6\,\tau_D(D)} = 180 \pm 10\ \mathrm{l./mole}$$

and is independent of naphthalene concentration (D) over the
range 0.0008 – 0.01 M. This suggests that self-quenching is
not important in this region, in qualitative agreement with the
findings of Dammers de Klerk[12] in deoxygenated n-hexane of
much lower viscosity; in this case

$$\frac{d\left(F_D{}^\circ/F_D\right)}{d\left(A\right)} = k_1\,\tau_D = 180 \pm 10\ \mathrm{l./mole}$$

The excellent agreement between the values of $k_1\,\tau_D$ obtained
from the sensitization of acceptor fluorescence and the quenching of donor fluorescence confirms the identity of the donor as
the lowest excited singlet state of naphthalene; this could con-
ceivably sensitize a higher singlet state of biacetyl which undergoes a radiationless conversion to the lowest singlet state
responsible for the observed sensitized emission. However
according to the absorption spectrum of biacetyl shown in Figure
1, the excited donor produced by absorption at 320mμ has insufficient energy to sensitize any but the lowest excited singlet

state of biacetyl and it must be concluded that this is the product of the transfer process.

The efficiency of the transfer process can be estimated from the value of $k_1 \tau_D$ if the lifetime τ_D of naphthalene in aerated solutions of cyclohexane is known. In the absence of this information a diffusion-controlled limiting value may be assigned to k_1 and a lower limit obtained for τ_D. According to the Debye equation[14]

$$k_1 = \frac{8\,RT}{3000\,\eta} = 7.5 \times 10^9 \text{ l./mole/sec.}$$

with $\eta = 0.89$ centipoise for cyclohexane at 25°C; thus

$$\tau_D \geqslant 180/(7.5 \times 10^9) = 2.4 \times 10^{-8} \text{ sec.}$$

Dammers de Klerk[12] obtains the value

$$\tau_D^{\circ} = \frac{1}{k_3 + k_4} = 4.7 \times 10^{-7} \text{ sec.}$$

for naphthalene from self-quenching data. If the oxygen quenching of naphthalene fluorescence is diffusion-controlled[15], a concentration of dissolved oxygen in the aerated solutions used here of

$$(O_2) = \frac{1}{k_5} \left\{ \frac{1}{\tau} - \frac{1}{\tau_o} \right\} = 5.3 \times 10^{-3} \text{ mol./l.}$$

would be sufficient to reduce τ_D to the limiting value of τ_D obtained above. In view of the reported value[16] of

$$(O_2) = 1.0 \times 10^{-2} \text{ mol./l.}$$

for the concentration of dissolved oxygen in cylcohexane at 25°C under 1 atm. of pure oxygen, this value is not unreasonable.

THE ACETONE-BIACETYL AND BENZENE-BIACETYL SYSTEMS

The initial slopes of the sensitization curves shown in Figures 5 and 6 for the benzene- and acetone-sensitization of biacetyl fluorescence exhibit no clear-cut dependence on acceptor concentration as in the case of the naphthalene-biacetyl system. According to equation (II) the sensitizing effect should decrease with increasing acceptor concentration if 1 – 11 are the only operative processes; however, since both benzene and acetone fluoresce in regions of relatively strong absorption by biacetyl, reabsorption of the donor fluorescence by the acceptor, which increases with acceptor concentration may be sufficient to offset the decrease in sensitization predicted by equation (II) and account for the observed effect. In the same way absorption of donor fluorescence by the acceptor would lead to an increase in the observed quenching of donor fluorescence at higher acceptor concentrations which is evident from the quenching curves for acetone and benzene shown in Figure 7.

If this interpretation is correct, the sensitization curves should be least affected by photon transfer at the lowest concentrations of acceptor *i.e.* 0.03 M and 0.002 M biacetyl for acetone and benzene sensitization respectively. With these values for (A) and the extinction coefficients quoted in Table 1, the analysis of the data in Figures 5, 6 and 7 according to expressions (III) and (V) provide the data given in Table 2.

Table 2

Sensitization and Quenching Data for Acetone-Biacetyl
and
Benzene-Biacetyl Systems in Cyclohexane

Donor	$\left\{\dfrac{d(F_A/F_A^\circ)}{d(D)}\right\}_{(D)\to 0}$	$\lambda m\mu$	$\dfrac{\epsilon_D}{\epsilon_A}$	$k_1\tau_D$	$\left\{\dfrac{d(F_D^\circ/F_D)}{d(A)}\right\}_{(A)\to 0}$
Acetone	14 ± 2	320	1.0	22 ± 2	26 ± 3
Benzene	370 ± 30	265	1.7	270 ± 30	200 ± 20

At the concentration of benzene used (0.008M) for the biacetyl quenching measurements, self-quenching is negligible[12] even in deoxygenated solutions of n-hexane where the benzene lifetime is longer and its diffusional rate faster than in aerated cyclohexane; consequently

$$\frac{d(F_D^\circ/F_D)}{d(A)} \simeq k_1\tau_D = 200 \pm 20 \ 1./\text{mol}.$$

which is in fair agreement with the value of 270 ± 30 obtained from sensitization, and for the benzene-biacetyl system

$$k_1\tau_D = 240 \pm 60 \ 1./\text{mol}.$$

Again assigning k_1 the upper limit of a diffusion controlled process we find that for benzene

$\tau_D > 3.2 \pm 0.8 \times 10^{-8}$ sec.

Using Dammers de Klerk's[12] value of

$$\tau_D^{\circ} = \frac{1}{k_3 + k_4} = 1.7 \times 10^{-6} \text{ sec.}$$

obtained from self-quenching measurements and the dissolved oxygen concentration required for consistency of the data obtained for naphthalene

$$(O_2) = 5.3 \times 10^{-3} \text{ mol./l.}$$

we obtain

$$\tau_D = \frac{\tau_D^{\circ}}{1 + k_5 \tau_D^{\circ} (O_2)} = 2.5 \times 10^{-8} \text{ sec.}$$

in agreement with

$\tau_D > 3.2 \pm 0.8 \times 10^{-8}$ sec.

obtained from the energy transfer measurements.

An examination of the data for acetone in Table 2 shows that in this case also self-quenching is unimportant although an acetone concentration of 0.08 M was used in the quenching experiments. If this is the case then

$$k_1 \tau_D = 25 \pm 5 \text{ l./mol.}$$

whence

$$\tau_D > 3.3 \pm 0.7 \times 10^{-9} \text{ sec.}$$

if k_1 is assigned an upper limit equal to the diffusion controlled rate constant. Since acetone fluorescence is not quenched by oxygen[17]

$$\tau_D = \frac{1}{k_3 + k_4} = \tau_D^{\circ} \gamma$$

where $\tau_D^{\circ} = 1/k_3$ is the natural radiative lifetime and γ is the quantum yield of acetone fluorescence. Use of the value

$$\tau_D^{\circ} = 3 \times 10^{-6} \text{ sec.}$$

calculated from the integrated absorption coefficient[18] leads to a value of $\sim 10^{-3}$ for the quantum yield of acetone fluorescence which is the order of magnitude obtained in the vapor phase.[19] The unimportance of self-quenching even in an 8×10^{-2} M solution would be expected for a molecule of such a short lifetime.

In the absence of oxygen, the experiments reported above would have resulted in the indirect sensitization of biacetyl phosphorescence by virtue of the high yield of intersystem crossing to the lowest triplet of biacetyl. Under these conditions, it would have been extremely difficult to measure the fluorescence of biacetyl, which is overlapped by the more intense phosphorescence, and the systems reported would manifest the symptoms of direct sensitization of a phosphorescent state by excited singlet states which contravenes the condition of spin-conservation.

FOOTNOTES

[1] H. L. J. Bäckström and K. Sandros, Acta Chem. Scand. 12, 823 (1958).
[2] H. L. J. Bäckström and K. Sandros, Acta Chem. Scand. 14, 48 (1960).
[3] E. J. Bowen and B. Brocklehurst, Trans. Faraday Soc. 49, 1131 (1953).
[4] E. J. Bowen and R. Livingston, J. Am. Chem. Soc. 76, 6300 (1954).
[5] T. Förster, Z. Elektrochem. 53,93 (1949); Z. Naturforsch. 4, 321 (1949).
[6] W. F. Watson and R. Livingston, J. Chem.Phys. 18, 802 (1950).
[7] G. Porter and F. Wilkinson, this conference.
[8] B. Stevens, Discussions Faraday Soc. 27, 34 (1959).
[9] J. T. Dubois, J. Phys. Chem. 63, 8 (1959).
[10] J. W. Sidman and D. S. McClure, J. Am. Chem. Soc. 77, 646 (1955).
[11] G. W. Luckey and W. A. Noyes, J. Chem. Phys. 19, 227 (1951).
[12] A. Dammers de Klerk, Mol. Phys. 1, 141 (1958).
[13] W. H. Melhuish, J. Phys. Chem. 64, 762 (1960).
[14] P. Debye, Trans. Electrochem. Soc. 82, 265 (1942).
[15] E. J. Bowen and A. Norton, Trans. Faraday Soc. 35, 44 (1939).
[16] H. C. Barnett and R. R. Hibbard, NASA TN 3276, p 114.
[17] H. J. Groh Jr., G. W. Luckey and W. A. Noyes Jr., J. Chem. Phys. 21, 115 (1953).
[18] G. E. Kaskan and A. B. F. Duncan, J. Chem. Phys. 16, 223 (1948).
[19] E. W. Luckey and W. A. Noyes Jr., J. Chem. Phys. 19, 227 (1951).

[20] H. Okabe and W. A. Noyes, Jr., J. Am. Chem. Soc. 79, 801 (1957).

[21] D. S. Weir, N. Ichikawa, J. S. Michael, N. Padnes, C. S. Parmenter and W. A. Noyes, Jr. Paper presented at 18th International IUPAC Congress, Montreal, August, 1961.

ENERGY TRANSFER FROM THE TRIPLET STATE

G. Porter, F.R.S.
Chemistry Department
The University, Sheffield, England

and

F. Wilkinson
Physical Chemistry Laboratory
Oxford, England

ABSTRACT

The transfer of electronic excitation energy from the triplet state of a donor molecule resulting in quenching of the donor and the elevation of the acceptor molecule from its singlet ground state to its triplet state has been observed between a number of donor-acceptor pairs in fluid solvents. Using the technique of flash photolysis, the mechanism of transfer has been unequivocally established by observation of the triplet state absorption spectra of both species in most of the cases studied. Energy transfer from excited singlet donors to the triplet state of the acceptor is not observed.

The transfer is diffusion controlled when the energy of the acceptor triplet is considerably lower than that of the donor but there is no evidence for long-range resonance transfer of the kind found in the analogous singlet energy transfer processes. As the triplet energies become comparable the transfer probability is reduced and no quenching is observed by molecules with triplet levels higher than that of the donor. Transfer of triplet energy between pairs of aromatic hydrocarbons has been illustrated, and it has been established that complex formation between donor and acceptor cannot be responsible for the transfer observed under the conditions of these experiments.

An electronically excited molecule may lose its excitation energy by any one of the following processes; (a) light emission (b) non radiative transition (c) photochemical reaction or (d) energy transfer. In recent years great interest has been focussed

on the various processes of energy transfer and a large number of papers have dealt with such subjects as sensitized fluorescence, concentration depolarization and concentration
quenching of fluorescence. (See for example references 1-4
and references therein). These effects are all due to energy
transfer from molecules in their excited singlet states. In 1952
Terenin and Ermolaev[5] clearly demonstrated the production of
sensitized phosphorescence in rigid media, thus illustrating
for the first time unambiguous transfer from molecules in
their triplet states.

The triplet state, the lowest excited state in most molecules,
has a lifetime several orders of magnitude greater than excited
singlet states, even in fluid solvents and might therefore be expected to have a greater probability of meeting other molecules
to which it can transfer energy. Quenching of the triplet state
has been established for a number of paramagnetic molecules[6]
e.g. O_2, NO, aromatic triplets, transitional and inner transitional metal ions. The quenching efficiency is not proportional to
the magnetic susceptibility and probably occurs by the process

$$A* \text{ (triplet)} + Q \text{ (multiplet)} \rightarrow A \text{ (singlet)} + Q \text{ (multiplet)}$$

with overall spin conservation. The energy is considered to be
dissipated as heat by the solvent, the multiplicity of Q remaining unchanged.

Singlet molecules cannot quench in this way because of spin
restrictions but the energy transfer process

$$A* \text{ (triplet)} + Q \text{ (singlet)} \rightarrow A \text{ (singlet)} + Q* \text{(triplet)}$$

is spin allowed and can lead to quenching of triplet states by
singlet molecules. This paper is mainly concerned with this
process and the nature of the interaction responsible for this
type of energy transfer. Using the technique of flash photolysis
we have been able to provide unambiguous proof of the occurrence of this process in fluid solvents at room temperature in
a variety of systems. During the course of this work Bäckström
and Sandros[7,8] by quite different methods have also provided
clear evidence of this process in fluid solution.

Sensitized Phosphorescence.

Terenin and Ermolaev[9] studied the sensitized phosphorescence of naphthalene and its derivatives (acceptors) with benzophenone and similar compounds as donors in ethanol-ether mix-

tures at $-195°C$ using light absorbed only by the donors. They detected both the sensitized phosphorescence of the acceptors and the quenching of the donor phosphorescence and obtained rate constants for the transfer process, the highest being 5×10^2 l. moles.$^{-1}$ sec.$^{-1}$, for benzaldehyde as donor with naphthalene as acceptor. In a later paper Ermolaev and Terenin[10] have gone on to study the efficiency of the transfer as a function of the triplet-singlet transition probability in the acceptor. Using the 1-substituted halogen derivatives of naphthalene as acceptors no change in the transfer efficiency could be found for either of the donors, benzophenone or benzaldehyde. They therefore concluded that their results were not consistent with transfer due to dipole-dipole interaction but could be explained in terms of an exchange mechanism.

TRIPLET TRANSFER IN FLUID MEDIA

When dissolved in ordinary fluid solvents at room temperature most compounds show no phosphorescence except in the case of a few compounds which have short radiative lifetimes[11] Bäckström and Sandros[17] have studied quenching of the phosphorescence of one of these exceptions, diacetyl, in benzene solution at $20°C$. A number of aromatic hydrocarbons were examined. Those with higher triplet levels showed almost no quenching but those with lower levels quenched with almost unit collision frequency. Bäckström and Sandros suggested that the quenching was due to 'triplet transfer'. However they had no means of detecting the triplet state of the acceptor which they assumed to be formed. We have confirmed this mechanism by observing the triplet state of 1.2 benzanthracene produced by light absorbed by diacetyl in our experiments. Bäckström and Sandros[8], in a more recent paper have illustrated sensitized phosphorescence of diacetyl, benzil and anisil by light absorbed primarily by benzophenone in fluid solutions containing both benzophenone and one of these three substances.

Fortunately measurements on energy transfer from the triplet state in solution are not confined to the few substances which phosphoresce in solution as the triplet states of many molecules are readily observed by means of their absorption spectra using flash photolysis techniques. Previous workers who have studied triplet energy transfer have dealt almost exclusively with carbonyl compounds as energy donors. In order to establish the general nature of this type of process we first of all studied pairs of compounds where both the energy donor and acceptor were unsubstituted aromatic hydrocarbons. Having established that transfer did occur in these cases (see *e.g.* Figure 1), the next step was to investigate the factors upon which the efficiency of the transfer process depends. The energy levels and other relevant data for the compounds investigated are given in Table 1. The results obtained by a combination of flash spectroscopy and kinetic spectrophotometry are summarized in Table 2 for every pair of compounds studied. A description of the apparatus and the experimental details have been given elsewhere.[12]

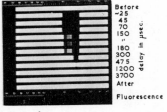

6.9×10⁻³ M Naphthalene.

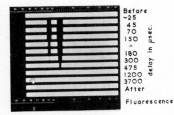

2.3×10⁻³ M Phenanthrene.

6.9×10⁻³ M Naphthalene.
& 2.3×10⁻³ M Phenanthrene.

Fig. 1 – Triplet energy transfer in ethylene glycol.

The first six pairs of donor and acceptor compounds have energy levels as shown in Figure 2 and it was therefore possible to filter the exciting light so that only the donor was being irradiated. Both the quenching of the donor triplet and the formation of the acceptor by energy transfer have been directly observed thus providing unequivocal proof for the occurrence of the process.

Donor (triplet) + Acceptor (singlet)

→ Donor (singlet) + Acceptor (triplet)

The only energetically possible alternative

Donor (upper singlet) + Acceptor (singlet) → Donor (singlet) + Acceptor (triplet)

violates Wigners spin rule[13] and would not lead to quenching of the triplet donor but instead to quenching of the fluorescent state. This process is experimentally excluded by our observation that in all cases where fluorescence was observed the

Table 1

Energies of First Excited Singlet and Triplet States,
Phosphorescence Lifetimes (τ), Lifetimes in Solution (τ solution)
and Phosphorescence Yields (Φ)

Compound	First excited singlet level (cm^{-1})	First triplet level (cm^{-1})	τ (secs)	τ solution (secs $\times$ 10^4)	Φ
Benzophenone	27,800	24,400[b]	0.006[f]	1.6 × 10^{-2} (benzene)[h]	0.84[f]
Triphenylene	28,200	23,500[c]	15.9[b]	0.56 (hexane)	0.6[f]
Phenanthrene	28,900	21,600[c]	3.3[c]	0.93 "	0.23
Naphthalene	31,200	21,300[b]	2.6[c]	0.91 "	0.09[f]
1 Bromonaphthalene	31,200	20,700[b]	0.018[c]	0.83 "	0.55[d]
1 Iodonaphthalene	31,200	20,500[d]	0.0025[c]	—	0.7[d]
Diacetyl	21,750	19,700[b]	0.00225[c]	0.60 (benzene)	—
1:2 Benzanthracene	20,600	16,500[c]	0.3[c]	1.59 (hexane)	0.001
Anthracene	26,000	14,700[b]	0.09[g]	9.1 (benzene)	0.0001
Iodine	33,774[a]	11,888[e]	—	—	—

The values of Φ for which references are not given have been calculated from the
ϕ_p/ϕ_f ratios in reference (c) by assuming $\phi_p + \phi_f = 1$.
The first excited singlet level has been taken as the long wavelength limit of singlet
absorption.

(a) Elliot, A., Proc. Roy. Soc., 1940, 174A, 273.
(b) Lewis, G. N. and Kasha, M., J. Amer. Chem. Soc., 1944, 66, 2100
(c) McClure, D. S. J. Chem. Phys., 1949, 17, 905.
(d) Terenin, A. N. and Ermolaev, V. L., J. Chim. Phys., 1958, 55, 698.
(e) Brown, W.G. Phys. Rev., 1931, 38, 1187.
(f) Gilmore, E. H., Gibson, G.E., and McClure, D. S., J. Chem. Phys., 1952, 20, 829.
(g) McGlynn, S.P., Padhye, M.R. and Kasha, M., J. Chem. Phys., 1955, 23, 593.
(h) Backstrom, H. L. J. and Sandros, K., Acta Chem. Scand., 1960, 14, 48.

fluorescence yield of the donor was unchanged by the presence of the acceptor.

With iodonaphthalene and iodine as acceptors the sensitized production of their triplet states could not be illustrated as these compounds do not show triplet-triplet absorption when they are flashed alone in solution. Iodonaphthatlene however only quenches molecules with higher triplets (e.g. phenanthrene and naphthalene) but does not affect the lifetime of those molecules with lower triplet states (e.g. anthracene) and it clearly operates by the same mechanism.

The mechanism for quenching by iodine is less certain as iodine quenches all the molecules investigated. This is however in keeping with this mechanism as iodine has a lower triplet state than all the donors used. Quenching by iodine is further complicated by the fact that chemical changes occur which result in the consumption of iodine. Whether this is due to a separate mechanism of quenching, a reaction which follows quenching by energy transfer or a process which is quite distinct from the quenching is not yet known.

The possibility must be considered that quenching by iodine occurs as a result of heavy atom enhancement of spin-orbit coupling. Previous work on the effect of heavy atoms such as Zn^{2+}, Ga^{3+} and Pb^{2+} [14] and also our observation that ethyl iodide has a negligible effect on triplet lifetimes seems to exclude this possibility. Finally the well known tendency of iodine to form change transfer complexes with aromatic molecules suggests a further mechanism by which iodine might operate. However the concentration of iodine in the mixtures studied was so low that even if it were all complexed it would only result in a reduction of the concentration of free donor molecules by less than one per cent. Similar considerations rule out complex formation as a significant factor in most of the other systems studied. For the two pairs phenanthrene-naphthalene, benzophenone-naphthalene however the concentrations of donor and acceptor were comparable and therefore a close check was made on the absorption spectra of mixtures of these pairs. Absorption spectra were taken of all the mixtures studied, no new bands were observed and the absorption spectrum of the mixture was found in all cases to be simply the sum of the separate absorption of the two components.

Finally the 'trivial process' of light emission and reabsorption can be excluded in our experiments since the fraction of triplet molecules which decay by a radiative process in fluid solvents, diacetyl excluded, is entirely negligible.

Table 2

Quenching Rate Constants

	Donor	Acceptor	Solvent	k_Q (l. moles.$^{-1}$ sec.$^{-1}$)
1	Phenanthrene	naphthalene	hexane	$2.9 \pm 0.7 \times 10^6$
	"	"	ethylene glycol	$2.3 \pm 0.8 \times 10^6$
2	Triphenylene	naphthalene	hexane	$1.3 \pm 0.8 \times 10^9$
3	Phenanthrene	1-bromonaphthalene	hexane	$1.5 \pm 0.8 \times 10^8$
	"	"	ethylene glycol	$1.5 \pm 0.8 \times 10^7$
4	Phenanthrene	1-iodonaphthalene	hexane	$7 \pm 2 \times 10^9$
	"	"	ethylene glycol	$2.1 \pm 0.2 \times 10^8$
5	Benzophenone	naphthalene	benzene	1.2×10^9
6	Diacetyl	1:2-benzanthracene	benzene	$3 \pm 2 \times 10^9$
7	Naphthalene	1-iodonaphthalene	ethylene glycol	$2.8 \pm 0.3 \times 10^8$
8	1-Bromonaphthalene	1-iodonaphthalene	ethylene glycol	$8 \pm 4 \times 10^7$
9	Phenanthrene	Iodine	hexane	$1.4 \pm 0.6 \times 10^{10}$
10	Anthracene	Iodine	hexane	$2.4 \pm 0.2 \times 10^9$

Systems showing no quenching, for which upper limits were obtained.

	Donor	Acceptor	Solvent	k_Q (l. moles.$^{-1}$ sec.$^{-1}$)
1	Naphthalene	phenanthrene	hexane	$\leqslant 2 \times 10^4$
	"	"	ethylene glycol	$\leqslant 1 \times 10^5$
2	Naphthalene	triphenylene	hexane	$\leqslant 5 \times 10^4$
3	1-Bromonaphthalene	phenanthrene	ethylene glycol	$\leqslant 5 \times 10^4$
4	Naphthalene	benzophenone	benzene	$\leqslant 1 \times 10^4$
5	1:2-Benzanthracene	diacetyl	benzene	$\leqslant 5 \times 10^4$
6	Anthracene	phenanthrene	ethylene glycol	$\leqslant 5 \times 10^3$
7	Anthracene	naphthalene	hexane	$\leqslant 4 \times 10^4$
8	Anthracene	1-iodonaphthalene	ethylene glycol	$\leqslant 2 \times 10^4$
9	Anthracene	ethyl iodide	hexane	$\leqslant 1.6 \times 10^4$
10	Phenanthrene	ethyl iodide	hexane	$\leqslant 3 \times 10^5$

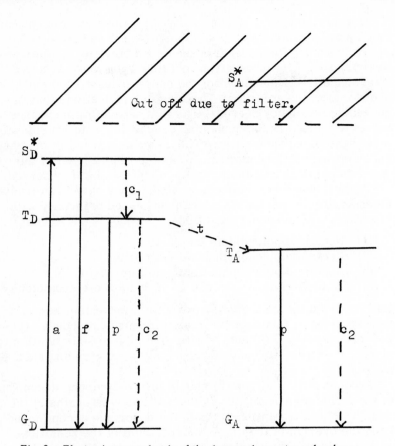

Fig. 2 — Electronic energy levels of the donor and acceptor molecules.

The Nature of the Interaction Responsible for Triplet Transfer.

The rate constants in Table 2 fall broadly into three groups depending upon the relative heights of the triplet states of the donor and acceptor molecules. When the triplet level of the donor is considerably greater than that of the acceptor the rate approaches that expected for a reaction determined by the rate of diffusion of the reactants together. Such reactions are said to be diffusion controlled and the rate constant, k_d, may be calculated from the following equation of Debye [15]

$$k_d = \frac{8RT}{3000\eta} \quad \text{l. moles.}^{-1} \text{ sec.}^{-1}$$

where η is the solvent viscosity.

This is illustrated by comparing the values calculated from this equation which are 2.0×10^{10}, 1.0×10^{10} and 3.3×10^8 l. moles.$^{-1}$ sec.$^{-1}$, for hexane, benzene and ethylene glycol respectively at 20°C with those given in Table 2 for those systems which have the triplet level of the donor at least 1000 cm^{-1} above that of the acceptor. There are no indications that the quenching efficiency decreases as this separation increases but as it decreases the quenching occurs at a rate considerably less than the encounter rate. This is most marked in the phenanthrene-naphthalene system. When the triplet level of the donor is below that of the acceptor no quenching is observed.

The following intermolecular interactions have been treated theoretically by Dexter[16] who was concerned primarily with sensitized luminescence in solids.

(1) Electric dipole-dipole interaction.
(2) Electric dipole-quadrupole interaction
(3) Electric dipole-magnetic dipole interaction
(4) Exchange interaction due to overlap of electron clouds

He concluded that process (3) is highly improbable, being, in typical cases, a factor of 10^8 less efficient than process (1) and that processes (1), (2) and (4) will give rise to sensitization of about $10^3 - 10^4$, 10^2 and 30 lattice sites surrounding each sensitizer.

Processes (1), (2) and (3) should lead to a strong dependence of the transfer probablility on the oscillator strengths of the singlet-triplet transitions in both the donor and acceptor and upon the overlap of the emission spectrum of the sensitizer with the absorption spectrum of the acceptor. No dependence on the singlet-triplet transition in either the donor or acceptor has however been found. Förster[17] has derived the following equation from which quantative predictions can be made for the critical transfer distance R_o (the distance at which excitation transfer and spontaneous deactivation are of equal probability) for energy transfer due to dipole-dipole interaction.

$$R_o = \sqrt[6]{\frac{9 \times 10^6 (\ln 10)^2 X^2, c, \tau^S}{16 \pi^4 n^2 N^2 \bar{\nu}^{\circ 2}}} \int \epsilon_a^A (\bar{\nu}) \, \epsilon_e^S (\bar{\nu}) \, d\bar{\nu}$$

where N is Avogadro's number, n, the refractive index, τ^S, the actual mean lifetime of the energy donor, c, the velocity of light, $\bar{\nu}^\circ$ is the 0,0 wavenumber for the emission of the donor, X^2 is an orientation factor which, for a random directional distribution, can be taken as equal to $2/3$. $\epsilon_a^A(\bar{\nu})$ represents the molar extinction coefficient of the acceptor and $\epsilon_e^S(\bar{\nu})$ the intensity of the emission of the sensitizer measured in the same units as the extinction coefficient.

For typical cases of sensitized fluorescence R_o values from 50-100 Å have been calculated from this equation in good agreement with experimental values.[18] However the values of R_o, calculated for sensitized phosphorescence in rigid media and also for triplet transfer between the pairs of donors and acceptors given in Table 2 in fluid solvents, are so small (~ 1 Å or less) that they only serve to illustrate that the equation is no longer valid since it only applies to transfer over distances greater than normal collisional diameters. Clearly therefore no long range transfer due to dipole-dipole interactions is expected or found.

Triplet transfer has been found to occur during an encounter at normal collisional separation and under these conditions exchange transfer, i.e. process (4) is quite possible. According to Dexter[16] not only has spin momentum to be conserved for an exchange mechanism but M_D^* must equal M_A^* and $M_D = M_A$ where M_D^* and M_A^* refer to the multiplicity of the donor and acceptor molecules in their excited states and M_D and M_A to multiplicities in their ground states. This condition is satisfied in the cases being considered here.

The probability of energy transfer by an exchange mechanism between two molecules is given by Dexter[17] as

$$P_{DA} = \frac{4\pi^2}{h} Z^2 \int f_D(E)\, F_A(E)\, dE$$

where $\int f_D(E)\, F_A(E)\, dE$ is a type of overlap integral between the emission spectrum of the donor and the absorption spectrum of the acceptor. Z^2 which has the dimensions of energy squared cannot, according to Dexter, be directly related to optical experiments. The transfer probability falls off exponentially with distance and one would therefore expect quenching constants due to exchange transfer not to exceed those calculated for diffusion controlled encounters between molecules having normal cross sections. The experimental results on triplet energy transfer are perfectly consistent with an exchange mechanism.

REFERENCES

[1] Förster, Th., Disc. Faraday Soc., 1959, 27, 7.
[2] Bowen, E. J., Trans. Faraday Soc., 1954, 50, 97.
[3] Perrin, J., 2me conseil de Chemie, Solway Garetheir-Villars, Paris, 1925.
[4] Watson, W. F., and Livingston, R., J. Chem. Phys., 1950, 18, 802.
[5] Terenin, A.N., and Ermolaev, V.L., Doklady Akad. Nauk. S.S.S.R., 1952, 85, 547.
[6] Porter, G., and Wright, M.R., Disc. Faraday Soc., 1959, 27, 18.
[7] Bäckström, H.L.J., and Sandros, K., Acta.Chem. Scand., 1958, 12, 823.
[8] Bäckström, H.L.J., and Sandros, K., Acta. Chem. Scand., 1960, 14, 48.
[9] Terenin, A.N., and Ermolaev, V.L., Trans. Faraday Soc., 1956, 52, 1042.
[10] Terenin, A.N., and Ermolaev, V.L., J. Chim. Phys., 1958, 55, 698.
[11] Lewis, G.N., and Kasha, M., J. Amer. Chem. Soc., 1945, 67, 994.
[12] Porter, G., and Wilkinson, F., Proc. Roy. Soc. 1961, 264A, 1.
[13] Wigner, E., Göttingen Nachrichten, 1927, 375.
[14] Porter, G., and Wright, M.R., J. Chim. Phys., 1958, 55, 705.
[15] Debye, P.J.W., Trans. Electrochem. Soc., 1942, 82, 205.
[16] Dexter, D.L., J. Chem. Phys., 1953, 21, 836.
[17] Förster, Th., Ann. Physik, 1948, 2, 55.
[18] Bowen, E. J., and Brocklehurst, B., Trans. Faraday Soc., 1955, 51, 774.

DELAYED FLUORESCENCE AND PHOSPHORESCENCE IN CRYSTALS OF AROMATIC MOLECULES AT 4.2°K

H. Sponer
Department of Physics, Duke University, Durham, N. C.

ABSTRACT

Delayed fluorescence has been observed in crystals of naphthalene, phenanthrene and chrysene at 4.2°K. The naphthalene spectrum consists of two systems, one belonging to naphthalene and another belonging to β-methylnaphthalene. The 0,0 level of the first is placed at 31,574 cm^{-1}. The main portion of this spectrum originates at 30,964 cm^{-1} which represents a 0-1 transition with a 610 cm^{-1} vibration excited in the ground state (M series in the crystal). The second system begins at 31,062 cm^{-1} with a strong 0,0 band. The view is confirmed that it belongs to β-methylnaphthalene, present as an impurity in naphthalene. This spectrum appears in delayed fluorescence. Phenanthrene crystals at 4.2°K emit a rather extended fluorescence spectrum originating at 28,636 cm^{-1}. Analysis confirms it as the true fluorescence. It also appears in the delayed emission. Chrysene crystals show a broad, diffuse fluorescence built upon the 25,180 cm^{-1} level. This system is of short extension, appears likewise in the delayed emission, and is the true fluorescence of chrysene. All three crystals exhibit extended phosphorescence spectra. The lifetimes of the emissions have been measured; in all three cases the decay is exponential for the phosphorescence in the absence of oxygen.

INTRODUCTION

Absorption and luminescence studies of organic material, crystalline and in solution, have been pursued for many years but there are still old and new questions to be answered. It is

143

an intriguing field and a source of information about intrinsic properties of such crystals. We became interested when, while pursuing phosphorescence studies in simple organic crystals at low temperatures, it was found[1] that naphthalene crystals had a fluorescence of $10^{-3} - 10^{-2}$ sec. instead of the expected $10^{-6} - 10^{-7}$ sec. The regular fluorescence was first observed and analyzed in 1943 by Obreimov and Shabaldas.[2] The "delayed" fluorescence does not start from an exciton level and was explained as a vibration-induced M series of naphthalene.[3-5] Recent results of Prikhotjko and Shpak[6] and of Wolf[7] have indicated, however, that the 31 062 level from which delayed fluorescence was observed must belong to an impurity, recognized by them as β - methylnaphthalene. The beginning of true fluorescence of naphthalene crystal was placed at 30 950 cm^{-1} by Wolf. We have added new experiments, some in naphthalene crystal and others in phenanthrene and chrysene crystals in which we had also found a delayed fluorescence to occur.

EXPERIMENTAL

The essential features of our experimental set-up for observation of phosphorescence and of delayed fluorescence have been described in detail in the first papers of our group.[8,9,10] Crystalline flakes of the purified sample were put in the sample cell which was evacuated. The crystals were randomly oriented. Before sealing off the sample cell, oxygen-free helium gas was introduced into the cell to ensure a temperature close to 4°K at the emitting surface. The sample cell was then immersed in liquid helium. The optical arrangement was essentially the same as described by Heckman,[8] except that the two right-angle quartz prisms in his arrangement were replaced by two small front-aluminized plane mirrors. Excitation was from a G.E. AH-6 high pressure mercury lamp. A Bausch and Lomb medium quartz spectrograph was employed for recording the spectra. 103a-F plates were taken when delayed fluorescence and phosphorescence were photographed simultaneously. With a 100 μ slit exposures required about 12 hrs.

For observations of fluorescence alone, radiation from a high pressure Xe lamp was passed through a small quartz prism monochromator. Excitation was into the second singlet system in order to isolate the scattered and reflected radiation from the emitted fluorescence spectrum. This seemed preferable to

the usual method of exciting into the first singlet system with
filtered light from a high pressure Hg arc since with this
latter technique there always appear some Hg lines, but absorption lines of the crystalline material show up as well.
103a - 0 plates were used when photographing the regular
fluorescence. Purification of the samples will be described in
a later, more detailed paper.

RESULTS AND DISCUSSION OF FLUORESCENCE

1. Naphthalene

We observed that fluorescence of purified randomly oriented
crystals sets in at 4°K with a weak band at 31 448 cm⁻¹. It lies
126 cm⁻¹ below the exciton level 31 574 cm⁻¹ measured by
Zmerli,[4] is not observed in the weaker delayed fluorescence,
and is not related to the 31 062 system. As mentioned before
this system is now believed to belong to β - methylnaphthalene
present in naphthalene crystals in very small concentration
(0.1 − 0.01%). This was shown convincingly by Prikhotjko and
Shpak,[6] and by Wolf.[7] The previous assignment was plausible
because 31 062 fits numerically a transition from the center
at 31 559 of the exciton levels 31 643, 31 476 to a vibrational
level of ∼ 510 cm⁻¹ in the ground state. We convinced ourselves
of the correctness of the new interpretation by irradiating our
"pure" naphthalene at 4°K with a narrow monochromatic beam
of light, and obtained a sharp absorption line at 31 062 cm⁻¹.
Weak absorption at this level had been found before in napththa-
lene crystals of at least 10-20 microns thickness. Since it is
the strongest emission line, it must be from an impurity. Wolf
observed the 31 062 line strongly in fluorescence at 14°K but
found a 30 950 cm⁻¹ line of higher intensity at 4.2°K.

Both lines appear in delayed fluorescence. In fact, our first
plates taken with Dr. Kanda in 1956 showed some interesting
intensity relations. On plates taken with a commercial sample
which we had purified the 31 062 was strong, whereas the 30 968
was strong on plates from a highly purified sample left over
from vapor absorption work.* Our present sample is also not

---

*The intensity variation with concentration of the two zero bands 31
062 and 30 964 has been well demonstrated by Shpak and Sheka.[11]

free from β - methylnaphthalene. Thus, the observed spectrum
is the result of different excitation mechanisms. If Zmerli's
observation of a small splitting into exciton levels 31 574 and
31 562 in fluorescence is correct, the 30 964 may result from
a transition 31 574-611 (ground state) = 30 963. Another alternative is a transition from the lower Davydov component 31 476
to a 512 vibration in the ground state: 31 476-512 = 30 964.
This would be an a-polarized system. These and other relations may be seen from Fig. 1. For example, the strong 31 062
fluorescence fits into two different schemes numerically: in

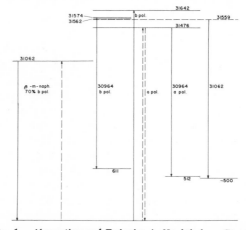

Fig. 1 — Absorption and Emission in Naphthalene Crystal

naphthalene crystal as transition from the center at 31 559 to
a ground state vibration 512 (this had been noticed previously),
and as an impurity transition from 31 062 to its ground state.
McClure and Schnepp[12] have mentioned that their a- and b-
polarized fluorescence spectra of naphthalene crystal at 20°K
are identical, except for intensity, at or below 31 062. The b
spectrum was reported as being twice as intense as the a spectrum. In spite of the various coincidences in the excitation of
the naphthalene crystal spectrum, most of the 31 062 fluorescence comes from β - methylnaphthalene excited by sensitization and exciton migration from the upper Davydov component.

2. Phenanthrene.

Phenanthrene (tech.), obtained from Eastman Kodak, was
purified using the method of Bachmann.[13] It was then placed

in the sample cell in the same way as described for naphthalene. The optical arrangement and procedure were also the
same. Several plates were measured in each case. Accuracy
is within 15 cm⁻¹ for the stronger bands and may be ± 30 cm⁻¹
for the weaker bands.

The fluorescence spectrum recorded by us is essentially the
same as that reported by McClure[14] except that it extends
further on the long wavelength side. Forty-four bands were
measured in the region 3540 − 4702 Å. On the whole the spectrum is not as sharp as the fluorescence of naphthalene. Fixa-
tion of the zero band is somewhat problematic. McClure placed
it at 28 636 in absorption which is the mean of the two Davydov
components 28 660 and 28 613. The transition to the upper
level is b-polarized, to the lower it is a-polarized. The zero
band does not appear in fluorescence. However, Wolf[15] reported
an a-polarized fluorescence from the lower Davydov component
28 590 cm⁻¹ at 90°K which was stronger than that from the b-
polarized level. Studies of the fluorescence of phenanthrene in
methyl pentane glass and absorption in EPA led McClure to
assume 28 275 as origin for fluorescence, and another one at
the weak band 28380. A later similar investigation by Prikhotjko
and Fugol[16] on establishing a relation between the luminescence
and the weak long wave absorption of phenanthrene crystals was
not available at this time. The same reasoning (relation between luminescence and environmental effects) was recently
used by these authors for stilbene crystals.[17]

Our fluorescence started with a band at 28 239 cm⁻¹. Assuming that it might belong to a transition from the vibration-
less level of the first excited singlet state, *i.e.* from 28 636
cm⁻¹, the absorption of a thick (2mm) phenanthrene crystal was
then examined at 4.2°K but the 28 239 band (at which fluorescence begins) did not show up. However, absorption bands of
anthracene appeared in the spectrum of the thick crystal of
phenanthrene[18] although none of them were discovered in the
fluorescence spectrum. Hence we believe the latter to be the
emission from pure phenanthrene crystal. Apparently our
technique of front face illumination and observation reduces the
effects of small amounts of impurity and consequently occurrence of sensitized fluorescence connected with them. The intensity maximum of the fluorescence lies at ∼ 4053 Å. The first

band is 397 cm^{-1} away from the absorption zero band. The separation corresponds to the Raman line 406 cm^{-1} which is the analogue of 606 in benzene and 512 in naphthalene. We made sure that this is not an accidental coincidence as in naphthalene by performing the same type absorption experiment in phenanthrene crystal with a narrow beam of light. No absorption line was observed in phenanthrene. The detailed analysis of the spectrum will be included in a later publication.

3. Chrysene.

Much less is known about absorption and fluorescence of this compound as far as crystals are concerned. On the other hand, absorption spectra in solutions have been reported by many workers.[19] Fluorescence in various solvents was observed by Kasha[20] and recently by Nurmukhametov and al.[21] Birks and Cameron[22] examined the fluorescence spectrum of micro-crystalline samples grown from solutions on a quartz plate. They noticed that different solvents would give specimens of varying degrees of uniformity and spectra of varying degrees of differences. Nurmukhametov *et al.*, in their recent work, also studied absorption and fluorescence of chrysene powders. There seem to be, however, some errors (probably typographical) in their report. The beginning of fluorescence in solution and in the powder is more than 7000 cm^{-1} apart, and this is also the case for absorption. It seems doubtful that the spectra are genuine chrysene products.

Our chrysene sample was of Eastman Kodak White Label grade and was recrystallized twice from toluene. The experimental conditions for delayed fluorescence were the same as described for naphthalene and phenanthrene. As in the other cases, delayed fluorescence and phosphorescence appeared on the same plate. All bands of chrysene crystals are more diffuse and broader than even the phenanthrene bands so that the accuracy of measurement is not better than ± 30 cm^{-1}. The spectrum extends from 4002 to 4613 Å and consists of 8 bands. The first band was measured at 24 980 which is 200 cm^{-1} distant from the origin at 25 180 (absorption). Three other vibrations, 350, 708 and 1590, occur in strong bands. The last one is the main vibration in the spectrum and appears twice excited in two bands.

RESULTS AND DISCUSSION OF PHOSPHORESCENCE

1. Naphthalene.

Phosphorescence in naphthalene crystals at 4.2°K starts from a level at 20 973 which we have verified under different experimental conditions with different coworkers. The phosphorescence region is rather extended, ranging from 20 973 to 14 860 cm^{-1}. In EPA solution at 77°K the phosphorescence emission is shifted to 21 274 cm^{-1}. Analysis of the bands is fairly straightforward. For comparison, onset of phosphorescence in the crystalline state has been added for β - methylnaphthalene in Table I.

Table I

Energy Relations and Phosphorescence Lifetimes in Some Aromatic Crystals

Substance	Exciton Levels Davydov Splitting		Zero Band of Phosphorescence	Phosphorescence τ at 4°K
naphthalene	(b) 31 643	166	21 274 EPA, 77°K	2. 31 ± 0. 03 sec.
	(a) 31 476		20 973 crystal, 4°K	
β-methylnaphthalene	(a) 31 155	31	20 843 EPA, 77°K	1. 78 ± 0. 05 sec.
	(b) 31 124		20 646 crystal, 4°K	
phenanthrene	(l) 28 660	47	21 720 EPA, 77°K	2. 81 ± 0. 02 sec.
	(a) 28 613		21 033 crystal, 4°K	
chrysene	25 186	11	19 800 EPA, 77°K	1. 38 ± 0. 03 sec.
	25 175		18 316 crystal, 4°K	

2. Phenanthrene.

We had expected the phosphorescence emission to start from a level lower than in naphthalene in analogy to the situation for fluorescence. However, as seen in Table I, the phenanthrene phosphorescence begins at a higher level than in naphthalene whereas the energy difference between the lowest singlets in the two crystals is of the order of 3000 cm^{-1} in the opposite direction. Another difference is in the shift of the phosphorescence levels from EPA solution[23] to the crystal. The shift in naphthalene is 300 cm^{-1} and in phenanthrene it is $\sim$ 700 cm^{-1}.

3. Chrysene.

Going to chrysene, the solution[24] – crystal shift of the phosphorescence becomes ~ 1500 cm^{-1}. The shift of the fluorescence level from phenanthrene to chrysene is ~ 3500 cm^{-1}, *i.e.* of the same order as the corresponding shift naphthalene-phenanthrene. Vibrational analysis of the phosphorescence spectra will be given in a later detailed paper where they will be discussed in relation to molecular and crystal symmetries where it is possible.

4. Lifetime Measurements of Phosphorescence.

The experimental method can be described here only briefly. A photomultiplier was mounted in such a way that, when the rotating sectors of the phosphoroscope blocked the light from reaching the sample, the light emitted from the sample – passing through suitable filters – would reach the photomultiplier. The latter is connected to the vertical plates of a Tektronix 532 oscilloscope. The resulting sweep pattern, obtained with sweep speeds of 0.5–2 sec/cm, were photographed and analyzed. It was observed that the decay curves of the phosphorescence lifetimes became exponential after one half to one seconds. The lifetime figures in the Table were measured over a period of 2–4 mean half lives. The low intensity of the phosphorescence prevents measurements for a longer period of time. It was found that the decay was a pure exponential in all three cases. The error in the measured values is estimated at 5%. However, the temperature could have been slightly above 4.2°K making the values obtained a little too short.

5. Remarks on the Mechanism of Delayed Emission.

Occurrence of delayed fluorescence must necessarily be connected with a long-living storage mechanism of the excitation energy in the crystal. Such processes are: formation of exciton traps, formation of metastable states, trapping of electrons. The first two lie energetically below the exciton bands, hence a delayed return to the exciton level has to be ruled out at 4°K at which temperature most of our observations were made. However, whether we consider the 31 062 system or the one from 30 964, it is always necessary to reach again the exciton levels of the naphthalene crystal for delayed emission.

This would be possible if the trap state has a long enough life to be visited by another exciton so that a higher excited state would result. Internal conversion will bring it down to the lowest excited level as usual but the fluorescence will appear "delayed". This would apply to the naphthalene system starting from 30 964 cm^{-1}. If there is present an impurity with much lower energy the singlet excitation energy will mainly be used for its excitation like for the 31 062 system of β - methylnaphthalene. The accidental closeness of the two levels favors occurrence of both processes. The other possibility, trapping of electrons, might materialize, if the two-quantum step leads into the conductivity band for free electrons so that photoionization could set in. The free electrons may then be trapped and stored until they are released from the traps by thermal fluctuations and can recombine with holes under light emission. As in the case of the exciton traps, the trap depth for electrons is not shallow enough for their release at 4° or 20°K. Should, however, light waves or migrating excitons come very close to such traps the electrons may be liberated in a way as they are from color centers in inorganic phosphors.

This discussion leads to the conclusion that delayed fluorescence is not caused by the long lifetime of a trapped exciton only. If it were, its decay curve should be exponential, whereas the experiments[1b] showed a deviation from exponentiality. Although the lifetimes and decay curves of the delayed fluorescence may be influenced by several mechanisms, this should not noticeably influence the phosphorescence decay which has a lifetime two or three orders of magnitude longer than the lifetime of the delayed fluorescence. These conclusions may be drawn from our exponential phosphorescence decay curves.

Acknowledgment: The research described in this report was carried out with the participation of Drs. Yoshiya Kanda, Herbert Renner, Dolores Olness, and Indra Sen Singh.

REFERENCES

[1] a. H. Sponer, Y. Kanda and L. A. Blackwell, J. Chem. Phys. 19, 721 (1958); b. N. W. Blake and D. S. McClure, J. Chem. Phys. 29, 722 (1958).

[2] W. Obreimov and K. Shabaldas, J. Phys. USSR 7, 168 (1943).

[3] D. Griesbach, G. Will and H. C. Wolf, Z. Naturforsch. 11a, 791 (1956); H.C. Wolf, Advances in Solid State Phys.9, 1 (1959).

[4] Adnan Zmerli, J. Chim. Phys. 1959, 387.

[5] H. Sponer, paper in "Electrical Conductivity in Organic Solids", Interscience Publishers, in press.

[6] A. F. Prikhotjko and M. T. Shpak, Optics and Spectroscopy (English translation) 6, 119 (1959).

[7] H. C. Wolf, Naturwiss. 48, 43 (1961).

[8] Richard Heckman, J. Mol. Spectroscopy 2, 27 (1958).

[9] Y. Kanda and H. Sponer, J. Chem. Phys. 28, 798 (1958).

[10] Lawrence A. Blackwell, Yoshiya Kanda and H. Sponer, J. Chem. Phys. 32, 1465 (1960).

[11] M. T. Shpak and E. F. Sheka, Optics and Spectroscopy (English translation) 8, 32 (1960).

[12] D. S. McClure and O. Schnepp, J. Chem. Phys. 23, 1575 (1955).

[13] W. E. Bachmann, J. Am. Chem. Soc. 57, 555 (1935).

[14] D. S. McClure, J. Chem. Phys. 25, 481 (1956).

[15] H. C. Wolf, Z. Naturforsch. 13a, 420 (1958).

[16] A. F. Prikhotjko & I. Y. Fugol, Optika i Spektroskopiya 5, 582 (1958).

[17] A. F. Prikhotjko and I. Y. Fugol, Optics and Spectroscopy (English translation) 7, 19 (1959).

[18] J. W. Sidman, J. Chem. Phys. 25, 115 (1956).

[19] See: H. M. Hershenson, Ultraviolet and Visible Absorption Spectra-Index for 1930-54, New York Acad. Press, 1956.

[20] M. Kasha, Chem. Rev. 41, 401 (1947).

[21] P. N. Nurmukhametov et al., Optics and Spectroscopy (English translation) 9, 313 (1960).

[22] J. B. Birks and A.J.W. Cameron, Proc. Roy. Soc. A 249, 297 (1959).

[23] Yoshiya Kanda and Ryoichi Shimada, Spectrochem. Acta 1959, 211.

[24] D. S. McClure, J. Chem. Phys. 17, 905 (1949).

THE EFFICIENCY OF SOLUTION FLUORESCENCE

E. J. Bowen and D. Seaman
Physical Chemistry Laboratory
Oxford, England

ABSTRACT

Solutions of 1- and 2-naphthylamines and certain of their sulphonates in a number of solvents have been examined for fluorescence properties. Fluorescence yields were found to increase in general with a lowering of temperature to a constant value which in many cases is not unity. Such limiting yields of less than unity seem to arise from interaction of excited molecules with the solvent, since they are correlated with absorption and fluorescence band maxima separations.

Solutions of certain fluorescent molecules in paraffins of different viscosity show temperate quenching which correlates with diffusional characteristics of the solvents for flexible molecules, while for rigid molecules solvent viscosity has a much smaller influence.

The fluorescence yield from solutions is affected by a number of factors. Concentration dependent factors are dimer formation in the ground[1,2] or in the excited[3] state, collisional self-quenching[4] or energy transfer[5]. Those independent of concentration are pH effects on ionization of ground and excited states,[6,7] H-bond formation in ground or excited states,[8] dipole relaxation effects,[9] and specific effects by solvent molecules on transition probabilities or on quasi-chemical reactions. The action of strong quenching agents such as oxygen and the above concentration dependent factors are not considered in this paper.

Fluorescence normally diminishes with rise of temperature and reaches a limiting value at low temperatures. It is often possible to realize a constant fluorescence yield over a wide temperature interval. The apparently reverse temperature-fluorescence slopes of the curves shown by Bowen and West[10]

153

become in many cases horizontal when corrected for refractive
index changes.[11] Such limiting yields often fall short of unity.
The results of Bowen and Sahu[12] indicated that yields F could
be related to the temperature by the equation:

$$\frac{1}{F} - 1 = k_1 e^{-E/RT} + k_2$$

The right-hand side terms represent two degradation processes, one dependent and the other independent of temperature.
The physical significance of these terms is the present subject
of discussion. The work described below is of measurements on
dilute solutions of 1- and 2- naphthylamines and of a number
of their sodium sulphonates and dimethyl derivatives. Under
the conditions used these substances absorb and emit in the
$-NH_2$ form, although in very acid or very alkaline solutions
the $-NH_3{}^+$ or the NH^- ions appear. The solutions were contained in a small transparent Dewer vessel, in which they could
be heated or cooled, and excited by light of wave-length 3660Å
from a mercury lamp at a fixed optical density (0.4). The fluorescence emerging at 90° was spectrally dispersed by a monochromator -photomultiplier combination, and the intensity determined from the area of the fluorescence band, corrected
for instrumental characteristics and for the refractive index
of the solution. Absolute values of fluorescence yield F were
obtained by comparison with the band area of the emission of
a dilute aqueous solution of sodium 1-naphthylamine 4-sulpho-
nate ($F = 0.8$ at 18-20°C). Dissolved oxygen was removed from
the solutions by a stream of CO_2; for organic solutions oxygen
quenching was marked, but was very small for solutions in
water.

Over the range -40 to + 80°C F values were found to vary
with temperature according to the above equation, and to reach
constant values $(1/1 + k_2)$ at lower temperatures. For 1- and 2-
naphthylamines and 1-naphthylamine 4- sulphonate this constant
value was near unity, while for 2- naphthylamine 1- sulphonate
it was $0.24 - 0.3$ in all the solvents studied. Three substances,
however, were found to show marked variations of the limiting
value of F depending on the solvent.

Figures 1—3 show the yield values F plotted against temperature °K for 1-naphthylamine 5-sulphonate, 1-naphthylamine
8-sulphonate, and 1 dimethylamino naphthalene 5-sulphonate.
These clearly show that limiting values of F less than unity
are reached at low temperatures; the independence of F with

T for the compounds in several solvents being particularly striking.

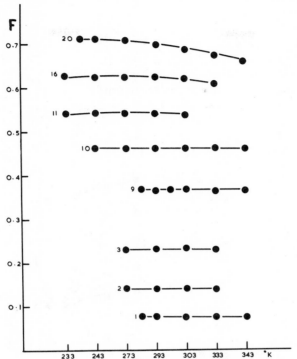

Fig. 1 — Yield-temperature curves for 1-naphthylamine,
5-sulphonate in various solvents.

Text for Figures.
Solvent key for Figs. 1-4.

1. Water
2. 3 methanol, 7 water.
3. 5 methanol, 5 water.
4. 2 ethanol, 7 water.
5. 5 ethylene glycol, 5 water.
6. 7 ethylene glycol, 3 water.
7. 5 ethanol, 5 water.
8. 5 isopropanol, 5 water.
9. Formamide.
10. Ethylene glycol.
11. Methanol.

12. Ethanol.
13. n-pentanol.
14. n-octanol.
15. n-butanol.
16. Isopropanol.
17. 5 formamide, 5 dimethyl formamide.
18. 5 ethylene glycol, 5 dimethyl formamide.
19. 3 methanol, 7 dimethyl formamide.
20. Dimethyl formamide.

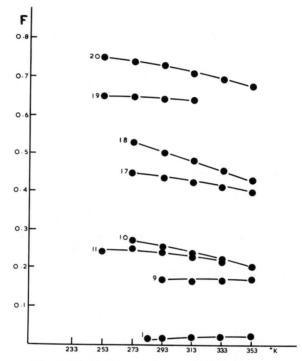

Fig. 2 — Yield-temperature curves for 1-naphthylamine,
8-sulphonate in various solvents.

The maxima of the absorption bands of these substances
do not vary very much with solvent, but those of the fluorescence bands do. At very low temperatures and very high viscosities the fluorescence bands move towards the blue, because
of the slow relaxation of the newly excited molecule, and at
high temperatures they move towards the blue again because of
the diminution of solvent interactions.[9] In the temperature

interval studied, however, the excited molecules are largely
relaxed before emitting, and because of the dissipation of the
relaxation energy the fluorescence band maximum has a large
separation from the absorption band maximum.

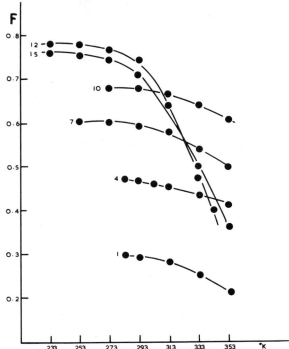

Fig. 3 — Yield-temperature curves for 1-dimethyl-amino-
naphthalene, 5-sulphonate in various solvents.

Fig. 4 shows that this separation is a function of the low-
temperature limiting value of the yield F. Comparison of the
solvents methanol and ethylene glycol shows that viscosity
plays little part in these systems.

Among the large number of substances investigated in this
laboratory all appear to have k_2 values of zero except where
quasi-chemical reactions of the excited state are probable.
Hexane solutions of 2-methyl anthracene, at first sight an exception,[12] show at very low temperatures a rapid rise of yield.
Typical examples are anthracene in chlorobenzene or chloroform, 1-chloranthracene in hexane (electron-transfer to Cl),
aromatic hydrocarbons in aromatic solvents[13,14] (Mulliken
force interactions), acridine in alcohol,[15] or the naphthylamine

derivatives described in this paper (H -bonding effects). Such

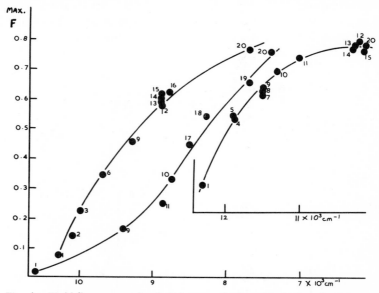

Fig. 4 — Yield-fluorescence band shift curves for 1-naphthylamine, 5-sulphonate; 1-naphthylamine, 8-sulphonate; and 1-dimethyl-amino-naphthalene, 5-sulphonate in various solvents.

quasi charge-transfer reactions of the excited singlet may be assumed to facilitate passage to the triplet state. If this is of general validity, there is then no reason to attribute the temperature-dependent term of the above equation to a ground-state degradation, but rather to relate it to a potential-surface crossing to the triplet state. Unfortunately the precision of measurement available does not enable E - values to be obtained very accurately; they lie in the range of a few k. cal. per mole. It will be seen from Figure 3 that differences of E-value must exist for different solvents, as indeed would be expected from interaction effects.

Measurements have been made by Mr. A. U. Khan in this laboratory on solutions in paraffins of widely different viscosities with fluorescent substances having yields tending to unity at low temperatures, i.e., having $k_2 = 0$. Table 1 shows a selection of activation energy data (E cal/mole). The E values from the expression

$$1/F - 1 = k_1 e^{-E/RT}$$

for the molecule di-9-anthryl ethane are very near to those characterizing the diffusional properties of the pure liquid solvents. This behavior resembles that found by Oster and Nishijima[16] for solutions of diphenylmethane derivatives, except that the latter showed large k_2 terms. It would appear that

Table 1

Paraffin Solvent	Viscous			Very fluid
	A	B	C	D
Solvent Fluidity E- value	8940	5200	4690	3310
Di-9-anthryl ethane. E value	8550	5750	5610	4530
Anthracene E-value	1380			1330
9:10 dichloro Anthracene E-value	6160			5790

the excited molecule of this substance can degrade its energy by relative thermal diffusional movements of the two large rings joined by the flexible chain. The effect of the viscosity on the E-values of the more rigid molecules of anthracene and its derivatives is much less, and energy must be lost in other ways. The E-value for 9:10 dichloro anthracene is 5790 cal./ mole in a paraffin solvent of diffusional E value only 3310, indicating that vibrational energy quantities relating to the solute molecule are more involved than solvent energy quantities. A completely satisfactory interpretation of E-values for fluorescence however is still lacking. For substances with high values of E, k_1 values also become large, sometimes reaching 10^6. If one is to regard thermal quenching as a reaction competing with the radiational process in time, $k_1 = k_0 \tau$ where τ is the radiational life-time and k_0 is an absolute rate. For $k_1 = 10^6$ and $\tau = 10^{-8}$ sec., k_0 is 10^{14} sec.$^{-1}$. Whether this is too fast a rate to allow of the above method treatment without modification remains at present a debatable matter.

REFERENCES

[1] V. L. Levschin, Acta Physiocochim., U.R.S.S. 1 685; 2 331 (1935)

[2] E. Rabinowitch and L. F. Epstein, J.A.C.S., 63 69 (1941)

[3] Th. Förster and K. Kasper, Zeit, Elektrochem., 59 977 (1955)

[4] E. J. Bowen and A. Norton, Trans. Farad. Soc., 35 44 (1939)

[5] R. Livingston, J. Physical Chem., 61 860 (1957)

[6] Th. Förster, Zeit, Electrochem., 54 42 (1950)

[7] A. Weller, Zeit. Elektrochem., 56 662 (1952)

[8] E. Lippert, Symposium on Hydrogen Bonding, Pergamon Press (1957)

[9] E. Lippert, W. Lüder and F. Moll, Spectrochimica Acta, 10 858 (1959)

[10] E. J. Bowen and K. West, J. Chem. Soc., 4394 (1955)

[11] J. Hermans and S. Levinson, J. Opt. Sci. Amer., 41 460 (1951)

[12] E. J. Bowen and J. Sahu, J. Physical Chem., 63 4 (1959)

[13] E. J. Bowen and E. Coates, J. Chem. Soc., 105 (1947)

[14] Majumdar and S. Basu, J. Chem. Phys., 33 1190 (1960)

[15] E. J. Bowen and J. Sahu, J. Chem. Soc., 3716 (1958)

[16] G. Oster and Y. Nishijima, J. Amer. Chem. Soc., 78 1581 (1956)

FLUORESCENCE OF AROMATIC ALDEHYDES

K. Bredereck, Th. Förster and H.-G. Oesterlin
Laboratory of Physical Chemistry, Technische Hochschule, Stuttgart

ABSTRACT

The fluorescence properties of some aromatic aldehydes were investigated. Some higher members of the aromatic series fluoresce in inert as well as in hydroxylic solvents, others only in the latter or in mixtures with inert ones. This can be explained by the differences in energy of the fluorescent $\pi \to \pi *$ and the quenching $n \to \pi *$ states of these aldehydes together with the solvent dependence of these energies. For pyrene-3-aldehyde the existence of two different mechanisms of fluorescence activation was demonstrated by the dependence of fluorescence yields and spectra on temperature and solvent composition. In the case of moderately activating agents solvent rearrangement during the lifetime of the excited molecule is most important. With a strong activator ground state interaction prevails at low concentration.

1. INTRODUCTION

The majority of aromatic aldehydes is nonfluorescent, at least in solution at room temperature. Several years ago, however, Kasper[1] found that pyrene-3-aldehyde, though non-fluorescent in hydrocarbon solution, fluoresces strongly in ethanol.

Similar effects had been observed earlier with other compounds of apparently different chemical nature. According to Livingston, Watson and McArdle,[2] and also to Evstigneev, Gavrilova and Krasnovski,[3] chlorophyll a and b are practically nonfluorescent in dry hydrocarbons but become fluorescent by traces of water or other polar admixtures. This so-called fluorescence activation was explained by Becker and Kasha[4]

161

by the existence of $n \rightarrow \pi *$ singlet states of nearly the same
energy as those of the emitting $\pi \rightarrow \pi *$ singlet states of these
molecules. An $n \rightarrow \pi *$ state results from the promotion of a
lone pair nonbonding electron from an N-, O- or similar atom
into an empty antibonding $\pi *$-orbital of the same molecule. As
demonstrated by Kasha[5], molecules with an $n \rightarrow \pi *$ state as
their lowest excited singlet state are generally nonfluorescent
(an exception was recently found by Lippert et al.[6]), because
the properties of such a state are favorable for nonradiative
deactivation via lower triplet states. Whereas $\pi \rightarrow \pi *$ state
energies are lowered by polar or hydrogen bonding solvents,
$n \rightarrow \pi *$ states behave in the opposite way. In suitable molecules
in inert solvents, it may therefore occur that the quenching
$n \rightarrow \pi *$ state be the lower, but the radiating $\pi \rightarrow \pi *$ state may be
lower in other solvents. In inert solvents these molecules will
be nonfluorescent, but fluorescence activation will occur by
polar admixtures or in pure polar solvents.

This situation is by no way unique for the chlorophylls.
Mataga, Kaifu and Koizumi[7] (compare also Mataga[8] and Mataga
and Tsuno[9]) have reported similar behavior of quinoline and
of acridine which, as N-heterocycles, would be expected to have
low $n \rightarrow \pi *$ states even though the corresponding absorption is
hidden under the much stronger $\pi \rightarrow \pi *$ bands.

Aldehydes, too, have $n \rightarrow \pi *$ states. In benzaldehyde the
$n \rightarrow \pi *$ absorption (0 - 0 band in heptane at 27.0 kK) is well
separated from the next $\pi \rightarrow \pi *$ absorption (0 - 0 band at 34.6
kK) so that the $n \rightarrow \pi *$ singlet state is the lowest excited one in
all reasonable solvents. Both kinds of states are shifted to
lower energies in the higher members of the aromatic series,
but, by their very nature, the $n \rightarrow \pi *$ states are shifted less
than the $\pi \rightarrow \pi *$ states so that they finally become the lowest
singlet states and the higher aromatic aldehydes are therefore
fluorescent.

In between, there should be aldehydes within which the
two states are of nearly equal energies so that their sequence
might be reversed by solvent interaction, thus making fluorescence activation possible. We suspect that pyrene-3-aldehyde
is representative of this intermediate case.

2. PYRENE-3-ALDEHYDE IN PURE SOLVENTS

Some fluorescence and absorption data of this aldehyde in

different solvents are presented in Table 1. It is nonfluorescent
in heptane and in diethylether. The fluorescence is weak in

Table 1

Fluorescence and Absorption Data for
Pyrene-3-Aldehyde in Different Solvents

Solvent	Quantum yield*	Fluorescence Maximum** kK	First Absorption Maximum kK
n-heptane	< 0.001	–	25.6
diethylether	< 0.003	–	25.6
chlorobenzene	0.008	24.0	25.2
acetonitrile	0.009	23.6	25.4
chloroform	0.045	23.7	25.2
ethanol	0.11	22.3	25.4
methanol	0.15	22.0	
acetic acid	0.26	21.2	25.4

* Approximate values, based on an energy yield of 0.12 for a
$3 \cdot 10^{-3}$ molar solution of pyrene-3-aldehyde in methanol
under excitation with 27.4 kK.[20] Values for other solvents
were obtained by comparison of integrated spectral intensities under complete absorption of exciting light.

**quanta per wavenumber interval as in Fig. 2.

chlorobenzene and in acetonitrile, but comparatively high in
ethanol, acetic acid (and also in a 1:1 mixture of water and
acetonitrile). Whereas the fluorescence is more violet in the
weakly activating solvents, it is blue in the stronger ones. This
results from a considerable red shift of the fluorescence maxima
in this series. By comparison, the absorption spectra (first
band of $\pi \rightarrow \pi^*$ absorption) are shifted to a much smaller extent.
    Fig. 1 shows in detail the absorption spectra in heptane,
ethanol and acetic acid. All maxima belong to the strong $\pi \rightarrow \pi^*$
absorption under which the much weaker $n \rightarrow \pi^*$ absorption must
be hidden. We have carefully examined the low frequency tail
down to $\log \epsilon$ values of 1.0 without finding any sign of it. This
does not, however, exclude the possibility that the maximum of
the hidden $n \rightarrow \pi^*$ absorption is on the red side of that of the
$\pi \rightarrow \pi^*$ absorption because it is several orders of magnitudes

weaker (in benzaldehyde, it has a $\log \epsilon_{max}$ value of only 1.4).

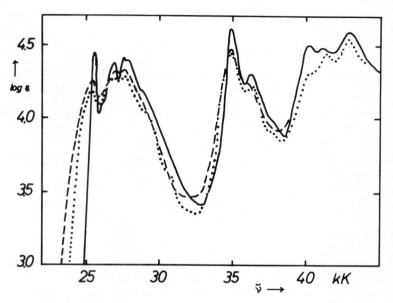

Fig. 1 — Absorption spectra of pyrene-3-aldehyde in heptane (——), ethanol (......) and acetic acid (— — —).

The fluorescence spectra in some of these solvents are depicted in Fig. 2. They show, when taken together with the data of Table 1, that with increasing fluorescence yield the spectra are shifted to the red in nearly the same sequence, and that this shift is connected with a loss of vibrational structure.

According to these spectral shifts, the activation of fluorescence is connected with a considerable decrease in the energy of the emitting $\pi \rightarrow \pi^*$ state due to solvent interaction. Since the shifts are much smaller in absorption than in fluorescence, this decrease results only to a minor extent from the equilibrium configuration of solvent molecules around the unexcited aldehyde molecule. It must mainly be due to some rearrangement of solvent molecules during the lifetime of the excited molecule in its fluorescent $\pi \rightarrow \pi^*$ singlet state.

Such rearrangement can take place because the electronic structure of the excited molecule differs from that of the unexcited one so that it exerts different forces on neighboring solvent molecules. Well known examples of this are unsymmetrically 4,4' substituted stilbenes and other compounds, where the solvent dependence of fluorescence spectra has been investigated by Lippert et al.[10-12] These molecules become highly polar by excitation so that they force the reorientation of surrounding dipole molecules. A somewhat different case has been investigated by Mataga et al.[13] β-naphthol in the excited state seems to be able to form well defined hydrogen bonds with suitable proton acceptors at much lower concentrations than in the ground state. The detailed mechanism of solvent interaction in the present case is discussed at a later stage.

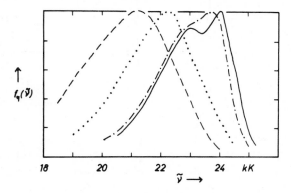

Fig. 2 — Fluorescence spectra F_q ($\tilde{\nu}$) (quanta per wave number interval, maxima normalized) of pyrene-3-aldehyde in chlorobenzene (——), chloroform (–.–) ethanol (......) and acetic acid. Room temperature, concentrations about 10^{-4}M. Spectra obtained with quinine in 0.1 N H_2SO_4 as standard and based on the data published by Lippert et al.[21])

The shifts of fluorescence spectra between weakly and moderately activating solvents in Table 1 are equivalent to energy differences of about 3 kcal/mole. This exceeds by far the thermal energy at room temperature and is sufficient to alter the relative populations of $\pi \rightarrow \pi^*$ and $n \rightarrow \pi^*$ states and, therefore, the ratio of competing radiative and nonradiative deactivation processes. It is thus possible that the decrease in $\pi \rightarrow \pi^*$ excitation energy is the main reason for fluorescence activation by these solvents.

Some further conclusions may be drawn from measurements at lower temperatures. Fig. 3 represents the fluorescence yield of pyrene-3-aldehyde in the polar solvent isobutanol (with 5% aliphatic hydrocarbon added to prevent crystallization).

With decreasing temperature, the yield at first rises to a maximum at 230°K and then decreases. Corresponding altera-tions occur in the fluores-cence spectra. These are depicted in Fig. 4. They are at first shifted to the red and then back to the blue. The temperature of maximum red shift is ap-proximately the same as that of maximum yield. Here again, the relation between $\pi \rightarrow \pi^*$ excitation energy as deduced from the spectral position and fluorescence yield can be seen.

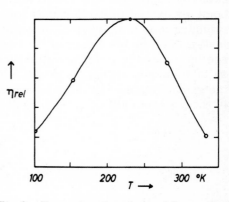

Fig. 3 — Temperature dependence of fluorescence quantum yield of pyrene-3-aldehyde in isobutanol.

Similar results were obtained in pure ethanol and in the common EPA solvent (volume proportions: ethyl-ether 5, isopentane 5, ethanol 2). In ethanol, the maximum yield occurs at 240°K while in EPA, which is less polar and also less viscous, maximum fluorescence and red shift occur at 180°K.

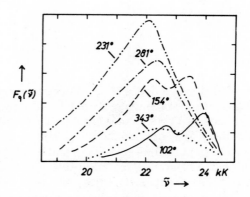

Fig. 4 — Fluorescence spectra $F_q(\tilde{\nu})$ (quanta per wave number interval, same units for all spectra) of pyrene-3-aldehyde in isobutanol at different tem-peratures.
—— 102°K, - - - 154°K, -..- 231°K, -.- 281°K, ... 393°K.

The temperature dependence of these fluorescence spectra is consistent with our general assumptions concerning the nature of solvent interaction with the excited molecule. At lower temperature, the equilibrium configuration of solvent molecules around the excited aldehyde molecule is less disturbed by thermal agitation and has, therefore, lower energy. Thus a further decrease of $\pi \rightarrow \pi*$ state energy occurs in an interacting solvent. But with decreasing temperature the rate constant of the rearrangement process must also decrease so that finally the equilibrium configuration will no longer be established during the short lifetime of the excited molecule. The fluorescing $\pi \rightarrow \pi*$ state energy then rises again and the spectrum is shifted back to the blue.* One may conclude once more from the corresponding decrease in fluorescence yield that at lower temperature the energy of the quenching $n \rightarrow \pi*$ state remains nearly the same and that the shift of $\pi \rightarrow \pi*$ state energy mainly determines the ratio of radiative and nonradiative deactivation within the molecule.

It is commonly accepted that nonradiative deactivation via $n \rightarrow \pi*$ states occurs by an intercombination process which finally populates the lowest triplet state of the molecule. One should therefore expect that under suitable conditions phosphorescence emission occurs in inert solvents as well as in polar ones below the inversion temperature. In methylcyclohexane-isooctane, actually, a yellow emission appears from 160°K downward. Although the nature of this emission was not investigated further, it looks like phosphorescence from the $\pi \rightarrow \pi*$ triplet state. In polar solvents, even below the inversion temperature, we were as yet unable to detect any emission in that region of the spectrum.

3. PYRENE-3-ALDEHYDE IN MIXED SOLVENTS

Further room temperature investigations were made in some mixtures of inert and activating solvents. Fig. 5 shows the

---

*A similar inversion of spectral shift with temperature was observed by Lippert et al.[12] with stilbene derivatives. However, the inversion temperatures in hydroxylic solvents are much lower in our case. This may result from a longer lifetime of the excited aldehyde molecule and, probably, from some difference in the relaxation process involved

fluorescence yields in mixtures of heptane with chloroform,
ethanol and acetic acid as a function of the mole fraction of the

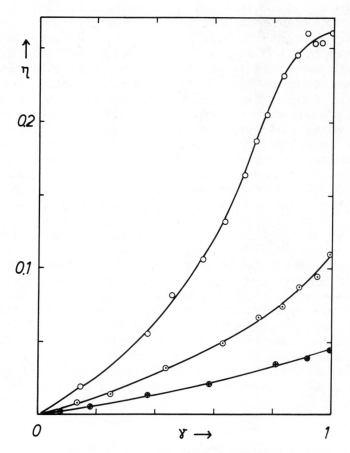

Fig. 5 – Fluorescence quantum yields of pyrene-3-aldehyde in mixtures
of heptane with chloroform: ⊕, ethanol: ⊝ and acetic acid: ○. γ : mole
fraction of the popular component. Exciting light 27.4 kK, other conditions as in fig. 2

polar component. These yields increase continuously and reach
their maximum in the pure solvents. This behavior is different
from that of the chlorophylls and of acridine which obtain maximum fluorescence yield at much lower concentrations of the
same activating agents. Thus their activating efficiency on py-

rene-3-aldehyde is much less, even though high quantum yields are obtained in the pure solvents.

For comparison, we have investigated absorption spectra in mixtures of heptane and ethanol. Although these spectra show isosbestic points, it has not been possible to determine ground state association constants by simple mass action law calculations such as the Benesi-Hildebrandt procedure.[14] It can be stated, however, that half of the aldehyde is hydrogen bonded at an alcohol mole fraction of about 0.1. At the same mole fraction the fluorescence yield is only one tenth of its maximum value in the pure solvent. This indicates again that ground state interaction is not responsible for fluorescence activation by this agent.

It seemed desirable to investigate a still stronger activator which might be efficient at lower concentrations. We tried trichloroacetic acid, which had also been used by Mataga et al.[7-9] in their experiments with N-heterocycles. Our results with pyrene-3-aldehyde are represented in Figs. 6 and 7. Fig. 6

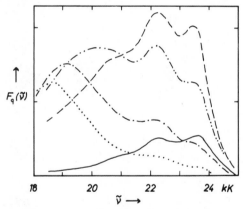

Fig. 6 – Fluorescence spectra $F_q(\tilde{\nu})$ (quanta per wave number interval, same units for all spectra) in heptane with varying molar concentrations, c, of trichloroacetic acid: —— $1.1 \cdot 10^{-3}$, ––– $1.1 \cdot 10^{-2}$, –..– $7.4 \cdot 10^{-2}$, –.– 0.3, ... 1.0.
Room temperature, aldehyde concentrations $2 \cdot 10^{-3}$M, exciting light 27.4 kK.

shows some spectra in heptane containing different concentrations of trichloroacetic acid. Appreciable fluorescence is obtained even at 10^{-3} M, and at 10^{-2} M it considerably exceeds that of an alcoholic solution. Nevertheless, these fluorescence spectra resemble those in weakly activating pure solvents inso-

far as they possess well developed structure and their maxima
are at comparatively high wavelengths (22.2 and 23.5 kK). The
whole character of the spectra changes considerably at higher
concentrations of trichloroacetic acid. An additional maximum
appears on the low frequency side and seems to be shifted more
and more to the red with increasing concentration. In a 1M
solution the fluorescence appears green and has its maximum at
about 19 kK. This red shift exceeds considerably that in alcoholic solutions, even at their inversion temperatures.

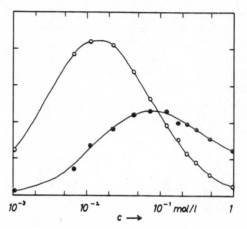

Fig. 7 — Fluorescence of pyrene-3-aldehyde in
heptane with varying concentrations, c, of trichloroacetic acid. Spectral yields at 23.5kK : O and at
19.5 kK: ● in arbitrary units.

Obviously, the fluorescence of these solutions consists of
two different components. With increasing activator concentration, the high frequency component develops first, but is then
replaced by the other. This behavior can be best visualized
from Fig. 7 where the spectral yields are represented for the
wave numbers of 23.5 and 19.5 kK which correspond approximately to the maxima of both components. Due to the considerable overlap of these, and also to the varying location of the low
frequency maximum, they are not exactly proportional to the
yields of the two components. But the half value concentrations
of about $5 \cdot 10^{-3}$ M for the increase and of about 0.1 M for the decrease of the high frequency component deduced therefrom
might be regarded as reliable.

Since fluorescence activation by trichloroacetic acid in the low concentration range occurs without an appreciable red shift, it cannot result from a decrease in the energy of the fluorescing $\pi \rightarrow \pi*$ state. It should then be due to an increase in energy of the quenching $n \rightarrow \pi*$ state. Furthermore, it can scarcely result from an interaction during the lifetime of the excited state because this is not long enough for a diffusion process involving free activator molecules at such low concentrations. Therefore, ground state interaction seems more probable in this case.

Some confirmation of this can be derived from absorption spectra. Upon addition of trichloroacetic acid, the first $\pi \rightarrow \pi*$ absorption maximum of pyrene-3-aldehyde at 26.6 kK in heptane decreases and a separate maximum appears at 24.5 kK. Fairly well developed isosbestic points indicate the formation of a separate species, probably a complex with strong hydrogen bonding. From the concentration dependence of these spectra, a half value concentration for complex formation of about $1 \cdot 10^{-2}$ M can be estimated. This is not too far from the half value concentration of fluorescence activation which therefore might result from only ground state interaction in this case.

It is very unfortunate that the $n \rightarrow \pi*$ absorption is hidden in these aldehydes so that the expected blue shifts cannot be observed. They should, however, be similar to those in benzaldehyde, where this absorption is well separated from $\pi \rightarrow \pi*$ absorption. In heptane solution containing 1M trichloroacetic acid, the $n \rightarrow \pi*$ absorption is no longer visible and must be blue-shifted under the stronger $\pi \rightarrow \pi*$ absorption. A minimum shift of 4 kK can be deduced from that observation. This is much more than the blue shift in ethanol which is only 1 kK, and even this seems to result mainly from a different intensity distribution among the individual vibrational bands and not from an actual shift of their positions.* In pyrene-3-aldehyde we may by analogy expect a considerable rise of $n \rightarrow \pi*$ state energy by hydrogen bonding with trichloroacetic acid, but no comparable rise with ethanol.

---

*This behavior is similar to that observed by Krishna and Goodman in alcoholic solutions of pyrazine.

4. OTHER ALDEHYDES

Our investigations were extended to some other aromatic aldehydes. Naphthalene-1-aldehyde and phenanthrene-9-aldehyde behave like benzaldehyde insofar as they are nonfluorescent in hydrocarbon-and hydroxylic solvents. Apparently, their $n \to \pi^*$ states are the lower ones in both kinds of solvents. For naphthalene-1-aldehyde this is confirmed by a well defined shoulder in the low frequency tail of the $\pi \to \pi^*$ absorption, appearing in heptane at $\log \epsilon < 2.5$. In ethanol, a blue shift takes place at $\log \epsilon < 1.5$, corresponding to wave numbers below 25.5 kK. Its magnitude cannot be evaluated because the $n \to \pi^*$ absorption is hidden in that solvent. But it is improbable that it is much more than 1 kK, the corresponding blue shift in benzaldehyde. As the maximum of the first $\pi \to \pi^*$ absorption of naphthalene-1-aldehyde is at 30.5 kK, the hidden $n \to \pi^*$ absorption will be at lower wave numbers even in ethanol.

Naphthalene-2-aldehyde, anthracene-9-aldehyde and acenaphthene-3-aldehyde show fluorescence activation similar to that of pyrene-3-aldehyde. They are nonfluorescent in heptane, but fluorescent in ethanol. In the case of naphthalene-2-aldehyde only, a weak $n \to \pi^*$ absorption shoulder was detected in heptane. But this shoulder only appears below $\log \epsilon \sim 1.6$ and in ethanol the red shift prevails in the total absorption down to our experimental limit of $\log \epsilon = 1.0$. Apparently, the $n \to \pi^*$ absorption is much closer to the $\pi \to \pi^*$ absorption in naphthalene-2-aldehyde than in its isomer. By this one may understand that solvent activation of fluorescence is possible here similarly to the case of the higher members of the aromatic series.

Tetracene-9-aldehyde and pyrene-4-aldehyde, finally, are fluorescent in both heptane and ethanol. As would be expected, the fluorescence spectra show large red shifts in the hydroxylic solvent. But even in the inert solvent the $\pi \to \pi^*$ state in these higher members of the aromatic series seems to be lower than the $n \to \pi^*$ state. The difference in behavior of the two pyrene aldehydes is not unreasonable, because the $\pi \to \pi^*$ excitation energy in the 4-isomer is lower than that in the 3-isomer (first absorption maxima in heptane 24.7 and 25.6 kK, respectively).

5. CONCLUSIONS AND FURTHER CONSIDERATIONS

It has been established by our investigations that the separation of $n \rightarrow \pi^*$ and $\pi \rightarrow \pi^*$ singlet state energies determines essentially the ability of an aromatic aldehyde to fluorescence. If this separation is small enough, its magnitude or even its sign can be altered by solvent interaction so that the aldehyde may be nonfluorescent in inert solvents but fluorescent in hydrogen bonding or polar ones or in their mixtures with inert solvents. This alteration of excitation energies can be accomplished in two different ways. Weakly or moderately activating agents, such as chloroform or ethanol, do this mainly by decreasing the $\pi \rightarrow \pi^*$ state energy. But the strongly activating agent trichloroacetic acid does it by raising the $n \rightarrow \pi^*$ state energy. While this results mainly from ground state hydrogen bonding, the $\pi \rightarrow \pi$ state lowering by the other activators occurs essentially by an interaction process during the lifetime of the excited molecule.

The nature of this process deserves some further consideration. Basically, either hydrogen bond formation or some less specific solvent relaxation by reorientation of dipole molecules is possible. It can be predicated by simple valence theoretical considerations that aromatic aldehydes in their $\pi \rightarrow \pi^*$ states are much more polar than in their ground states so that a decrease in excitation energy by rearrangement of solvent dipoles might be possible. Actually, all our activating agents are more or less polar. But we have found some highly polar solvents which only weakly activate (acetonitrile) or not at all (N-dimethylformamide). Furthermore, in hydroxylic solvents the inversion temperature of the fluorescence red shift accompanying activation is essentially lower than in other cases of dipole relaxation.[12]

All our moderately as well as strongly activating agents have, however, proton donating properties so that they are able to transfer protons to the carbonyl group of the aromatic aldehyde or, at least, form hydrogen bonds with them. Proton transfer must be excluded insofar as there are continuous alterations of the fluorescence spectra obtained with different activators and also with the same activator at different temperatures. Hydrogen-bonding in the excited $\pi \to \pi^*$ state, due to its enhanced proton affinity,† would thus seem probable.

However, the decrease in $\pi \to \pi^*$ state energy which is responsible for fluorescence activation by weak or moderate activators cannot result from mere hydrogen bonding. Our experiments, in particular those at lower temperatures, demonstrate the necessity of a rearrangement process even in pure hydroxylic solvents where all aldehyde molecules must already be hydrogen-bonded in the ground state. A mere strengthening of an existing hydrogen bond, due to the enhanced proton affinity in the excited state, would certainly occur without activation energy so that it would be difficult to understand its absence at lower temperature. This, together with the difference between half value concentrations for ground state hydrogen bonding and for fluorescence activation in ethanol-heptane mixtures, suggests the participation of other hydrogen bonding (or perhaps only polar) molecules in addition to the one already involved in ground state hydrogen bonding. The same must be assumed for the extremely large fluorescence red shift in the presence of higher concentrations of trichloroacetic acid. In this case, an actual proton transfer, but with the assistance of further activator molecules, seems probable. Though there are many possibilities for this, our present experiments do not allow discrimination between them. It may be mentioned, however, that some observations by Weller and Grellmann[19] on the fluorescence spectra of aromatic hydroxy compounds in the presence of proton acceptors also lead to the assumption of such cooperative action.

Moreover, the complete understanding of fluorescence activation, especially that by moderate or weak agents, might require a more detailed kinetic picture. During the lifetime of the excited molecule hydrogen bonds can be established and broken again and the molecule change over from $\pi \to \pi^*$ to $n \to \pi^*$ state and back. If nonradiative deactivation in the latter state is fast enough, the molecule might be practically nonfluorescent even if the energy of that state exceeds that of the $\pi \to \pi^*$ state by more than the average thermal energy. Nevertheless, our basic assumption that the energy separation of the two states essentially determines the fluorescence ability of

---

†This enhancement of proton affinity in the excited state follows from simple valence theoretical considerations and has been confirmed by fluorescence observations made by Weller et al.

these aldehydes seems well enough supported by the experiments reported here.

The authors wish to thank Dr. E. Lippert and Dr. A. Weller for valuable discussions. They also wish to express their gratitude to the Deutsche Forschungsgemeinschaft and to the Fonds der Chemischen Industrie for financial support of this investigation.

REFERENCES

[1] K. Kasper, unpublished work at this laboratory.
[2] R. Livingston, W. F. Watson and J. McArdle, J. Amer. Chem. Soc. 71, (1949) 1542
[3] B. V. Evstigneev, V. A. Gavrilova and A. A. Krasnovsky, Compt. rend. (Doklady) Acad. Sci. USSR 66 (1949) 1133; 70 (1949) 261
[4] R. S. Becker and M. Kasha, J. Amer. Chem. Soc. 77 (1955) 3669
[5] M. Kasha, Discuss. Faraday Soc. 9 (1950) 14
[6] E. Lippert, Zeitschr.f.Physikal.Chemie (1961) in print.
[7] N. Mataga, Y. Kaifu and M. Koizumi, Bull. Chem. Soc. (Japan) 29 (1956) 373
[8] N. Mataga, ibid. 31 (1958) 459
[9] N. Mataga and S. Tsuno, ibid. 30 (1957) 368
[10] E. Lippert, J. Physique Radium 15 (1954) 627
[11] E. Lippert and F. Moll, Z. Elektrochem. 58 (1954) 718
[12] E. Lippert, W. Lüder and F. Moll, Spectrochim. Acta 10 (1959) 858
[13] N. Mataga, Y. Kaifu and M. Koizumi, Bull. Chem. Soc. (Japan) 29 (1956) 1
[14] H. A. Benesi and J.H. Hildebrand, J.Amer.Chem.Soc. 71 (1949) 2703
[15] V.G. Krishna and L. Goodman, J.Chem.Phys. 33 (1960) 381
[16] A. Weller, Naturwiss. 41 (1955) 175
[17] A. Weller, Z. Elektrochem. 60 (1956) 1144
[18] W. Urban, unpublished work at this laboratory
[19] A. Weller and K. H. Grellmann, to be published.
[20] W. Gann, dissertation Stuttgart 1953
[21] E. Lippert, W. Nägele, I. Seibold-Blankenstein, U. Staiger and W. Voss, Z. analyt. Chem. 170 (1959) 1.

THE LUMINESCENCE SPECTRA OF SOME
TRAPPED ORGANIC RADICALS

Sydney Leach

Laboratoire de Chimie-Physique,
Faculté des Sciences de Paris,
Orsay, (Seine-et-Oise), France.

SUMMARY

Important information on trapped organic radicals can be obtained from their luminescence spectra but this has hitherto been a neglected field of study. The fluorescence spectra of benzyl, deuterated benzyl and triphenylmethyl radicals trapped in low temperature rigid glasses are discussed. Some remarks are made concerning the sensitivity of the luminescence technique in observing trapped radicals and other species produced by low temperature photolysis.

The rigid matrix technique has been extensively used in studies of the fluorescence and phosphorescence spectra of organic molecules.[1] Solute molecules dissolved in a rigid glassy or crystalline matrix are excited by ultraviolet radiation and the luminescence emission is recorded. In recent years, a further application of the rigid matrix technique has been developed: the formation and trapping of organic radicals in situ by photochemical decomposition of the solute.[2,3] However, apart from some work on the fluorescence spectrum of triphenylmethyl[4] and other triarylmethyl radicals,[5] the possibility of observing luminescence spectra of trapped organic radicals has been neglected. Identification of these species has usually been carried out by absorption spectroscopy in the u.v. and visible spectral regions and in some cases by electron paramagnetic resonance spectroscopy.[6]

The luminescence spectra of trapped organic radicals can provide information on the energy and symmetry of the lowest excited doublet (fluorescence) and quartet (phosphorescence) electronic states. However, up to the present time, the phosphorescence spectrum of a trapped organic radical has not been reported.

Luminescence spectra can also give useful information on ground state vibrational frequencies of trapped radicals since emission transitions involve excitation of ground state vibrational modes. Such information is particularly important in that it has not yet proved possible to study the infra-red and Raman spectra of organic radicals. It should be noted that in most absorption studies on trapped organic radicals the observed spectra correspond to high electronic transitions since the first transition is generally very weak. Relatively few bands are observed and their characterization as electronic or vibrational structure is uncertain because the higher electronic transitions tend to crowd together in the energy spectrum. Some work on the first doublet-doublet transition in absorption has been reported for triarylmethyl radicals [4,5] and for the benzyl radical.[7] Distinct vibrational structure has been observed in these cases. The long absorption path technique of Porter and Strachan[7] holds promise for investigation of the lowest absorption transition in other trapped organic radicals. However, as has been shown by work on the benzyl radical,[8] the possibility of performing a vibrational analysis of the lowest absorption transition is much enhanced if the corresponding fluorescence spectrum is also observed.

Although few luminescence spectra of trapped organic radicals have been reported,[4,5,8] it is not unlikely that certain luminescence spectra observed by earlier workers were actually emitted by such species, particularly some of the spectra reported by Goldstein in his studies on the photolysis and radiolysis of aromatic solids.[9]

A systematic study of the luminescence spectra of trapped organic radicals is being carried out in this laboratory. Work in progress on benzyl, deuterated benzyl, triphenylmethyl and diphenylmethyl radicals is discussed below.

Benzyl

The luminescence spectrum of benzyl was observed by 2537Å excitation of trapped radicals formed by photochemical decomposition of either toluene, dibenzyl or benzyl chloride in the following rigid solutions at 77°K:

   a) M.P. (2 parts methylcyclohexane, 3 parts isopentane)
   b) E.P.A. (5:5:2 proportions of ethyl ether, isopentane and
       ethyl alcohol)
   c) Isopentane.

Solute concentrations were in the range 10^{-1} M to 10^{-4} M. The experimental technique is described elsewhere.[10],[11]

Identical spectra, consisting of a series of bands in the 4621-5400Å spectral region were obtained from the three solutes (Figure 1). In the M.P. and E.P.A. solutions absorption bands in the 3180Å region characteristic of the benzyl radical[3]

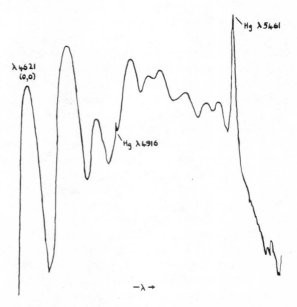

Fig. 1 — Densitometer tracing of benzyl radical fluorescence in E.P.A. solution at 77°K.

were observed under the same conditions.* After heating to room temperature and cooling to 77°K the luminescence and the absorption bands were no longer observed. The spectral region and vibrational structure[8] of the luminescence observed, coupled with the facts reported above, point to the benzyl radical $C_6H_5CH_2$ as being the fluorescence carrier. The mechanism of photochemical decomposition of the solute and of radical

---

*The benzyl emission in isopentane solutions is much weaker than in E.P.A. or M.P. solutions; the corresponding 3180A benzyl absorption is not observed in isopentane owing to insufficient concentration of trapped benzyl radicals in this less rigid matrix.

trapping is discussed elsewhere.[10]

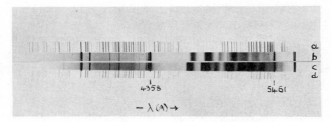

Fig. 2 — Fluorescence spectra of $C_6H_5CD_2$ and $C_6D_5CD_2$ radicals in rigid solutions at 77°K: a = Fe arc; b = $C_6H_5CD_2$; c = $C_6D_5CD_2$; d = Fe arc.

Similar luminescence spectra, but showing isotopic displacement, have been obtained from the deuterated toluenes $C_6H_5CD_3$ and $C_6D_5CD_3$, the respective fluorescence carriers being $C_6H_5CD_2$ and $C_6D_5CD_2$ (Figure 2). The O,O bands in M.P. solutions are given in Table 1.

Table 1

Benzyl Radical Fluorescence Origins (O,O band)
At 77°K In M.P. Solution

	$\lambda_{o,o} A$	$\nu_{o,o} cm^{-1}$
$C_6H_5CH_2$	4621	21630 ± 15
$C_6H_5CD_2$	4623	21625 ± 15
$C_6D_5CD_2$	4597	21747 ± 15

Deuterium substitution in the CH_2 group alone should have a very small effect on the zero point vibrational energies of the first excited and ground electronic states of benzyl. This is borne out by the fact that no isotopic displacement of the O,O band is found within experimental error in going from $C_6H_5CH_2$ to $C_6H_5CD_2$. A noticeable isotope shift of 120 ± 30 cm^{-1} to the violet is observed in going to $C_6D_5CD_2$. Deuterium substitution of the aromatic ring hydrogens should lead to considerable changes in frequencies of modes involving mainly skeletal C-H vibrations. This gives rise to a larger modification of zero-point vibrational energies than in the case of $C_6H_5CD_2$.*

A detailed study has been made of the effect of deuterium substitution on the vibrational structure of the fluorescence spectrum.[13] The results support the analysis of the $C_6H_5CH_2$ spectrum previously reported.[8]

This analysis has shown that the fluorescence spectrum of the benzyl radical is to be attributed to a partially forbidden 1^2A_2-1^2B_2 transition, the benzyl radical having C_{2v} symmetry in both electronic states. The active vibrations are very similar in nature to those of the $^1B_1$ - $^1A_1$ transition of toluene.[14] The structure of the benzyl spectrum is indeed very similar to the first singlet-singlet transition of toluene in having both an allowed part: $O,O - n\nu_s$, where ν_s = frequency of a totally symmetric vibrational mode, n = vibrational quantum number; and a forbidden part: $O,O - \nu_a - n\nu_s$, where ν_a = frequency of a non-totally symmetric vibrational mode related to benzene e_g^+ vibrations. The forbidden part is derived in structure from the forbidden $^1B_{2u} - {}^1A_{1g}$ transition of benzene.

The presence of both allowed and forbidden parts in the first electronic transition is characteristic of the spectra of those monosubstituted benzenes in which the electronic perturbation of the aromatic ring π electrons by the substituent radical is insufficient to alter the fundamental π - π character of this transition. The first benzyl transition can therefore be considered as a typical monosubstituted benzene case. It is to be noted that the intensity of the allowed part, I_p, is less than that of the forbidden part, I_i, in the case of benzyl.

Following Sklar[15] and Platt,[16] it is possible to separate the total oscillator strength f of the first transition of a monosubstituted benzene into two parts: $f = f_i + f_p$ corresponding to the forbidden (i) and allowed (p) structures. The f_i contribution comes from the non-totally symmetric vibrations analogous to the benzene case, and its value is taken as approximately that of the $^1B_{2u} - {}^1A_{1g}$ transition of benzene: $f_i \sim 1.6 \times 10^{-3}$. The I_p/I_i ratios should be proportional to f_p/f_i and should increase with increasing f. The I_p/I_i ratio has been determined from work on gas phase emission spectra carried out in this laboratory on a number of monosubstituted benzenes.[17]

---

*In the case of the $^1B_1$-$^1A_1$ transition of toluene the O,O band shifts 196 cm-1 to the violet in going from $C_6H_5CH_3$ to $C_6D_5CD_3$ (observations in the gas phase[12]).

Values of I_p/I_i, f_p/f_i and f are given in Table 2. Interpolation of $I_p/I_i \sim 0.5$ for benzyl gives a value of $f \sim 2.5 \times 10^{-3}$ for the oscillator strength of the $1^2A_2 - 1^2B_2$ transition.

Table 2

Monosubstituted Benzenes : Intensity Relations For The First Electronic Transition

C_6H_5X	$f \times 10^3$	f_p/f_i	I_p/I_i
$C_6H_5CH_3$	3.1(a)	1	~ 1
C_6H_5F	8.9(a)	4.5	~ 2.5
C_6H_5CN	10.4(b)	6.5	~ 3
C_6H_5OH	19.7(c)	12	~ 6
$C_6H_5NH_2-$	24.6(c)	15	~ 10
$C_6H_5CH_2$	2.5	< 1	~ 0.5

f = oscillator strength
i = forbidden part
p = allowed part
I_p/I_i = Ratio of the intensities of i and p bands.

(a)   = M. Sponer and D. S. Lowe. J. Opt. Soc. Am. 39, 840 (1949)
(b)   = R. S. Mulliken and C. A. Rieke. Rep. Prog. Phys. 8, 231 (1941)
(c)   = A. L. Sklar. J. Chem. Phys. 10, 135 (1942)

Theoretical calculations have predicted that this transition should have a forbidden character.[18] The presence of an allowed part, although weaker than the forbidden part, indicates that the approximation by which the ring carbon atom attached to the CH_2 group is considered as being equivalent to the other ring carbons[18] is not entirely justified.

Triphenylmethyl

Triphenylmethyl radicals were formed and trapped by u.v. irradiation of triphenylmethane in E.P.A. and M.P. rigid solutions at 77°K. The fluorescence spectrum was excited by the 2537Å mercury line. This spectrum consists of ten bands in

the 5135–6270Å region and the results are in good agreement
with those previously reported by Lewis, Lipkin and Magel.[4]
Pauling[15] has pointed out that there is a close similarity between the frequency differences observed and certain Raman
frequencies of monosubstituted benzenes. Chu and Weissman[5]
have examined the polarization of the luminescence bands of
triphenylmethyl and have classified certain bands as corresponding to excitation of totally symmetric or antisymmetric
vibrations in the ground state.* However, no detailed analysis
has yet been achieved.

The fluorescence spectrum is a good mirror image of the
corresponding absorption spectrum.[4] The O,O band, which
occurs at 5135Å in our experiments, is the most intense band.
This indicates that the transition is more allowed† than in the
corresponding benzyl case. This is to be expected in view of
the fact that the triphenylmethyl radical is not completely
planar.[20] Maximum resonance stabilization would require planarity, under which conditions the first electronic transition
should be forbidden. However, true planarity is incompatible
with the consequent repulsion between adjacent ortho hydrogen
atoms. The exact structure of this radical and the symmetries
of the electronic states involved in the first transition have not
yet been clarified.[20,21]

Diphenylmethyl

Attempts were also made to observe the fluorescence spectrum of the diphenylmethyl radical after low temperature photolysis of diphenylmethane solutions in E.P.A. and M.P. at
77°K. Although absorption bands attributed to this radical[22]
were observed in the 3120–3350Å region, no luminescence
characteristic of the diphenylmethyl radical was found. Instead,
the fluorescence spectrum of the benzyl radical was observed
in the 4620–5400Å region. This indicates that in diphenylmethane there is competition between breaking of a C-H bond
of the methylene group, leading to the formation of diphenylmethyl, and a C-C_6H_5 bond, leading to formation of benzyl.

---

*See, however, the postcript in reference 20.
†The oscillator strength of this triphenylmethyl transition is of the order of 0.01.[5]

Sensitivity of the luminescence technique

In studies of the photolysis of $C_6H_5CH_2X$ compounds (X = H, Cl, $CH_2C_6H_5$) in low temperature rigid media[10,11] the use of luminescence spectral techniques has revealed the existence of a number of primary and secondary low temperature photochemical reactions which were not detected in the purely absorption studies of Porter and his co-workers.[3,22]

The luminescence technique can often be used to detect much smaller concentrations of photochemical products than can absorption spectroscopy under the same experimental conditions. This is due not only to the fact that weak emission is easier to observe experimentally than weak absorption but also to intrinsic characteristics of the luminescence process in favorable cases.

The lowest electronic transition of aromatic molecules (singlet-singlet) or radicals (doublet-doublet) is invariably weak. Observation of this first transition in absorption therefore requires relatively high concentrations of species. Higher electronic transitions are stronger by a factor of 10 to 100 than the first transition and in principle can be observed with correspondingly smaller minimum concentrations. However, these higher transitions of photochemical products often have sufficient energy to fall in a region of absorption of the parent molecule. Observation of low concentrations of photochemical products by their absorption spectra will therefore be difficult in such cases. However, absorption of energy by the product molecule directly in its strong transitions, or by transfer from the parent species, can lead to relatively high stationary concentrations of the first excited level through a process of internal conversion. The fluorescence emission from the lowest level will therefore correspond to a much higher stationary concentration in the first excited state than could be obtained by direct absorption to that level. The detection of a product species by its fluorescence is thus correspondingly easier (requiring a lower minimum concentration of species) than by its absorption spectrum in the same region or when the higher absorption transitions overlap the parent molecule absorption.

The favorable cases for observation of product species by luminescence are therefore:
  a) that quantum yield of fluorescence or phosphorescence be non-negligeable;

    b) that the product luminescence spectrum fall in a spectral region where the parent molecule has negligeable absorption;

    c) that higher absorption transitions of the product be relatively intense (and/or efficient energy transfer from the parent molecule).

Observation by luminescence spectra of products formed by the photolysis of toluene and substituted toluenes in rigid media[10,11] has clearly demonstrated the value of this technique. This is illustrated, for example, by the observation of the 4600Å fluorescence of the benzyl radical under the following conditions:

    1) dibenzyl photolysis in E.P.A. solutions

    2) toluene and benzyl chloride photolysis in isopentane solutions.[10,11]

No benzyl absorption was detected in these experiments, even in the 3180Å region which corresponds to a benzyl transition of higher oscillation strength ($f \sim 0.025$)[23] than the $1^2A_2 - 1^2B_2$ 4600Å transition ($f \sim 0.0025$). Absorption in still higher benzyl electronic levels, corresponding to strongly allowed transitions in the region below 2700Å,[18] followed by internal conversion to the first excited 1^2A_2 state, would explain why 4600Å benzyl emission was observed in these cases.

Acknowledgment is gratefully made to Mlle. Lydie Grajcar, Dr. Gianna Mazzucato and Dr. Ugo Mazzucato for their contributions to the experimental part of this work.

REFERENCES

[1]   P. Pringsheim. "Fluorescence and Phosphorescence", Interscience, N.Y. (1949).

[2]   G. N. Lewis and D. Lipkin. J.Am.Chem.Soc. 64,2801 (1942).

[3]   I. Norman and G. Porter. Proc.Roy.Soc. A230, 399 (1955).

[4]   G. N. Lewis, D. Lipkin and T.T. Magel. J. Am. Chem. Soc. 66, 1579 (1944).

[5]   T. L. Chu and S. I. Weissman. J.Chem.Phys., 22, 21 (1954).

[6]   "Formation and Trapping of Free Radicals", edited by A.M. Bass and H. P. Broida, Academic Press, N.Y. (1960).

[7]   G. Porter and E. Strachan. Spectrochimica Acta, 12, 299 (1958).

[8] L. Grajcar and S. Leach. Comptes Rendus, 252, 1014 (1961).

[9] P. Pringsheim. "Fluorescence and Phosphorescence", Interscience, N.Y. (1949), references 510 to 516 cited.

[10] S. Leach and L. Grajcar. Fifth International Symposium on Free Radicals, Uppsala Sweden, July 1961; to be published J. Chim. Phys.

[11] L. Grajcar and S. Leach. Comptes Rendus, 252, 3377 (1961).

[12] J. Robert. Diplôme d'Etudes Supérieures, Univ. Paris, 1961.

[13] L. Grajcar and S. Leach. J. Chim. Phys. to be published.

[14] J. Kahane-Paillous and S. Leach. J. Chim. Phys. 55, 439 (1958).

[15] A. Sklar. J. Chem. Phys. 10, 135 (1942).

[16] J. R. Platt. J. Chem. Phys. 19, 263 (1951).

[17] J. Kahane-Paillous and S. Leach. Fourth International Meeting on Molecular Spectroscopy, Bologna, (1959), in the press; J. Kahane-Paillous, thesis, Univ. of Paris, (1960).

[18] W. Bingel. Z. Naturforschg. 10a, 462 (1955); H. C. Longuet-Higgins and J. A. Pople. Proc. Phys. Soc. 68A, 591 (1955); H. Brion, R. Lefebvre and C. Moser, J. Chim. Phys. 54, 363 (1957).

[19] L. Pauling. J. Am. Chem. Soc. 66, 1985 (1944).

[20] J. N. Murrell. J. Chem. Phys. 26, 1738 (1957).

[21] F. C. Adam and S. I. Weissman. J. Am. Chem. Soc. 80, 2057 (1958).

[22] G. Porter and E. Strachan. Trans. Faraday Soc. 54, 1595 (1958).

[23] Calculated from the experimental value ϵ_{3180} (benzyl) $\simeq 1100$ 1/mol cm given by R. L. McCarthy and A. MacLachlan. Trans. Faraday Soc. 56, 1187 (1960).

INTERDEPENDENCE OF EXCITED STATES
OF DICHROIC MOLECULES*

Gerald Oster

and

Gisela Kallmann Oster
Polytechnic Institute of Brooklyn

ABSTRACT

Triphenylmethane dyes which lack trigonal symmetry of their substituent groups are colored green in solution. Apparently the two absorption bands at each end of the visible spectrum are associated with the two dichroic axes. Although the free dye is photochemically inactive, the dyes when bound to high polymers in solution are capable of being photoreduced. Furthermore, the bound dye is fluorescent while the free dye is not, due to competing internal conversion processes which are suppressed on binding.

Excitation with near ultraviolet light gives a green fluorescence (positively polarized) while excitation with red light gives a deep red fluorescence (negatively polarized). Hence it appears that the two absorption bands are independent electronic systems. Excitation with blue light, on the other hand, gives green fluorescence plus a little red fluorescence. Flash spectroscopy of bound dye was carried out using extremely high intensity filtered light. Excitation with red light caused a reversible decrease of the long wavelength absorption band while excitation with blue light resulted in a reversible decrease in both peaks.

The production of metastable species is not appreciably influenced by the presence of oxygen. Furthermore no self-quenching of these species is observed. It is concluded that the excited molecule imbedded in the polymer is protected from external quenching influences.

---

*Supported by the United States Air Force through the Air Force Office of Scientific Research of the Air Force Research and Development Command under Contract No. AF 96(638)-293 and the Air Force Cambridge Research Center under Contract No. AF 19(604)-3065.

I. PHOTOCHEMISTRY OF TRIPHENYLMETHANE DYES

Triphenylmethane dyes are normally insensitive to light.·
That is, they do not undergo photoreduction in the presence of
mild reducing agents. When bound to high polymers in solution,
however, they undergo photochemical changes. Specifically,
when cationic triphenylmethane dyes are bound to the negatively
charged polymer, polymethacrylic acid, in the presence of an
electron donor for the light-excited dye, photoreduction to the
colorless (leuco) form takes place.[1] Such electron donors include ascorbic acid, glutathione, and other mild reducing agents
as well as certain chelating agents such as ethylenediamine
tetraacetic acid.[2]

Whereas other dyes, such as those of the xanthene and
thiazine families, show a marked decrease of quantum yield at
higher concentrations due to concentration quenching, bound
triphenylmethane dyes are photoreducible at high dye concentrations. In fact, the quantum yield for bound triphenylmethane
dyes is increased with increasing dye concentration. This system has an obvious analogy with photosynthetic systems where
chlorophyll is present in high concentrations yet is photochemically active. Apparently, the fact that chlorophyll is in the
bound state in the chloroplast enables it to react in this way.
It is of interest that water-soluble chlorophyll (potassium
chlorophyllin) exhibits certain photochemical reactions only in
the bound state.[3]

It has been demonstrated (see refs. 2, 4, for example) that
photoreduction of dyes proceeds via a long-lived excited state
since small amounts of certain substances (e.g., potassium
iodide, nitrobenzene, etc.) retard the reaction. Calculations
based on diffusional encounter arguments show that in water the
lifetime of such long-lived species is of the order of 10^{-4} sec.
The kinetics[1] of the photoreduction of the bound triphenylmethane dye ethyl violet requires that the long-lived chemically
reactive species (D') be produced by interaction with the singlet
excited dye $(D*)$, namely

$$D* + D \rightarrow D' + D \tag{1}$$

This proposed step is further supported by the fact that self-
quenching of fluorescence of these systems occurs at extremely
low dye concentrations (in the neighborhood of 5×10^{-6} molar,

Fig. 1). Reaction (1) is a competitor for fluorescence and occurs at a faster rate (about a factor of a hundred) than is allowed by diffusional encounters. The kinetics of the reaction

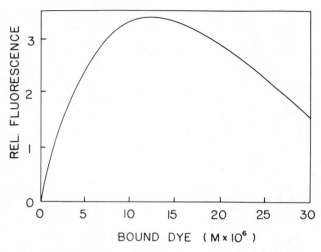

Fig. 1 — Self-quenching of ethyl violet bound to polymethacrylic
acid (0.6%) at pH 5.0.

further require that the metastable state is formed in this way
and not by a simple direct transition from the excited singlet
state. Furthermore there is no evidence of self quenching of
the metastable species. Certainly quenching arising from diffusional encounters is suppressed when the dye molecules are
imbedded in large polymer molecules but it is not clear why
this should encourage energy transfer.

II. ABSORPTION SPECTRA AND LUMINESCENCE

Triphenylmethane dyes are not fluorescent in aqueous solution or in most organic solvents. However, in highly viscous
media, for example, glycerol, these dyes exhibit a pronounced
fluorescence.[5] This phenomenon, which also occurs for diphenylmethane dyes and for stilbene derivatives, has been interpreted
as meaning that internal conversion due to internal rotation in
these non-rigid dye molecules is suppressed by the high viscosity. This suppression of rotation is also achieved by binding
the dye to certain high polymers, for example, polymethacrylic

acid in the case of cationic dyes.

Triphenylmethane dyes exhibit a phosphorescence in extremely rigid media, for example glucose glass, and this is of the alpha, or delayed fluorescence type at room temperature.[6] This phosphorescent species is undoubtedly the species involved in photochemical reactions since the phosphorescence and photochemical activity are closely correlated.[6]

Triphenylmethane dyes are perhaps the most strongly visible light absorbing substances and have molar extinction coefficients in the neighborhood of 10^5. Their absorption spectra, like those of other dyes, are correlated with their substituent groups. For example, the amino, methylamino, and ethylamino substituents lead to progressively longer wavelength maxima. Among the triphenylmethane dyes are a group of green dyes (*e.g.*, malachite green, brilliant green, ethyl green, etc.) which have two maxima at both ends of the visible region (and hence their green color), Fig. 2. These dyes differ from other dyes

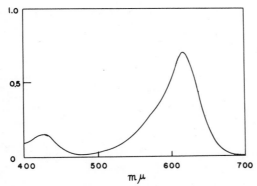

Fig. 2 — Absorption spectra (optical density for 1 cm. pathlength) of bound malachite green (0.005%).

of this family in that they do not have trigonal symmetry, that is, not all three phenyl groups are substituted equally (Fig. 3). Hence these molecules should be dichroic with polarizable axes of similar magnitude (called x and y bands by G. N. Lewis[7]).

Normally, for green substances, *e.g.*, chlorophyll, the two peaks correspond to two excited successive singlet levels (S_1 and S_2). Excitation of the short wavelength band of chlorophyll leads to the same fluorescence spectra as excitation of the long

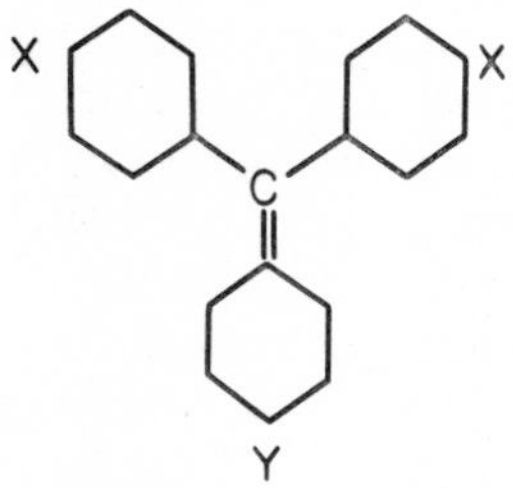

	X	Y
CRYSTAL VIOLET	$N(CH_3)_2$	$N(CH_3)_2$
ETHYL VIOLET	$N(C_2H_5)_2$	$N(C_2H_5)_2$
PARA ROSANILIN	NH_2	NH_2
MAGENTA III	$NH_2(O\cdot CH_3)$	$NH_2(O\cdot CH_3)$
MALACHITE GREEN	$N(CH_3)_2$	H
BRILLIANT GREEN	$N(C_2H_5)_2$	H
LIGHT GREEN SF	$N(C_2H_5)CH_2\phi SO_3^-$	SO_3^-

Fig. 3 — Chemical formulae of some triphenylmethane dyes.

wavelength band since fluorescence emanates from the lower excited singlet state. We found that malachite green at room temperature when either dissolved in glucose glass or bound to polymer exhibits a fluorescence whose spectrum depends on the wavelength of exciting light. G. N. Lewis and coworkers[7,8] had noticed this effect in pentane-ether-ethanol glasses at −158°C. For both bound malachite green as well as the dye in rigid media excitation of the long wavelength band with orange light gives a red fluorescence while excitation with near ultra-violet light (365 mμ) gives a green fluorescence. Excitation with blue light (435 mμ), on the other hand, gives a strong green fluorescence with some red fluorescence as well.

On excitation of the long wavelength band with unpolarized or vertically polarized light the red fluorescence is strongly negatively polarized, that is, the fluorescence is mainly horizontally polarized (compare refs. 7 and 9). For the short wavelength band, on the other hand, the fluorescence is polarized positively to a small degree. This behavior is different from that observed for other dyes (fluorescein, rhodamine B, etc.[10]) where the long wavelength band, that is the visible light band, is positively polarized while the near ultraviolet band is negatively polarized, the fluorescence spectra being the same in both cases. The near ultraviolet excitation of those dyes must correspond to higher electronic states whose absorption axes are at right angles to those of the lowest excited electronic state where emission occurs. In this connection it should be noted that the polarization of fluorescence of chlorophyll is always positive regardless of the wavelength of exciting light.[11] For malachite green the emission of red light apparently arises from a dichroic axis which lies perpendicular to that from which the green fluorescence emanates.

III. FLASH SPECTROSCOPY

In order to identify the long-lived photochemically active species a study of the flash spectroscopy of bound triphenylmethane dyes was undertaken. Thanks to the generosity of Prof. Stig Claesson of the Institute of Physical Chemistry, University of Uppsala, their huge flash unit was made available to us. The technical assistance of Mr. Carl Eklund is also greatly appreciated. This flash apparatus is of the general form first employed by Norrish and Porter[12,13] and is capable of supplying 43,000 joules to an oxygen-filled discharge tube.[14,15] Simultaneous absorption spectra were obtained with a xenon lamp continuously operated. The solution is contained in a 20 cm or 60 cm pathlength cell surrounded by a transparent jacket in which appropriate liquid filters could be introduced. Such a powerful unit (20-40 times greater than conventional systems) was particularly desirable for our studies since the quantum yield for production of metastable species was low and furthermore, light filters which necessarily entail a large decrease in light intensity could be employed.

It was found from photochemical studies[1] that of all the triphenylmethane dyes studied ethyl violet (in the bound state) has the greatest quantum yield of photoreduction. For this reason this dye was studied by means of flash spectroscopy in greatest detail.

Two qualitatively new phenomena were observed at the outset. Namely that the metastable species was only formed when the dye was bound and that oxygen had no large effect on the concentration of the metastable species. It has been well established from flash spectroscopy studies of chlorophyll,[16,17] fluorescein,[18] and eosin[19] that the system must be thoroughly degassed (as much as nine alternate freezing and degassing steps[18]) in order to properly observe the metastable species. With bound triphenylmethane dyes, however, there is only little quenching by oxygen and therefore the system need not be degassed.

The effect of binding of the dye is illustrated in Fig. 4. As

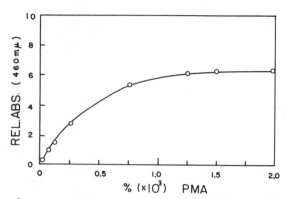

Fig. 4 — Absorption at 460 mμ of long-lived intermediate for bound ethyl violet as a function of polymethacrylic acid (molecular weight 45,000) at pH 5.0.

little as 0.01% polymethacrylic acid gives by flash spectroscopy an intermediate species which absorbs maximally 460 mμ. From the known molecular weight of the polymer (45,000 in this case) we calculate that at saturation, *i. e.*, excess polymer, there is on an average one dye molecule per polymer chain. This curve follows exactly the adsorption isotherm for the dye-polymer system. Furthermore, the quantum yield for the photoreduction of the dye follows the same curve. Hence we can conclusively say that only those dye molecules which are bound are photochemically active and that the long-lived species is the chemically active species. The production of the new species with its maximum absorption at 460mμ is accompanied by the parallel disappearance of the absorption peak of the original dye at 550 mμ (Fig. 5). The small downward pip on the lower curve is due to stray light from the flash. The lifetime of the metastable species is about one millisecond.

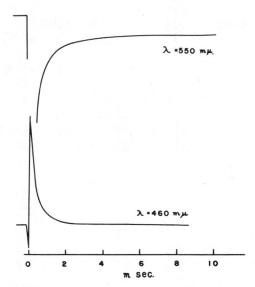

$\lambda = 550 \; m\mu.$

$\lambda = 460 \; m\mu$

0   2   4   6   8   10

m sec.

Fig. 5 — Flash spectroscopic tracings for bound
ethyl violet. Upper curve: recovery of the ground
state dye. Lower curve: disappearance of the metastable species.

Increasing the bound dye concentration gives a proportion-
ally higher amount of metastable species in direct contrast to
the results obtained with other dyes which show, at least when
they are unbound, a strong self-quenching between the long-
lived excited species.[16-19] Unfortunately the flash spectroscopic
studies do not help to explain the nature of the energy transfer
process. Obviously such a process takes place over a much
shorter time than can be observed by the present techniques.

We attribute this lack of self-quenching (between metastable
species) for bound dyes to mean that the polymer, because of
its very low diffusion constant, drastically reduces the number
of diffusional encounters between the excited bound dye molecules. The polymer protects the excited dye molecule from
quenching by oxygen as well. Here again we have an analogy
with photosynthesis which obviously takes place in the presence
of oxygen. The polymer (at pH 5 in all these experiments) may
immobilize several water molecules by virtue of solvation in
the interstices of its coiled up configuration and this could prevent the diffusion of oxygen to the bound dye.

Crystal violet and malachite green both in the bound states exhibit long-lived species (absorption maxima at 480 mμ and 470 mμ), respectively, when flashed with light but to a lesser extent than that for ethyl violet. In fact, the quantum yield for the production of metastable species exactly follows their relative quantum yields for photoreduction.[1] With malachite green some interesting phenomena appear if the light flash is in different spectral regions. For this purpose we filled the jacket surrounding the tube containing the dye solution with either a potassium bichromate solution to isolate the red region or a copper ammonium solution to isolate the blue region (Fig. 6).

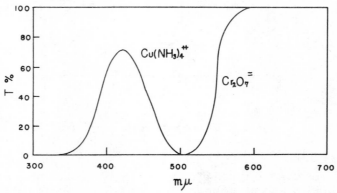

Fig. 6 — Filters used to produce an orange-red flash (potassium bichromate) and a near ultraviolet-blue flash (copper sulfate and ammonia).

On excitation of bound malachite green with red light the long wavelength peak disappears with a parallel production of an intermediate species with an absorption maximum at 480 mμ. The shorter wavelength peak, however, remains unchanged showing that only the longer wavelength dichroic axis is excited, leaving the shorter wavelength one undistrubed. On exciting with blue light, however, both the short wavelength as well as the long wavelength absorption bands disappear. The disappearance of the short wavelength band is greater than that of the longer wavelength band. Furthermore only a slight production of the 480 mμ absorbing species is produced. Obviously there is an interdependence of electronic excitation of the two dichroic axes when blue light is employed in conformity with our observations of the fluorescence using blue light. Since under this condition much less long-lived species are observed we conclude that

excitation with blue light produces a long-lived species which
has a very low absorption coefficient.

IV. REFERENCES

1 G. Oster and J. S. Bellin, J. Am. Chem. Soc., 79, 294 (1957)
2 *cf* G. Oster and N. Wotherspoon, J. Am. Chem. Soc., 79,
  4836 (1957).
3 G. Oster and S. B. Broyde, Nature, 192, 132 (1961).
4 A. H. Adelman and G. Oster, J. Am. Chem. Soc., 78, 3977
  (1956).
5 G. Oster and Y. Nishijima, J. Am. Chem. Soc., 78, 1581 (1956).
6 G. Oster, J. Joussot-Dubien, and B. Broyde, J. Am. Chem.
  Soc., 81, 1869 (1959).
7 G. N. Lewis and J. Biegeleisen, J. Am. Chem. Soc., 65,
  2102 (1943).
8 G. N. Lewis, D. Lipkin and T.T. Magel, J. Am. Chem. Soc.,
  66, 1579 (1944).
9 P. P. Pheofilov, Doklady Akad. Nauk S.S.S.R., 57, 447 (1947).
10 P. P. Pheofilov, Doklady Akad. Nauk S.S.S.R., 44, 147 (1944).
  See also chapter 4 of P. P. Pheofilov "Polarization of Luminescence of Atoms, Molecules, and Crystals" (in Russian),
  Moscow, 1959.
11 F. Perrin, Ann. physique, 12, 169 (1929).
12 R. G. W. Norrish and G. Porter, Nature, 164, 658 (1949).
13 G. Porter, Proc. Roy. Soc., A200, 284 (1950).
14 S. Claesson and L. Lindqvist, Arkiv. Kemi, 11, 535 (1957).
15 S. Claesson and G. Wettermark, Arkiv Kemi, 11, 561 (1957).
16 R. Livingston, J. Am. Chem. Soc., 77, 2179 (1955).
17 H. Linschitz and K. Sarkaanen, J. Am. Chem. Soc., 80,
  4826 (1958).
18 L. Lindqvist, Arkiv Kemi, 16, 79 (1960).
19 L. I. Grossweiner and E. F. Zwicker, J. Chem. Phys., 34,
  1411 (1961).

THE PHOTOCONDUCTIVE AND EMISSION SPECTROSCOPIC PROPERTIES OF ORGANIC MOLECULAR MATERIALS[1]

M. Kleinerman[2], L. Azarraga[3] and S. P. McGlynn
Coates Chemical Laboratories
Louisiana State University
Baton Rouge 3, Louisiana

ABSTRACT

The initiating act in the generation of a photocurrent is the absorption of a light quantum or quanta. Thereafter, three energy-dissipative processes ensue: 1. luminescence emission, 2. nonradiative degradation into vibrational motion of lattice and/or molecule, and 3. production of current carriers. It is noted that processes 1 and 2 are subtractive with respect to 3. Despite this, it is the thesis of the present paper that (a) the better photoconductors will be found among luminescent species, (b) the occurrence of intermolecular interaction, as exemplified for instance by fluorescence self-quenching, enhances process 3, and (c) a significant triplet state population density, somewhat contrary to existing belief, indicates improbability of process 3.

I. INTRODUCTION

It has been suggested by many authors[4] that the triplet state of the organic molecule in some way conditions the dark conductivity of the single crystal formed therefrom. It would seem that this suggestion is based on two observations: (a) the fact that there is a degree of metastability associated with triplet states,[5] and (b) the reasonably good agreement which exists between lowest triplet state energies and twice the thermal

196

activation energies for dark-conduction.[4] It must be said initially that the agreement implied in condition (b) is not as good[5,6] as is generally supposed; however, even if this agreement were excellent it would still be possible to dismiss the triplet state theory very succinctly by noting (a) that the dark-conduction process is thermally equilibrated since there is no significant hysteresis in plots of dark-current *versus* temperature, and (b) that the equilibrium triplet state population density is so extremely small[7] (approximately one triplet anthracene per seven cubic yards of anthracene single crystal at room temperature), that it cannot under any realizable conditions, account for the observed dark-currents.[8]

This paper will consider triplet state involvement in the dark-conduction process as being no longer a moot question. However, the possibility of triplet state involvement in the photoconduction process in organic crystals, as suggested by many authors,[5,9,10] may not be readily eliminated, any more than it can be readily substantiated, on the basis of existing data. The experiments reported on here, as well as elsewhere[11] were initiated in order to provide direct experimental information *pro* or *con* the triplet state photoconduction thesis; the results are such that one may conclude that again in the photoconductive process the triplet state is not kinetically intermediate to charge carrier generation. Above and beyond this, the results obtained do provide a number of experimental criteria for significant photoconductivity of a given crystalline material, and it is this latter positive aspect of the work contained herein which the authors wish to stress.

II. A SPECIFICATION OF RESEARCH AIMS AND LIMITATIONS

It is well in discussing the photoconductive properties of organic materials, a subject so mistreated and in which so much of the literature is confusing, to be very specific both with regard to ones aims, and the assumptions or approximations made in order to realize those aims.

Questions relating to carrier mobility or to the actual charge generative act[12] are not of primary importance in the present work. Rather attention is directed to the events succeeding the absorption act and preceding the generative act, and which in one way or another make available the absorbed radiant energy for charge carrier production. The generative act itself, whether it be bimolecular or monomolecular with respect to absorbed photons, whether it involve extrinsic or intrinsic traps or for that matter any traps at all, or whether it be no more than a barrier activation necessary to electrode injection, is not of immediate relevance to the discourse, but will be referred to later.

The operational research method used by the authors consists of a comparison of a photocurrent, i_p, measured in a single crystalline material, with the manner in which the absorbed light energy is bipartitioned between the excited singlet and triplet states of the molecules which constitute the single crystalline material in question. A comparison of these quantities for any one material is insufficient, in the absence of information relating the rate of charge carrier formation to either excited singlet or triplet state population densities, to enable one to reach any relevant conclusion; instead one must resort to investigation of series of reasonably similar molecular materials in which the ratio of triplet to excited singlet population densities vary considerably in the illuminated steady state, and to endeavour to induce some correlation between i_p and the magnitude of this bipartitioning factor. There are many difficulties and uncertainties inherent in an effort such as this, and these undoubtedly are well exemplified in the present work; they will be discussed individually:

A. Carrier Lifetime and Mobility:

In the case of a uniformly excited single crystal, one may write[13]

$$i_p = R\tau\mu EqA \tag{1}$$

where R is the rate of carrier generation, τ is carrier lifetime, μ is their mobility and E is the applied field; q is the electronic charge and A the electrode area. Very little is known regarding either τ or μ; it is known that μ is of the order of $1 cm^2$ per volt-sec in anthracene,[14] naphthalene[15] and terphenyl[16] but the quantity τ is generally an unknown. Since it is the authors' aim to calculate R, or relative values of R, from known values of i_p, and since this is palpably impossible because of the lack of knowledge of the product $\tau\mu$, or the manner in which it varies in proceeding from one compound to another in a given series, an alternative approach is desirable. It will be assumed that within a series of closely related compounds $\tau\mu$

remains essentially constant; R is then proportional to i_p.
If, further, it is observed that a large i_p is always associated,
say, with a large singlet excited state population, $n_{s'}$, then it
may be concluded that the singlet excited state, S', is kinetically
intermediate to the photoconductive state. It is clear that this
sort of argument attains credibility only on a probabilistic
basis; in other words a large number of different compounds,
belonging to different series must show complete conformity
to the imposed regularities.

B. The Relation of R to Excited State Populations:[17]

If it is presumed that it is the singlet excited state which is
directly intermediate to the photoconductive state then one
may write $R = \beta_s n_{s'}$, where β_s is a proportionality constant:
if the triplet state is thought to be the intermediate, one obtains
$R = \beta_T n_T$, where β_T does not necessarily equal β_s, and where
n_T is the number of excited triplet molecules. (It would be
better to write R as an increasing function of either $n_{s'}$ or n_T
or both, since it might be bimolecular with respect to excited
species.) It will be assumed that the β's do not vary significantly from compound to compound. Again this assumption is
only credible probabilistically; to be more specific, and to anticipate the results of the present work, it seems peculiar that
when n_T is large β_T must always be decreased by *circa*
$10^3 \leftrightarrow 10^5$ in order to attain conformity to experiment. It is
more reasonable to presume β_T constant and to consider
the triplet intermediate hypothesis invalid.

On the other hand, as will be evident later, when self-
quenching of fluorescence occurs, the authors will be guilty of
presuming β_s to be a very sensitive increasing function of the
bimolecular self-quenching rate constant, k_{SQF}. This somewhat unjustified assertion, made in order to conform to experiment, is obviously based on their belief that charge carrier
formation is not monomolecular, and is usually more probable
the greater the extent of intermolecular interaction, one manifestation of which is self-quenching of fluorescence.

C. The Extrapolation of Spectroscopic Data to the Solid at Room Temperature:

The phosphorescence $(T \rightarrow S)$ emissions of organic compounds are generally observed with difficulty except when they

are embedded in some solid matrix at low temperatures (most conveniently $-195.8°C$). Consequently, the only direct meas-urements of the bipartition of energy between singlet and trip-let states are available to us from investigational work on solid glassy solutions at $-195.8°C$. Some further triplet state data are available from the flash-photolytic work of Porter,[18] in-variably carried out on dilute liquid solutions at room tempera-ture. Most fluorescence data relate to liquid solutions at room temperature or to glassy solutions at $-195.8°C$, and the extent of room temperature single-crystalline data is indeed very scant. However, all photoconduction data have been obtained in the crystalline state at or close to room temperature, and in order to be consistent it is necessary that the spectroscopic data refer to the crystal also. In view of the amazing dearth of such data, the authors have had to extrapolate from the results of work on glasses at low temperature, on solutions at room temperature, and from their own qualitative observations on crystal fluorescence at room temperature, in order to compile some knowledge of the bipartioning ratio in the crystal. It is believed that this extrapolation can generally be validly carried out, but it is nonetheless another uncertainty in the present work.

III. THE CALCULATION OF RELATIVE POPULATIONS OF EXCITED STATES

The first question to be answered is: if an observation of no-fluorescence or no-phosphorescence is made under fairly strin-gent experimental conditions, what, may one conclude, is the maximal emissive quantum yield? It is to be noted that the principal operative restriction is not that of excitation source intensity, species absorptivity or detector sensitivity, but rather one of background discrimination. In other words it becomes difficult to distinguish a low yield intrinsic emission from im-purity emissions, solvent emissions, apparatus emissions (of filters, quartz, etc.) and scattered light. The only answer the authors can give is one based on experience; while working with anthracene which has a quantum yield of fluorescence of the order of unity ($\phi_F \sim 1$), they have observed background luminance to be less than 10^{-6} times that of the fluorescence intensity. There seems no reason why background could not be further re-duced, and as a consequence the presumed answer to the initially posed question is ϕ_F (or ϕ_P) $\leqslant 10^{-6}$, where ϕ_P is the phosphorescence quantum yield. Kasha[19] has been somewhat more conservative; for instance, in discussing the fact that emission occurs only from the lowest excited level of a given manifold of levels,[20] he attributes this to internal radiationless interconversion of all excited levels to the lowest excited one with a first order rate constant k_{IC} of the order of 10^{13} sec^{-1}. Since the majority of higher excited singlet states of aromatic hydrocarbons have intrinsic fluorescence lifetimes of the order of 10^{-8} sec, it follows that Kasha, without having said so explicitly, considers a $\phi_F < 10^{-5}$ as being non-observable. The present authors would prefer to consider k_{IC} of the order of 10^{14} sec^{-1}, and $\phi_F \leqslant 10^{-6}$ as normally unobservable; we will use this latter number in the following calculations, but we stress that the use of $\phi_F \leqslant 10^{-4} \geqslant \phi_P$ will not appreciably alter any of our conclusions.

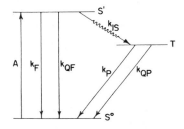

In view of Kasha's emission rule cited above the kinetics of excited state population may be discussed in terms of the Jablonski diagram of Fig. 1. It is generally conceded that direct absorption in the triplet manifold is unimportant in populating the triplet state T, since the $T \leftarrow S°$ absorption probability is less by 10^6 times than the $S' \leftarrow S°$ absorption probability. It is possible to be more explicit: in anthracene, for example, if a polychromatic excitation is effected with a lamp of equal photon output in the $T \leftarrow S°$ and $S' \leftarrow S°$ absorption regions, only one triplet molecule in 10^4 has achieved the triplet state by the direct absorption process, and this ratio will be relatively independent of temperature (at least, for anthracene). The direct $T \leftarrow S°$ process will henceforth be neglected in this work. Bimolecular self-quenching modes

Fig. 1 – Jablonski diagram of the states of an organic molecule. Only the lowest excited singlet state, S' the lowest triplet state, T, and the ground state, $S°$, are shown, since it is understood that higher excited states rapidly convert to S' and T. The absorption process, A, may be considered to populate all excited states of the singlet manifold. k_F is the fluorescence rate constant, k_{QF} the rate constant for internal quenching of fluorescence, k_{IS} the intersystem crossing rate constant, k_P the phosphorescence rate constant and k_{QP} the rate constant for internal quenching of phosphorescence. An absorption process leading directly to population of the triplet manifold is not shown, nor are bimolecular quenching rate constants considered.

for fluorescence and phosphorescence are not shown in Fig. 1; in actuality these modes will be discounted only when experiment indicates that this is valid, and in some cases they will be considered explicitly.

In the absence of luminescence quenching modes, verifiable by the fact that the total quantum yield, ϕ_T, where $\phi_T = \phi_F + \phi_P$, equals unity, and under steady state illumination conditions we may write

$$(n_T/n_S') = (k_{IS}/k_P) \tag{2}$$

and

$$(\phi_P/\phi_F) = (k_{IS}/k_F) \tag{3}$$

In the absence of self-quenching we may more generally write

$$n_S' = \alpha I/(k_{IS} + k_F + k_{QF}) \tag{4}$$

and

$$n_T = k_{IS} n_S'/(k_P + k_{QP}) \tag{5}$$

where I is the incident intensity and α is a proportionality factor. Furthermore, the fluorescence quantum yield becomes

$$\phi_P = k_F/(k_{IS} + k_{QF} + k_F) \tag{6}$$

In the presence of self quenching, Equations 4, 5, and 6 have to be modified by adding terms to their denominators which may be functions of all, or only one, of n_S', n_{S^o} and n_T. These equations are straightforward kinetic relations; it remains only to use them to deduce relative populations of the excited states of different illuminated molecular species.

A. An Example: The Related Molecules Anthracene, Acridine and Phenazine:

The formulae for these three compounds are shown in Fig. 2 where it will be noted that the principal difference between them consists of the possession of a lone pair of $2p$-electrons (the n-electrons) by each nitrogen atom. These $2p$-electrons, actually sp^2 hybrids, are differentiated from the π-electrons by the fact that they are non-bonding and symmetric with respect to reflection in the molecular plane. Despite the fact that these n-electrons do not appear to alter the absorption spectrum significantly, they dominate the luminescence characteristics. The energy level diagrams of these molecules are shown in Fig. 3.

The absorption from $S°$ to the highest energy illustrated $S_{\pi,\pi}$ state governs the general shape of the absorption spectra, which are shown in Fig. 4. However, there are lower energy transitions possible in both acridine and phenazine which, because of their relative forbiddenness, manifest themselves primarily in the long wavelength tail-absorption in both acridine and phenazine.[21] The dramatic effect of these lower lying levels on the fluorescence yields is conditioned by the greater amount of spin-orbital

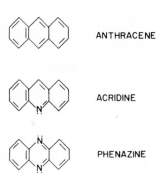

ANTHRACENE

ACRIDINE

PHENAZINE

Fig. 2 — Structural formulae of the three planar molecules: anthracene, acridine and phenazine.

coupling between singlet and triplet states arising from the same n, π^* electron configuration,[22] and by the inherently long radiative lifetimes of $S_{n,\pi}$ states which makes intersystem crossing more competive with the emissive decay process. In fact it is generally supposed that this increase of intersystem crossing is responsible for the non-observation of any significant fluorescence, even at $-195.8°C$, from molecules containing lowest singlet excited states of n, π^* type.

The validity of the above conclusions is indicated in Table I, which contains data on the lowest triplet state (of π,π^* nature in all three cases). Despite an apparent constancy of ϕ_T, the ratio ϕ_P/ϕ_F increases tremendously, indicating that at least at liquid N_2 temperatures the increasing singlet state depopulation on going from anthracene to phenazine is due entirely to increased intersystem crossing; it seems not unreasonable to suppose that it is the same effect which governs the room temperature fluorescence behavior of the crystalline materials (listed under RTF in Table I).

The following distinctions may now be made: (a) <u>A material for which at room temperature $\phi_T \sim 1$ in both crystal and highly dilute neutral solution</u>: It is obvious that here all bimolecular quenching processes, whether self or extraneous, are unimportant. In particular, in anthracene where ϕ_F may be 0.99, it becomes apparent from Eq. 6 since $k_F \sim 10^8 \ sec^{-1}$, that $k_{IS} + k_{QF} \sim 10^6 \ sec^{-1}$, and that the measured radiant decay time is very nearly identical to the true radiative lifetime $1/k_F$. (b) <u>A ma-</u>

terial for which at room temperature $\phi_T \sim 0$ in both crystal and highly dilute solution: In this case, even though bimolecular

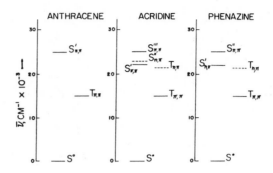

Fig. 3 — The energy level diagrams of anthracene, acridine, and phenazine. The data for anthracene are taken from S. P. McGlynn, M. R. Padhye and M. Kasha, *J. Chem. Phys.* 23, 593 (1955); those for acridine and phenazine are from R. W. Harrell, Ph.D. Dissertation, The Florida State University, Jan., 1959. The solid lines indicate experimentally fixated levels, the dashed lines theoretically computed ones. The subscripting π,π, implies a state derived from S^0 by excitation of one of the highest energy π-electrons to the lowest energy vacant π-orbital; n,π implies a state derived from S^0 by excitation of an n-electron to the lowest energy vacant π-orbital. The two $S_{\pi,\pi}$ levels of acridine are due to the fact that acridine belongs to the point group C_{2V}, while phenazine and anthracene belong to D_{2h}.

As is evident from the text, the present authors are not satisfied that the energy level diagram given for acridine is correct.

quenching need not necessarily be unimportant in the crystal, it is obvious from the dilute solution work that $k_{IS} + k_{QF}$ must alone be of sufficient magnitude to explain the absence of fluorescence. Putting a detectability limit of 10^{-6} on ϕ_F when observation records no fluorescence, we find, using Eq. 6, and noting that k_F for an n,π^* fluorescence is $\sim 10^{+6}$ sec^{-1}, that

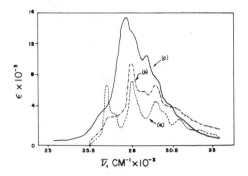

Fig. 4 — The dilute solution absorption spectra of (a) anthracene, (b) acridine and (c) phenazine, taken from R. W. Harrell, Ph.D. Dissertation, The Florida State University, Jan., 1959. Since the absorption spectra are so similar one may use the unfiltered output of any light source for comparative measurements of photoconductivity; one does not have to consider as a variable the spectral distribution of emitted intensity in the source. The extinction depth for the three crystals will be virtually identical also.

$k_{IS} + k_{QF} \sim 10^{12}$ sec^{-1} for phenazine. Our observations do not record any fluorescence for crystalline acridine, or for its solutions in benzene. This would imply that the lowest excited singlet level is an $S'_{n,\pi}$ level, and by similar reasoning to that immediately above would yield $k_{IS} + k_{QF} \sim 10^{12}$ sec^{-1}. Sangster[23] reports, however, that $\phi_F \sim 10^{-3}$ for acridine; this would imply that the lowest excited singlet state is $S'_{\pi,\pi}$, which with $k_F \sim 10^8$ sec^{-1} would yield $k_{IS} + k_{QF} \sim 10^{11}$ sec^{-1}. We are inclined to attribute Sangster's results to impurity luminescence, since the material which we used was highly zone-refined and very pure.

Using Eq. 4 and noting from Fig. 4 the similarity of αI for all three compounds, the relative values of $n_{S'}$ may be calculated as $n_{S'}$ (anthracene) $= 10^{-8} : n_{S'}$ (phenazine) $= 10^{-12} : n_{S'}$ (acridine) $= 10^{-12}$: In actuality there exists some uncertainty about the species of the lowest singlet state of acridine, and we might more thoroughly specify the relative value of $n_{S'}$ acri-

Table I

SOME SPECTRAL DATA FOR ANTHRACENE, ACRIDINE
AND PHENAZINE

Compound	$\bar{\nu}_T{}^a$	τ_T(calc.)^b	τ_T(obs.)	ϕ_T	ϕ_P/ϕ_F	RTF^c
anthracene	14850^d	0.09^e	$\sim 0.01^f$	1^d	$10^{-3}{}^d$	strong
acridine	15625^g	0.0092^g	—	1^g	$10^{-2}{}^g$	weak or absent
phenazine	15504^g	0.011^g	0.023^g	1^g	$\sim \infty^g$	none

a) The 0,0 band of the phosphorescence spectrum, in cm^{-1}
b) Lifetime of the phosphorescence emission calculated from
the converse absorption, in secs.
c) Room temperature fluorescence of the crystal.
d) From S. P. McGlynn, J. D. Boggus and E. Elder, J. Chem.
Phys. 32, 357 (1960).
e) From M. R. Padhye, S. P. McGlynn and M. Kasha, J. Chem.
Phys. 24, 588 (1956).
f) From G. Porter and M. W. Windsor, J. Chem. Phys. 21,
2088 (1953).
g) From R. W. Harrell, Ph. D. Dissertation, The Florida State
University, Jan., 1959.

dine) = 10^{-12} if (1) the lowest excited singlet state is $S'_{n,\pi}$ and
no fluorescence is observed at room temperature; $n_{S'}$, (acridine) = 10^{-11} if (2) the lowest excited singlet state is $S'_{\pi,\pi}$ and
Sangster's result[23] is correct and $n_{S'}$ (acridine) = $10^{-14'}$ if (3)
the lowest singlet excited state is $S'_{\pi,\pi}$ and our observation is
correct.

The data of Table I obtained for glassy solutions at $-195.8°C$
may now be used to calculate k_{IS} from Eq. 3, and using this and
the relative values of $n_{S'}$ previously obtained, n_T may be deduced from Eq. 5. A number of reservations must be remarked
on. Firstly it is presumed that k_{IS} can only increase with temperature, but that it more likely will remain constant. Secondly
it is presumed that the quenching constants of phosphorescence
both bimolecular and mono-molecular are roughly the same
for all three compounds, which seems not unreasonable in view
of the results of Linschitz[24] on liquid solutions at room temperature. The results obtained are presented in Table II,

Table II

RELATIVE POPULATIONS AND SOME OTHER DATA FOR ANTHRACENE, ACRIDINE AND PHENAZINE

Molecule	Acridine				Anthracene	Phenazine
Case	$(1)^a$	$(2)^a$	$(3)^a$	$(4)^b$		
ϕ_P/ϕ_F	10^{-2}	10^{-2}	10^{-2}	∞	10^{-3}	1
k_{IS}	10^4	10^6	10^6	10^{12}	10^5	10^{12}
n_T	10^{-2}	10^{-3}	10^{-5}	10^3	: 1	: 10^3
$n_{S'}$	10^{-3}	10^{-4}	10^{-6}	10^{-4}	: 1	: 10^{-4}
i_p^+		$10^{-3\,c}$			: $1^{\,c}$	: $6 \times 10^{-3\,c}$

a) Refers to type of lowest excited singlet state and to luminescence characteristics; defined on page 11 paragraph 1 of text.

b) Lowest singlet state is $S'_{n,\pi}$. The value of 10^{-2} for ϕ_P/ϕ_F is considered here to be due to the fact that the EPA glass used by R. Harrell, Ph.D Dissertation, The Florida State University contained some water and caused an inversion of n,π^* and π,π^* singlet states, and that actually $\phi_P/\phi_F = \infty$ would be observed in a dry hydrocarbon glass.

c) at 7v/mil applied field (see reference 11 of text).

whence it will be evident that state population versus photo-current correlation is achieved only if we presume that it is the singlet state which is the direct kinetic intermediate to the photoconductive state.

It is hoped that the many approximations made in the argument presented are sufficiently clear to leave no doubt as to their nature. Henceforth presentation of argument will be brief.

IV. EXPERIMENTAL

A. Instrumental and Technique

Sandwich cells were prepared by melting the compounds between two quartz squares coated with a transparent film of tin dioxide (SnO_2). Excess melt was squeezed out under pressure and a slow cooling effected. Cell thickness was maintained at 1 mil by use of Teflon spacers. An exploded view of a cell various modifications of which were used in the present work is shown in Fig. 5, and is essentially similar to the type used by

Northrop and Simpson.[25] Electrode contact to the SnO_2 film
was made by conductive Ecco-Bond cement, and was made
rigid with epoxy resin. The cell, when prepared, was further

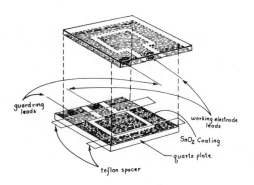

Sandwich Cell with Guard Rings

Fig. 5 — An exploded view of a sandwich cell of
which various modifications were used in the present work.

coated around the edges with epoxy resin to maintain good
physical contact and to aid (possibly) in oxygen exclusion. Leak-
age currents were of the order of 10^{-14} amps.

A G.E. AH-6 high pressure mercury lamp was used to excite
the crystals. Infrared was removed from the excitation source
with a water filter; otherwise excitation was polychromatic.
Some photoconduction action spectra were obtained with a
Bausch and Lomb monochromator, and in general reproduce
those in the literature. Cell to cell reproducibility of photocurrent for any given material was good only within an order of
magnitude, but this was sufficient for our purposes.

Cells of p-quaterphenyl, phenazine, 9,10-dichloroanthracene,
p-terphenyl, perylene, dibenzophenazine and dibenzanthracene
were prepared under nitrogen. All other cells were prepared in
air. Cells of phenazine, p-quaterphenyl, dibenzanthracene and
dibenzophenazine prepared in air showed no different behavior
from those prepared in nitrogen; in other words the effect of
O_2 on the one cell was less than the cell to cell reproducibility
of i_p for that compound, in accord with recent observations by
Kuroda and Flood.[26]

The photocurrents as quoted here are DC measurements

made with a Keithley 610 voltmeter. Such measurements suffer from a number of defects, the most serious of which are contact effects, space-charge effects, surface effects, etc. Space-charge effects may be ameliorated by working at either or both low intensity of illumination or high applied voltage; as far as can be ascertained space-charge effects are either negligible (or of comparable significance) in the results described here. Some investigations were performed using the transient method of Kepler,[14] illumination being effected with a General Radio Strobotac flash source. No transient photocurrent was detected in p-terphenyl, since the noise level was too high; the peak transient i_p for anthracene and rubrene were of the same order of magnitude ratio as those measured by the DC method. It is submitted then, because of the comparative results obtained by both methods for p-terphenyl, anthracene and rubrene that (at least for these compounds) the results obtained by transient and DC methods are comparable.

Present theories of radiant energy utilization for carrier formation are based entirely on DC measurements. Consequently, and in proper context, these theories may be either refuted or substantiated by the present work. However, the present authors, not wishing to dispose of the more general validity of DC measurements when used as an order-of-magnitude sampling tool, and not deriving any particular pleasure from supplanting theories based on poor i_p data with other theories based on further poor i_p data, do believe, in view of their comments above concerning the various defects in DC measurements, that at least as used here, the method has provided reliable data.

B. Chemicals:

The sources of the various chemicals used and the methods of purification are briefly described. The term "extensively zone refined" implies at least twenty passes through the heated zone.

Anthracene, Acridine and Phenazine: as previously described.[11]

Anthracene-sym-Trinitrobenzene complex: as previously described.[27]

1,2,3,4-Dibenzanthracene: Rutgerswerke—Aktiengesellschaft, Germany; extensively zone-refined.

1,2,3,4-Dibenzophenazine: Synthesized from phenanthrenequinone and o-phenylenediamine; recrystallized several times from acetic acid, and then extensively zone-refined.

POPOP: Phenyl-oxazolyl-phenyl-oxazolyl-phenyl: Pilot Chemicals; extensively zone-refined.

BOPOB: Biphenyl-oxazolyl-phenyl-oxazolyl-biphenyl: Pilot Chemicals; recrystallized from acetic anhydride.

Carbazole: Eastman D.P.I.; repeated sublimation in air.

Rubrene: K and K Labs; vacuum-sublimed twice.

Naphthalene: Eastman D.P.I.

α-Chloronaphthalene and α-Iodonaphthalene: Eastman D.P.I.: vacuum distilled.

9,10-Dichloroanthracene: Eastman D.P.I.; recrystallized several times from acetic anhydride and then extensively zone-refined.

9,10-Diphenylanthracene: Pilot Chemicals; extensively zone-refined.

p-Terphenyl: Pilot Chemicals; extensively zone-refined.

p-Quaterphenyl: Chemicals Procurement Co.; extensively zone-refined.

Decacyclene: Rutgerswerke Aktiengesellschaft, Germany; recrystallized several times from cumene and then vacuum sublimed three times.

Tetraphenyl-1,1',4,4'-butadiene-1,3: Arapahoe Scintillators.

Acridine Orange (non-ionic): Recrystallized from benzene; prepared from the ionic dye by addition of NH_3 to form aqueous solution and extracting with benzene.

Selection of chemicals was made on the basis of their availability in quantities sufficient to enable use of good purification procedures and of their possession of a low melting point in order to avoid contamination by decomposition products during the cell formation process.

V. RESULTS AND DISCUSSION

A. Dependence of Photocurrent on Triplet State Population

It is intended to discuss here various series of molecules in which, within a given series, significant changes in n_T are effected. Increase of n_T is occasioned by increasing k_{IS}; alone, however, this is not sufficient since a number of other variables, particularly k_{QF}, k_{QP} and k_P, are of significance. Because of this latter aspect, some series in which increase of k_{IS} and decrease of n_T occur simultaneously will be considered for completeness. Various ways of increasing k_{IS} will be utilized.

1. Anthracene, Acridine and Phenazine: Increase of k_{IS} occurs from left to right in this series because of the insertion of a $T_{n,\pi}$ level, or both $S_{n,\pi}$ and $T_{n,\pi}$ levels between $S_{\pi,\pi}$ and $T_{\pi,\pi}$ levels. The measured photocurrents are shown in Fig. 6, and these results have been discussed in detail on page 202 to 207. where the pertinent conclusions have been drawn.

2. 1,2,3,4-Dibenzanthracene and 1,2,3,4-Dibenzophenazine: The structure of these two planar molecules is shown in Fig. 7. Dibenzanthracene solid fluoresces strongly at room tempera- ture while dibenzophenazine does not. By analogy with the case of anthracene and phenazine, the reason for the room tempera- ture luminescence-lack of dibenzophenazine is presumed due to a very large k_{IS} ($\sim 10^{12}$). Immediately it follows that n_T (di- benzophenazine) : n_T (dibenzanthracene) : : 10^3 : 1; yet the photocurrents measured are at least 10^2, and probably 10^3 times less in the dibenzophenazine than in dibenzanthracene. In other words, n_T versus i_p correlation is off by a factor of at least 10^5, and more probably by a factor of 10^8. On the other hand $n_S{}'$ versus i_p correlation is very good since $n_S{}'$ (diben- zophenazine) : $n_S{}'$ (dibenzanthracene) : : 10^{-4} : 1.

The sandwich cells used contained oriented needles rather than single crystals. The majority current carriers in dibenz- anthracene are positive; it was not possible to establish the sign of the majority carriers in dibenzophenazine because of the low signal to noise ratio.

3. Anthracene and Phenanthrene: The structures and energy levels of these molecules are shown in Fig. 8, wherein it will be noted that the $S' \rightarrow T$ split is much less in the phenanthrene; this generally implies that the mixing of S' and T states is greater in the phenanthrene and that as a consequence k_{IS} is larger also. Much of the data collected in Table III are rendered reasonable by this conclusion. For example, at $-195.8°C$ where ϕ_T (phenanthrene) ~ 1, $\phi_P/\phi_F \sim 1$ also; hence $k_{IS} \sim 10^8$ sec^{-1}. Since, according to Sangster,[23] $\phi_F \sim 0.4$ at room temperature, it follows from Eq. 6 that $k_{QF} + k_{IS} \sim 10^8$ sec^{-1}, and that no other quenching factor can exceed this value by any significant amount. In view of the low temperature value of k_{IS} just cal- culated it follows that intersystem crossing can account com- pletely for the reduced fluorescence yield of phenanthrene (com- pared to anthracene) at room temperature. The other conclu- sions of Table III follow automatically from Eq.'s 4 and 5, with

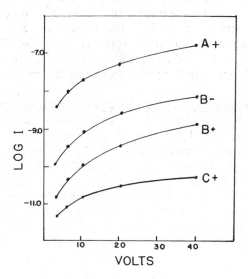

Fig. 6 — log i_p *versus* voltage for cells 1 mil
thick of A = anthracene, B = phenazine and C =
acridine,+ and - indicate sign of the illuminated
electrode. The illuminated area was 0.5cm². It is
unusual that i_{-p} should be greater than i_{+p} for
phenazine; more significantly i_{+p} and i_{-p} have
different activation energies. We know of no other non-ionic compounds, with the possible exception of some materials discussed by A. Terenin,
Proc. Chem. Soc. (London), 1961, 321, which exhibit this type of behavior. The present diagram
is abstracted from reference 11 of text.

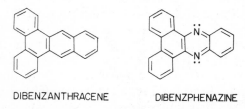

DIBENZANTHRACENE   DIBENZPHENAZINE

Fig. 7 — Structures of 1,2,3,4 - dibenzanthracene
and 1,2,3,4 - dibenzophenazine diagrammed.

the assumption that conditions of light absorption are similar for both compounds. Since the measurement of i_p were not carried out by the authors they cannot guarantee that this was so. In any case, n_T (anthracene)$/n_T$ (phenanthrene) $\sim$ 10^{-3}, and it must be realized that this is a maximal value since ϕ_P/ϕ_F for anthracene is less than 10^{-3} and since quenching of the triplet state of anthracene should be greater, if anything, than that of phenanthrene at room temperature. The n_T *versus* i_p discrepancy is then greater than 10^6, and this factor cannot be accounted for by variation of lamp output in the absorption regions of anthracene and phenanthrene. Once again the $n_{S'}$ *versus* i_p correllation is the better one.

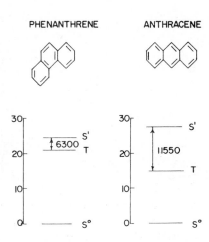

Fig. 8 — Structures and lower energy levels of anthracene and phenanthrene.

4. <u>Anthracene, Naphthalene and Benzene</u>: ϕ_P/ϕ_F as measured at low temperatures increases on proceeding from left to right in the above series. The room temperature photoconductivity behaves oppositely, at least for the first two members. It is tempting to use these data to negate the triplet thesis; however, this may not be done. For one thing it is entirely possible that k_{IS} decrease on going from left to right, and that the increasing ϕ_P/ϕ_F is conditioned entirely by a decreasing k_F; for another, it is difficult to say much about the relative values of k_{QF}, except that internal quenching is of importance in both naphthalene and benzene. The only valid conclusion which may be drawn is that data within the above series do not suffice to differentiate between a singlet or triplet intermediate.

5. <u>Anthracene and Antracene-TNB</u>: k_{IS} for the complex is of the order of 10^2 times that of anthracene. However, the complex is visually non-fluorescent. If the fluorescent quantum yield is significantly less than that of anthracene (say by a factor of 10^2 or better), as it appears to be, it is not possible to attach any differential significance to the fact that we have found needles of the 1:1 complex to be at least 10^2 times less photo-

Table III

SPECTRAL AND PHOTOCONDUCTION DATA
FOR ANTHRACENE AND PHENANTHRENE

Datum [a]	Anthracene		Phenanthrene
ϕ_T	~ 1 [b]		~ 1 [c]
ϕ_P/ϕ_F	~ 0.001 [b]		~ 1 [c]
k_{IS} (sec^{-1})	10^5		10^8
$k_P + k_{QP}$ (RT, sec^{-1})		$\geqslant$	
τ_P (sec)	~ 0.09		3.3 [d]
τ_F (RT, sec)	12×10^{-9} [e]		60×10^{-9} [e]
$\phi_F(RT)$	~ 1 [f]		0.4 [f]
$n_T(RT)$	1	:	~ 10^3
$n_S'(RT)$	1	:	~ 1
$i_p(RT)$	10^{-7} [g]		10^{-10} [g]

a) Low temperature datum except where specified by RT
(= room temperature).
b) Reference 27 of text.
c) Reference 19 of text.
d) H. Sponer, this conference.
e) A. Schmillen, this conference.
f) Reference 23 of text.
g) L. E. Lyons and G. C. Morris, J. Chem. Soc. 1957, 3648.

conductive than anthracene.[28] We do not refer here to the experimental work of Calvin and coworkers on the surface conductivity of layered cells of acceptors and donors,[29] since this is of no relevance to our considerations, and we are cognisant of the fact that the action spectrum of the slight photoconductivity exhibited by cells like ours does (perhaps significantly) include the charge transfer bands.[30]

6. Naphthalene, α-Chloronaphthalene and α-Iodonaphthalene: Despite the fact that there is a significant increase in k_{IS} from left to right in this series, since both the halogen derivatives are non-fluorescent visually at room temperature, it is impossible to attach much differentiation ability to the fact that both are not photoconductive within our limits of measurement.

7. Various Other Compounds: Anthraquinone behaves spectroscopically in identical fashion to phenazine. It should have

a very high triplet population density, yet in actual fact it is a very poor photoconductor.[31]

Carbazole has $\phi_P/\phi_F \sim 1$ at low temperatures; it is at most very weakly fluorescent in the crystal at room temperature. Conclusions similar to those for phenanthrene apply, and again despite a high light-induced triplet population density, it has, according to our measurements, a negligible photoconductivity.

Azo-compounds, in which the presence of n,π^* levels can increase k_{IS} to a value of $10^{10} \rightarrow 10^{12}$ sec^{-1} have been found by Terenin[32] to be non-photoconductive.

On the other hand in trans-stilbene where we may set $k_{IS} \sim 10^4$ sec^{-1}, and which is fluorescent at room temperature the photoconductivity is of the same order of magnitude as in anthracene.[33]

It will be evident from this discussion that there exists no evidence in favor of a triplet state intermediate theory of photo-conductivity, and considerable evidence against it. Despite the fact that the compounds listed above yield examples in which k_{IS} has been increased by at least four different ways, and despite the somewhat cautious approach of the writers, it must be concluded that the only possible kinetically intermediate state is the excited singlet state. It is also concluded that the diversity of compound-type investigated, and the concordance of i_p with $n_{S'}$ in all cases suffices to relax the restrictive arguments of II.

B. Dependence of Photocurrent on Fluorescence Efficiency

Only molecules which are good room-temperature fluorescers have significantly high room-temperature singlet state populations. Let us suppose that a detectable fluorescence is of quantum yield not less than $\phi_F = 10^{-4}$. If $k_F = 10^8$ sec^{-1}, then $k_{IS} + k_{QF} \sim 10^{12}$ sec^{-1}. Since k_F generally lies in the range $10^7 \rightarrow 10^9$ sec^{-1} we conclude, almost self-evidently, that a good fluorescer is good ($\phi_F > 10^{-1}$), primarily because $k_{IS} + k_{QF}$ is small. As a consequence of this reasoning we estimate that a good fluorescer has a singlet state population $n_{S'}$ which, under similar conditions of light absorption, is some 10^3 times greater than $n_{S'}$ for a marginal fluorescer and may equal 10^6 times the value of $n_{S'}$ in a non-fluorescer. These conclusions are also true in the presence of bimolecular quenching.

For these reasons it is imperative to investigate the photo-conductivities of highly fluorescent species. It becomes immed-

Table IV

ROOM TEMPERATURE LUMINESCENCE, PHOTOCONDUCT-
ANCE AND PHOTOCONDUCTANCE ACTIVATION ENERGIES
OF COMPOUNDS DISCUSSED IN THE PRESENT WORK

Compound	Fluorescence[a]	$i_p{}^b$	$E_p{}^c$ (ev)
Tetraphenyl-1,1',4,4'- -butadiene-1,3	+	+	-----
POPOP	+	+	-----
BOPOB	+	+	-----
Napththalene	±	±	0.078
Anthracene	+	+	0.17
Dibenzanthracene	+	+	0.25
9,10-Dichloroanthracene	+	±	-----
β-Methylanthracene	+	+	0.17
p-Quaterphenyl	+	+	0.12 ± 0.015
p-Terphenyl	+	±	0.104
Biphenyl	+	−	0.087
Phenazine	−	∓	$0.11(+)^d, 0.17(-)^e$
Acridine	−	−	-----
Anthracene-TNB	−	−	-----
α-Chloronaphthalene	−	−	-----
α-Iodonaphthalene	−	−	-----
Dibenzophenazine	−	−	-----
Anthraquinone	−	−	-----
Azo-dyes	−	−	-----
Carbazole	−	−	-----
Benzoquinone	−	−	-----

a) + indicates a good crystalline fluorescer, − indicates the absence and ± indicates intermediate yield of fluorescence.

b) + indicates a good photoconductivity, − indicates poor photo-conductivity and ± indicates intermediate behavior; these distinctions are at best qualitative.

c) Photoconduction thermal activation energy in ev.

d) Activation energy when illuminated electrode is positive.

e) Activation energy when illuminated electrode is negative.

iately apparent that the better photoconductors are generally to be found among fluorescent species; this is indicated very clearly in Table IV. The voltage vs i_p curves for a representative range of scintillators are shown in Fig. 9. It becomes apparent that a high concentration of singlet excited state species predicates photoconductivity, and that any large non-radiative degradative process is detrimental to the observation of a photocurrent. Two other isolated observations accord with

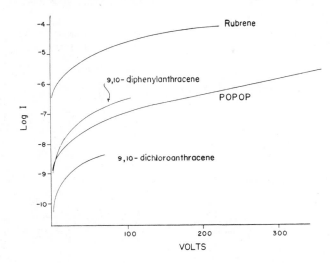

Fig. 9 — log i_p *versus* voltage for some luminescers. It will be noted that the photocurrent measured by us in 9,10 - dichloroan-thracene is considerably less than that reported by E. Bock, J. Ferguson and W. G. Schneider, *Canadian J. Chem. 36*, 507 (1958). Our material was highly purified and our measurements refer to a sandwich rather than a surface. The 9,10 - diphenyl-anthracene and POPOP cells were polycrystalline, and only one run of i_p *versus* V was carried out.

these conclusions: Impurities which quench the fluorescence proper of a hydrocarbon quench the photocurrent in roughly the same ratio. Naphthacene-doped anthracene, so much studied from the point of view of fluorescence quenching, provides a striking example since at naphthacene concentrations as low as 0.01%, anthracene is no longer photoconductive.[25] Compton, Schneider and Waddington,[34] noted that the effects of neutron bombardment of anthracene was to decrease ϕ_F and i_p in the same rough ratio.

C. Self-Quenching, Intermolecular Interaction and Bimolecu-
   larity

The experiments reported in this section and the conclusions
drawn are to be regarded as very preliminary and tentative in
nature.

The molecule rubrene of which the structure is shown in
Fig. 10 is strongly fluorescent in dilute neutral solution, but not

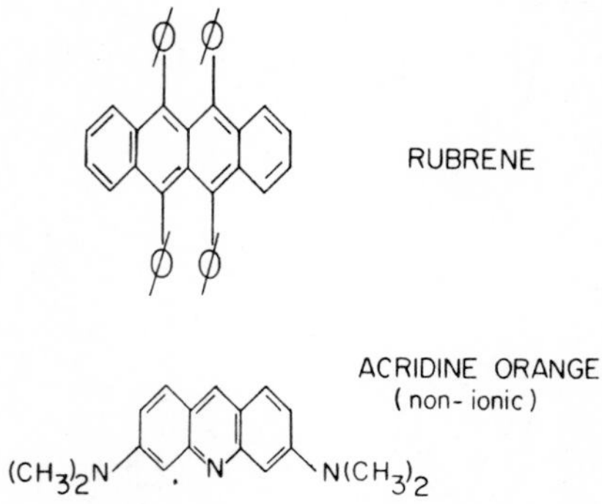

RUBRENE

ACRIDINE ORANGE
(non- ionic)

$(CH_3)_2N$ $N(CH_3)_2$

Fig. 10 — Structures of rubrene and acridine
orange. The symbol ϕ indicates a phenyl
group.

in the single crystal. Acridine orange exhibits similar behavior.
It follows that these compounds must be considered as having
very large external self-quenching rate constants. It is perhaps
significant that rubrene is such a very good organic photoconductor (see Fig. 9). Acridine orange, however, has a photoconductivity some 10^2 times less than anthracene. The rubrene results are tantalizing in that they suggest to us that the specific
singlet degradative process which leads to the photoconductive
state is extramolecular in nature. It should not be deduced from
this that these authors expect all such self-quenched materials
to be photoconductors; they merely would not be surprised if the
very best photoconductors exhibited considerable self-quenching.

It might be further reasoned that it is not the self-quenching
which is important, but rather the intermolecular interaction
which causes it. In this way, for example, may be explained the
increasing photoconductivity with size of the polyacenes and
polyphenyls. However, if we are to regard the extent of the fluorescence wavelength shift on going from solution to solid as an
indicator of strong intermolecular interaction, we are disap-

pointed in that decacyclene and 9,10-dichloroanthracene have
photoconductivities $\sim 10^2$ times less than that of anthracene.
1. Plastic Solutions: One other experiment performed in these
laboratories is perhaps of some significance in this latter regard. We failed to observe any photoconductivity in different
polystyrene solutions which contained individually 10% anthracene, 20% stilbene, 20% acridine orange and 20% tetraphenyl-1,
1', 4, 4'-butadiene-1, 3, all of which are good photoconductors in
the pure crystalline state. Since the plastic solutions retained
in entirety their luminescence characteristics it is to be concluded from the negative results that the production of charge
carriers requires the participation of two or more molecules of
photoconductor in intimate contact. This conclusion results
from two observations: namely that injected carriers have a
finite mobility in the pure polystyrene matrix, and that sus-
pensions of the same or less over-all concentrations of some
of the same materials, do indeed photoconduct significantly.
Since the resistive barrier of interposed insulating polystyrene
film between adjacent molecules of the solution should on the
average be somewhat thinner than the equivalent barrier in the
case of the suspension (because there are obviously more molecules than particles), if incipient carrier formation could occur within the one molecule then the photoconductivity of the
solution might be expected to be actually greater than that of the
suspension. It becomes obvious then that carrier generation is
communal. And there is only one qualifying appendage necessary
to this statement-namely the possibility that "streamer" formation of particles occurs in the case of the suspension, such that
there are virtual line-ups or "streamers" of particles with
good inter-particle contact, extending randomly throughout the
suspension.[35]

VI. PHOTOCONDUCTIVE ACTIVATION ENERGY

It is recognized that these energies are of the order of a
vibrational quantum or two (0.1 → 0.4 ev) and that they may
therefore be vibrational in origin. A few facts are to be noted
in this regard. Firstly, there exist many normal modes in
these molecules, the frequency difference between which, in
most cases, is less than the error made in measuring photoconduction energies. Consequently any comparison of E_p, measured
as $i_p = i_p^{\circ} e^{-E_p/kT}$, with a specific vibrational quantum is

suspect. Secondly it is not obvious that the particular active vibration should be one of those which is strongly coupled to the electronic transition, unless it be because those are the ones most strongly activated in the absorption process; and finally, it is not obvious that only one particular frequency (out of 66 in anthracene) should be active in whatever process it is that leads to carrier production.

The next point to note is that the behavior of E_p is contrary to that of E_s (semiconduction activation energy) since E_p increases with molecular size, a fact obvious from Table IV. This simply implies that the activation barrier for photoconductivity is larger the lower the singlet excited state energy. However, vibrational frequencies of a given type generally decrease in frequency with increasing molecular size; it becomes necessary therefore to use larger frequency vibrations (and therefore of different type) to fit the data on larger molecules; this is indeed disconcerting in view of the fact noted previously that only one particular vibrational quantum seems to be involved.

The thermal activation plots of anthracene and of the p- and n-photocurrents of phenazine have been shown elsewhere.[11] It was previously noted that phenazine is an n-conductor, the only non-ionic aromatic known to us to be such.[36] This in itself is not too surprising; what is of interest is that the n- and p- photocurrents have different activation energies, since this very clearly shows that the measured n-current is not a back p-current. The question then becomes why this is so. The presumed answer is that molecules in n,π^* excited states may very well function as intrinsic hole traps, for the simple reason that the non-bonding hole is localized on one atom, thus making its capture cross-section for electrons small, compared to that of a π-hole. The authors do not take any correllation with vibrational frequencies too seriously, but do suggest that the idea of aza-aromatics functioning as intrinsic hole traps seems reasonable and worthy of further investigation.

VII. CONCLUSIONS

The materials investigated in this work were of three extreme types with regard to their fluorescence characteristics.

(a) materials which are strongly fluorescent at room temperature in both the solid and the dilute neutral solutions, and in which it is obvious that quenching of all sorts is small;

(b) materials which are non-fluorescent in both solid and dilute neutral solution at room temperature and also at $-190°C$, but which are strongly phosphorescent at $-190°C$, and in which as a consequence the intersystem crossing rate constant is very large $(k_{IS} \sim 10^{12} \sec^{-1})$;

(c) materials which fluoresce strongly in dilute neutral solution at room temperature, but in which the fluorescence efficiency decreases markedly with increasing concentration until in the single crystal it may be absent or weak, and in which as a consequence the self-quenching rate constants of a bimolecular or higher order process must be very large.[37] Many materials intermediate in their luminescence behavior between these extremes were investigated, and in particular, materials in which k_{IS} was increased by a number of different ways were studied. These methods all function by increasing the spin-orbital coupling in the molecule and are:

(a) Appending a heavy atom, as a substituent, to the molecular framework,

(b) Decreasing the $S' \to T$ energy split,

(c) Forming charge-transfer complexes,

(d) Designing the molecule such that $n,\pi *$ levels intervene between $S'_{\pi,\pi}$ and $T_{\pi,\pi}$.

The conclusions to be drawn are as follows, and it is to be emphasized that the reservations appended to them in the text are not to be forgotten here:

(1) Photogeneration of carriers proceeds with significantly higher probability from the lowest singlet excited state than from the lowest triplet state.

(2) As a corrolary of (1) it may be concluded that the better photoconductors will be found among those species which have simultaneously the highest quantum yield of fluorescence and the lowest fluorescent rate constant.

(3) The difference in probability quoted in (1) is such that the intersystem crossing process leading to triplet state population may be considered in a kinetic sense to be competitively concurrent with charge carrier formation.

(4) Photoconductivity increases in a fashion which corresponds roughly to the extent of increasing intermolecular interaction in the solid.

(5) As one corrolary of (4) it is not surprising that the best photoconductor investigated by us, namely rubrene, shows complete self-quenching of fluorescence in the solid.

(6) Charge-carrier generation is predominantly, or perhaps even completely, communal; it requires the participation of two or more molecules of photoconductor. It may be first order, but it is not monomolecular.

(7) It seems not unreasonable that the non-bonding orbitals of aza-aromatics should function as intrinsic hole traps.

(8) Since the rise-time of pulsed photoconductivity in anthracene[15] may be of the order of 10^{-7} sec, and since k_{IS} is of the order of 10^5 sec^{-1}, any kind of triplet state participation in the photogenerative act seems ruled out. The authors here consider that perhaps conclusion (2) is relevant only because the singlet exciton is more mobile than the triplet exciton and it can more readily attain the surface or an appropriate defect where it then degrades to a triplet, or because a biphotonic bimolecular process is involved, one molecule being a S' species, the other a triplet species. A simple biphotonic process in which the second photon causes excitation entirely within the triplet manifold of a previously excited molecule seems similarly excluded.

(9) Neither the lowest excited singlet or triplet states are photoconductive states. There exists no reason why they should be, and many reasons why they should not. At most they are kinetic intermediates.

(10) The exact nature of the photoconductive thermal activation energy is still unclear. It could be vibrational in nature.

VIII. ACKNOWLEDGMENT

The authors wish to express their gratitude to the Petroleum Research Fund of the American Chemical Society and to Humble Oil and Refining Company for their generous support of this work. They are grateful to Mrs. Charles Neely for some of the diagrams contained herein, and to Dr. G. M. Spruch for her patience.

REFERENCES

[1] Read by S. P. McGlynn on Tuesday, October 10, 1961 at the International Conference on Luminescence at New York University, Washington Square, New York.

[2] Post-doctoral Research Fellow 1960-61; supported by a Research Grant 638-A from the Petroleum Research Fund of the American Chemical Society to the Louisiana State University; present address: Research Division, American Optical Co., Southbridge, Massachusetts.

[3] Pre-doctoral Research Fellow 1960-; supported by a Research Grant from Esso Laboratories—Humble Oil and Refining Co. to the Louisiana State University.

[4] Most recently by B. Rosenberg and J. F. Camiscoli, J. Chem. Phys. 35, 982 (1961).

[5] M. Wilk, Z. Electrochem. 64, 930 (1960). This is only one of the possible interpretations which can result from a reading of Wilk's work.

[6] B. Pullman, "Proceedings of the Third Biennial Conference on Carbon", edited by S. Mrzowski, M. L. Studebaker and P. L. Walker, Pergamon Press, New York, N. Y., 1959; see Fig. 13, p. 20.

[7] W. Moore and M. Silver, J. Chem. Phys. 33, 1671 (1960).

[8] It is obvious that any singlet excited state theory of dark-conductivity, such as might be deduced from the observation [A. T. Vartanyan, Izvest. Akad. Nauk S.S.S.R., 20, 154 (1956)] that there is good correlation of the singlet absorption edge energy and twice the thermal activation energy, is similarly negated.

[9] A. N. Terenin, Radiotekhnika i Elektronikha 1, 1127 (1956).

[10] B. Rosenberg, J. Chem. Phys. 31, 238 (1959); 34, 63 (1961).

[11] M. Kleinerman and S. P. McGlynn, Proceedings of the Inter-Industry Conference on Organic Semiconductors, Chicago, April 18-19, 1961; to be published by Macmillan and Co., New York.

[12] It should be evident by now that the authors give no credence to any theory which makes either the excited singlet or triplet state the photoconductive state. They are presently considering only the kinetic intermediacy of excited singlet or triplet states to the photoconductive state.

[13] This equation is over-restrictive, since it does not apply to the non-uniformly illuminated sandwich cells used

in the present work. It does not take into account space charge effects, nor the difference in τ and μ between n- and p-carriers. The equation is used here merely to indicate some functional dependencies.

[14] R. G. Kepler, Phys. Rev. 119, 1226 (1960).

[15] M. Silver, private communication.

[16] P. Mark, private communication.

[17] It is not entirely proper to effect separation of β and $\tau\mu$, as has been done in II.B and II.A, respectively. It would be better to discuss the product $\beta\tau\mu$ alone, which is very tersely done in reference 11 of the text. The present separation is entirely in the interest of clarity.

[18] G. Porter and M. R. Wright, Discussions Faraday Soc. No. 27, 18 (1959).

[19] M. Kasha, Radiation Research, Supplement 2, 243 (1960).

[20] The word "manifold" here implies that all the contained levels are of the same multiplicity.

[21] It may be said quite generally that $\epsilon (S' \leftarrow S^\circ) \simeq 10^6 \epsilon (T \leftarrow S^\circ)$ and $\epsilon (S_{\pi,\pi} \leftarrow S^\circ) \simeq 10^2 \epsilon (S_{n,\pi} \leftarrow S^\circ)$. A very excellent discussion of the nature of n,π^* transitions is given by M. Kasha, "Light and Life", The Johns Hopkins University Press, 1961, page 31, edited by W. D. McElroy and B. Glass.

[22] E. Clementi and M. Kasha, J. Mol. Spectroscopy 2, 197 (1958).

[23] R. C. Sangster and J. W. Irvine, Jr., J. Chem. Phys. 24, 670 (1956).

[24] H. Linschitz, Radiation Research, Supplement 2, 182 (1960).

[25] D. C. Northrop and O. Simpson, Proc. Roy. Soc. 244A, 377 (1958).

[26] H. Kuroda and E. A. Flood, Can. J. Chem. 39, 1981 (1961).

[27] S. P. McGlynn, J. D. Boggus and E. Elder, J. Chem. Phys. 32, 357 (1960).

[28] This particular experiment, being our first in this area, was rather crude, and surfacial.

[29] D. Kearns, Radiation Research, Supplement 2, 207 (1956)

[30] D. Hausterey, private communication.

[31] A. Bree and L. Lyons, J. Chem. Soc. 1960, 5179.

[32] A. Terenin, E. Putzeiko and J. Akimov, Discussions Faraday Soc. 27, 83 (1959).

[33] D. Drefahl and H. J. Henkel, Naturwissenschaft, 42, 624 (1955).

[34] D.M.J. Compton, W. G. Schneider and T. C. Waddington, J. Chem. Phys. 28, 742 (1959).

[35] The results obtained above are not to be compared with the plastic systems considered in the recent patents of Kalle and Co. (Kalle, Belg. Pat. 593,002).

[36] Some further examples of molecules which may possess low energy n,π^* states are given by Terenin, Proc. Chem. Soc. 1961, 321. They are also n-photoconductors.

[37] It is possible that some self-quenching takes place *via* triplet states, a fact which might possibly be construed as detrimental to some of the conclusions to be drawn below— see G. A. Mokeeva and B. Ia. Sveshnikov, Optika i Spektroskopiya 9, 601 (1960).

p-OLIGOPHENYLENE STUDIES

by H. O. Wirth
University of Mainz

p-oligophenylenes are defined initial members of the homologous p-polyphenylene series, such as biphenyl, p-terphenyl, p-quaterphenyl, etc.

Because of the rapid decrease of solubility as the number of rings increases, this class of materials could not be investigated thoroughly beyond p-quaterphenyl. For example, the solubility of p-sexiphenyl, (I) in Table 1, is only 10^{-4} g/l. This property causes great difficulties not only in synthesis, but also in handling the materials. In particular, investigations in solution have been completely impossible.

Table 1:   Solubilities of p-sexiphenyls (Toluene, $20°C$)

Structural Formula	Solubility (g/l)
I	$\sim 10^{-4}$
II	87

In the course of our investigations we found that the solubility of the p-oligophenylenes can be greatly enhanced by substitution.[1] Thus, the solubility of the sixiphenyl increases up to 87 g/l (II) .

With this knowledge we were in a position to open a very interesting research field; very interesting also for systematic luminescence studies, since the fluorescence of these compounds is one of their identifying characteristics.

According to two different principles of synthesis - which cannot be demonstrated here - we have up to now prepared more than 70 p-oligophenylenes with from three to eight rings.

Now a few words on the spectral properties of this class of materials: Ultraviolet spectroscopic investigations of unsubstituted p-oligophenylenes have already been carried out by various authors.[2] These compounds show a broad structureless absorption band which is shifted toward longer wavelengths as the degree of condensation increases (Table 2).

Table 2:   UV-Absorption Behavior of Homologous
           p-oligophenylene Series (in Chloroform)

n	λ mμ	λ
1	–	254
2	251	269
3	280	277
4	300	281
5	312	–
.	.	.
.	.	.
	344	287

This shift takes place, though, in the sense of a converging series with a limiting value of 344 mμ. A polyphenylene with an infinite degree of condensation absorbs in the ultraviolet and is therefore colorless.

The absorption behavior of the methyl-substituted series (shown in Figure 2) can also be described with the aid of a converging series.[3] The range of absorption is much narrower, however, and the limiting value for the corresponding polyphenylene is 287 mμ.

We see as the cause of these convergence phenomena the inner rotations of the benzene rings around the longitudinal axis of the molecules. That means that the absorption is produced by a statistical chromophoric element which does not increase with the total length of the molecule. In addition the substituted methyl groups sterically disturb the coplanar con- stellation of the molecule and, therefore, the mesomeric co- operation of the single chromophors. This leads to a hypso- chromic effect in comparison with the corresponding unsub- stituted compounds.

Because of the correlation between absorption and emission, the fluorescence bands of the p-oligophenylenes also show a convergence. This fact not only diminishes the practical appli- cations of these compounds, but also restricts systematic re- search.

If this spectral convergence phenomenon is caused by the inner rotations of the benzene rings, a blocking of this move- ment with the help of suitable substituents must lead to an ideal coplanarity and in connection with this to a significant red shift of the spectral bands. With this concept in mind we synthesized some bridged p-oligophenylenes using, for instance, oxygen as bridging element,[4] and our expectations were confirmed (Table 3).

Table 3:   UV Spectra of Oxido-p-Oligophenylenes
            (in Chloroform)

Structural Formula		Absorption Data	
		$\lambda_{long.}$ (mμ)	$\varepsilon_{mol.}$
	III	298	10,000
	IV	340	35,000
	V	365	88,000

The strongest absorption band of the trioxido-p-quaterphenyl (V) has a longer wavelength than the limiting value of
the unsubstituted polyphenylene (Table 2).

Unfortunately, these bridged oligophenylenes are very
sparingly soluble. It is seen that the solubilities of compounds
III, IV, and V are considerably lower even than those of the
unsubstituted substances. Since solubility is very important
for luminescence research, our present situation might seem
hopeless.

However, the dependence of solubility on structure is also
a very important part of our work. Recently, we have succeeded in finding out some fundamental relationships which will
enable us to make compounds of the above type soluble without
changing their favorable optical properties.

Because of the narrow frame of this report and finally also
because our investigations in this field are not yet finished, I
cannot go more deeply into this very interesting complex of
questions.

The investigations which I have reported were carried out in
the Institute of Professor W. Kern in Mainz. I should like to
thank Professor Kern for his interest in and support of this
work and Professor Kallmann for the generous invitation to
present this report at the conference.

REFERENCES:

[1] W. Kern, W. Gruber and H. O. Wirth; Makromolekulare
   Chem. 37, 198 (1960).
[2] A. E. Gillam and D. H. Hey; J. Chem. Soc. (London) 1939, 1170
   E. Clar; Chem. Ber. 82, 495 (1949).
   W. Kuhn; Helv. Chim. Acta 31, 1780 (1948).
[3] W. Gruber; Thesis, University of Mainz, 1958.
[4] G. Waese; Diplomarbeit, University of Mainz, 1961.

FLUORESCENCE LIFETIME STUDIES OF PYRENE SOLUTIONS

J. B. Birks and I. H. Munro

The Physical Laboratories, The University
Manchester, England

The fluorescence emission spectrum of a solution of pyrene consists of two components: M, the normal emission from singlet excited molecules at $\lambda = 360$-420 mμ, and D, the emission from excited dimers (excimers) at $\lambda = 420$-550 mμ. As the pyrene concentration c is increased, the quantum intensity of M decreases and that of D increases (Förster and Kaspar, 1955).

In the present investigation the rise and decay times of the two components have been studied, both in the absence and presence of dissolved oxygen, as a function of concentration c and of solvent viscosity η. The pyrene was of high purity (Rütgers), and spectroscopic grade cyclohexane was used as the solvent in the concentration studies. Dissolved oxygen was expelled by boiling for a few minutes, this method being found more effective in eliminating oxygen quenching than other methods described in the literature. The solvent viscosity was varied by using mixtures of cyclohexane and paraffin oil, with a fixed pyrene concentration of 10^{-3} M.

Each specimen was contained in a quartz-windowed cell and excited by $\lambda = 230$-350 mμ radiation from a pulsed hydrogen discharge lamp, passed through a saturated $CoSO_4$-$NiSO_4$ solution filter. The components M and D were separated by appropriate filters. The emission was observed with a 56 AVP photomultiplier, feeding a Hewlett-Packard 185 A pulse sampling oscilloscope. The oscillogram of the light pulse from the lamp had a decay time of 3 nsec and a width at half-intensity of 5 nsec. The shape and intensity of the light pulse could be varied by changing the hydrogen pressure and applied voltage, and was adjusted to an optimum. Such measurements indicate that the observed time spread is due primarily to the photomultiplier transit time spread and the oscilloscope response time, and that the width of the primary light pulse is 1 nsec or less.

Typical results for a deoxygenated solution in cyclohexane of $c = 5 \times 10^{-3}$ M are shown in Figure 1. The monomer fluorescence M (curve A) decays exponentially with a decay time τ_M.

The intensity of the dimer fluorescence D (curve B) varies
with time t according to an equation of the form

$$I_D = C(e^{-t/\tau_F} - e^{-t/\tau_R}) \qquad (1)$$

where τ_R is the rise time and τ_F the decay time of the emission. The light pulse shape is shown in curve C.

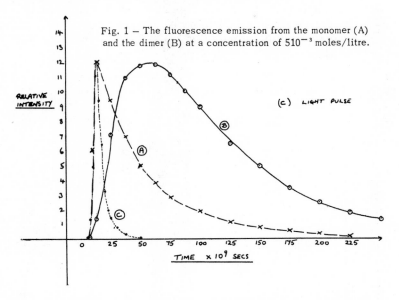

Fig. 1 — The fluorescence emission from the monomer (A)
and the dimer (B) at a concentration of 510^{-3} moles/litre.

The variation of $1/\tau_M$ with c for deoxygenated solutions is
shown in Figure 2. A linear relation is observed of the form

$$\frac{1}{\tau_M} = \frac{1}{\tau_{M_0}} + k_D c \qquad (2)$$

where k_D is the quenching rate parameter due to dimer formation, and τ_{M_0} is the monomer decay time in the absence of
external quenching. For the full concentration range up to
$c = 10^{-2}$ M a least-squares fit yields τ_{M_0} = 290 nsec,
k_D = 3.3 × 10⁹ liter mole⁻¹ sec⁻¹. However, the results at
$c > 10^{-3}$ M are a little less reliable due to the reduced intensity
of the monomer fluorescence, and possible reabsorption effects
which would increase the apparent value of τ_M. The data at
$c \leqslant 10^{-3}$ M, which also vary linearly with c, yield τ_{M_0} = 340
nsec, k_D = 4.5 × 10⁹ liter mole⁻¹ sec⁻¹.

The theoretical value (Smoluchowski 1917, Bowen 1954) for the rate parameter of a diffusional controlled quenching process is

$$k = \frac{8\,aRT}{3000\eta} \tag{3}$$

where the collisional parameter $a \sim 1.0$, and the case a = 1.0 corresponds to collisions between spherical molecules in which every collision is effective. For cyclohexane at room temperature, $\eta = 0.01$ poise, and $k = 6.5a \times 10^9$ liter mole^{-1} sec^{-1}, so that comparison with k_D yields $a = 0.5$ to 0.7.

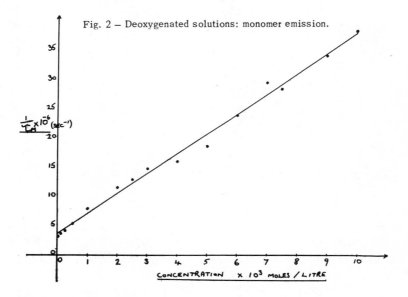

Fig. 2 – Deoxygenated solutions: monomer emission.

The observed dependence of τ_M on solvent viscosity η of deoxygenated solutions of $c = 10^{-3}$ M is shown in Figure 3. A linear relation between $1/\tau_M$ and $1/\eta$ is observed, in agreement with the theoretical equation obtained from (2) and (3)

$$\frac{1}{\tau_M} = \frac{1}{\tau_{M_0}} + \frac{8aRTc}{3000\eta}. \tag{4}$$

Comparison of (4) with the experimental data yields $\tau_{M_0} = 340$ nsec, $a = 0.7$ in agreement with the previous data.

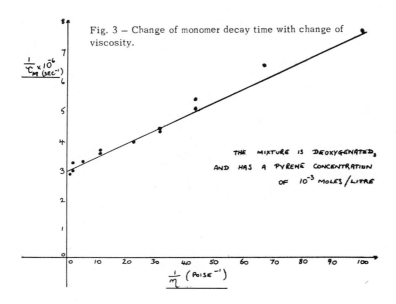

Fig. 3 — Change of monomer decay time with change of viscosity.

THE MIXTURE IS DEOXYGENATED, AND HAS A PYRENE CONCENTRATION OF 10^{-3} MOLES/LITRE

Figure 4 shows the observed dependence of $1/\tau_M$ on $1/\eta$ for oxygen saturated solutions of $c = 10^{-3}$ M. The variation is linear over most of the range, with a similar rate constant to that for dimer formation, indicating that oxygen quenching is also diffusion controlled.

The dimer decay time τ_D is independent of c in deoxygenated solutions and equal to 40 nsec. This value is obtained from an analysis of the observed dimer emission curves in terms of equation (1), to be published. At low c, where $\tau_M > \tau_D$, $\tau_R = \tau_D$, $\tau_F = \tau_M$. At high c, where $\tau_M < \tau_D$, $\tau_R = \tau_M$, $\tau_F = \tau_D$.

The value of τ_D agrees well with the fluorescence decay time of crystalline pyrene, which is known from its fluorescence spectrum (Birks and Cameron 1959) and crystallographic structure to be dimerized. Decay time measurements were made on several microcrystalline specimens, the values obtained ranging from 50 to 80 nsec. Schmillen (1961) and Birks and Cameron (1959) have reported values of $\tau_x = 80$ nsec and 46 nsec, respectively.

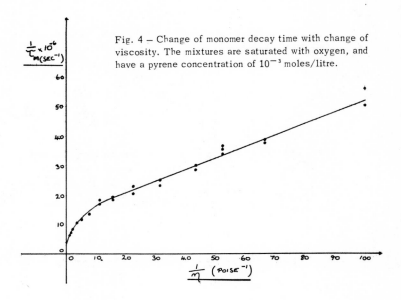

Fig. 4 – Change of monomer decay time with change of viscosity. The mixtures are saturated with oxygen, and have a pyrene concentration of 10^{-3} moles/litre.

REFERENCES

J. B. Birks and A. J. W. Cameron; Proc. Roy. Soc. A249, 297 (1958).
E. G. Bowen; Trans. Faraday Soc. 50, 97 (1954).
Th. Förster and K. Kaspar; Z. für Elektrochem. 59, 976 (1955).
A. Schmillen; Naturwiss. 16a, 5 (1961).
M. v. Smoluchowski; Z. Phys. Chem. 92, 129 (1917).

INTERNAL STRUCTURE OF POLYMER SOLUTIONS AS STUDIED BY A FLUORESCENCE POLARIZATION METHOD

Yasunori Nishijima

Department of Polymer Chemistry
Kyoto University, Kyoto, Japan

ABSTRACT

The fluorescence technique has been applied to study the internal structure of polymer solutions over a wide range of polymer concentrations. The relaxation time of rotation of fluorescent residues dispersed in a polymer solution is estimated from the degree of polarization of fluorescence emitted from the solution. (A) The local viscosity, which is a measure of the internal architecture of the solution, can be obtained by dispersing free fluorescent molecules in the polymer solution. (B) The micro-Brownian motion of a polymer chain in solution can directly be observed by placing fluorescent residues on the polymer chain by appropriate methods of chemical bond formation between the polymer chain and the fluorescent molecules. Measurements have been carried out under various conditions so as to investigate the effects of chain length and polymer concentration on the internal structure of polymer solution.

1. INTRODUCTION

Diffusion processes especially in systems containing macromolecules are very complicated because of the fact that the rate of diffusion cannot be expressed by a simple function of T/η, where T is the absolute temperature and η is the viscosity of the medium (macroscopic viscosity), and the diffusion is controlled by the internal structure of the local environment through which particles are diffusing.[1]

A fluoreometric method has been introduced for studying the internal structure of polymer systems throughout every phase, that is, polymer solutions of a wide range of concentration, polymer melts and polymer solids.[2] This method is based on the theory which gives the correlation between the degree of polarization of fluorescence and the rotational diffusion of fluorescent molecules in the medium.[3] When fluorescent residues dispersed randomly in a polymer system are excited with a beam of plane-polarized light, the fluorescence radiation emitted from the system is partially polarized. The degree of polarization of the fluorescence is determined by the following factors:

(1) Optically anisotropic characteristics of the fluorescent residues.

(2) Lifetime of excitation of the fluorescent residues, τ. and (3) Relaxation time of rotation of the fluorescent residues in the medium, ρ.

Hence, if the factors (1) and (2) are known, the degree of polarization of fluorescence is a measure of the factor (3), which is a function of T/η^* of the system. The viscosity, η^*, is not the macroscopic viscosity of the medium but the "local viscosity" that is a measure of the hydrodynamic frictional force of the local environment in which the fluorescent residues are rotating. The relaxation time of rotation, ρ, and hence the local viscosity, η^*, are a measure of the internal structure of the polymer system. The lifetime of excitation, τ, is usually of the order of 10^{-9} sec., therefore, any change in the internal structure corresponding to the time-scale comparable with this value can be observed. The concentration of the fluorescent residue in the system required for the measurements is only less than 10^{-5} mole/1. and hardly influences the behavior of polymer chains in the system. These features of the present method are uniquely utilized for measuring changes in the internal structure of polymer systems during the transformations.

In the present paper, two cases of observations are discussed, that is, (A) fluorescence emitted from a polymer solution in which free fluorescent molecules are dispersed, and (B) fluorescence from solution of fluorescent polymer molecules in which fluorescent residues are directly attached on the polymer chains by some chemical bondings. The results obtained in the case (A) show the internal structure of polymer solutions, such as degree of overlapping of polymer molecules in solution, in terms of the local viscosity. The micro-Brownian motion of polymer chains in solution can directly be investigated by measurements of the polarization of fluorescence in the case (B).

2. EXPERIMENTAL PROCEDURES

The degree of polarization of fluorescence, p, is measured in an optical system as shown in Fig. 1, in which the exciting light beam, I_o, plane-polarized with the electric vector along ab which is parallel to the Z-axis, falls on the cell, C, in the direction parallel to the X-axis, and the fluorescence, I_f, is observed in a direction within the XY-plane. The value of p is determined from the fluorescence intensity with the electric vector parallel to ab (I_n) and that with the electric vector perpendicular to ab ($I_\perp$) by the following definition;

$$p = \frac{I_n - I_+}{I_u + I_+} \tag{1}$$

Uraine (fluorescein Sodium) was chosen for the present study. The first maximum of the absorption spectrum in aqueous solution is at 490 mμ, and the fluorescence spectrum is a mirror image of the principal absorption peak and the maximum fluorescence intensity is observed at 517 mμ. No appreciable changes in the absorption spectrum and the fluorescence intensity are observed in the solutions used in the following studies, except that in some solutions the absorption maximum is shifted to longer wave-lengths by about 5 mμ.

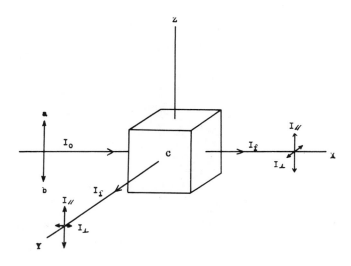

Fig. 1 — Components of polarized fluorescence.

3. POLARIZATION OF FLUORESCENCE OF URANINE IN GLYCEROL-WATER MIXTURE

In order to obtain the relation between the degree of polarization of fluorescence, p, and the local viscosity, η^*, measurements of the degree of polarization of fluorescence of uranine
were carried out in mixtures of glycerol and water at various
glycerol contents ranging from 0 to 85% and at various temperatures from 5°C. to 30°C. In Fig. 2, the values of the reciprocal of the degree of polarization, $1/p$, are plotted against
T/η^*, where η^* is the local viscosity of the mixture which has
been found to be identical with the macroscopic viscosity of the
mixture at the temperature of observation.[4] The linear relationship between $1/p$ and T/η^*, as expected from the Perrin's
equation expressed in the following form,

$$\left(\frac{1}{p} - \frac{1}{3}\right) = \left(\frac{1}{p_o} - \frac{1}{3}\right)\left(1 + \frac{kT}{\eta u}\tau\right) \tag{2}$$

is obeyed in the region of T/η^* upto $10^{40} K$/poise but for higher
values of T/η^* the plots tend to deviate from the straight line
upwards. In the following experiments, however, the value of
the local viscosity is estimated from the degree of polarization
using this experimental result.

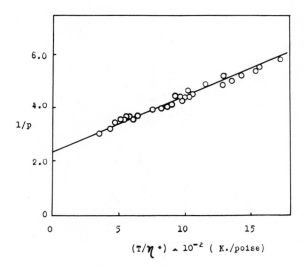

Fig. 2 — $1/p$ versus $T\eta^*$, for uranine in glycerol-water mixtures.

4. POLARIZATION OF FLUORESCENCE OF URANINE IN POLYMER SOLUTIONS

A typical result is shown in Fig. 3, in which the local viscosity obtained from the degree of polarization is plotted against concentration of polyacrylamide in the aqueous solutions. The features of these curves are similar to those of curves obtained from the translational diffusion of small molecules in polymer solutions.[1] The critical concentration, at which the rise in the local viscosity commences, for PAA-H is about 0.5 g/100 ml. and for PAA-L is about 1.5 g/100 ml. After the critical concentration is exceeded, the local viscosity begins to rise gradually due to the overlapping of polymer chains in solution. At about 10 g/100 ml. in this case, the local viscosity becomes independent of the molecular weight of polymer, indicating the formation of a network in the solution in which the polymer chains are so entangled that they lose their identity.

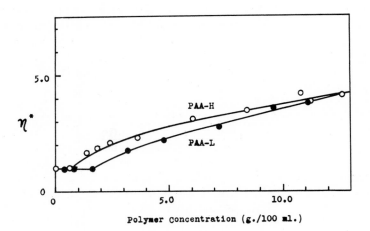

Fig. 3 — Relative local viscosity, η^*, versus polymer concentration, for aqueous polyacrylamide solutions. Molecular weights; PAA-H:12.5 × 10⁴, PAA-L:6.0 × 10⁴.

5. MICRO-BROWNIAN MOTION OF POLYMER CHAINS IN SOLUTION

When some fluorescent residues are directly attached onto polymer chains, the degree of polarization of fluorescence emitted from a solution of such fluorescent polymers should be a measure of the micro-Brownian motion of the polymer chain in the solution.

A.   Preparation of Fluorescent Polymers

The fluorescent polymer for the present purpose may be prepared by either of the following methods; (1) polymerizing a monomer in the presence of fluorescent molecules which can act as an initiator or a chain transfer agent on the polymerization, (2) conjugating fluorescent residues on a polymer chain whose monomeric units are capable of forming chemical bonds with some fluorescent molecules by means of appropriate reactions, or (3) copolymerizing ordinary monomers with some monomer molecules which originally possess fluorescent residues.

A wide variety of systems for preparing fluorescent polymers has been examined. In the present paper, as an example, the case of uranine-conjugated polyacrylamide is discussed. This fluorescent polymer could be obtained when an acrylamide monomer was polymerized in aqueous solution in the presence of uranine molecules using hydrogen peroxide as the initiator.

The fluorescence characteristics of this fluorescent polymer are identical with those of the free uranine molecule, and it is also proved that the fluorescent uranine residues are directly attached to the ends of polyacrylamide chains.

B. Polarization of Fluorescence of Uranine-Conjugates of Polyacrylamide in Dilute Aqueous Solutions

The degree of polarization of fluorescence emitted from dilute aqueous solutions of the fluorescent polymer (polymer concentration less than 0.2 g/100 ml.) was measured as a function of temperature ranging from 5°C. to 30°C. Using the viscosity of water at each temperature as the local viscosity of the medium, $1/p$ is plotted as a function of T/η^* in Fig. 4, for three fractions of the fluorescent polymer having different chain length. The plots give a straight line for each fraction in agreement with the theory described above. The intercepts of these straight lines coincide at $1/p_0 = 2.0$, which is identical with that of free uranine.

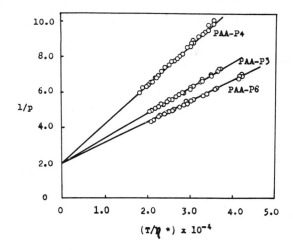

Fig. 4 — $1/p$ *versus* T/η^*, for uranine-conjugates of polyacrylamide in dilute aqueous solutions. Molecular weights:
PAA-P3:8.4 × 10^4, PAA-P4:3.5 × 10^4, PAA-P6:23.0 × 10^4.

From the slope of the straight line, knowing the lifetime of
excitation, the relaxation time of rotation of the fluorescent
residue in solution can be estimated. In order to clarify the effect of chain length on the rotational motion of the chain segments, the uranine-conjugates of polyacrylamide were carefully
fractionated with regard to the chain length and the degree of
polarization of fluorescence was measured as a function of the
chain length. A typical result is shown in Fig. 5. The value of
p, hence, the mean relaxation time of rotation of terminal
segments increases with increasing chain length up to a certain
limited value and then levels off for longer chain lengths. The
mean relaxation time corresponding to the value of p at this
plateau is calculated to be about 7×10^{-9} sec. It should be
noted here that this value is about ten times as long as that of
free uranine in water, which is about 7×10^{-10} sec.

From the features of the curve in Fig. 5, it may be reasonable to consider that the effect of chain length on the rotational
movements of the terminal segment can be divided into two
parts, that is, (1) direct contributions of the movements of
neighboring segments of the terminal segment; (2) some indirect contributions of the movements of segments situated in

the local environment of the terminal segment. For the cases
of very short chains, the effect (1) would be predominant but
this effect should become independent of the chain length for
longer chains. The effect (2) is, of course, dependent on the
segmental distribution of the chain length for very long chains.
In the present case, the rotational movements of terminal segments become independent of the chain length at the length of
about 3,000 Å.

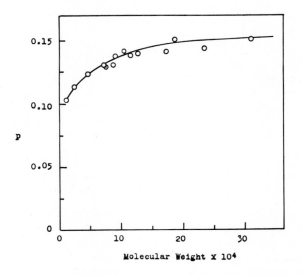

Fig. 5 — The degree of polarization of fluorescence as a
function of molecular weight, for dilute aqueous solutions
of uranine-conjugates of polyacrylamide.

The further detailed study on the chain length dependence
should reveal the inside view of the segmental motion of polymer chains in solution.

6. CONCLUSION

The fluorescence polarization method could effectively be
applied to the study of the internal structure of polymer solutions. The diffusion processes occuring in systems involving
macromolecules would be more clearly interpreted in terms of
the local viscosity of the system or the rotational relaxation
time of the particle in question.

This method is now being extended to the study of the internal structure of polymer solids under various conditions.

REFERENCES

[1] Y. Nishijima and G. Oster, J. Polymer Sci., 19, 337 (1956) .
[2] Y. Nishijima and A. Teramoto, Reports on Progress in Polymer Physics in Japan 4, 1 (1961).
[3] See, for example, (a) P. Pringsheim, "Fluorescence and Phosphorescence", Interscience Publishers Inc., New York, N.Y., 1949, Secs. 118-123, (b) T. Förster, "Fluoreszenz Organischer Verbindungen" Vandenheock und Reprecht, Gottingen, 1951, Secs. 33-37, and (c) E. J. Bowen and F. Wokes, "Fluorescence of Solutions", Longmans, Green and Co., New York, N. Y., 1953, Chapter 3.
[4] G. Oster and Y. Nishijima, J.Am.Chem.Soc.,78,1581 (1956) , see also, Y. Nishijima and G. Oster, Bull. Chem. Soc. Japan, 33, 1649 (1960) .

ENERGY TRANSFER PHENOMENA IN PURE AND MIXED CRYSTALS OF DURENE

Hartmut Kallmann, Sohachiro Hayakawa* and Peter Magnante

Physics Department, New York University

INTRODUCTION

Recently, mixed crystals of aromatic compounds have been studied because of interest in energy transfer mechanisms in molecular crystals.[1] Anthracene-naphthalene and napthalene-anthracene systems have received attention because of their remarkable energy transfer properties.[2,3,4,5]

In this paper some energy transfer phenomena in pure and mixed crystals of durene will be reported. The measurements and interpretation of absorption and fluorescence spectra of crystalline durene has been reported recently in detail by Schnepp and McClure.[6] Their interest was related to the lower excited level of the simpler aromatic compounds. Our experimental results suggest the electronic interaction among luminescence centers introduced by guest molecules and photochemical reactions.

EXPERIMENTAL PROCEDURE

Some pure and mixed crystals were prepared by the Bridgman method. The purest commercial durene was zone-purified. After more than fifty passages of purification, the durene was ready to be used as a host material for clear crystals.

The crystal slices which were used had a diameter of about 15 mm, a thickness of 1 mm, and were quite clear. The concentration of a guest material in mixed crystals was determined by measurements of the intensity of fluorescence of liquid solutions.

Photometric measurements were carried out by a photomultiplier (DuMont 6292) with a stabilized power supply and a micro-micro-ammeter (R-I-E meter, Leeds and Northrup Co.)

---

*On leave from the Tokyo Institute of Technology, Tokyo, Japan.

APPEARANCE OF GREEN EMISSION IN DURENE CRYSTALS

The fresh pure durene crystal showed no visible fluorescence. However, a visible green emission band appeared after long time irradiation by gamma-rays, X-rays, and 254 mμ ultraviolet light. Fig. 1 shows spectra of green emission under excitation by 254 mμ at room temperature and at liquid nitrogen temperature.

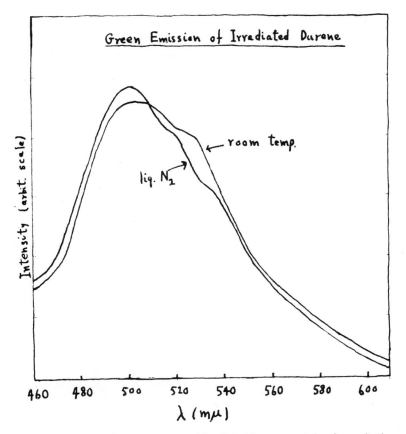

Fig. 1 — Spectrum of green emission of irradiated durene crystal under excitation by 254 mμ.

The intensity of green emission induced by 254 mμ was about proportional to the intensity of excitation as shown in Fig. 2. The bleaching of the green emission centers took place in the dark and was measured by excitation of short duration with 254 mμ every ten minutes. The green emission centers were bleached after a few hours at room temperature, but the bleaching was very slow at liquid nitrogen temperature. The build-up curves were almost independent of temperature.

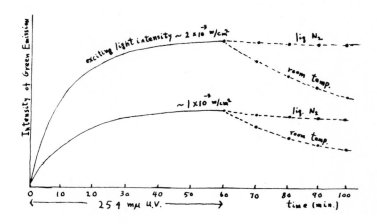

Fig. 2 — Build-up and Bleaching of green emission centers.

This green emission center is considered to be produced by some photochemical reaction. Photo-oxidation, however, is not probable because the build-up and bleaching curves were independent of the oxygen pressure. Almost the same curves were obtained in vacuum as those obtained at atmospheric pressure.

The green emission of durene crystals was never observed under excitation by 313 mμ ultraviolet light as shown in Fig. 3. Immediately after the irradiation by 254 mμ, however, the green emission centers were formed in the crystal. 365, 405, and 430 mμ also neither produced nor excited the green emission centers. We could detect no absorption spectrum corresponding to direct excitation of the centers in the range from 300 to 500 mμ, and this seems quite consistent with the above facts.

We are not sure of the nature of this center. However, this center interacted with other kinds of luminescence centers introduced by guest molecules embedded in durene crystals. These interactions are described below.

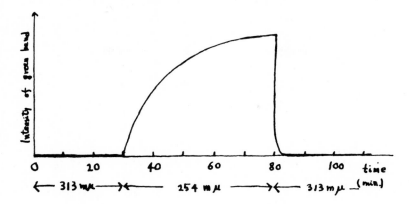

Fig. 3 — Green emission of durene under excitation by 313mμ and 254 mμ (light intensity $\sim 10^{-2}$ w/cm² for 313 mμ, $\sim 2 \times 10^{-2}$ w/cm² for 254 mμ)

ENERGY TRANSFER PHENOMENA IN ANTHRACENE-IN-DURENE

A fresh crystal of anthracene-in-durene emitted an ultra-violet durene band with a peak near 310 mμ and a blue anthracene band with a peak near 430 mμ. The concentration of anthracene in the slice we used was approximately 0.002 M%.

A green emission band was induced and the blue anthracene band was quenched during irradiation by 254 mμ. Figure 4 shows emission spectra in the fresh state, and in the irradiated state, which corresponded to the crystal exposed to 254 mμ radiation of about 1×10^{-2} w/cm² for one hour. These spectra were measured at room temperature. Dependency of the intensities of the blue and green emissions on time during excitation and during curing is shown in Figure 5(a). The respective intensities were measured separately by means of nearly monochromatic color filters (Corning glass filter #5-74 for the blue band and #4-105 for the green band). At the initial stage, only the blue emission was observed. As green emission was induced by irradiation, the blue emission was quenched. When the bleaching of the green emission took place in the dark, the blue emission recovered.

When a crystal was irradiated first with 313 mμ, it did not induce a green emission, but excited anthracene molecules as shown in Figure 5(b). Notice also that after irradiation by

254 mμ, 313 mμ light did not excite the green emission centers, although surely these centers then existed. The green
emission band was neither induced nor excited by 313, 365,
405 and 430 mμ.

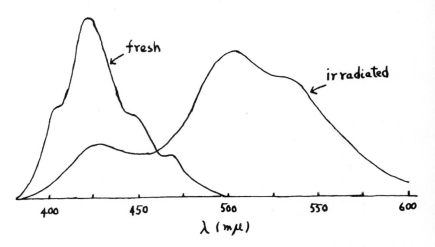

Fig. 4 — Emission spectra of a fresh and irradiated anthracene (0.002%)-indurene crystal under excitation by 254 mμ (Irradiation condition: 1 hr. in 10^{-2} w/cm^2 at 254 mμ u.v.)

It is concluded that no electronic transition between the
excited levels of anthracene and green emission center is
allowed, but a competition for sharing the energy absorbed by
the host durene crystal may take place.

ENERGY TRANSFER PHENOMENA IN NAPHTHALENE-IN-DURENE

Pure crystals of durene showed an almost undetectable
phosphorescence although powdery crystals sublimed at low
temperature and roughly treated cracked crystals showed a
fairly intense phosphorescence. But crystals of naphthalne-in-
durene showed a remarkably long phosphorescence under

excitation by 254 mμ. The fluorescence and phosphorescence
excited by alternating 254 mμ were measured by an oscilloscope. This phosphorescence was quite different from the
phosphorescence reported earlier[7] in the two following
points. The first fact is that neither 313 mμ nor 365 mμ excited phosphorescence in our case. The other is that the
decays were exponential instead of hyperbolic.

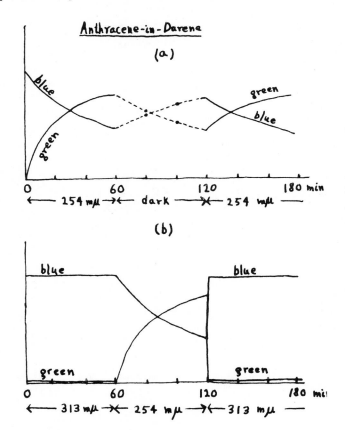

Fig. 5 — Changes of intensities of blue and green emission under
excitation by 254 mμ and 313 mμ.

After irradiation with 254 mμ, the phosphorescence consisted of two parts - a rapidly decaying part and a slowly decaying part.

The extent of the rapidly decaying part was almost propor-
tia to the intensity of the induced green fluorescence and it

produced the same spectral response as the green fluorescence. The above facts indicate that this fast part can be considered to be a delayed fluorescence and that a direct transition between trap levels induced by naphthalene and the excited
levels of the induced green centers took place.

The slowly decaying part was expressed completely by an
exponetial decay, as shown in Figure 6. The decay constant
was 0.5 second at room temperature and 1.3 second at liquid
nitrogen temperature for the used crystal with an approximate
concentration of 0.002 M% naphthalene.

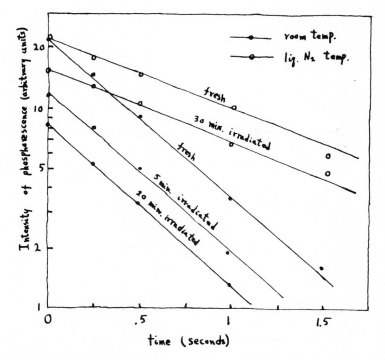

Fig. 6 — Time-dependence of phosphorescence of naphthalene-in-durene crystals.

The extent of the delayed fluorescence was much smaller at
liquid nitrogen temperature than at room temperature for
similar intensities of the induced green emission.

Therefore, it is concluded that the electronic transition between the traps introduced by naphthalene and the excited levels
of the green emission centers is quite allowed in naphthalene-
in-durene crystals contrary to anthracene-in-durene crystals.

REFERENCES

[1] Reviewed in S. I. Ganguly and N. K. Chaudbury, Rev. Mod. Phys. 31, 990 (1959).
[2] E. J. Bowen et al, Nature 153, 663 (1944), 159, 706 (1947), 164, 572 (1949); Proc. Phys. Soc. London, A62, 26 (1949).
[3] F. R. Lipsett and A. J. Dekker, Nature 173, 736 (1954).
[4] J. W. Sidman, J. Chem. Phys. 25, 115 (1956).
[5] H. C. Wolf, Z. f. Physik 145, 116 (1956).
[6] O. Schnepp and D. S. McClure, J. Chem. Phys. 30, 874 (1959).
[7] H. Kallmann, B. Kramer and E. Sucov, J. Chem. Phys. 23, 1043 (1955).

INVERSE CORRELATION BETWEEN LUMINESCENCE AND PHOTOCONDUCTIVITY OF DIAMOND

A. Halperin[*] and J. Nahum
Department of Physics, The Hebrew University of Jerusalem,
Jerusalem, Israel

ABSTRACT

The luminescence and photoconductivity excitation spectra of type I and IIa diamonds are described. The excitation spectra show a band structure near the absorption edge and at longer wavelengths. The photoconductivity excitation spectrum shows inverted peaks just at the wavelengths of maxima in the absorption and in the luminescence excitation spectrum. At temperatures above 240°K the inverted peaks in the photoconductivity excitation near the edge turn into real maxima, while those at longer wavelengths (in the region of the 415 mμ system) remain inverted.

A model is proposed to account for the results.

INTRODUCTION

Robertson, Fox and Martin[1] have classified diamonds into two types, I and II, according to their physical properties. One of the characteristic properties in this classification was the UV absorption. While the rare type II diamonds transmitted down to about 2250 Å, the type I diamonds showed a strong continuous absorption up to about 3000 Å. The same authors found type I diamonds to exhibit strong blue luminescence and only very weak photoconductivity, while type II luminesced only weakly and showed strong photoconductivity. Raman[2] and Bai[3] agreed that type II diamonds usually luminesce very weakly, if at all. They claimed, however, that there was no correlation between the absorption (due to nitrogen[4]) at 2200-3000 Å and the luminescence intensity. Moreover, they found the luminescence intensity to <u>decrease</u> with <u>increasing</u> absorption at 2200-3000 Å.

---

*Now at Mellon Institute, Pittsburgh, Pa. While on leave from the Hebrew University of Jerusalem.

Only very recently it has been realized by Male,[5] and independently in our laboratory,[6] that the UV excited luminescence depended rather on a fine structure in the absorption at 2200-2500 Å and not on the nitrogen absorption. The structure near the edge is difficult to detect in type I diamonds, where it is completely covered by the stronger nitrogen absorption. It is, however, revealed clearly in the luminescence excitation spectrum as shown below.

Still less clear was the situation with regard to the photoconductivity excitation spectra. Various authors[1, 7, 8, 9] obtained maxima of the photocurrents at various wavelengths between 2200 and 2450 Å. A secondary maximum has been found[1,7] near 3400 Å. Neither of these maxima could be correlated to maxima in the excitation of the luminescence.

Careful examination of both the luminescence and photoconductivity excitation spectra carried out in the present work revealed interesting relations between the two. Some of the results, particularly on the luminescence, were reported previously.[6] These will therefore be given only briefly in the present paper, in which the relation between the luminescence and photoconductivity will be emphasized.

The present work deals with type I and type IIa or intermediate diamonds.[10] This excludes the semiconducting type IIb diamonds. The latter do not show the phenomena described in the present work. Some of their properties were described in a previous report.[11]

EXPERIMENTAL

The experimental arrangements were as described previously.[6] The combination of the light-source, monochromator and detector enabled one to obtain luminescence excitation spectra with a resolution of about 0.2 mμ through the whole range of 210-420 mμ. The resolution in the photoconductivity measurements was nearly the same near the absorption edge (at about 220 mμ) but was much worse at longer wavelengths at which the photoconductivity response was much lower.

Photoconductivity measurements were carried out in a d.c. circuit with heat resistant silver-paint electrodes painted on the diamond. Polarization effects were observed when switching the field on or off. Measurements were taken only when stationary currents were reached, and spectra were always scanned from longer to shorter wavelengths.

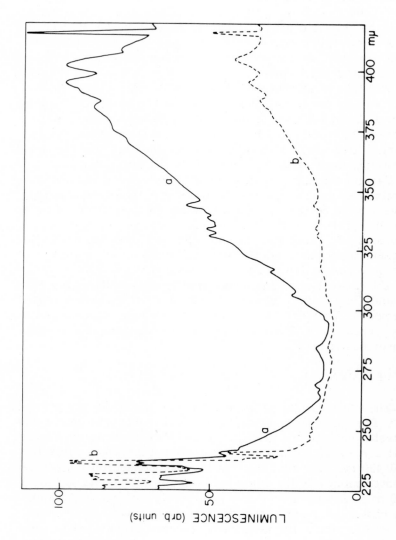

Fig. 1 – Typical luminescence excitation spectra at 77°K for a type I diamond (sample TI, curve a) and an intermediate one (sample T5, curve b).

RESULTS

Fig. 1 shows two typical luminescence excitation spectra as obtained at 77°K. Curve a describes the spectrum for a type I diamond (sample T1), and curve b for an intermediate[10] (sample T5), which is a type IIa showing a band structure in absorption at 225-240 mμ.

At wavelengths around 400 mμ the excitation spectra reproduce the so called[10] 415 mμ absorption system. Diamond T1 actually showed this system in absorption. The absorption of T5, however, was too weak in this region to be detected directly.

Sharp bands appear in the excitation spectra near the absorption edge. These bands were found[6] to fit the absorption of the intermediate diamond (T5) in this region. The absorption could not be observed directly in type I because of the strong nitrogen absorption.

We shall describe now the relation between luminescence and photoconductivity. Fig. 2a shows the structure near the absorption edge in the excitation of the luminescence (curve L) and the photoconductivity (curve P'), both for T5 at 77°K. Curve P gives the photoconductivity response of the same diamond but at 300°K. The excitation spectrum of the thermoluminescence glow peak at 150°K of the same diamond is given in Fig. 2b.

The interesting feature of the curves is that minima appear in P' and in Fig. 2b at 230, 236 and 240 mμ which are just the wavelengths of the main maxima in L. The inverted peaks in the photoconductivity appear only on excitation at low temperatures. At higher temperatures the minima are reduced until a nearly smooth curve is obtained at 240°K. At still higher temperatures maxima appear at the same wavelengths as shown in Fig. 2a curve P.

Longer wavelengths beyond 250 mμ are much less effective in producing photoconductivity even in type I diamonds which absorb strongly in this region. Fig. 3 shows photoconductivity excitation spectra for the wavelength range 200-450 mμ for a type I (T3, curve a) and a type IIa diamond (T5, curve b) - both on excitation at 77°K. The curves show a broad maximum at 340 mμ as reported by earlier workers[1,7]. Closer examination, however, shows a finer structure. This appears more clearly in Fig. 4 obtained with exciting light intensities increased by a factor of 25. Fig. 4 gives the absorption A, luminescence excitation L, and photoconductivity excitation P, all as obtained at 77°K with a type I diamond. Type IIa diamonds gave similar results except for the absorption which is negligibly small in this region in type IIa. We have again inverted peaks in the photoconductivity curves, and they follow almost exactly the maxima in A and L. There is one exception, at 393 mμ, where a maximum appears in the photoconductivity. This maximum nearly disappears at room temperature (see Fig. 5).

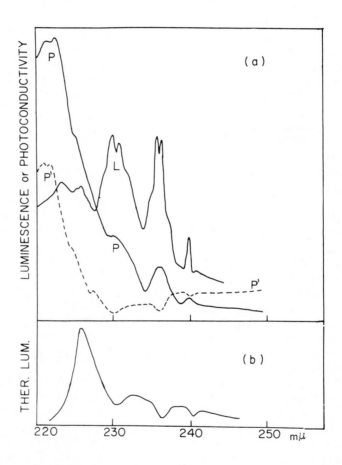

Fig. 2a — Structure near the absorption edge in the excitation spec-tra: L - luminescence at 77°K, P' - photoconductivity at 77°K, and P - photoconductivity at 300°K. All for sample T5.

Fig. 2b — Excitation spectrum for the thermoluminescence peak at 150°K of sample T5, excited at 77°K.

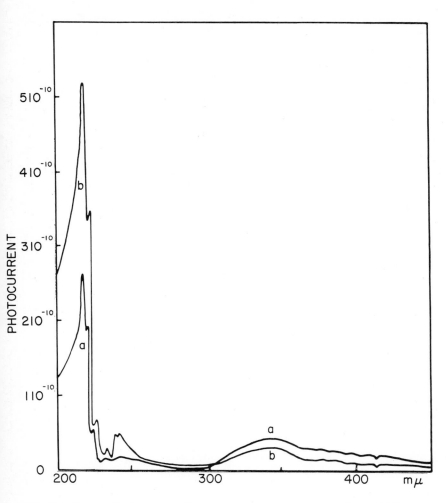

Fig. 3 — Photoconductivity excitation spectra for: curve a - a type I diamond (T3); curve b - an intermediate diamond (T5). Both at 77°K.

The effect of temperature on the inverted peaks in this region differs from that near the edge. This is shown in Fig. 5, where the luminescence and photoconductivity response curves are given (for T3) as obtained at 77, 300 and 350°K. Measurements at still higher temperatures were difficult because of the high dark currents at these temperatures. It is clear from Fig. 5 that, unlike the behavior near the edge, the 415 mμ system of minima remains inverted at least up to 350°K.

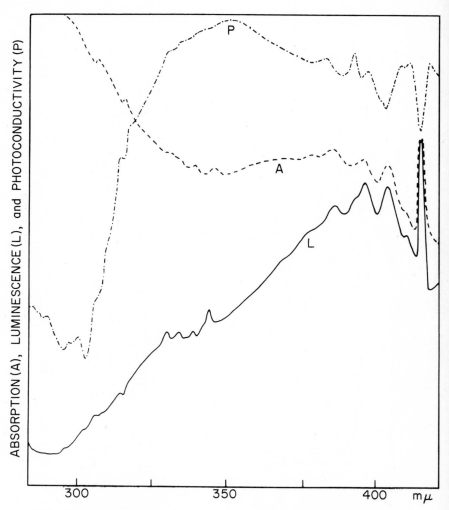

Fig. 4 – Comparison of absorption A, luminescence excitation L, and photoconductivity excitation P, all for a type I diamond at 77°K.

The opposite behavior of the luminescence and photocon-ductivity appears also in their temperature dependence. This is shown in Fig. 6, where the temperature dependence is given for two exciting wavelengths, one (236 mμ) to represent the be-havior for excitation near the edge, and the other (400 mμ) to represent longer wavelengths (250-420 mμ). We see that for excitation near the edge the luminescence (upper part of Fig. 6

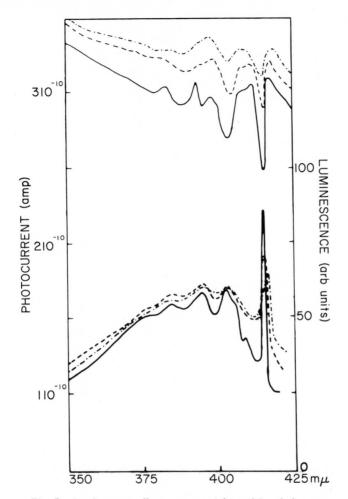

Fig. 5 — Luminescence (lower curves, right scale) and photoconductivity (upper curves, left scale) excitation spectra of a type I diamond (T3) at various temperatures.
————at 77°K, -----------at 300°K, and -.-.-.-.-.-at 350°K.

drops almost to zero, while the photoconductivity (lower part of Fig. 6) increases rapidly on warming the crystal from 200 to 400°K. On the other hand, on excitation with longer wavelengths both the luminescence and photoconductivity are nearly temperature independent up to above 400°K, a fact which is evident also from the curves in Fig. 5.

DISCUSSION

As was already pointed out by Pant,[9] there is a clear inverse correlation between photoconductivity and luminescence in diamond. Pant's statement was based on comparison of luminescence and photoconductivity in different diamonds. The present work extends this inverse relation to include effects of wavelength and temperature on luminescence and photoconductivity in the same diamond. The observations indicate a competition between the two phenomena in which one increases at the expense of a decrease in the other. This can help in

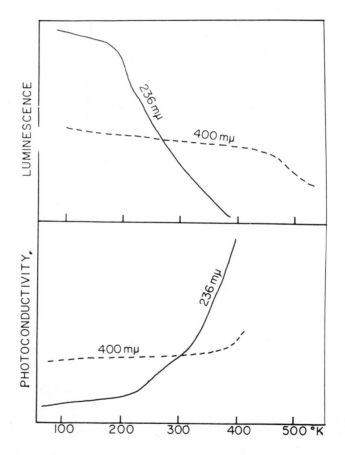

Fig. 6 — Temperature dependence of the luminescence (upper curves) and photoconductivity (lower curves) of sample T3 (type I) excited with 236 and 400 mμ.

establishing a model for the transitions involved. The presence of photoconductivity implies that free carriers are involved. Because of the nearly equal mobilities of electrons and
holes in diamond[12] either free electrons in the conduction band
or free positive holes might be responsible for the photoconductivity. For the sake of the present discussion we shall assume
that the photocurrent is carried by electrons in the conduction band.

As was already discussed previously[6] we assume that the
fine structure near the edge is due to impurity excitons.[13]

Fig. 7 is a schematic model of the transitions involved.
Defect levels D are assumed to exist in the forbidden gap near
the valence band. Exciting light with energy insufficient for
direct excitation of electrons at D up to the conduction band,
may still contribute to the photoconductivity by indirect transitions to the conduction band by phonon interaction.[14] If, however,

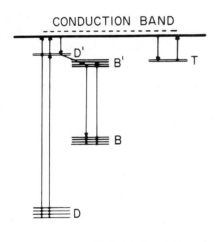

Fig. 7 — A schematic model of the transitions involved in the process of
luminescence (blue), photoconductivity
and thermoluminescence.

the exciting light is of a wavelength which fits one of the transitions D → D', the electron may reach the excited state B'
of the blue luminescence center and emit luminescence on recombination at B. The process should of course involve emptying of B by a transition B → D. Electrons available for luminescence by this process will not controbute to the photoconductivity, which explains the minima in the photoconductivity
excitation spectra at low temperatures. At higher temperatures, thermal ionization of the excited electrons at D' becomes important, and causes the rise in photoconductivity and

the decrease in luminescence with increasing temperature as observed. When the temperature is high enough practically all the electrons will be ionized, and one should then expect the photoconductivity to be proportional to the absorbed energy; the photoconductivity response curve should then show maxima fitting the absorption curves as in Fig. 2a curve P.

This mechanism is supported also by the thermoluminescence excitation spectrum (Fig. 2b). Excitation of the thermoluminescence means filling up the trapping levels T. For this to be accomplished one has to excite the electrons up to the conduction band, which explains why the thermoluminescence excitation spectrum follows that of the photoconductivity at the wavelengths of the fine structure near the edge.

At wavelengths of the 415 mμ absorption system excitation produces the transitions B → B' and the luminescence is obtained by return to the ground state. The appearance of minima in the photoconductivity response curve in this region can again be explained assuming indirect transitions to the conduction band. The lifetime of the excited electrons at B' is however very short, and the probability for recombination at the center is still high compared to the probability for thermal ionization even at 350°K. The photoconductivity excitation spectrum retains the minima as observed (Fig. 5). The temperature independence of the luminescence and photoconductivity for excitation with wavelengths within the 415 mμ absorption system fits into the described picture.

It is worth noting that according to the given model the levels D' and B' should be within a phonon energy distance from the conduction band. This energy limit seems to be about 0.23 eV[15].

REFERENCES

[1] R. Robertson, J.J. Fox and A.E. Martin, Trans.Roy.Soc. (London) A263, 463 (1934).

[2] C.V. Raman, Proc. Indian Acad. Sci. A19, 199 (1944).

[3] K.S. Bai, Proc. Indian Acad. Sci. A19, 253 (1944).

[4] W. Kaiser and W. L. Bond Phys. Rev. 115, 857 (1959).

[5] J. C. Male, Proc. Phys. Soc. (London) 77, 869 (1961).

[6] J. Nahum and A. Halperin, J. Phys. Chem. Solids, in press.

[7] B. Gudden and R. W. Pohl, Z. Phys 17, 331 (1923).

[8] H. Lenz, Ann. Phys. Lpz. 83, 941 (1927).

[9] D. D. Pant, Proc. Indian Acad. Sci. A19, 314, 325 (1944).

[10] C. D. Clark, R.W. Ditchburn and H.B. Dyer, Proc.Roy.Soc. (London) A234, 363 (1956).

[11] A. Halperin and J. Nahum, J.Phys.Chem.Solids 18, 297 (1961).

[12] T.S. Moss, Optical Properties of Semiconductors, p. 107, Butterworth's Scientific Publications, London (1959).

[13] D.G. Thomas and J.J. Hopfield, Phys.Rev. 116, 573 (1959).

[14] See for example: R.H. Bube, Photoconductivity of Solids, p. 212, John Wiley and Sons, Inc., New York (1960).

[15] See reference 12, p. 111.

THEORY OF WEAK-FIELD EPR TRANSITIONS AMONG THE SUBLEVELS OF THE LOWEST TRIPLET STATE OF ETHYLENE

P. Csavinszky

General Dynamics/Electronics, Rochester, New York

I. INTRODUCTION

Since the observation of electron paramagnetic resonance in the lowest triplet state of naphthalene by Hutchison and Mangum[1,2] there has been a renewed interest in the nature of the paramagnetic states of organic molecules. These authors, and independently van der Waals and de Groot,[3] have found that the lowest triplet level of naphthalene is split into three distinct levels even in the absence of a magnetic field. The theory of the zero-field splittings has been worked on by several authors[4-7] and explained by the spin-spin interaction among the π-electrons. In the EPR experiments[1,2,6] on the naphthalene system linearly polarized r.f. magnetic fields were applied and the constant magnetic field was such that the magnitude of the spin-spin interaction was comparable to or smaller than, the spin-constant magnetic field interaction.

In contrast to the above, the present work investigates how the lowest triplet state of linear hydrocarbon molecules with one double bond is expected to behave in EPR experiments when circularly polarized r.f. fields are applied and the spin-constant magnetic field interaction is smaller than the spin-spin interaction. The approach is based on perturbation theory and the ethylene molecule is discussed in the π-electron approximation. The coordinate system is chosen in such a way that the C-C direction in the ethylene molecule coincides with the z-direction.

II. THEORY

1. <u>Spin-spin Interaction</u>. The term scheme of ethylene, as shown schematically in Fig. 1, consist of a sequence of singlet levels, denoted by S, S', S'',..., and a sequence of triplet levels, denoted by T, T', T'',.... It is assumed that the corresponding orthonormal orbital wave functions $\psi_S(O)$, $\psi_{S'}(O)$,..., $\psi_T(O)$, $\psi_{T'}(O)$ and energy eigenvalues W_S, $W_{S'}$,..., W_T, $W_{T'}$,... are

known and are associated with a Hamiltonian H. Throughout this work the argument(O)refers to all spatial (orbital) variables of a wave function.

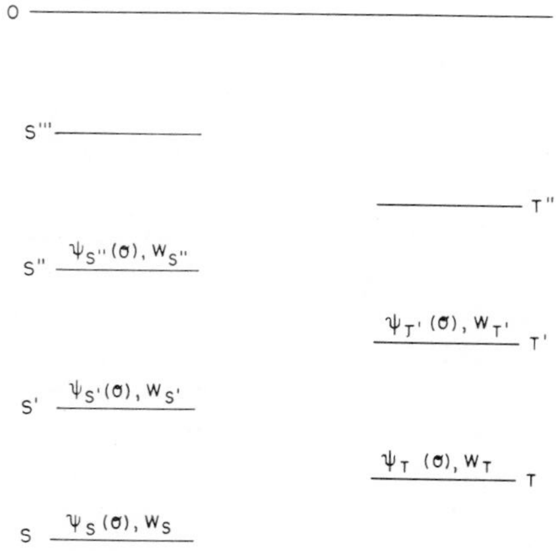

Fig. 1 — Energy level scheme of the ethylene molecule.

The spin-spin interaction operator[8] (in atomic units) is given by

$$H_{SS} = g^2 \beta_0^2 \left[(\overline{S}_1 \cdot \overline{S}_2) \, r_{12}^2 - 3(\overline{S}_1 \cdot \overline{r}_{12})(\overline{S}_2 \cdot \overline{r}_{12}) \right] r_{12}^{-5} , \qquad (1)$$

where g is the spectroscopic splitting factor, β_0 is the Bohr magneton and r_{12} is the distance between electrons 1 and 2 of spins S_1 and S_2.

In the π-electron approximation the sublevel wave functions of the lowest degenerate triplet state can be written as products of an orbital and a spin wave function

$$\Psi_{T1} = \psi_T(\text{O}) \times \alpha(1)\,\alpha(2) \qquad\qquad\qquad (2)$$

$$\Psi_{T2} = \psi_T(\text{O}) \times \beta(1)\,\beta(2)$$

$$\Psi_{T3} = \psi_T(\text{O}) \times 1/\sqrt{2}\,[\alpha(1)\,\beta(2) + \beta(1)\,\alpha(2)],$$

where α and β are the customary one-electron spin wave functions.

By carrying out a first-order degenerate perturbation calculation[9] one finds that the degeneracy is resolved and that the first order corrections to W_T are

$$W_{T1}^{SS\,(1)} = -\frac{1}{2}g^2\beta_0^2\,(D + E)$$

$$W_{T2}^{SS\,(1)} = -\frac{1}{2}g^2\beta_0^2\,(D - E) \tag{3}$$

$$W_{T3}^{SS\,(1)} = g^2\beta_0^2\,D \, ,$$

where

$$D = \,<\psi_T(0)\left|\frac{1}{2}\frac{3z_{12}^2 - r_{12}^2}{r_{12}^5}\right|\psi_T(0)> \tag{4}$$

$$E = \,<\psi_T(0)\left|\frac{3}{2}\frac{x_{12}^2 - y_{12}^2}{r_{12}^5}\right|\psi_T(0)>$$

The corresponding zeroth-order wave functions are found to be

$$\phi_{T1}^{(0)} = \frac{1}{\sqrt{2}}\,(\Psi_{T1} + \Psi_{T2}) = \psi_T(0)\times\frac{1}{\sqrt{2}}\,[\,\alpha(1)\,\alpha(2) + \beta(1)\,\beta(2)\,]$$

$$\phi_{T2}^{(0)} = \frac{1}{\sqrt{2}}\,(\Psi_{T1} - \Psi_{T2}) = \psi_T(0)\times\frac{1}{\sqrt{2}}\,[\,\alpha(1)\,\alpha(2) - \beta(1)\,\beta(2)\,]$$

$$\phi_{T3}^{(0)} = \Psi_{T3} = \psi_T(0)\times\frac{1}{\sqrt{2}}\,[\,\alpha(1)\,\beta(2) + \beta(1)\,\alpha(2)\,]. \tag{5}$$

It is seen from the above wave functions, which are approximate solutions of the operator $H + H_{SS}$ belonging to the energy levels $W_T + W_{T1}^{SS(1)}$, $W_T + W_{T2}^{SS(1)}$ and $W_T + W_{T3}^{SS\,(1)}$, that the effect of spin-spin interaction consists in mixing the "spin-up" and "spin-down" states.

2. Spin-Constant Magnetic Field Interaction. If a constant magnetic field is applied along the z-direction, for instance, then the interaction operator of the field with the spin magnetic moments is given by[10]

$$H_{sm}^{(z)} = -g\beta_0 H_z\,(S_{1z} + S_{2z})\,, \tag{6}$$

where the field, H_z, is measured in oersteds.

Application of non-degenerate perturbation theory[11] shows that the first-order energy corrections to the sublevels are zero. In second order one finds for the correction terms

$$^{(z)}W_{T1}^{Sm\,(2)} = -\frac{H_z^2}{E}$$

$$^{(z)}W_{T2}^{Sm\,(2)} = \frac{H_z^2}{E} \tag{7}$$

$$^{(z)}W_{T3}^{Sm(2)} = 0 .$$

The lowest triplet sublevel wave functions, correct to first order, are found to be

$$\chi_{T1}^{(z)} = \phi_{T1}^{(0)} + \Omega_z\,\phi_{T2}^{(0)} = \psi_T(O) \times \frac{1}{\sqrt{2}}[(1+\Omega_z)\,\alpha(1)\,\alpha(2) +$$

$$+ (1-\Omega_z)\,\beta(1)\,\beta(2)]$$

$$\chi_{T2}^{(z)} = \phi_{T2}^{(0)} - \Omega_z\,\phi_{T1}^{(0)} = \psi_T(O) \times \frac{1}{\sqrt{2}}[(1-\Omega_z)\,\alpha(1)\,\alpha(2) -$$

$$- (1+\Omega_z)\,\beta(1)\,\beta(2)] \tag{8}$$

$$\chi_{T3}^{(z)} = \phi_{T3}^{(0)} = \psi_T(O) \times \frac{1}{\sqrt{2}}[\alpha(1)\,\beta(2) + \beta(1)\,\alpha(2)] ,$$

where

$$\Omega_z = \frac{H_z}{g\beta_0 E} .$$

It is seen from Equation (8) that the effect of the constant magnetic field consists in giving different weights to the "spin up" and "spin-down" states. These wave functions are approximate solutions of the operator $H + H_{SS} + H_{Sm}^{(z)}$ and belong to the energy levels

$$W_{T1}^{(z)} = W_T + W_{T1}^{SS\,(1)} + {}^{(z)}W_{T1}^{Sm(2)} = W_T - \frac{1}{2}\,g^2\beta_0^2(D+E) - \frac{H_z^2}{E}$$

$$W_{T2}^{(z)} = W_T + W_{T2}^{SS\,(1)} + {}^{(z)}W_{T2}^{Sm\,(2)} = W_T - \frac{1}{2}\,g^2\beta_0^2(D-E) + \frac{H_z^2}{E}$$

$$W_{T3}^{(z)} = W_T + W_{T3}^{SS\,(1)} + {}^{(z)}W_{T3}^{Sm(2)} = W_T + g^2\beta_0^2\,D. \tag{9}$$

One infers from Equation (9) that the sequence of the energy sublevels depends on the sign of the quantities D and E. Paramagnetic resonance experiments on the "naphthalene-in-durene" system[1,2] which can be described[4] by the same spin Hamiltonian as ethylene, have led to the conclusion that D and E have opposite signs. The schematic sequence of the energy levels for the cases $D > 0$, $E < 0$ and $D < 0$, $E > 0$ respectively is illustrated in Fig. 2 cases a and b.

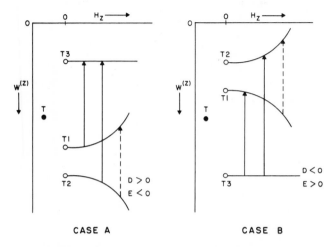

CASE A   CASE B

Fig. 2 — Schematic representation of the sequence of the lowest triplet sub-levels of ethylene in a constant magnetic field oriented along the z-axis. Full circles represent the degenerate triplet level. Open circles represent the positions of the sub-levels in zero magnetic field after the degeneracy is removed by spin-spin interaction. The solid arrows represent the transitions realizable in absorption and the broken arrows represent the transitions forbidden by selection rules.

3. Spin - r.f. Magnetic Field Interaction. Considering now a circularly polarized r.f. magnetic field with its plane of polarization in the (x,y) plane, its interaction with the spin magnetic moment is described by the operator

$$H_{S-r.f.m}^{(x,y)} = G(t) \left[(S_{1x} + S_{2x}) \pm i (S_{1y} + S_{2y}) \right],$$ (10)

where i is the imaginary unit and, for the present purposes, the time dependent quantity $G(t)$ need not be specified further.

It is seen from Fig. 2 case b, that for $E > 0$ the possible transitions in absorption are $T3 \rightarrow T1$, $T3 \rightarrow T2$ and $T1 \rightarrow T2$. Using Equations (8) and (10) one finds for the transition probabilities

$$P_{31}^{\pm} = \left| < \chi_{T3}^{(z)} \left| H_{S-r.f.m}^{(x,y)} \right| \chi_{T1}^{(z)} > \right|^2 = \left| G \left(1 \mp \frac{H_z}{g \beta_0 |E|} \right) \right|^2 ,$$

$$P_{32}^{\pm} = \left| < \chi_{T3}^{(z)} \left| H_{S-r.f.m}^{(x,y)} \right| \chi_{T2}^{(z)} > \right|^2 = \left| G\left(\mp 1 - \frac{H_z}{g\beta_0\,|E|}\right) \right|^2$$

$$P_{12}^{\pm} = \left| < \chi_{T1}^{(z)} \left| H_{S-r.f.m}^{(x,y)} \right| \chi_{T2}^{(z)} > \right|^2 = 0,$$

(11)

which shows that the $T1 \to T2$ transition is forbidden. The $\pm$ signs in Equations (10) and (11) correspond to the two possibilities of circular polarization.

The total energy absorbed in a transition, that is the intensity of a transition, is evidently

$$I = N(h\nu)\,P,$$

where N is the number of molecules capable of making the transition whose probability is P and which involves a quantum of energy $h\nu$.

On this basis one can write the ratio of the intensity of a transition induced by a clockwise (+) polarized r.f. magnetic field to that of the same transition induced by an anti-clockwise (−) polarized field as

$$\frac{I_{31}^{+}(+E)}{I_{31}^{-}(+E)} = \frac{N_{31}^{+}(h\nu_{31})P_{31}^{+}}{N_{31}^{-}(h\nu_{31})P_{31}^{-}} = \frac{N_{31}^{+}\left| 1 - \dfrac{H_z}{g\beta_0|E|} \right|^2}{N_{31}^{-}\left| 1 + \dfrac{H_z}{g\beta_0|E|} \right|^2}$$

$$\frac{I_{32}^{+}(+E)}{I_{32}^{-}(+E)} = \frac{N_{32}^{+}(h\nu_{32})P_{32}^{+}}{N_{32}^{-}(h\nu_{32})P_{32}^{-}} = \frac{N_{32}^{+}\left| 1 + \dfrac{H_z}{g\beta_0|E|} \right|^2}{N_{32}^{-}\left| 1 - \dfrac{H_z}{g\beta_0|E|} \right|^2}$$

(12)

If one assumes now that $N_{31}^{+} = N_{31}^{-}$ and $N_{32}^{+} = N_{32}^{-}$ then it follows from Equation (12) that

$$\frac{I_{31}^{+}(+E)}{I_{31}^{-}(+E)} = \frac{1}{\dfrac{I_{32}^{+}(+E)}{I_{32}^{-}(+E)}} \quad ,$$

(13)

which offers an interesting point for experimental verification.

One can justify the equating of N_j^+ to N_j^- ($j = 31,32$) as follows. Suppose the experiment is carried out on a sample which is a dilute solid solution of ethylene-type molecules in an organic host crystal. To populate the lowest triplet sublevels the sample is illuminated by a light source. Upon illumination the guest molecules are excited from their singlet ground states (S) into one of their higher lying excited singlet states (S'', S''' ...). From these states the molecules usually return to the first excited singlet state (S') by a radiationless transition. The lowest singlet state, in turn, looses its population by a non-radiative transition to the first excited triplet state (T). If this mechanism leads to a Boltzmann-type distribution of population over the sublevels then the $T3 \rightarrow T1$ and $T3 \rightarrow T2$ transitions are realizable in absorption. In this case if one uses the sample repeatedly under "identical" excitation conditions then always the same number of molecules will be involved in a given transition irrespective of the polarization direction of the inducing r.f. magnetic field.

Finally, it is mentioned that in the case of $E < 0$, shown in Fig. 2 case a, the $T1 \rightarrow T3$ and $T2 \rightarrow T3$ transitions are possible and calculation shows that

$$\frac{I_{13}^+(-E)}{I_{13}^-(-E)} = \frac{1}{\dfrac{I_{23}^+(-E)}{I_{23}^-(-E)}} \tag{14}$$

It is, therefore, concluded that the relations between the intensities in the cases considered are not dependent on the sign of D and E.

III. DISCUSSION

The present treatment of EPR transitions is restricted to the case of a weak constant magnetic field. The range of validity can be estimated by considering that the spin-spin interaction energy should be larger than the spin-magnetic field interaction energy. Using Equations (3) and (7) the conditions for this can be written as

$$\frac{1}{2} g^2 \beta_0^2 \left| D + E \right| > \frac{H_z^2}{|E|}$$

$$\frac{1}{2} g^2 \beta_0^2 \mid D - E \mid > \frac{H_z^2}{\mid E \mid}$$

$$g^2 \beta_0^2 \mid D \mid > 0 \, . \tag{15}$$

The last one of the above relations is always satisfied. If one considers that Gouterman and Moffitt[4] have calculated that $\mid D \mid \gg \mid E \mid$, then, one can approximate both $\mid D + E \mid$ and $\mid D - E \mid$ by D. In this case the first two relations in Equation (15) reduce to

$$\frac{1}{2} g^2 \beta_0^2 \mid D \mid \mid E \mid > H_z^2 \, ,$$

which upon substitution of numerical values[4] (using $g = 2$) shows that the inequality is satisfied as long as the constant magnetic field is weaker than 760 oersteds.

REFERENCES

[1] C. A. Hutchison, Jr., and B. W. Mangum, J. Chem. Phys. 29, 952 (1958).
[2] C. A. Hutchison, Jr., and B. W. Mangum, J. Chem. Phys. 34, 908 (1961).
[3] J.H. van der Waals and M. S. deGroot, Mol. Phys. 3, 190 (1960).
[4] M. Gouterman and W. Moffitt, J. Chem. Phys. 30, 1107 (1959).
[5] M. Gouterman, J. Chem. Phys. 30, 1369 (1959).
[6] J. H. van der Waals and M. S. de Groot, Mol. Phys. 2, 333 (1959).
[7] R. McWeeny, J. Chem. Phys. 34, 399 (1961).
[8] M. Tinkham and P. Strandberg, Phys. Rev. 97, 937 (1955).
[9] H. Eyring, J. Walter and G. E. Kimball, Quantum Chemistry, (John Wiley and Sons, Inc., New York, 1947) p. 96ff.
[10] See Ref. 9 p. 127
[11] See Ref. 9 p. 92ff.

THE FRANCK-CONDON PRINCIPLE APPLIED TO SOLUTIONS
OF AROMATIC COMPOUNDS

E. Lippert
Technische Hochschule, Stuttgart

I should like to make some comment on the papers of the morning session. The first is concerned with the Franck-Condon Principle and relaxation mechanisms and their temperature dependence.

Let us consider p-cyano-dimethylaniline. The electronic structure of this compound is composed mainly of two resonance structures, a non-polar one and a highly polar one with a positive charge on the amino nitrogen and a negative charge on the cyano nitrogen. The molecule emits a fluorescence band which is polarized in the direction of the long axis.

From a plot of the Stokes red shift, the absorption frequency minus the fluorescence frequency, as plotted over the orientation polarization of the solvent, one can calculate the dipole moment of the excited state. We have done this and found that in the first excited singlet state the polar structure amounts to about 50%. This compound emits not only one fluorescence band, the long wavelength band, but it possesses also a second fluorescence band which is shown in Fig. 1. The full line is the fluorescence spectrum at room temperature and the dotted line is the fluorescence spectrum at nearly liquid nitrogen temperature. In cooling, this second fluorescence band increases in intensity, but the frequency position is almost the same at all temperatures. With this change in temperature the long wavelength absorption band is not altered very much. When the temperature is lowered, the absorption band is shifted slightly towards the red, as it is commonly the case. The blue fluorescence band remains nearly constant. The blue fluorescent band is that which is polarized perpendicular to the long axis, the short axis being in the plane of the molecule. It is emitted by the state ^1L_b. The long axis polarized fluorescence band has a special temperature dependence. In cooling, the Stokes red shift is increased until it reaches a maximum value, which means the fluorescence frequency reaches a minimum value, and then increases again. At high temperatures thermal motion acts against the orientation of the polar solvent molecules, and at very low temperatures the relaxation times become too long to allow orientation to take place within the lifetime of the excited molecule. We found that as the lifetimes of the excited singlet states are always of the order of 10^{-9} sec, the temperature position of this minimum or maximum depends only on the solvent, that is, on the first solvent relaxation time, and does not depend on the nature of the compound we investigate.

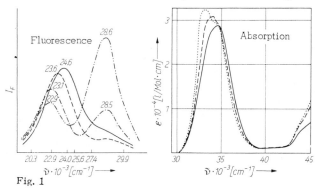

Fig. 1

The mechanism is the following. The transition to ^1L_a has a higher transition moment than that to ^1L_b, and the absorption bands to ^1L_b and ^1L_a are nearly at the same frequency position. The energy of ^1L_a is a little higher. Thus, the exciting light brings the molecule first to the state ^1L_a, afterwards internal conversion takes place, first to the lowest singlet state in the non-polar solvent, that is ^1L_b. Now the ^1L_b fluorescence may be emitted, but when the temperature is high enough, a certain activation energy might be supplied to the system. Then orientation takes place from near disorientation to orientation around the high dipole of the excited molecule and the result is a high interaction energy; and the state ^1L_a of the system, and not of the molecule itself, now is lower, and we have a red fluorescence from the state ^1L_a. After the emission process the system returns to its original state. Now what we have to expect is that, when temperature is lowered, we have less a fluorescence and more and more b fluorescence, since the activation energy is no longer supplied. When raising the temperature, the a fluorescence increases more and more in intensity. From the slope of the plot of the logarithm of the intensity ration of the a to the b fluorescence versus the inverse temperature, we can calculate the activation energy, which is in accordance with the activation energy which one gets if one plots the logarithm of the viscosity versus the reciprocal temperature. At higher temperatures the intensity ratio decreases again. That means at higher temperatures the intensity of the a band decreases faster than that of the b band because of thermal quenching processes which quench the a fluorescence in addition to the b fluorescence, since for both emission processes the molecule had first been in the state ^1L_b and could then emit either the b fluorescence, or the a fluorescence from the ^1L_a equilibrium state.

REFERENCE

E. Lippert et al., Angewandte Chemie 73, (1961) 659; European Conference on Molecular Spectroscopy, Bologna (1959), H.W. Thompson, Ed., Pergamon Press, London (1962).

$\pi^* - n$ TRANSITIONS

E. Lippert

Technische Hochschule, Stuttgart

The compound I should like to deal with is 9, 10-diaza phenanthrene. As you know neither quinoline, nor pyridazine, nor ethyl benzene in its cis- or trans-form emit fluorescent light, but this compound does. The dotted line in Fig. 1 is the absorption spectrum of phenathrene and the full line is the absorption spectrum of 9,10-diaza phenanthrene. You see that in the shorter wavelength part the spectra are rather similar, the transition to L_b is somewhat more intense, but then in addition there occurs this $\pi^* \leftarrow n$ absorption band. Now in the figure we have also plotted the light with which we have excited the fluorescence of this diaza compound: mercury 313, 365, 404 and 435 mμ.

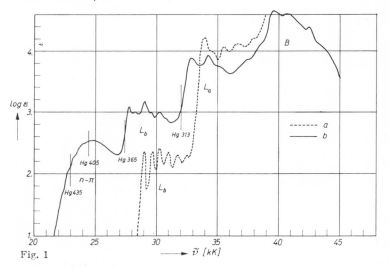

Fig. 1

If one adds ethanol to an inert solvent, then the $\pi^* \leftarrow n$ absorption band is shifted to the blue, but the $\pi^* \leftarrow n$ transition is still situated at the long wavelength side of the absorption band with respect to L_b. The maximum extinction coefficient is about 400, which means that this is an absorption to a singlet state and not to a triplet state. On the other hand, you can also see that the emission is nearly a mirror image of the absorption. Thus, it is the same transition in emission and means it is the $\pi^* \to n$ fluorescence (Fig. 2).

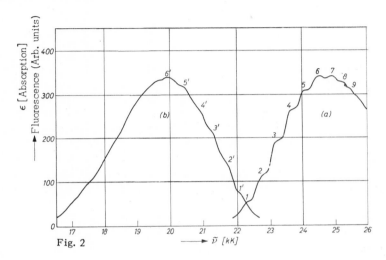

Fig. 2

The phosphorescence band and the fluorescence band taken at low temperatures are seperated very much from one another, one being at 21,000 wave numbers and the other at 13,000 wave numbers. That means that the energy of the $^3(\pi^*,\pi)$ triplet level and of the energy of the $^1(n,\pi^*)$ excited singlet level show a marked difference. Thus, the $n \leftarrow \pi$ fluorescence may compete with the radiationless transition, as there will be little mixing between these states.

REFERENCE

E. Lippert et al., Angewandte Chemie, 73, 659 (1961). Z. f. Physik. Chemie N. F. (1962) in press.

PHOTOCONDUCTIVITY IN ORGANIC MATERIALS

M. Pope
Physics Department, New York University

What I shall talk about represents the work of Dr. Kallmann and myself. I am sure that after McGlynn's talk on photocon-ductivity, everyone is convinced that excitation to the triplet state is not a necessary prerequisite for the creation of car-riers. I would like to sell you on the idea that excitation to the singlet state is not necessary either.

More seriously, in this brief period I should like to address myself to some aspects of conductivity in organic materials, in particular bulk conductivity as distinguished from surface conductivity.

Two problems face workers in this field. The first is the apparent discrepancy between the energy requirements for ionization in the solid crystal and the much lower optical ener-gy threshold at which conductivity starts. For example, in solid anthracene the ionization energy is about 5.6 e.v. while the optical threshold for photoconductivity is about 3.3 e.v. The second problem relates to the method by which the carriers move inside the crystal from one molecule to the other, from óne side of the crystal to the other.

Much effort has been expended in an analysis of the possible energy states within the crystal with the goal of finding some energy levels inside the crystal that can make photoconductivity understandable. These efforts still continue. In our opinion, however, most, if not all, of the energy requirements for car-rier creation are provided at the surface of the crystal by an electrode-crystal interaction.[1]

As for the second problem, we in our laboratory still have no definite results as yet, but recently, Le Blanc has succeeded in providing a rational basis for a conductivity band picture for anthracene. This band appears to have a width of less than kT which would account for the low mobility observed by Kepler.[2]

Before proceeding, some definitions are in order. In these photoconductivity measurements, the highly absorbed light is shone on one side of the crystal. Polarity of current is then determined from that side; if the illuminated side is at a positive potential, then the current which flows is called i^+; if the illuminated side is at a negative potential, that current is called i^-. The current i^- can be caused either by a true flow of electrons from the illuminated side or by a flow of holes from the opposite side caused by fluorescent light, or both. We have more to say about this a little later.

Using evaporated metal electrodes on an anthracene crystal, we can drive saturation photocurrents through a crystal using sufficiently high fields. Using sodium chloride electrolyte electrodes, we can drive saturation photocurrents through a crystal of anthracene at a field strength about one tenth of those used with metal electrodes.[3] Using sodium iodide[4] electrolyte electrodes, we get one tenth the saturation currents that we get when using sodium chloride electrodes. Using iodine electrodes,[5] we have been able to get a large conductivity through anthracene using light of 4360 Å to which the anthracene is normally transparent. Finally, using a ceric sulfate electrode,[6] we can drive saturation currents through anthracene in complete darkness.

In Fig. 1, there is a graphical summary of some of the conductivity behavior we have observed with anthracene. Curve A represents the dark current in the case where both electrodes are solutions of NaCl. Here i^+ equals i^-, and there is no polarity effect. Curve B represents the current observed when one side of the crystal has a NaCl solution electrode and the other has an I_3^- (I^- - I_2) electrode. In this case a larger dark current flows when the iodine electrode is at a positive potential; the dark current flowing when the iodine electrode is at a negative potential is about the same as in Curve A. Curves C and D represent the normal i^+ and i^- photocurrent respectively, using the NaCl solution electrodes, and highly absorbed radiation. Notice the much larger i^+ current. Curve E on the other hand shows the current flowing through the crystals when light to which the anthracene is normally transparent is used; however in this case, the back electrode consisted of a solution of I_2 in I^-, whereas the front electrode consisted of a NaCl solution. The 4360 Å light passed through the NaCl solution, through the anthracene crystal, and into the iodine solution, where it was highly absorbed, creating more of the injecting species (I atoms) which in turn produced larger currents in the anthracene.

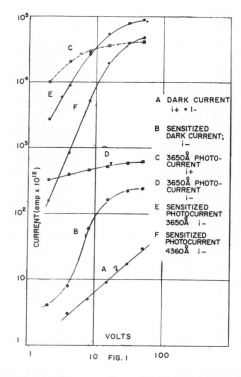

A DARK CURRENT
i+ = i-

B SENSITIZED
DARK CURRENT;
i-

C 3650Å PHOTO-
CURRENT
i+

D 3650Å PHOTO-
CURRENT
i-

E SENSITIZED
PHOTOCURRENT
3650Å i-

F SENSITIZED
PHOTOCURRENT
4360Å i-

FIG. I

In Fig. 2, we have the results with the ceric sulfate elec-trode. In this case, the front electrode consisted of a NaCl solution, and the back electrode consisted of a solution of ceric sulfate in 0.5M sulfuric acid. Curves A and B represent the photocurrents i^+ and i^- respectively, when both electrodes are 0.5M H_2SO_4 solutions. Curve C represents the dark current when the ceric sulfate was at a positive potential. The dark current flowing when the ceric sulfate solution was at a nega-tive potential is practically the same as the normal dark cur-rent. Curve D shows the effect of shining light (3650 Å) on the front side (NaCl solution) of the crystal. The light reaching the ceric sulfate solution was the fluorescent light generated inside the crystal after the absorption of the 3650 Å radiation. Curve D was calculated by subtracting Curve B from Curve E; in this way, the effect of the ceric sulfate could be separated from the normal i^- photocurrent. It is apparent that the light reaching the ceric sulfate had very little effect on the saturation photo-current; in other words, no additional injecting species appeared. At low voltages, however, there was a significant increase in current produced by the absorbed light. We attribute this to the discharge of a dark polarization caused by hole trapping; this is accomplished by the small electron current produced by the light absorbed at the surfaces of the crystal.

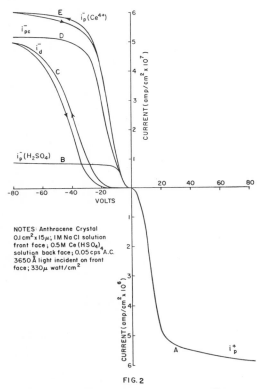

FIG. 2

DARK AND PHOTOCURRENT IN ANTHRACENE WITH 0.5M Ce^{4+} ELECTRODE

In Table 1, there is a summary of some of the results we have observed with different electrodes. The letters A and B under the heading <u>Electrode System</u> refer to the faces of the crystal facing the light and distant from the light respectively, when light is used. In any case, the polarity of the current corresponded to the polarity of side A. On line 1, with NaCl on both sides, the ratio of photocurrents i^+/i^- was about 60. As was mentioned earlier, i^- can be a true electron current, or it could be due to holes coming from the back side of the crystal. This was tested on line 3, when the back electrode was a NaI solution. The photocurrent ratio i^+/i^- was about 300, which means that if there was a true electron current, it was not more than 0.3% of the positive hole current. The mechanism of the I$^-$ effect may be related to that proposed today by Weller. He suggests that the I$^-$ exerts a fluorescence quenching effect in some cases by hastening the transition from the singlet to the triplet state; in our case, this would deprive the excited anthracene molecules of the energy necessary for charge creation.

Table I

Effect of Electrodes on Conductivity in Anthracene

Electrode System		Dark Current		Photocurrent	
A	B	i^+	i^-	i^+	i^-
		(amp/cm² × 10¹¹)		(amp/cm² × 10¹¹)	
1. NaCl	NaCl	3	3	328,000	5,400
2. NaI	NaI	3	3	42,000	620
3. NaCl	NaI	4	5	328,000	1,150
4. NaI	NaCl	4	6	35,000	•5,000
5. NaI	NaI	3	3	19*	18*
6. NaI	I₂ (in I⁻)	11	245	20*	48,000*
7. NaCl	Picric Acid	45	100	40*	4,500*
8. NaCl	Ce⁴⁺ 1M	10	260,000	400,000	420,000

Note: 1. Currents are approximately saturated.

2. *refers to measurements with 4360 Å light; all other photocurrents were made with 3650 Å light incident on side A.

On line 8, the large rectification ratio in the dark currents may be noted. On line 7, we mention the results with a picric acid electrode. The efficiency of the picric acid electrode may be due to its ability to form a complex with anthracene. This is an interesting electrode system in that it is the undissociated picric acid that is the active injecting species; since the concentration of this species is sensitive to pH, it was found that by changing the pH of this solution, we could change the photo-current passing through the crystal.

To summarize, photoexcitation is not necessary for the induction of high conductivity in organic crystals. By a suitable choice of the electrodes, considerable charge injection can be effected. When photoexcitation is involved, the excitation diffuses to the surface where dissociation takes place as a result of an interaction with the electrode, the electron passing preferentially into the electrode or being trapped there and the hole becoming free to move through the crystal. When the electrode is absent or blocking, dissociation may occur at an impurity at the surface. The mobility of the carriers as determined by Kepler[2] is about 1 cm^2/vsec. In the case of anthracene the extent of the true negative electron current is not greater than about 0.3 of a percent of the hole conductivity, and there is also some trapping of holes.

REFERENCES

[1] Kallmann, H. and Pope, M., Nature 186, 31-3 (1960)
[2] Kepler, R. G., Phys. Rev. 119, 1226 (1960)
[3] Pope, M. and Kallmann, H., Proc. Int. Conf. on Electrical Cond. in Organic Solids, Interscience Pub. Co., N.Y. (1962)
[4] Kallmann, H. and Pope, M. Nature 185, 753 (1960)
[5] Kallmann, H. and Pope, M. J. Chem. Phys. 32, 300 (1960)
[6] Pope, Kallmann, Chen and Gordon, J. Chem. Phys. (in press)

Dennis Eric Galati, M. D., discussed experiments, which showed that the human heart fluoresces under pathological conditions, and that diseased tissues, such as blood vessels, fluoresce while normal tissue does not fluoresce.

GENERAL DISCUSSION OF ORGANIC SYSTEMS

1. DISCUSSION OF SHORT COMMUNICATIONS

<u>McGlynn</u>: I presume Dr. Lippert must have some reason for
drawing the $n \rightarrow \pi^*$ triplet state above the $n \rightarrow \pi^*$ singlet state
in this diethyl compound which he had on the board. I know of
only one other case where such a situation has been postulated (but again not verified), that is in the case of β-carotene
where perhaps it is not so unreasonable on the basis of a
molecular exciton picture. There you get much splitting of
the singlet level due to the strong interactions of the various
oscillators along the chain. But I can find no reason at all on
any basis for making it so in this particular molecule. Now
my question, in essence, is: do you have reason, Dr. Lippert,
for drawing the triplet state of the diethylphenanthrene type
molecule higher in energy than that of the singlet $n \rightarrow \pi^*$?

<u>Lippert</u>: For common aromatic compounds it is well known
due to Hund's rule that the triplet state is at lower energy,
but I think for $n \rightarrow \pi^*$ excited states there is no knowledge as
to whether it is higher or lower. Some examples are known,
however, where indeed the triplet state is higher than the
singlet state. There have been calculations by Mataga on
this.

<u>Förster</u>: Let me say something on this point. Certainly, in a
state which results mainly from a single configuration it is
impossible for the triplet state to be higher than the corresponding singlet state. Now in this case with these two adjacent nitrogen atoms the lowest $n \rightarrow \pi^*$ state will certainly not
result from a single configuration. In the case of such states
it is difficult for me to understand why Hund's rule should
apply. Calculations have been made on nitrogen heterocyclic
compounds, calculations which I was not able to understand
in detail. In these calculations the corresponding triplet states
came out higher than the corresponding singlets.

McGlynn: I see no reason why the Hund type of reasoning should apply to an excited state. Probably I am very naive, because I just simply think of the triplet state as having much better spacial correlation in it than does the singlet. I feel for this reason that it should always lie below the singlet level unless one has a lot of configurational mixing. I cannot believe this to be the case for a diazo compound.

Lippert: I think that in the n → π excited states the two electrons are separated in the average more than in the π → π* states, because one electron remains located in the nitrogen atom and the other is in an anti-bonding π orbital.

Tsou: I have two questions to address to Dr. Wirth:
1.—I want to know which of the oligophenylenes substituted with methyl groups is the most efficient as a solute in a scintillation system, and how this compound compares with the p-terphenyl which we use today.
2.—When you introduce methyl substituents on oligophenylenes, you are affecting the coplanarity of the system, because, as I see, the ultraviolet spectra which you indicated reach a limit of about 287 mμ, whereas in the unsubstituted system these spectra extend to a higher wavelength. I am wondering to what extent you have investigated the possibility of the coplanarity, because I think this may have an effect on energy transfer in this type of system.

Wirth:
1.—We have measured about twenty-five compounds so far using the instrument described by Hayes *et al* and found for most of them efficiencies from 1.0 to 1.3 compared to 3 g/1 PPO in toluene. The highest value was given by a dimethoxy-p-quaterphenyl. A tetramethyl-p-sexiphenyl also proved to be very effective. We have recently reported on these investigations in the *Zeitschrift für Elektrochemie*.
2.—Now to your second question. It is correct to say that the position of the absorption bands is a reliable measure of coplanarity for compounds which are derived from the same basic structure. We have, for instance, a p-quaterphenyl derivative which absorbs as low as 205 mμ; this compound is ideally non-coplanar. The trioxido-p-quaterphenyl, which I mentioned in my report, is ideally coplanar; it therefore absorbs at much longer wavelengths, namely at 365 mμ.

Because of the Stokes effect we have to expect emission
bands at about 305 and 465 mμ, respectively, for these two
compounds. We have not yet tested either of these p-
quaterphenyl derivatives or other related compounds with
regard to their scintillation properties, since their solubilities are too low. However, it is easy to estimate which compound will have higher scintillation efficiency if one considers
the optical data.

2. TRIPLET STATES

Lim: I just want to make one comment on the heavy ion effect. Let us assume that the heavy ion effect is in part due
to charge transfer forces operating between the heavy ion
species and the molecule. For the triplet state one can then
understand the heavy ion effect very clearly. If I recall the
discussion between Dr. McGlynn and Dr. Lippert on the
heavy ion effect, the conclusion drawn was that at room
temperature the heavy ion effect is very small, but at lower
temperatures the heavy ion effect may become large. Now,
if we assume that at low temperature the overlapping of donor and acceptor orbitals becomes larger, that is contact
becomes closer, a consequence of this will be that charge
transfer forces become greater at lower temperature. This
is shown in the case of iodine or oxygen dissolved in numerous solvents. By cooling down one can clearly show that the
charge transfer absorption band increases in intensity
drastically as the temperature goes down and down, and I
think, if we can assume that the heavy ion effect is greater
at lower temperatures, then we have to assume that the
charge transfer forces must be operating under the same
conditions.

McGlynn: The fluorescence quantum yield of naphthalene is
at least ten times greater than the phosphorescence yield.
As is indicated in the accompanying table, ϕ_P/ϕ_F increases
upon formation of the charge transfer complex with trinitrobenzene. This enables one to say that the intersystem crossing probability has been increased by the complexation; and
because of the fact that trinitrobenzene is not paramagnetic
and does not contain heavy atoms, one concludes that either
charge transfer forces increase spin-orbital coupling

considerably, or that the insertion of a new level, the charge transfer level, between the singlet and triplet $\pi \rightarrow \pi^*$ states, decreases a presumed activation energy necessary to the crossing process.

RELATIVE PHOSPHORESCENCE TO FLUORESCENCE QUANTUM YIELD RATIOS OF NAPHTHALENE AND SOME OF ITS CHARGE TRANSFER COMPLEXES

(N. Christodouleas and S. P. McGlynn)

Species[a]	φ_P[b]	ϕ_F[c]	ϕ_P/ϕ_F
Naphthalene	0.06	0.68	0.09
Naphthalene-TNB	0.23	0.78	0.29
Naphthalene-TCPA	0.20	0.40	0.50
Naphthalene-TBPA	0.19	0.29	0.64
Naphthalene-TIPA	0.46	0.35	1.32

a) TNB: *sym*-trinitrobenzene; TCPA: tetrachlorophthalic anhydride; TBPA: tetrabromophthalic anhydride; TIPA: tetraiodophthalic anhydride.

b) Relative intensities at 21300 cm^{-1}.

c) Relative intensities at 29400 cm^{-1}.

In complexes of naphthalene with tetrachloro-, tetrabromo-, and tetraiodophthalic anhydride one can study ϕ_P/ϕ_F as a function of the atomic number of the halogens appended to the acceptor (the word 'acceptor' here means the Lewis acid, and not 'energy acceptor'). These systems are quite complicated spectroscopically, since one has considerable self-absorption probability, considerable energy transfer probability, and the further complication that these three acceptors themselves luminesce. It seems possible to say, however, that the observed effects cannot be accounted for on this basis, and it becomes necessary to say that there is a distinct heavy-atom effect of considerable magnitude.

Two components then are relevant. Firstly, that charge transfer complexation increases intersystem crossing probability, and secondly, that heavy atoms appended to the acceptor have a significant effect on the luminescence properties of the donor.

We have also examined the phosphorescence decay of dilute solutions of propyl halides and naphthalene at -195.8°C. There is no effect that we can detect. However, the effects of the halide on τ_p at high concentrations are very distinct, as is shown in the accompanying table. This type of behavior is consistent with very weak complexation.

Oster: I simply want to know whether anybody has tried inducing a phosphorescence with ionizing radiation. Is the source too weak? Or has anybody tried the Terenin system, that is the benzophenone-naphthalene combination?

Kallmann: We have tried to excite phosphorescence in all kinds of systems (pure crystals, mixed crystals) with high energy radiation and we have compared this to the normal fluorescence, so that we have a measurement of how much the phosphorescence would be, percentagewise. We have compared this with excitation by light. We took a mixed system, for instance durene mixed with small amounts of naphthalene, less than one percent, and we excited it with both high energy radiation and UV radiation. We were very careful to avoid direct excitation of the naphthalene. The experiments were carried out in our laboratory by Dr. Adelman. The results were at first sight amazing. With a pure crystal, no phosphorescence was seen, even at low temperature, with high energy radiation. The same system excited by UV light, gives a weak phosphorescence, i.e. less than one tenth of a percent of the corresponding singlet radiation. If you use—and this is the same result that Dr. Wilkinson found—a system where the solute has a higher excitation energy than the bulk material, you get also no phosphorescence. But in the case where you have a system like durene and naphthalene or diphenyl and naphthalene, where the bulk material has a higher excitation energy than the solute, then you get an unusually high phosphoresence with high energy radiation, much higher than with light. We

MEAN LIFETIMES (IN SECONDS) OF NAPHTHALENE AND ITS HALOGEN DERIVATIVES IN SEVERAL SOLVENTS

(S. P. McGlynn, M. J. Reynolds, G. W. Daigre and N. Christodouleas)

SOLVENT / EMITTER	EPA[a]	(RATIO)	PROPYL[b] CHLORIDE	(RATIO)	PROPYL[b] BROMIDE	(RATIO)	PROPYL[b] IODIDE
NAPHTHALENE	2.6	(5.0)	0.52	(3.6)	0.14	(18.9)	0.076
(Ratio)	(1.8)		(3.0)		(1.2)		(0.27)
ALPHA FLUORONAPHTHALENE	1.4	(8.3)	0.17	(1.4)	0.12	(4.2)	0.029
(Ratio)	(6.3)		(2.3)		(2.0)		(1.3)
ALPHA CHLORONAPHTHALENE	0.23	(3.1)	0.075	(1.3)	0.059	(2.6)	0.023
(Ratio)	(16.4)		(10.2)		(8.0)		(3.6)
ALPHA BROMONAPHTHALENE	0.014	(1.8)	0.0073	(1.0)	0.0073	(1.2)	0.0063
(Ratio)	(5.9)		(5.1)		(6.2)		(6.7)
ALPHA IODONAPHTHALENE	0.0023	(1.6)	0.0014	(1.2)	0.0012	(1.2)	0.00095

a) EPA: ether, isopentane and alcohol in 5:5:2 ratio by volume.
b) Emitter and solvent were in 5:2 mole ratio. These systems formed cracked glasses at -195.8°C.

excited durene with 2537 Å and observed the phosphorescence of naphthalene, which in this case was roughly one percent of the singlet radiation. If you do the same with high energy radiation, then you get about 10 to 15% naphthalene phosphorescence with the correct lifetime of naphthalene. You get the same result for diphenyl-naphthalene. If we use the system durene-diphenyl, we also get the same result: diphenyl phosphorescence is excited by high energy radiation via durene.

But if you reverse the concentrations and take durene or diphenyl in naphthalene, you see little phosphorescence with light and practically none with high energy radiation. The explanation for this is, according to Dr. Adelman and myself, the following: with UV light you excite only the singlet state of the bulk material, from which energy is transferred to the singlet state of the solute, and from there eventually to its triplet state. This of course occurs only when the excitation energy of the solute singlet state is smaller than that of the bulk material. There is also the possiblity that energy is transferred to the triplet state of the solute directly from the singlet state of the bulk material, even if the singlet state of the solute has a higher singlet excitation energy than that of the bulk material. This process does not occur, however, as Dr. Wilkinson has already pointed out. The reason is that when the excitation energy gets to the spot where the solute is, it remains there for only such a short time, 10^{-10} or 10^{-11} sec, that it cannot transfer energy to the triplet state of the solute.

With fast electrons the situation is the following. Many higher states are excited, and there is also ionization. If you excite naphthalene in durene with high energy radiation, positively charged durene molecules are created in the main, but the positive charges migrate and are trapped by the naphthalene. Now there are only ionized napthalene molecules surrounded by neutral durene, which will finally recombine with the free electrons produced. This recombination will go about 75% to the triplet state and 25% to the singlet state. In this way ionization can really excite phosphorescence of the solute, but only if the ionization energy of the solute is less than that of the bulk material. This is the reason why you find an anomalously strong phosphorescence with high energy radiation, but not with UV radiation, but only in cases for which the above condition holds.

Lippert: I should like to learn whether intersystem crossing is possible in the case of an absolutely spontaneous process or whether there is always some kind of interaction necessary, such as inhomogeneous electric or magnetic fields.

McGlynn: My answer to this question will be in two parts. Firstly, any intercombination is in a sense an intersystem crossing process, and to the extent that this be true, the latter process will be spin-orbit coupling in nature. Spin-orbital coupling can and does occur in the spherically symmetric (and isolated) atom, and the external inhomogeneous fields are not necessary to its occurrence, as has been pointed out by Dr. Linschitz. Spin-orbital coupling and thus presumably intersystem crossing should be increased, however, by application of strongly inhomogeneous magnetic fields; apparently paramagnetic species are capable of such perturbation, but there seems to exist now a rather general feeling that there must be charge transfer before the expected effect becomes of observational significance. My second comment is that some intersystem crossings could very well be activated processes; thus far we have discussed only the nature of the frequency factor, and it is obvious that externally applied perturbations could also affect the activation energy. In this way significant changes of intersystem crossing probabilities could occur without any particularly large change in spin-orbit coupling.

Linschitz: May I ask you a question, Dr. McGlynn? I should like to ask you a question which actually has a bearing on Dr. Lippert's question. If you make a charge transfer complex with the naphthalene, for example, or between naphthalene and trinitrobenzene, you make this complex with the ground state of the naphthalene, presumably. Is that right? Now, I do not understand why you can see the phosphorescence and the fluorescence of ordinary naphthalene if the complex ties up all the naphthalene to begin with.

McGlynn: It is, of course, quite impossible to tie up all the naphthalene in any situation where one has a finite equilibrium constant. There are, however, other reasons for worry. For example, in the work of Czekalla and Briegleb excitation of charge transfer fluorescence seems always to have been effected in the charge transfer absorption wavelength region.

There is no indication in their work of their having excited elsewhere and having observed a charge transfer emission.

In our work which was done in glassy solutions at -195.8°C by N. Christodonleas, the concentrations used were as low as 10^{-4} moles/liter. We have measured equilibrium constants at room temperature, and conclude from the usual thermo-dynamic extrapolation that $K_c \sim 11$ lit/m at -195.8° C for trinitrobenzene-naphthalene. Yet we have not thus far been able to observe any charge transfer emission unless we ex-cite in the charge transfer absorption region. Yet there is complex present, and the emission observed is, of course, the sum of that from the uncomplexed naphthalene and the complexed naphthalene. Thus, from concentration studies, and a knowledge of K_c, one can, from the intercept of a plot which is reasonably linear, deduce ϕ_P/ϕ_F, the phosphorescence to fluorescence quantum yield ratio, for complexed naphthalene. It turns out to be about two orders of magnitude greater than for free naphthalene.

One might explain the apparent absence of charge transfer fluorescence by presuming that all states other than the CT state are dissociative, but this then makes it virtually im-possible to interpret the ϕ_P/ϕ_F studies.

Linschitz: That is the whole difficulty. Is there any chance that the charge transfer band can overlie the fluorescence band, so that you absorb the fluorescence and the apparent ratio of ϕ_P/ϕ_F would go up?

McGlynn: No, I do not believe this to be the case. The effect does occur, but it seems capable of accounting for about 1/3 only of the effect found.

Murty: In answer to Dr. Lippert's question as to whether the intersystem crossing is *spontaneous* or not, I would like to say that this phenomenon has been defined by Kasha (Disc. Faraday Soc., 9, 14 (1950)) as the spin-orbital-coupling-dependent internal conversion process. When no change in multiplicity is involved, the transition probabilities are of the order of 10^{-6} in the case of radiative transitions. For radia-tionless transitions also a similar prohibition factor is in-volved. Kasha estimated the rate constant for this process, from a study of ϕ_P/ϕ_F, the yield to have a value of the order of 10^{-7} sec^{-1}. This process, although much slower than the

internal conversion between electronic states of like multiplicity, is quite fast enough to compete with the *spontaneous*
fluorescence emission from excited singlet-levels in many
molecules.

Wilkinson: I just want to clear up the fact that I have not done
  any gas phase work. I have been interested in Dr. Lippert's
  questions and the probability of non-radiative transitions and
  what they depend upon. I think we know far too little about the
  a priori reasons for crossing under the gas phase conditions.
  But I have not worked in the gas phase; it is just that I think
  that if we knew what happens in the gas phase, things would
  be much better.

Porter (British Columbia):   I just want to comment on Dr.
  Lippert's question. That is that the molecules biacetyl and
  acetone phosphoresce and fluoresce in the vapor phase. The
  intersystem crossing there is first order, in other words, no
  bimolecular quenching processes, self-quenching that is,
  occur in the case of biacetyl. The fluorescence to phosphorescence ratio remains constant down to as low pressures as
  have been studied. It is also, incidentally, the same in solution.

Williams: I should like to comment on what I understand to be
  Dr. Lippert's question from the theoretical point of view.
  These singlet and socalled triplet states in general are in a
  sense an approximation, that is due to spin orbit interaction.
  As in atomic systems there is some mixing of these states,
  and it is this mixing, the departure from pure spin states,
  that facilitates the interaction, that is the transitions between
  the singlet and the triplet state.
     Now the other point I would like to make is that in these non-
  radiative transitions one has to look very carefully at the
  adiabatic approximation. During these non-radiative transitions between singlet and triplet states the adiabatic approximation is no longer valid because the energy separations
  are now too small.

3. LIFETIMES

Kallmann: I want to put a question to this audience. I am
  worried about the following results. If you compare lifetime

measurements in single anthracene crystals, the values which
you find in the literature are rather diversified. The most
probable value I found was 14 nsec., which is roughly what we
found in our measurements. Other values go down to about 7
nsec. I wanted to ask those people who work in the field if
they still believe that those low values represent the true
time constant of solid anthracene.

If you calculate the emission lifetimes from the absorption
strengths, the values you get are higher than 10 nsec. Therefore, values below 10 nsec. are really astonishing. Results
for lifetime measurements in the vapor phase are even more
astonishing. In Oxford the lifetime of anthracene in the vapor
phase was measured or extrapolated. They also got very low
values. I should like to ask whether anybody can comment on
this, because these very short lifetimes are amazing to me.

Birks: The molecular fluorescence decay time τ_o of an organic
crystal may be defined as that of a lamina sufficiently thin as to
eliminate self-absorption. In a thicker crystal self-absorption
increases the decay time to the technical value τ, given by[1]

$$\tau = \frac{\tau_o}{1 - aq_o}$$

where q_o is the quantum efficiency of fluorescence, and a is
the fraction of primary photons that are reabsorbed.

For anthracene at room temperature $q_o = 0.9$[2], and a value of τ_o
= 10 nsec has been extrapolated from measurements[3] on thin la-
minae. For a crystal of thickness $\geq$ 5mm, a attains a constant
value, which can be determined from a comparison of the technical
and molecular fluorescence spectra.[4] We may distinguish three
cases for thick crystals.

(i) <u>Volume excitation</u> (by γ-rays, X-rays or other penetrating
radiations). Here $a = 0.76$, so that $\tau = 31.6$ nsec from (1), which
agrees excellently with the experimental value of $\tau = 31 (\pm 2)$ nsec,
from the results of 6 independent observers.[5]

(ii) <u>Surface excitation</u> (ultra-violet, $\propto$-rays etc.) <u>with observation by reflection.</u> Here $a = 0.54$, so that $\tau = 19.4$ nsec
from (1). This may be compared with the sole experimental
value[3] of $\tau = 16 (\pm 2.6)$ nsec, which might be influenced by
surface oxidation.

(iii) <u>Surface excitation with observation by transmission.</u>
Here a is the mean of that in cases (i) and (ii), namely
$a = 0.65$, so that $\tau = 24.1$ nsec from (1). This agrees excellently with the experimental values of $\tau = 24.2$ nsec,
from photo-excitation of freshly cleaved surfaces[6], and of
$\tau = 23.8 (\pm 1.1)$ nsec, from $\propto$-particle excitation.[3]

In (iii) normal atmospheric oxidation reduces τ to 18 nsec[7] or 17 nsec[8], while aged sufaces yield τ = 14 nsec[9] or 12.6 nsec[6]. The theory explains why a reduction of the crystal thickness reduces the decay time to a value intermediate between τ and τ_0, and why surface excitation gives a lower value of τ than volume excitation of the same specimen.[10]

When the crystal dimensions are reduced to ~ 0.1μ, which is comparable with the exciton mean free path in the bulk crystal[11], the decay time is reduced below τ_0, due to the premature conversion of excitons into photons on encountering the crystal surface. This accounts for the low value of 6.4 nsec observed for microcrystals[6], and for the monotonic decrease in τ towards ~3 nsec observed as the microcrystalline size is reduced.[12]

The relation of the molecular decay time τ_0 of the crystal, which is the exciton lifetime, to the decay time τ_m of the isolated molecule in the vapor phase or in dilute solution is of particular interest. In p-terphenyl, where a is negligible, τ_0 = 5.5 nsec,[6] while in solution τ_m = 2.2 nsec,[13] yet q_0 is similar in the two cases. From the limited experimental data available it appears that τ_0 is generally greater than τ_m and this effect is being currently studied.

A fuller account of this work is being published elsewhere.[14]

[1] J. B. Birks. Phys. Rev., 94, 1567 (1954)
[2] E. J. Bowen, E. Mikiewicz and F. W. Smith. Proc. Phys. Soc. A, 62, 26 (1949)
[3] H. Kallmann and G. J. Brucker. Phys. Rev., 108, 1122 (1957)
[4] J. B. Birks and G. T. Wright. Proc. Phys. Soc. B, 67, 657 (1954)
[5] R. C. Sangster and J. W. Irvine. J. Chem. Phys., 24, 670 (1956)
[6] T. D. S. Hamilton. Proc. Phys. Soc. B, 70, 144 (1957)
[7] G. T. Wright. Proc. Phys. Soc. B, 68, 241 (1955)
[8] S. H. Liebson. Nucleonics, 10, No. 7, 41 (1952)
[9] J. B. Birks and W. A. Little, Proc. Phys. Soc. A 66, 921 (1953)
[10] W. Hanle and H. G. Jansen. Z. Naturforsch., 9a, 791 (1954)
[11] I. I. Kucherov and A. N. Faidysh. Izv. Akad. Nauk SSSR, Ser. Fiz., 22, 29 (1958)
[12] A. Schmillen. Private communication (1961)

[13] R. K. Swank, H. B. Phillips, W. L. Buck and L. J. Basile. I.R.E. Trans.Nuc.Sci., NS-5, 183 (1958).

[14] J. B. Birks. Proc. Phys. Soc. In press.

Förster: I would like to ask about something I have not understood. You get lower values in the microcrystals because you have some surface effect, but why do you get higher values by surface excitation of thick crystals without reabsorption?

Birks: You get reabsorption in the thick crystal. You are getting it from the other side.

Weller: Dr. Birks, do you know anything about the measurements which, I think, were carried out by Stevens in Sheffield on the lifetimes in anthracene in the vapor state?

Birks: I can just refer to Dr. Kallmann's other point. I would agree with him quite definitely that there is a discrepancy which is not an experimental discrepancy; a true discrepancy which has to be accounted for theoretically between the lifetimes in the crystal phase and the lifetimes in either the vapor or the solution phase. Crystalline terphenyl shows quite definitely that there is a difference in the lifetimes although the counting efficiencies are similar. It looks as if the crystalline environment for the molecule does have an influence on its lifetime, and, of course, this is obviously relevant to the exciton theory of crystals.

Porter (British Columbia):   I would like to ask a question of group as to what information there is, either experimental or theoretical, concerning the lifetimes of upper singlet states, with regard to conversion to the lowest singlet.

Kallmann: I will make a very weak comment. The only result which I know which could give some idea is the concentration dependence of the fluorescence when excited with high energy radiation. We have tried this with substances which have practically no concentration quenching, so that one would expect a flat plateau, or, if higher states are excited and have a finite lifetime, then by increasing the concentration, one should find increasing fluorescence. This is not the case, however. You see, this effect is so weak that we suspect from these experiments, which are really very rough, that the life

time of the excited state must be smaller by one or two orders of magnitude. Otherwise one should see an increase in
the concentration curve with higher concentration of some of
these solutes.

Buck: In connection with the pulsed fluorescence of pyrene
   dimers observed by Dr. Birks, I was wondering what conclusions could be drawn from the shape of the rising portion
   of these pulses of fluorescence from the dimer emission.

Birks: If I may be allowed to show one slide which contains
   this particular result, this may answer your question. I did
   not get round to it under the nine minute rule, but the last
   slide brings out one of the important points I wanted to bring
   out from this investigation. That is, we make the very surprising discovery - it is very surprising in terms of the
   existing ideas previous to this work - that the rise time of
   the dimer fluorescence is faster, about twice as fast as
   decay time of the monomer fluorescence. The slide shows
   the inverse of the monomer decay time as a function of concentration in deoxygenated solutions, and on the same
   diagram is plotted the dimer rise time, that is the quantity
   τ_R in the double exponential equation. You see that the slope
   of the second curve is about twice that of the first curve.
   They both, incidentally, are of the right order of magnitude
   for a viscosity controlled process, but here we have a specific case which indicates that the dimer is being produced not
   only from the state of the monomer which is fluorescent.
   That is, there is indication here that there is a second state
   of the monomer, a non-fluorescent state, which is probably
   localized below the normal monomer emitting state, which is
   also giving rise to dimers. So far this is the only explanation
   of this particular result. The result itself is sufficiently
   astonishing. We made quite independent measurements using
   the phase and modulation fluorometer developed by Dyson and
   myself. This instrument is essentially like the instrument
   described by Dr. Schmillen which has got a degree of modulation on it as an additional parameter. Since you measure two
   parameters, phase and degree of modulation, you can determine a double exponential, a rise and a decay. The
   results we obtain are in agreement with the results presented
   in this work, that is, we are quite convinced that there is this
   essential difference between the dimer rise time and the
   monomer decay.

Weller: Does this ratio of the rate constants obtained from
  dimer rise and monomer decay time depend on the solvent?

Birks: It was only done in cyclohexane.

4. ENERGY TRANSFER

Birks: Considering energy transfer between two solutes, that
  is, not between the solvent and the solute but between two
  solutes, measurements made by Kucherov and myself on
  transfer between terphenyl and tetraphenylbutadiene showed
  that there was no viscosity effect in the system. On the other
  hand, from results obtained by other workers it appears likely that when the magnitudes of the fluorescence intensity and
  of the absorption, that is the magnitudes of the dipole moments
  involved, are much less than in that situation, you might expect to find the viscosity dependence.

Kallmann: I want to make a short remark on energy transfer
  in plastics. We have compared energy transfer and quenching, and for both processes you need energy transport according to our theoretical picture. In plastics you have no
  energy transport by material diffusion, but only by migration
  of excitons. Now I will give one example of how tremendously
  careful one must be in these experiments. First, we investigated in plastics, especially in polyvinylnaphthalene, the
  concentration quenching of normal solutes, and we find - this
  was also found by other people - that concentration quenching
  does not exist in plastics because material diffusion is necessary in order to bring two solute molecules close to one
  another. Then we investigated the effect of quenchers. There
  was very little quenching when the solutes were excited directly, which is quite reasonable.
     Then, we investigated the quenching of polyvinylnaphthalene
  with the fluorescence method described this morning by F.
  Brown. That is, energy is transferred from the bulk to a
  fluorescent solute which is not quenched. First we investigated
  the quenching of polyvinylnaphthalene by hexachloro-p-xylene.
  Since we get good energy transfer to the fluorescent solute,
  we expected that we would get energy transport to the hexachloro-p-xylene and that polyvinylnaphthalene would be
  quenched, since we know that in methylnaphthalene and
  in the monomer the hexachloro-p-xylene quenches the excited states very strongly. The result, however, was that with
  hexachloro-p-xylene the fluorescent radiation was hardly

quenched at all. Hexachloro-p-xylene is not a quencher
for polyvinylnaphthalene.

Our first conclusion was that there is no energy transport by
migration as we had assumed, but we were not quite satisfied
with this experiment. Then we tried a similar quenching experiment with diphenyl mercury, the experiment Brown discussed this morning. There we found strong quenching. From
these experiments with hexachloro-p-xylene and diphenyl mercury we conclude that some substances simply do not quench
if they are in a rigid medium. It is not only that the excited
molecule must be close to the quencher, but in some way it
must be in a certain position, or, it must come especially
close, as is possible in liquids where there can be a much
closer collision than in plastics.

Paris: I would like to ask a question of either the Kasha or the
Weissman school on the energy transfer of metal organics,
the chelates, primarily rare-earth chelates where the absorption of the energy is in the ultraviolet, and in the case of
Tb^{+3} chelates the emission is in the near infrared. The
question, then, is: how is the energy transferred and why is
the efficiency so high in these cases?

Lipsky: I have always been confused about the diffusion of
excitation energy. One can ask whether excitation energy
really diffuses, that is, whether it obeys a diffusive equation.
It seems to me that one can say that excitation does diffuse
if the probability per unit time of transfer from one molecule
to another is independent of the presence of other molecules.
But for a crystal, I think it is meaningless to speak about the
diffusion of excitation. I would doubt that a diffusion equation
is applicable for describing an excited state of the crystal. I
was speaking with Dr. Franck this morning about this, and he
has not really convinced me that there is a qualitative difference between what he calls sensitized fluorescence and exciton motion. I certainly feel that, if you do have exciton
splitting in the case of a crystal, you cannot speak of a diffusive type of motion for the energy.

Förster: I think this depends on whether you are able to consider the excitation to be localized at a single molecule or
only delocalized between a certain number of molecules. And
I think it depends on the amount of coupling energy between
the different electronic systems. This is to be compared with
the coupling which exists in the individual molecule between
the electronic system and the nuclear vibrations. If the

coupling between the different electronic systems exceeds the coupling between the electronic system and nuclear vibrations within the molecule, then it is of no use to consider the excitation as localized. But in the other case, if the coupling within the molecule is larger, then I think it is quite reasonable to consider the excitation as localized. When we are able to consider this for a certain instant, we can talk about motion from one molecule to the other. I think that in a theoretical development of this we get something like a diffusion equation. I do not know whether this is an answer; it is a somewhat complicated matter.

Weller: This means that when we can localize the energy, then we can talk about diffusion. Is that so?

Förster: Yes, that's right.

DuBois: This is on the same topic and it is also in the form of a question. If I understand correctly some of the results we saw this morning, it seems that when the transferring substances have energy levels that are close to one another, the transfer is poorer. Now I would like to ask, if this is so, how does one look at the transfer from one molecule to another of the same species? It is presumable that the coupling in this case would be as good as can be on a resonance basis.

Kallmann: I will comment on this question in a slightly different way. When you use a system such as polystyrene plus naphthalene, then you get very strong energy transfer from naphthalene to the solute. Now we have found that this energy transfer is almost perfect with 25 g naphthalene per liter, which is a concentration of about two tenths of a mole.
The naphthalene molecules are really not spaced very close together. In this case I am certain that you cannot speak of an exciton which extends over several molecules; you must speak of a localized exciton, an excited molecule of naphthalene. Therefore, since the bulk material is polystyrene, we certainly have no material diffusion. I think that this is a perfect example where we really have exciton migration diffusion. There is no way out and no excuse any more. The direct answer to Dr. Dubois' question is this. If the energy levels of two molecules are very close to each other, the probability of transfer is much smaller than when the solute has a lower energy level. In the former case the excitation energy of a bulk molecule will go over to the many other

bulk molecules with greater probability than to the one solute molecule in its neighborhood.

McGlynn: I should like to attempt to answer Dr. Paris' question, although I do not fully have the right to do this, since the work to which he refers was done by Crosby and by Weissman. There are a number of points which are of relevance. Firstly, the fact that one excites in the ultraviolet and observes an emission in the infrared does not necessarily mean that one is going to have a low quantum yield. In fact there seems to no *a priori* reason to suppose that the yield should be either high or low. It is entirely a question of whether internal degradation of higher metal energy levels directly to the ground state can take place with higher probability than the internal degradation to the first excited level of the metal ion. This would seem improbable. In fact, the most seriously competitive process might very well be back-transfer of energy from the metal ion to the ligand, and in many of the cases studied by Crosby this is virtually impossible.

It is presumed that energy transfer to the metal ion can occur at higher levels than the first excited one. In a species of the sort being considered there is usually a high density of states above that one which is emissive. Furthermore, the coupling of a metal state to a ligand state can generally be considered to be small (i.e., the crystalline field perturbation does not generally induce much mixing of ligand and metal orbitals). This implies that, if energy transfer occurs to the metal *via* some strongly coupled metal state, then one may internally degrade through a high density of weakly ligand-coupled metal states to that one which is emissive - and thus have a high quantum yield.

Have I succeeded in answering your question in any way?

Paris: Yes, part of it. Could you amplify on the manner in which vibrational factors affect the transfer and/or the quantum yield?

McGlynn: No, I cannot. But I can make the following observations. Metal-ligand vibrations would presumably be the important coupling vibrations; we know very little about these vibrations since their frequencies are generally so low as to lie below the detection limit of available commercial infrared instruments. I believe that this fact of low frequency would decrease the effectiveness of metal-ligand vibrations in energy transfer. My reason for this supposition is that overlap of the vibrational levels of one state with those of a higher energy

state will occur only at large values of the vibrational quantum
number of the former. The peakedness of the wave functions
will then occur at the extremes of the vibration and overlap
with the lower vibrational levels of the higher state (if vertically disposed) will be small.

Indeed, my argument seems to be that the metal-ligand vi-
vibrations will be of not much importance, and that perhaps
other, initially less probable vibrations, will dominate. In
either case, I would not expect strong vibronic coupling.

Lipsky: I would like first to answer Dr. DuBois' question. If
one has two similar molecules, then whether transfer between
them will be rapid or not really depends on how strong the
coupling is. This is essentially what Förster just told me.
That is, if the coupling is very weak, then the molecule will
vibrationally relax before it transfers. Then, you have a
large Stokes shift. You have a Stokes shift generally in a
polyatomic molecule. Thus there will be very small overlap
between the dipole fields and, therefore, transfer will be
weak. But in order to get exciton motion, you must have such
molecules. If the coupling is strong, you would expect very
fast transfer between two benzene molecules.

I should like to ask Dr. Förster another question along the
same line and that is the following. You are aware of McGee's
calculation, where you take a linear array of H_2^+ molecules,
and you ask what is the probability of finding excitation at any
point along this chain of oscillators? You assume that the
probability per unit time depends on the presence of all other
oscillators along the chain. You do not get a diffusionlike
equation, no matter what the coupling strength is. This is
independent of his value for β, I think. This result, that is, the
fact that we do not get a diffusive equation, does not depend on
any assumption about the coupling strength. It only involves
the assumption that the molecule that is transferring knows
that all the other molecules are around.

Förster: I have seen the paper. The coupling with nuclear
motion is included only by the way of the potential energy
curves. When I looked at the paper, I tried to analyze the
different cases, which I would like to call strong, moderate,
and weak coupling. I got the impression that all this belonged
to the case of strong coupling, so that actually in this case a
diffusion equation might not be obtained. But perhaps I am
wrong.

Wilkinson: As no one seems to be coming forward, I might
take this opportunity to ask Dr. Förster a question. I said
yesterday that my reading of the work of theoreticians said
that we cannot make calculations on what we would expect for
exchange transfer. You have done such a wonderful job on the
dipole-dipole interaction. I wonder if you have thought about
exchange transfer, or if you have just confirmed my reading
of the theoreticians' work about it. Will it be possible? Is
there any work being done by theoreticians on this subject?

Förster: The only work which has been done so far in the extension of this theory is the work done by Dexter years ago,
but I am afraid nobody since that time has touched this field.
It would certainly be worthwhile. The problem is comparatively easy in the case of dipole-dipole coupling, but it is
somewhat complicated in these other cases of coupling by
higher momenta, and in the exchange case it comes certainly
to the qualitiative result that some penetration of the electronic cloud is necessary. This would lead in most cases to
diffusional quenching. If you want a more detailed answer, it
would be difficult to develop a theory for this.

Birks: I would just like to address a question to everybody.
That is, does anybody know of a case which has been studied,
of energy transfer from the first excited singlet to a second
excited singlet of another molecule? I also want to ask Dr.
Förster whether his theory would indicate that such things
should be highly allowed transfers.

Förster: I can only say that I do not know of any experiments
with the exception of some which we are now planning at our
laboratory. It is a question of whether energy transfer can be
faster than internal degradation of energy between singlet
states. Why should this transfer not occur? The donor does
not know whether the energy goes to the first or the second
singlet of the other molecule.

INORGANIC SYSTEMS

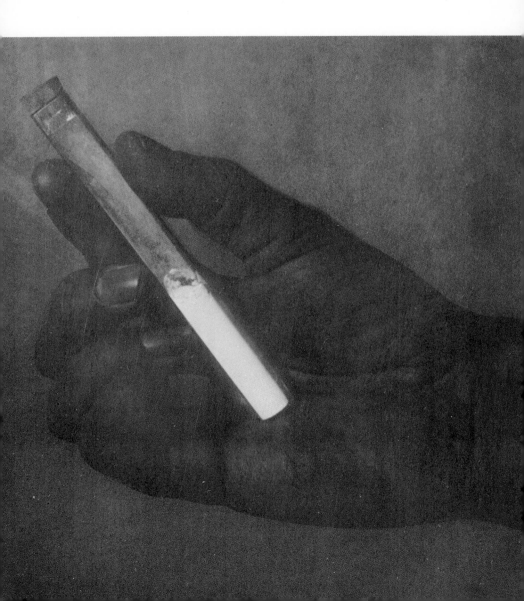

THEORETICAL CONSIDERATIONS OF THE LUMINESCENCE
OF ALKALI HALIDE AND ZINC SULFIDE PHOSPHORS*

Ferd E. Williams
Department of Physics, University of Delaware
Newark, Delaware

ABSTRACT

The semiempirical, tight binding calculations of the absorption and emission spectra of heavy metal activators in alkali halides are reviewed. The more recent quantum mechanical calculations of these spectra are discussed with particular emphasis on their relevance to the earlier theoretical investigations. The problem of the relative oscillator strengths for the principal impurity absorption bands in these materials is considered, and the effect of crystalline interactions on the pure spin states emphasized. Configuration interaction with electron transfer states and the Jahn-Teller effect are also invoked.

After identifying the activators and coactivators in zinc sulfide phosphors as acceptors and donors, respectively, we examine the evidence for the importance to the luminescence of pairing of donors and acceptors. In particular, a theoretical analysis of the optical properties of ZnS prepared with Zn^{65} which forms Cu by K capture is reported. The effective mass treatment of donor-acceptor pairs is reviewed, and the problem of the large central cell correction for acceptors in ZnS is discussed.

The general characteristics common to both alkali halide and zinc sulfide phosphors are considered. The broad absorption and emission bands and the Stokes shift arise in both classes of phosphors from the difference in electronic configuration of the activator system in the ground and excited states, from the

---

*Some of the research described herein was accomplished in part while the author was associated with the General Electric Research Laboratory.

polar character of the medium, and from the orbital electron or hole motion being rapid compared to lattice vibrations.

I INVESTIGATIONS OF ACTIVATOR SYSTEMS IN ALKALI HALIDES

Alkali halide crystals activated by heavy metal activators have been investigated during the past decade by increasingly sophisticated theoretical methods. In particular, the absorption and emission bands of thallium in potassium chloride have received more attention by theorists than have the properties of any other luminescent solid.

Following the earlier proposal of Seitz[1] that the activator system is comprised of Tl^+ substituted at K^+ sites in KCl and that the principal impurity absorption and emission bands could be attributed to transitions between the ^1S and $^3P_1^\circ$ and $^1P_1^\circ$ states of Tl^+ perturbed by crystalline interactions, Williams[2] calculated the excitation and emission spectra associated with the 2460 Å impurity absorption band. The principal emission maximum is at 3050 Å. In this calculation the parameters required to calculate crystalline interactions of the $^3P_1^\circ$ Tl^+ according to modified Born-Mayer[3] methods were estimated semiempirically from Hartree wave functions for the free activator ion. The calculation of spectra requires the determination of the energy of the activator system for each electronic state of the Tl^+ as a function of the nuclear coordinates for which the transition energy is most sensitive. It was shown that the transition energy is strongly dependent on the symmetric displacement of the nearest neighbor Cl^- toward and away from the Tl^+. This effect can be shown diagrammatically by the configuration coordinate model in which the energy for each electronic state is plotted as a function of the nuclear coordinates.

The configuration coordinate model was first applied qualitatively to activator systems by Gurney and Mott[4] and by Seitz.[1] It is based on the adiabatic approximation according to which the wave function for a state of the activator system can be separated as follows:

$$\chi(r,q) = \phi(q)\phi_q(r) \tag{1}$$

The electronic wave function $\phi_q(r)$ is a function of the electronic coordinates r and is smoothly modified by changes in the positions of the nuclei whose state of motion is described by $\phi(q)$. In the actual calculation for the activator system in KCl:Tl the harmonic approximation was also made, that is, the parametric dependence of $\phi_q(r)$ on q was neglected. Also, the configuration coordinate model involved only the symmetrical displacement of nearest Cl⁻ neighbors. Lax[5] has justified in general the use of a single configurational coordinate for impurity systems.

The spectra $P(\epsilon)$ at the temperature T, including the effect of the zero point energy $k\theta$, can be expressed in the form:[6]

$$P(\epsilon) = \left(\frac{K}{2\pi kT}\right)^{1/2} \exp\left[-Kq^2/2k\theta \coth\left(\frac{\theta}{T}\right)\right]\frac{dq}{d\epsilon} \qquad (2)$$

where K is the force constant for the activator system in the initial electronic state, q is the displacement in the configuration coordinate from the equilibrium value for the initial state, and ϵ is the transition energy at q. An additional term in the exponential of Eq. (2) can be added to include the effect of hydrostatic pressure on the spectra $P(\epsilon)$.[7] The calculated absorption and emission spectra for the $^1S \rightleftharpoons {}^3P^\circ$ transitions of Tl⁺ in KCl and their temperature and pressure dependences were found to be in good agreement with experiment considering the simplifications in the theory and approximations in the calculations.

More rigorous quantum mechanical calculations have been reported in the past few years on the interaction energies of heavy metal activators in alkali halide crystals. Knox and Dexter[8] pointed out that the introduction in the original calculation of a coulomb overlap term for the excited state could not be rigorously justified by them. Potekhina[9] examined this question by calculating the spectra of NaCl:Ag, first by the previously described method and then by strictly quantum mechanical methods, and concluded that the introduction of the coulomb overlap term is justified and is the major factor in determining the character of the spectra. In addition, Kristofel[10] reports a quantum mechanical calculation of the spectra of KCl:Tl and concludes that the semiempirical method is in general supported by his results. He obtains somewhat more quantitative agreement with experiment, principally because his results involve a smaller displacement of the equilibrium position of the ions in the excited state.

In addition, the problem of the ratio of the oscillator strengths of the two principal absorption bands, which involve the $^1S \rightarrow {}^3P_1{}^\circ$, $^1P_1{}^\circ$ transitions of Tl^+ in KCl, has received attention. The relative intensities of these transitions are determined by mixing of the $^3P^\circ$ and $^1P^\circ$ pure spin states by spin-orbit interaction. Knox and Dexter[8] reported a theoretical analysis of this problem using the characteristics of the free Tl^+ and neglecting the effects of crystalline interactions. Their results are in conflict with experiment. Because In^+ has the same energy level structure as Tl^+, the analysis can be applied to KCl:In, and in this case there is an even more serious discrepancy between experiment and their theory. Williams, Segall and Johnson[11] also used the free ion spin-orbit coupling constants but took account of crystalline interactions by determining the energy separation of the pure spin states in the crystal from the experimental absorption maxima and thereby obtained satisfactory agreement with experiment. Knox[12] has invoked configuration interaction with electron transfer states which form Tl° and Cl° to explain the experimental oscillator strength ratio and the energy separation of the two principal absorption bands. Configuration interaction with transfer states which form Tl^{+2} and K° provides the more diffuse charge density expected from the effects of the crystalline field on the atomic wave function of the $6p$ electron of the excited Tl^+. Sugano[13] has recently used the molecular orbital model and found that the constraints on the oscillator strength ratio obtained with the strictly ionic model are no longer valid.

The effect of spin-orbit interaction on the configuration coordinate model of KCl:Tl has been examined by Johnson and Williams.[14] These studies predicted that luminescent emission corresponding to the transition $^1P_1{}^\circ \rightarrow {}^1S$ of Tl^+ should occur in the same spectral region as the absorption corresponding to the transition $^1S \rightarrow {}^3P_1{}^\circ$. This has been verified experimentally and results in radiative transfer between the Tl^+ activators in KCl. The configuration coordinate model including the $^1P_1{}^\circ$ state, as well as the $^3P_1{}^\circ$ and ^1S states of Tl^+, was found to be simpler than was believed to be the case before the investigations of spin-orbit interaction. With appropriate modifications the detailed theoretical work on KCl:Tl can be used to propose configuration coordinate models for KBr:Tl and KI:Tl which are consistent with the experimental spectra of these phosphors. The models are shown in Fig. 1. These three luminescent materials differ in that the KCl:Tl exhibits radiative transfer

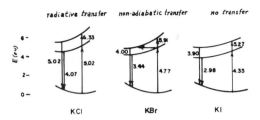

Fig. 1 — Configuration coordinate models for KCl: Tl, KBr:Tl, and KI:Tl.

of energy from the $^1P_1^{\,\circ}$ state to the $^3P_1^{\,\circ}$ state; the KBr:Tl, non-adiabatic energy transfer from the $^3P_1^{\,\circ}$ to the $^1P_1^{\,\circ}$ state; and the KI:Tl, neither mechanism except for a trace of radiative transfer.

There remains, however, the problem of the identification of the luminescent center and the transition responsible for the longer wavelength emission band with a maximum at 4750 Å in KCl:Tl. This emission has essentially the same dependence on concentration of thallium as the shorter wavelength emission attributed to isolated Tl^+ at K^+ sites and is independent of added divalent cations or annealing rate during preparation of the crystals. Therefore, the same center is probably responsible for the long wavelength as for the short wavelength emission. Kamimura and Sugano[15] have invoked the Jahn-Teller effect to account for this emission.

II INVESTIGATIONS OF ACTIVATOR SYSTEMS IN ZINC SULFIDE

During the past decade the problem of the identification of the impurity systems responsible for the multiple emission bands of zinc sulfide phosphors has received considerable attention. Kroger and associates[16] elucidated the role of the coactivator in the chemistry of phosphor preparation by the application of the principle of charge compensation. Bowers and Melamed[17] and Prener and Williams[18] independently identified by the application of semiconductor theory the activators and coactivators as acceptors and donors, respectively. The former investigators were concerned with the absence of paramagnetic impurities in ZnS:Cu,Cl; the latter, with the

luminescent characteristics of ZnS containing Zn^{65} which by
K capture transforms to Cu.

From the magnitude of recoil energy accompanying the
transmutation, Prener and Williams concluded that an appreciable fraction of the Cu remained at Zn sites and, since the
relative intensities of the emission bands were unaltered by
the progress of the transmutation, that the luminescent Cu
center differed from the center formed from Zn^{65} in other than
electron occupational probability or valence state. Specifically,
they suggested that the acceptor involved in luminescent emission is distinguished by the presence on an associated donor at
other than a nearest neighbor site. Schulman and Klick [19]
proposed that the parameters of the luminescent centers may
be such that the luminescent emission may be unaffected by
the Cu centers formed from Zn^{65} even if this center were
identical with the normal luminescent center except for electron occupational probability. We examined this possibility
and here give the analysis in some detail since it has not been
previously published.

As a consequence of its large band gap, zinc sulfide prepared by conventional methods is very nearly compensated,
that is, the activators or acceptors and coactivators or donors,
whether of impurity or defect origin, are present in approximately equivalent concentrations. If there is an excess of
donors over acceptors in the initial ZnS containing Zn^{65} which
is adequate to balance the Cu acceptors subsequently formed
from Zn^{65}, the Fermi level will remain well above the Cu acceptor levels; and the states of the Cu acceptors will have a
high electron occupational probability. In other words, the Cu
formed from Zn^{65} will be in the proper valence for luminescence; the Schön-Klasens [20,21] theory of positive hole migration
between the luminescent centers applies; and the results of the
transmutation experiment are understandable only on the basis
of the Cu formed from Zn^{65} differing from the luminescent Cu
in some other characteristic.

On the other hand, if there is not an intial excess of donors
over acceptors adequate to balance the Cu acceptors formed
from Zn^{65}, then the Fermi level will drop to an energy near the
Cu acceptor level and the occupational probability of these
states will be determined with ordinary excitation intensities

by the Fermi level, rather than by the excitation intensity.*
This is in contrast to zinc sulfide phosphors in which the occupation probability of acceptor states is established by detailed
balance between excitation, emission and the thermal processes
in accordance with the Schön-Klasens theory. With a typical
excitation intensity of 10^{14} photons/cm^2 sec the fraction of activator systems simultaneously excited in a representative
zinc sulfide powder is of the order of 10^{-8}, whereas the fraction ionized because of equilibrium conditions alone is for the
case of a low-lying Fermi level in excess of 10^{-5}.

We consider two types of acceptor states, associated with
the green and blue emission, respectively. For each we define
ϵ_i as the electronic energy and E_i as the lattice polarization
energy. This separation takes account of the energy of the
level being dependent on state of occupancy. The Cu centers
formed from Zn^{65}, N_G', are assumed to be equivalent to the
normal green emitting centers, N_G, in electron occupational
probability. If we apply the condition for charge balance and
make use of the fact that the blue centers, N_B, lie nearer the
valence band, we find that the Fermi level, ζ, is as follows;
for $g_B \ll g_G$, which we know from the emission spectrum:

$$\zeta \approx -kT \ln\left\{\frac{N_G'Z_G - N_B(1-Z_B) - N_G(1-Z_G)}{N_B[g_B + g_G(1-Z_B)] + N_G[g_G + g_B(1-Z_G)] - N_G'g_B Z_G}\right\}$$

(3)

where $Z_i = (kT)^{-1} \exp(-E_i/kT)$ and $g_i = \exp(\epsilon_i/kT)$. From
Eq. 3 the hole occupational probability for each of the G, G'
and B centers can be obtained, and if the intensity of the emission characteristic of each of these centers is taken as proportional to the concentration of those centers which are occupied by positive holes, we find the following for the ratio of
intensities of the green and blue emission:

$$\frac{I_G}{I_B} \approx \frac{\sigma_G}{\sigma_B} \cdot \frac{(N_G + \eta)}{N_B} \cdot \frac{(1 + g_G f - Z_G)}{(1 + g_B f - Z_B)} \cdot \frac{(1 + g_B f)}{(1 + g_G f)}$$

(4)

---

*Ga and Cl donors are also formed during the experiment, however,
for the later stage which was the period investigated in this work, the
concentration of Cu acceptors formed exceeds the concentration of donors formed.

where σ_G/σ_B is the ratio of cross sections for capture of conduction electrons by ionized green and blue centers, $f = \exp(-\zeta/kT)$, and $\eta = N'_G$ if the G' centers are assumed capable of emission and $\eta = 0$, if they are not. Both possibilities are considered separately for different values of Z_A and Z_B, and only two cases are found in which I_G/I_B is, for $N'_G > N_G, N_B$, independent of N'_G, as observed experimentally. These are the lower left and upper right elements of Table I.

Table I

Theoretical ratios of green emission to blue emission, as functions of concentrations of centers for different values of parameters of the centers.

	$\eta = N'_G$	$\eta = 0$
$Z_G \approx 1,$ $Z_B \ll 1$	$\dfrac{I_G}{I_B} \approx \dfrac{\sigma_G}{\sigma_B} \cdot \dfrac{(N'_G - N_B)}{N_B}$	$\dfrac{I_G}{I_B} \approx \dfrac{\sigma_G}{\sigma_B} \cdot \dfrac{N_G}{N_B} \cdot \dfrac{(N'_G - N_B)}{(N'_G + N_G)}$
$Z_G \approx 1,$ $Z_B \approx 1$	$\dfrac{I_G}{I_B} \approx \dfrac{\sigma_G}{\sigma_B} \cdot \dfrac{g_G}{g_B} \cdot \dfrac{N_G}{N_B}$	$\dfrac{I_G}{I_B} \approx \dfrac{\sigma_G}{\sigma_B} \cdot \dfrac{g_G}{g_B} \cdot \dfrac{N_G^2}{N_B(N_G + N'_G)}$

For the one of these in which it was assumed that the G' are capable of emission an increase in I_G/I_B by several orders of magnitude is predicted at low temperatures, whereas for the other case in which the G' are assumed incapable of emission, only a small temperature dependence is predicted. We find experimentally that in the temperature range from 300° to 80°K, I_G/I_B decreases by a factor of two as shown in Fig. 2. We conclude, therefore, that the Cu acceptors formed from Zn^{65} are incapable of luminescent emission.

Aven, Kastner and Potter[22] have made more detailed studies of ZnS containing Zn^{65}, which in general support the earlier work. They find some dependence of I_G/I_B on N'_G, particularly during the early stage of the transmutation. They also measured the diffuse reflectance during the transmutation and found two absorption bands which can be identified with hole transitions involving the Cu acceptors. These hole transitions in ZnS:Cu with a low-lying Fermi level have also been observed in materials prepared by chemical methods.[23] A high sulfur pressure minimizes the formation of sulfur vacancies, which as double donors, would compensate for the copper acceptors.

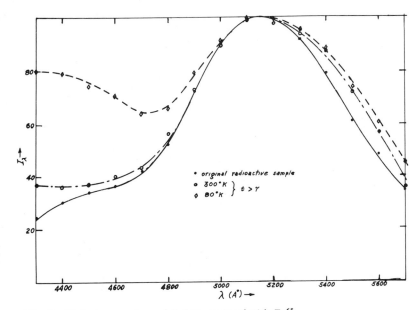

Fig. 2 — Emission spectrum of ZnS:Cu prepared with Zn[65].

On a purely theoretical basis the question of the association of donors and acceptors into pairs has been examined. The donors and acceptors, either impurities or imperfections, are ionized either by electron transfer or thermal ionization at the temperature of crystallization and therefore interact coulombically and are not distributed at random. Prener[24] derived by a statistical analysis the following expression for the fraction α_i of pairs characterized by the interimpurity distance r_i:

$$\alpha_i = AcS_i \exp\left(- \rho_A \rho_D /Kr_i kT\right) \exp\left(-c\sum_{j=1}^{i} S_j\right) \tag{5}$$

where c is the concentration of donors or acceptors, S_i is the number of sites at r_i, ρ_A and ρ_D are the charges on acceptor and donor, K is the static dielectric constant, A is a normalization constant dependent on c, and T is the temperature below which diffusion over interimpurity distances does not occur. Application of Eq. 5 to zinc sulfide with representative activator and coactivator concentrations indicates that association into pairs must be taken into account in the theory of the luminescence of this class of phosphors. In particular, Prener and Weil[25] have shown that the "self-activated" blue emission discussed earlier involves an impurity donor associated with a double acceptor, which is probably a zinc vacancy, and thus forms a singly ionizable acceptor. Apple and Williams[26] have attributed the red emission observed with zinc sulfide containing equivalent concentrations of Group IB and IIIB impurities to radiative transitions between the ground states of donor and acceptor. The spectra for the red emission are dependent on the identification of both donor and acceptor in accordance with this explanation. In addition, the dependence of the intensity of the red emission on temperature and impurity concentration is also consistent with the theory. Koelmans[27] has recently reported evidence that part of the red emission originates from an additional center.

The electronic energy levels of the donor-acceptor pair have been investigated theoretically in the effective mass approximation by Williams.[28] In the analysis, the cores are approximated by point charges; the medium, by a continuous dielectric with optical and static dielectric constants; and the two-particle wave functions, by a single product of the separated donor and acceptor wave functions:

$$\Psi\left(-,+\right) = \Psi_D(-)\,\Psi_A\left(+\right) \tag{6}$$

The permuted product is not included because the electron and positive hole are distinguishable particles. By applying the Hamiltonian, which includes all interparticle interactions, to the wave function of Eq. 6, it is found that for zinc sulfide the transition energies involved in absorption and emission between particular donor and acceptor states increase as a consequence of association. The transition energies for absorption and emission differ because the lattice modes are polarized differently immediately following optical creation of an electron-hole pair and following their optical annihilation.

In contrast to the effective mass approach, Birman[29] has recently proposed a model for the luminescent centers in ZnS:Cu based on the application of crystal field theory modified by relevant aspects of the band theory. This is a tight binding approach concerned with the localized d-orbitals of the activator

and can be considered as focusing attention on the central cell
correction to the effective mass analysis.

III GENERAL CHARACTERISTICS OF ACTIVATOR SYSTEMS

It is evident that the tight binding calculations for heavy
metal activators in alkali halides and the effective mass treatment of donor-acceptor pairs in zinc sulfide are both approximations. An exact theory of the impurities responsible for
luminescence must take account of both the part of the wave
function within the central cell which is atomic-like and of the
diffuse part which is effective mass-like. Within the central
cell, the electronic particle interacts with the total electrostatic
potential in accordance with the free electron mass, whereas
outside the central cell the electronic particle in the effective
mass framework interacts with the perturbing potential of the
impurity in accordance with the effective mass for the appropriate energy band.

The admixture of electron transfer states to the atomic
states of Tl^+ in KCl introduces effective mass character since
these transfer states can be in part described in terms of the
band structure. In the effective mass limit of describing the
Tl^+ in KCl as a deep donor with an electron coulombically
bound to the Tl^{++}, the energy difference between the triplet and
singlet state vanishes. This is in qualitative agreement with
the conclusion from the investigations of oscillator strengths
that the energy difference between the $^3P^\circ$ and $^1P^\circ$ pure spin
states of Tl^+ is reduced as a consequence of crystalline interactions.

The effective mass treatment is more nearly quantitative for
the donors than for the acceptors in zinc sulfide. This arises
in part because the effective mass for electrons in the conduction band is smaller than the effective mass for holes in the
valence band. The acceptor levels are, therefore, deeper and
with the associated more localized wave function become even
deeper because of the central cell correction. Configuration
interaction with the inner d-orbitals becomes increasingly
important.

It is reassuring that some of the most important general
characteristics of luminescent crystals activated by impurities
can be explained qualitatively either on the basis of tight-bind-
ing or effective mass considerations. In the case of KCl:Tl the

Stokes shift of emission compared to absorption arises from the difference in nearest neighbor interactions of the excited state compared to the ground state of Tl^+, whereas in the case of ZnS:Cu,Cl the Stokes shift arises in part from the long range lattice polarization for an exciton trapped at a donor-acceptor pair. The Stokes shift for KCl:Tl is understandable in terms of the local interactions of ions, whereas for ZnS:Cu,Cl the Stokes shift is understandable in part in terms of the polarization of a continuous dielectric.

In general, the broad absorption and emission bands and the Stokes shift arise from the difference in electronic configuration of the activator in the excited and ground states, from the polar character of the medium, and from the orbital electron or hole motion being rapid compared to lattice vibrations. The sharp lines observed with ruby[30] involve emitting and ground states which have the same electronic configuration except for spin; the Stokes shift for transitions involving deep donors or acceptors in germanium and silicon is negligible because of the absence of polar character; and the apparent absence of a Stokes shift for some of the emission from cadmium telluride[31] probably arises because the impurity states are so shallow that the period for orbital motion is less than for lattice vibration. On the other hand, the heavy metal impurities in alkali halides and the acceptors and donors in zinc sulfide satisfy the criteria for broad absorption and emission bands and for a Stokes shift.

REFERENCES

[1] F. Seitz, J. Chem. Phys. 6, 150 (1938)

[2] F. E. Williams, J. Chem. Phys. 19, 457 (1951)

[3] J. E. Mayer, J. Chem. Phys. 1, 220, 327 (1933)

[4] R. W. Gurney and N. F. Mott, Trans. Far. Soc. 35, 69 (1939)

[5] M. Lax, J. Chem. Phys. 20, 1752 (1952)

[6] F. E. Williams and M. H. Hebb, Phys. Rev. 84, 1181 (1951)

[7] P. D. Johnson and F. E. Williams, Phys. Rev. 95, 69 (1954)

[8] R. S. Knox and D. L. Dexter, Phys. Rev. 104, 1245 (1956)

[9] N. D. Potekhina, Optics and Spectroscopy 8, 437 (1960)

[10] N. N. Kristofel, Optics and Spectroscopy 7, 45 (1959)

[11] F. E. Williams, B. Segall and P. D. Johnson, Phys. Rev. 108, 46 (1957)

[12] R. S. Knox, Phys. Rev. 115, 1095 (1959)

[13] S. Sugano, private communication

[14] P. D. Johnson and F. E. Williams, Phys. Rev. 117, 964 (1960)

[15] H. Kamimura and S. Sugano, J. Phys. Soc. Japan 14, 1612 (1959)

[16] F. A. Kroger and J. Dikhoff, Physica 16, 297 (1950)

[17] R. Bowers and N. T. Melamed, Phys. Rev. 99, 1781 (1955)

[18] J. S. Prener and F. E. Williams, J. Electrochem. Soc. 103, 342 (1956)

[19] J. H. Schulman and C. C. Klick, Phys. Rev. 104, 548 (1956)

[20] M. Schon, Ann. Physik 6 (3), 333 (1948)

[21] H. A. Klasens, J. Electrochem. Soc. 100, 72 (1953)

[22] M. Aven, J. Kastner and R. M. Potter, private communication

[23] G. Meijer, J. Phys. Chem. Solids 7, 153 (1958)

[24] J. S. Prener, J. Chem. Phys. 25, 1294 (1956)

[25] J. S. Prener and D. J. Weil, J. Electrochem. Soc. 106, 409 (1959)

[26] E. F. Apple and F. E. Williams, J. Electrochem. Soc. 106, 224 (1959)

[27] H. Koelmans, J. Phys. Chem. Solids 17, 69 (1960)

[28] F. E. Williams, J. Phys. Chem. Solids 12, 265 (1960)

[29] J. L. Birman, Phys. Rev. 121, 144 (1961)

[30] T. H. Maiman, Nature 187, 493 (1960)

[31] G. F. J. Garlick, J. M. Hough and R. A. Fatehally, Proc. Phys. Soc. Lond. 72, 925 (1958)

LIGHT EMISSION BY RECOMBINATION OF FREE CARRIERS CREATED BY ELECTRON BOMBARDMENT

M. Balkanski

(Laboratoire de Physique, École Normale Supérieure, Paris - France)

F. Gans

(Laboratoire d'Infra-rouge Technique et Appliqué - Gif-sur-Yvette-France)

ABSTRACT

When a crystal of cadmium sulfide is bombarded with high energy electrons, avalanche phenomena occur giving rise to high densities of free carriers.

This paper deals with the thermalization of the electrons and recombination of the free carriers.

The process of ionization and creation of secondary carriers is a fast one, while the direct recombination is relatively slow. The carrier density is computed for an energy surface which has the form of a parabola, with its minimum outside the center of the zone.

Direct recombination takes place when the level of the occupied states reaches the abscissa $\vec{k} = 0$.

Experimentally, a blue emission band is observed for crystals irradiated by an electron beam of 20 KeV. The energy of this band at a given temperature is exactly the same as that of the band gap.

I. INTRODUCTION

When a CdS monocrystal is bombarded by a beam of monokinetic electrons with an energy of about 20 KeV, a green emission which corresponds approximately to the energy of the gap may be observed at room temperature. The actual experiments will be described here.

Various hypotheses have been put forward to explain the

phenomenon, but none is quite satisfactory. In view of the fact that the minimum of the conduction band of CdS is not situated in the center of the Brillouin Zone, direct recombination is prohibited in an intrinsic CdS crystal, and only the recombination where phonons take part in the process is possible. The avalanche induced by the beam of electrons produces a very high density of carriers. It is then conceivable that the conduction band is sufficiently filled and that direct transitions at $\vec{k} = 0$ become possible. We will now try to show that this effect may actually take place.

In order to prove this point, we must begin with a study of the penetration of the electrons into the crystal, and therefore of the volume in which the avalanche occurs. We will then try to determine the density of the free carriers resulting from their creation by the beam of electrons, and the recombination and diffusion processes. Lastly, we shall calculate the distribution of the free carriers in the conduction band.

II. PENETRATION OF THE ELECTRON BEAM INTO THE CRYSTAL

A. Depth of Penetration. When a high energy electron passes through a crystal, it suffers a large number of ionizing collisions with the atoms of the crystal. It is thus necessary to apply a statistical method to determine the deviation of the electrons.

In order to simplify the problem, we will suppose that the electrons of the beam propagate along a straight line inside the crystal.

It is possible to show experimentally that when a monokinetic parallel beam of electrons falls perpendicular to the surface of a crystal, the number of electrons penetrating into the crystal to a depth x is:

$$N = N_0 \exp\left[-\left(\frac{x}{cE_0^n}\right)^p\right]$$

E_0 is the initial energy of the electrons; n, c, p, are empirical constants depending on the nature of the crystal. With $X = cE_0^n$ and $\chi = x/X$ we obtain:

$$N = N_0 \exp\left[-\chi^p\right] = N_0 \eta(\chi) \qquad \text{(figure 1.)}$$

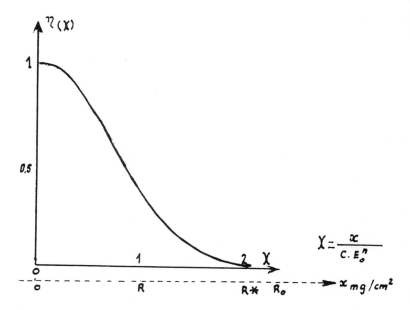

Fig. 1 — Relative number of electrons vs depth of penetration.

For light substances, such as: Al, Si, Cu, Ge, CdS ... $p = 2$ and the curves $N(\chi)$ are the positive halves of Gaussian curves.

$$N(\chi) = N_0 \exp\left[-\chi^2\right]$$

For heavy elements, such as Bi $p = 1$ and $N(\chi)$ follows Lenard's exponential law

$$N(\chi) = N_0 \exp\left[-\chi\right]$$

The relative number γ of electrons absorbed between 0 and x will be expressed as $\gamma = 1 - \eta$, and the relative number of electrons absorbed between x and $x + dx$ will be expressed by $f(x)dx$, with

$$f(xE_0) = \frac{d\gamma}{dx} = \frac{d\eta}{dx} = \frac{px^{p-1}}{(cE_0^n)^p} \exp\left[-\left(\frac{x}{cE_0^n}\right)^p\right]$$

$$f(xE_0) = \frac{p}{X}\,\chi^{p-1}\,\exp\left[-\chi^p\right]$$

For CdS we may take $p = 2$; therefore:

$$N(x E_0) = N_0 \exp[-\chi^2]$$

$$f(x E_0) = \frac{2}{X} \chi \exp[-\chi^2] \qquad \text{(figure 2.)}$$

f is at a maximum for $\chi = 0.7$; which corresponds to $x_{(max)} = 0.7\,X$ and $N(0.7) \simeq 0.6\,N_0$

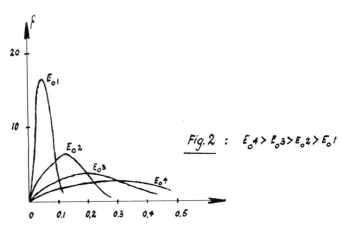

Fig. 2 : $E_04 > E_03 > E_02 > E_01$

Fig. 2 — Relative number of electrons absorbed at depth x, for an incident energy E_0.

f equals 0 for $x = 0$ and $f \simeq 0$ for $x = 2x_{(max)} = 1.4\,X$.

The penetration of the beam is thus undetermined, but it is possible to define an r.m.s. penetration

$$R = \sqrt{\overline{x^2}} = X \text{ (for } p = 2)$$

At depth R,

$$N_R = N_0 \exp[-1] \simeq 0.36\,N_0$$

Only two thirds of the electrons from the beam have been absorbed, but 0.9 of the energy has been absorbed.

At depth $2R$, $N_{2R} = N_0 \exp[-4] \simeq 0.018\,N_0$.

$R = X = c E_0^n$ is given in mg/cm^2 and E_0 in KeV.

If ρ is the crystal density:

$$R_{mg/cm^2} = R_{cm}\,\rho_{mg/cm^3} = c E_0^n$$

$$R_{cm} = \frac{1}{\rho}\,c E_0^n$$

The constants c and n are known for some substances and it is thus possible to plot the curve $R_\mu = f(\rho_\mu/{\rm cm^3})$ for a given E_0 and then compute an approximate value of R for CdS (Figure 3).

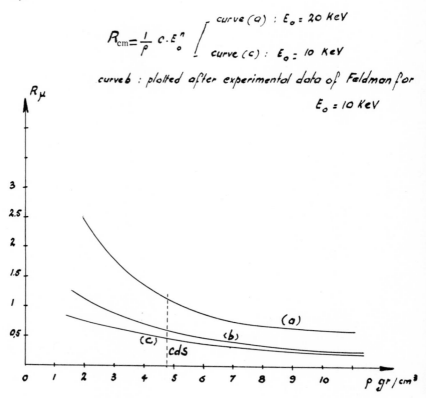

$$R_{\rm cm} = \frac{1}{\rho} \, c \cdot E_0^n$$

curve (a) : E_0 = 20 KeV

curve (c) : E_0 = 10 KeV

curve b : plotted after experimental data of Feldman for

E_0 = 10 KeV

Fig. 3 — r.m.s. penetration R_μ vs crystal density for an energy of the incident electrons E_0.

The density of CdS is $\rho = 4.82$ gr/cm^3; therefore

for $E_0 = 10$ KeV $\rightarrow R_1 \simeq 0.4\ \mu$
for $E_0 = 20$ KeV $\rightarrow R_2 \simeq 1.1\ \mu$

Thus, for CdS, we may take for the penetration of the beam:

$$R_\mu \simeq 13.9 \times 10^{-3}\ E_{0\,KeV}^{1.46}$$

Feldman[2] has studied the penetration into solids of electrons of 1 to 10 KeV energy; he finds also that the curve $N(\chi)$ is the positive half of a Gaussian curve.

He defines the practical maximum penetration R^*, which is the penetration as measured experimentally; he shows that:

$$R^* \simeq 250 \frac{A}{\rho} \left(\frac{E_0}{Z^{1/2}} \right)^{n'} \text{ with } n' = \frac{1.2}{1 - 0.29 \log_{10} Z}$$

A = atomic or molecular weight

Z = atomic number, or number of electrons for one molecule (in chemical compounds)

ρ = density

Some electrons must reach depth R^*, if this depth is to be
measured; R^* is thus smaller that R_0, the maximum electron
penetration depth.

From the curve

$R^* \simeq 2R$ may be deduced. (cf. Figure 1).

Feldman has calculated and measured experimentally R^*
for $E_0 = 10$ KeV and for various substances; we may then plot
the curve $R = f(\rho)$ for $E_0 = 10$ KeV and deduce R for CdS.
(cf. Figure 3).

This experimental method gives the result R (10 KeV) = 0.5 μ.

B. Mean Energy of the Electrons at depth x:

Makhov[1] shows that the mean energy of the electrons in the
beam, at depth x, is

$$\overline{E}(x) = \frac{E_0}{\eta(\chi)} \int_0^1 \exp\left[- \left(\frac{\chi}{1 - \xi^n} \right)^p \right] d\xi$$

with

$$\xi = \frac{E(x)}{E_0}$$

For CdS, we may take $p = 2$ and $n \simeq 1.46$. It is possible to
calculate an approximate solution:

$$\overline{E}_1(x) \simeq E_0 \exp. (-\chi^{0.9}) = E_0 \overline{\xi}_1(\chi)$$

In order to compute the time necessary for the thermalization of the incident electrons, a solution which is an approximation of the previous one may be taken:

$$\overline{E}_2(x) \simeq E_0 \left[1 - \frac{\chi}{1.5} \right] = E_0 \overline{\xi}_2(\chi) \quad \text{(cf. Figure 4)}$$

These curves cross at $\chi = 0$ and $\chi = 1$.

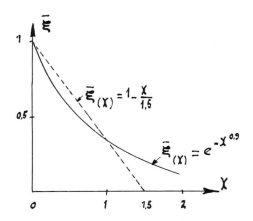

Fig. 4 — Relative mean energy of the electrons vs
depth of penetration x.

Let $\overrightarrow{v}$ be the drift of the electrons from the beam; if it is
supposed that they propagate along a straight line, their kinetic
energy at depth x will be

$$E(x) = \frac{1}{2} m \left(\overrightarrow{v}(x) \right)^2$$

and we may write

$$\left| \overrightarrow{v} \right| = \sqrt{\frac{2 \cdot E}{m}} = \frac{dx}{dt}$$

The thermalization time is thus

$$t_1 - t_0 = \sqrt{\frac{m}{2 \cdot E_0}} \int_0^{1 \cdot 5R} \frac{dx}{\sqrt{1 - \dfrac{x}{1.5\,R}}} = \sqrt{\frac{m}{2\,E_0}} \times 3R$$

This expression shows that for CdS, electrons with an
energy of 20 KeV thermalize in a period of time between 10^{-13}
and 10^{-14} sec. We may thus conclude that the recombination
process is very slow compared with the thermalization of the
carriers.

C. Absorption of the Beam Energy.

Young[3] has studied the passing of electrons through films of
Al_2O_3 and shown that the distribution as a function of depth of

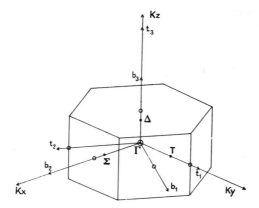

Fig. 5 – Brillouin Zone in CdS.

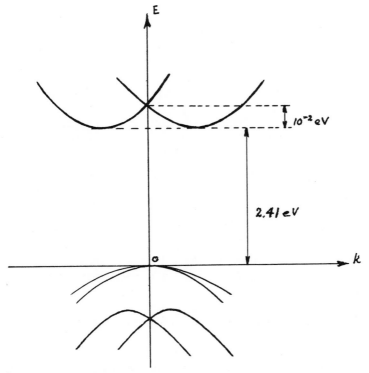

Fig. 6 – Band structure in CdS, near the center of the Brillouin Zone in the direction $k_{(x)}$ (or $k_{(y)}$).

the absorbed energy is practically constant over the whole
region penetrated by the electrons.

Let P_0 be the initial energy received by one cm² of the crystal in one second, and $W(x)$ the total energy absorbed between
0 and x in one second; we then obtain

$$\frac{d\,W(x)}{dx} \simeq \text{const.} \simeq \frac{P_0}{R}$$

Makhov[1] shows also that $(dW(x))/(dx)$ is practically constant between 0 and R and this quantity tends towards zero
when x becomes greater than R.

III. CREATION OF ELECTRON-HOLE PAIRS

When a high energy particle penetrates into a crystal, the
number of pairs created depends only on its energy, and not on
the nature of the crystal.

Shockley[4] determined the mean total energy necessary to
produce a pair in a reverse biased p-n junction.

$$E_p = E_i + 2E_f + E_R$$

E_i is the threshold energy for a carrier, measured from the
band edge, above which it may produce a hole electron pair;
$E_i = E_{gap}$.

E_R is the mean kinetic energy dissipated to phonons between
two ionizing collisions; unfortunately, it is very difficult to
estimate E_R in the case of the cathodoluminescence of CdS.

E_f is the mean final kinetic energy of the non ionizing
carriers (dissipated to phonons).

$E_f \simeq 0.6\,E_i$ (the energy surfaces are assumed to be parabolic).

For CdS, we have $E_g = 2.41$ eV and therefore $E_p \simeq 5.3 + E_R$ eV.

According to Spicer,[5] substances with a well ordered crystalline structure need an energy $E_p \sim 3E_{gap}$, while those with a
slightly disordered structure need only an energy close to E_{gap}.
For CdS, in which the structure is of this type, it may be assumed that $E_p \simeq 2.5\,E_g$, that is $E_p \simeq 6$ eV.

For the following calculations, it seems that $E_p = 6$ eV
would be a fair approximation.

Assuming that the absorption curve $W(x)$ is linear in the
region traversed by the beam, we may deduce the number of
pairs generated per cm³ per second:

$$g = \frac{1}{E_p} \cdot \frac{P_0}{R}$$

$P_0 = N_0 E_0$ and N_0 is the number of electrons falling per second on 1 cm² of the crystal $\simeq 10^{18}/cm^2$ sec.

If $E_0 = 20$ KeV, we will find, for CdS $R \simeq 1.1 \mu$ whence $g = 3 \times 10^{25} /cm^3$ sec.

Under permanent operating conditions, the actual density of the pairs is given by

$$g + D\frac{d^2n}{dx^2} - \frac{n}{\tau} = 0$$

However, between 0 and R, the diffusion may be neglected in comparison with the volume recombination, and we may write: $n \simeq \tau g$.

The volume lifetime of the carriers, τ, is difficult to evaluate with precision but we may assume that it is around 10^{-7} sec. This gives in the above mentioned example

$$n = 3 \times 10^{18} \text{ cm}^{-3}$$

IV. DISTRIBUTION OF FREE CARRIERS IN THE CONDUCTION BAND

In a semiconductor, the density of states in the conduction band of energy between the edge W_c and energy W is:

$$n' = \frac{8}{3} \cdot \frac{\pi}{h^3} \cdot \sum_i g_i \, (2\,m*)^{3/2}(W - W_c)^{3/2}$$

g_1 is a constant equal to the number of valleys in the conduction band in any given direction i.

For CdS, hexagonal in structure, only the directions perpendicular to axis c are of interest.

Thus

$$n' = \frac{8}{3} \cdot \frac{\pi}{h^3} \cdot 6\,(2\,m*)^{3/2}(W - W_c)^{3/2} \qquad m* = 0.2\,m$$

whence

$$n'_{\text{cm}-3} = 24.3 \times 10^{20} \, (W - W_c)^{3/2}_{\text{eV}}$$

At $\vec{k} = 0$, we have $W - W_c = 10^{-2}$ eV; whence $N' = 2.43 \times 10^{18}$ cm⁻³.

We have seen above that the density of the free electrons about 3.10^{18} cm⁻³ for $E_0 = 20$ KeV; consequently, since the density of states between the edge of the conduction band W_c and the center of the Brillouin Zone $W(\vec{k} = 0)$ is $N' = 2.43 \times 10^{18}\,\text{cm}^{-3}$, we may hope to find free electrons at $\vec{k} = 0$.

The whole crystal is no longer at thermal equilibrium in view of the avalanche induced by the beam and it is therefore not possible any more to speak of a Fermi level. However, as is the case for reverse biased p-n junctions, a quasi Fermi level E_q for electrons may be defined by the expression:

$$n = N_c \, \exp\left[\frac{E_q - E_c}{kT}\right]$$

n is the density of the free carriers. The energies are given with regard to the level

$$E_i = \frac{1}{2}\,(E_v + E_c + kT\,\log\frac{N_v}{N_c})$$

we may write:

$$n(x) = n_i \, \exp.\left[\frac{\phi_n(x)}{kT}\right]$$

n_i = intrinsic density $= \sqrt{N_c \cdot N_v}\,\exp\left[-E_g/2\,kT\right]$ and $\phi_n = E_q - E_i$ (at equilibrium $\phi_n = 0$). Whence:

$$n = 2\,\left(\frac{2\pi\,kT}{h^2}\right)^{3/2}(m_c^* \cdot m_v^*)^{3/4}\,\exp\left[\frac{\phi_n - E_g/2}{kT}\right]$$

if the density of the free carriers is $10^{18}\,\text{cm}^{-3}$ at 300°K, we find:

$$\phi_n = 1/2\,E_g - 0.05\text{ eV } (\text{ if we take } m_c^* = 0.2\,m \text{ and } m_v^* \simeq m).$$

It may occur, in certain cases, that the quasi Fermi level is in the conduction band, or close to it.

In the non disturbed region, it merges into the Fermi level. The diffusion current towards the non-disturbed region is:

$$j = \mu n\,\frac{\partial\,\phi_n}{\partial x}.$$

It is constant, being equal to the current emitted by the electron gun; whence $(\partial\,\phi_n)/(\partial x)$ varies thus as $1/n$.

The density of the beam is $n'' \simeq 1.2 \times 10^8\text{ cm}^{-3}$ in the perturbed region of the crystal, the density of the diffused electrons will be $\sim 10^5\text{ cm}^{-3}$, i.e., $n'' \ll n_i$. This region is almost intrinsic.

V. EXPERIMENT

When we began this work, we intended to build a source of very high luminance in the infrared or the visible region of the spectrum. To this end, we constructed a lamp in which electrons were projected onto a luminescent screen by using an electron gun. The anode of this gun was raised to a high potential, about 20 KeV. In order to avoid the destruction of the screen, the latter is made to rotate rapidly.

However, during the course of our experiments, evidence was found of a new property of the radiation of crystalline luminescent powders bombarded by electron beams of high density and energy. The technical characteristics of this radiation, particularly its very short duration, appeared to be remarkably favorable for application to optical telecommunications.

Moreover, this effect posed a scientific problem, the characteristics of the radiation emitted by the screen being quite unexpected.

The set up of the first experiments is to be seen in Figure 7. This set up was simplified later on.

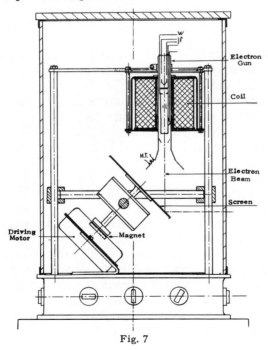

Fig. 7

The figure shows the gun, the beam of electrons, the rotating screen which is mounted on the same axis as a magnet. This magnet is itself driven by another magnet mounted on the axis of a motor. Motor and magnet are enclosed in a vacuum tight box.

In view of the results obtained with powders, we were led to bombard immobile monocrystals also (Figure 8). On the figure may be seen the set up of the experiment: the gun, the concentration coil and the target. The small Dewar flask permits the cooling of the crystal.

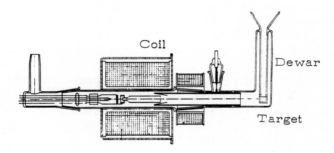

Fig. 8

The experiments have been carried out with cadmium sul·fide, either pure, or silver activated (the silver concentration is between 10^{-6} and 10^{-4}).

For the experiments with monocrystals, we always worked with non-activated crystals, as pure as possible.

The intensity of the electron beam did not exceed 100 μA, the acceleration voltage remained under 20 kV.

VI. RESULTS

Under these conditions, a brilliant spot, about 0.3 mm in diameter may be observed.

Our goal was the construction of point red source of high luminance capable of being modulated, obtained with silver-activated cadmium sulfide. We actually reached this result, and a luminance, difficult to estimate, but of the order of some tens of stilbs was observed; this is very high, considering the low sensitivity of the eye to the radiation (λ = 7200 Å) emitted.

However, besides this red radiation another one may be observed, green in color, in the enighborhood of 5100 Å. The ratio of the intensity of the green and red emission depends:

1° - on the current density; the larger this is, the more green is emissted;

2° - on the voltage applied between anode and cathode: the ratio green /red rises with the voltage.

3° - on the concentration of impurities contained in the substance; the purer this is, the easier it is to obtain the green radiation;

4° - on the state of the substance; for a given current it is easier to obtain the green radiation from a monocrystal than from a powder.

We also noticed that when the current intensity rises, the red band becomes wider, while the green band–of practically constant width–shifts towards longer wavelengths (around 5400 Å). It disappears for higher current densities and it is replaced by a new band around 6400 Å. The presence of this new

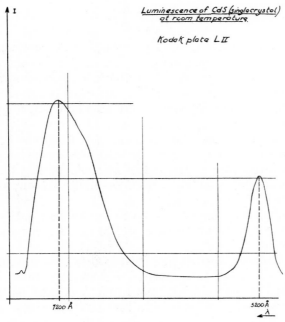

Fig. 9

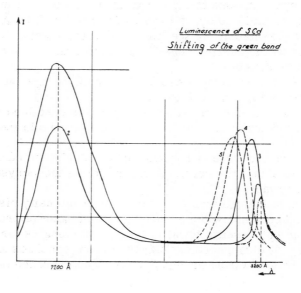

Fig. 10

band seems to be connected with a noticeable destruction of the substance. If the bombardment is carried out on a crystal cooled to a temperature close to liquid air temperature, a blue band (4900 Å) which corresponds closely to the absorption edge at liquid air temperature may also be observed, but not with all specimens.

Another effect becomes apparent, a new intense green band, so intense that in some specimens the blue emission disappears. This green emission which seems to compete with the blue one, has characteristics which closely resemble the emission known as "Ewles-Krȫger spectrum".

Similar effects may be observed in mercury sulfide; under cathodic bombardment, this substance emits a red radiation, close to 6400 Å.

When all these results are put together, one striking fact emerges: at a given temperature, the wavelength which may be observed at the farthest point of the spectrum on the violet side coincides very closely with the absorption edge of the spectrum, and therefore with the emission which would take place when an electron returns directly from the conduction band to the valence band.

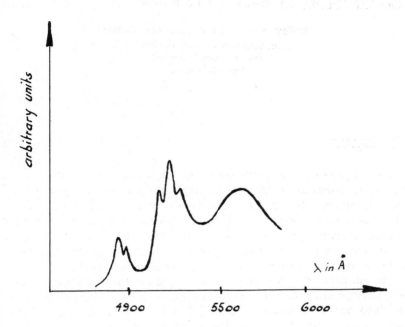

Fig. 11 — Light Emission in CdS crystal at 77°K.

We have shown above that in CdS, under the conditions prevailing in our experiments, this mechanism is indeed possible.

Other interpretations however cannot yet be excluded. We are continuing work on the subject to test their validity.

This work has been performed with the support of the U.S. Signal Corps under contract R & D 37 and 197 and the U.S. Department of the Navy under contract n° 62558-2720, and with the help of MM François Bombré and Gilles de Gaalon.

REFERENCES

[1] A. F. Makhov, Fiz. Tverd. Tela, 2, 2161 (1960)
[2] Feldman, Phys. Rev., 117, 455 (1960)
[3] Young, Phys. Rev., 103, 292 (1956)
[4] W. Shockley, Solid State Electronics, 2, 35 (1961)
[5] W. E. Spicer, R.C.A. Laboratories, Princeton, N.Y.

ON THE THEORY OF THERMAL QUENCHING OF LUMINESCENCE

H. Payen de la Garanderie and D. Curie
Laboratoire de Luminescence
Faculté des Sciences
Paris (France)

ABSTRACT

An expression is derived for the light efficiency, which is of
the same form as in Mott and Seitz's theory; but it is shown
that the probability of radiative transitions, which is usually
considered as a constant term, increases indeed for increasing
temperatures. While the probability of a transition starting
from a given quantum state is treated as a constant, the effective number of states leading to the transition increases.

In addition, the deviation from a Boltzmann distribution of
the energy distribution among the vibrational states of the light
centers has been studied. Such a deviation exists, but does not
seem as a general rule to play an important part.

1. DESCRIPTION OF THE EMITTING AND NON-EMITTING PROCESSES IN THE CONFIGURATIONAL CURVE MODEL.

Let us consider an activator center, which is described in
the configurational diagram by two configuration curves $U^f(r)$
and $U^e(r)$. U^f is the potential energy of the center in the fundamental electronic state, U^e is the same energy for the electronically excited state.

Let n_j $(j = 0, 1, 2, ...)$ be the number of centers which are
at the $j-$th vibrational level of the excited state, and ν_e the
frequency of vibration of the ions in this state.

A. The Emitting Process.

As a result of the absorption of the exciting radiation q, the
center reaches a high vibrational level j_0. Then it emits several
phonons and falls to a lower level j, and finally the light emit-

334

ting transition (emission of photons) occurs, with a rate p. We shall call

$$A = a \; \frac{1}{e^{h\nu_e/kT} - 1} \qquad E = a\left(1 + \frac{1}{e^{h\nu_e/kT} - 1}\right)$$

the respective rates of phonon absorption and phonon emission.

The equilibrium equations are:

(I) $\begin{cases} \dfrac{dn_0}{dt} = 0 = -A\,n_0 + E\,n_1 - p\,n_0 \\[2ex] \dfrac{dn_1}{dt} = 0 = A\,n_0 - (A + E)n_1 + E\,n_2 - p\,n_1 \\[2ex] \cdots\cdots\cdots\cdots \\[2ex] \dfrac{dn_j}{dt} = 0 = A\,n_{j-1} - (A + E)n_j + E\,n_{j+1} - p\,n_j \\[2ex] \cdots\cdots\cdots\cdots \\[2ex] \dfrac{dn_{j_0}}{dt} = 0 = A\,n_{j_0-1} - (A + E)n_{j_0} + E\,n_{j_0+1} - p\,n_{j_0} + q \end{cases}$

We are allowed to assume $p \ll A$ and E, in order to obtain between the n_j a distribution which differs only slightly from a Boltzmann equilibrium:

$$n_j = n_0\, e^{-jh\nu_e/kT} + \epsilon_j$$

ϵ_j is a small correction.

We assume also that p is independent of the emitting state j: p is supposed to have the same value for the emitting transitions coming from levels with different j's.

Both these approximations are needed in order to obtain simple results. They are actually satisfactory, as is shown by the study of the shape of the emission bands; at high temperatures (indeed, the temperatures where thermal quenching occurs), this shape is conveniently described by the classical Boltzmann factor:

$$I\,(h\nu)\,d\,(h\nu) \propto \exp\left[-U^e(r)/kT\right] \cdot \frac{dr}{d\,(h\nu)}\;d\,(h\nu)$$

Another simplification lies in the fact that we have described the absorption transition as leading to only one vibrational state with the quantum number j_0. Actually, the excitation leads to several levels in the vicinity of j_0, but all of them are located much higher than the emitting levels $j = 0, 1, 2, ...$
The results do not depend on the quantum number j_0.

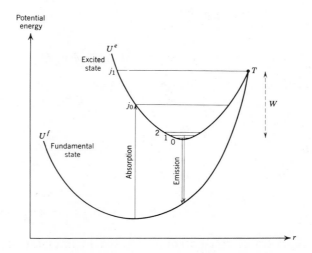

Fig. 1 — The well-known configurational curves for a light center.

B. The Radiationless Process.

At high temperatures, a competitive process may also occur. By a series of phonon absorption transitions, the center reaches the crossing point T. Let j_1 be the corresponding vibrational level. At the crossing point, the radiationless transition between the excited state U^e and the fundamental state U^f occurs with a high probability.

The j_1 level is supposed to be much higher than the j_0 level, in a good phosphor.

We thus complete the differential system (I) by:

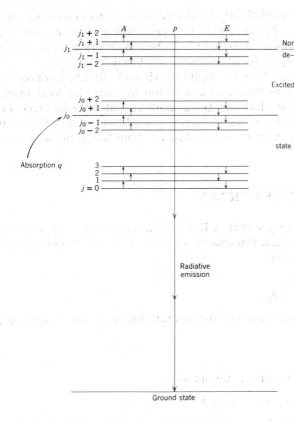

Fig. 2 – The different vibrational levels involved in the electronically excited state of the center.

$$(\text{II}) \begin{cases} \dfrac{dn_{j_0+1}}{dt} = 0 = A\,n_{j_0} - (A+E)n_{j_0+1} + En_{j_0+2} - pn_{j_0+1} \\[2mm] \cdots\cdots\cdots \\[2mm] \dfrac{dn_j}{dt} = 0 = A\,n_{j-1} - (A+E)n_j + En_{j+1} - pn_j \\[2mm] \cdots\cdots\cdots \\[2mm] \dfrac{dn_{j_1}}{dt} = 0 = A\,n_{j_1-1} - (A+E)n_{j_1} + En_{j_1+1} - pn_{j_1} - sn_{j_1} \end{cases}$$

where s is the probability of the radiationless transition at T. We assume $s \gg p$; otherwise no appreciable thermal quenching would occur. As a consequence of this assumption, we shall put all the n_j equal to zero above the level j_1.

We emphasize that the systems (I) and (II) are nothing else but a way for describing in a detailed manner the well-known principles of the Mott and Seitz theory. But we shall find in Section 2 that this detailed formulation leads to an expression for the light efficiency which differs from the generally accepted one.

2. THE LIGHT EFFICIENCY

The radiatively emitted light intensity being I_γ and the intensity of the radiationless transitions $I_{n\gamma}$, let us define the light efficiency by:

$$\eta = \frac{I_\gamma}{q} = \frac{I_\gamma}{I_\gamma + I_{n\gamma}}$$

A. First we shall neglect the deviations from the Boltzmann distribution:

$$\epsilon_j \equiv 0$$

Then the summation involved in

$$I_\gamma = p \left(n_0 + n_1 + \ldots + n_{j_1} \right)$$

is straightforward:

$$I_\gamma = p n_0 \frac{1 - e^{-j_1 h \nu_e / kT}}{1 - e^{-h \nu_e / kT}}$$

while the intensity of the radiationless transitions is:

$$I_{n\gamma} = s n_{j_1} = s n_0 e^{-j_1 h \nu_e / kT}$$

We put $W = j_1 h \nu_e$ (W is the activation energy leading to the crossing point T), and obtain:

$$(1) \quad \eta = \frac{p \dfrac{1 - e^{-W/kT}}{1 - e^{-h\nu_e/kT}}}{p \dfrac{1 - e^{-W/kT}}{1 - e^{-h\nu_e/kT}} + s e^{-W/kT}}$$

As j_1 is a highly excited level, $W \gg kT$, $e^{-W/kT} \ll 1$, and the simpler formula:

$$(1') \quad \eta = \frac{p \cdot \dfrac{1}{1 - e^{-h\nu_e/kT}}}{p \cdot \dfrac{1}{1 - e^{-h\nu_e/kT}} + s e^{-W/kT}}$$

appears to be valid in most cases.

This expression is not very different from the usual Mott and Seitz one. Both are indeed of the same form. But usually I_γ is considered to be a constant term, while here I_γ increases with increasing temperature.

We have assumed in the usual way that p is a constant; p means the probability of the transition starting from a given quantum state. I_γ increases because the effective number of states leading to a light transition increases with temperature.

At the Debye temperature $kT = h\nu_e$, $I_\gamma = 1.58 \, p n_0$.

B. Study of the Deviations from the Boltzmann distribution

We substitute in the differential system (I), (II) the expressions:

$$n_j = n_0 e^{-jh\nu_e/kT} + \epsilon_j$$

In this way we are led to a set of recurrence equations giving the ϵ_j. If in these equations we neglect the second order terms $p \epsilon_j$, we obtain:

$$\frac{dn_j}{dt} = 0 = A \epsilon_{j-1} - (A+E) \epsilon_j + E \epsilon_{j+1} - p n_0 e^{-jh\nu_e/kT}$$

for all j's, except $j = j_0$ and $j = j_1$. For $j = j_0$:

$$\frac{dn_{j_0}}{dt} = 0 = A\epsilon_{j_0-1} - (A+E)\epsilon_{j_0} + E\epsilon_{j_0+1} - pn_0 e^{-j_0 h\nu_e/kT} + q$$

while the equation obtained for $j = j_1$ is not interesting and only assures us that:

$$q = I_\gamma + I_{n\gamma}$$

This system is solved easily. The results are:

$$\epsilon_j = \frac{pn_0}{E}\left[\frac{E^2}{a^2}(1 - e^{-jh\nu_e/kT}) - \frac{E}{a}je^{-jh\nu_e/kT}\right]$$

for $j \leqslant j_0$, and

$$\epsilon_j = \frac{pn_0}{E}\left[\frac{E^2}{a^2}(1 - e^{-jh\nu_e/kT}) - \frac{E}{a}je^{-jh\nu_e/kT}\right]$$

$$- \frac{q}{a}\left[1 - e^{-(j-j_0)h\nu_e/kT}\right]$$

for $j > j_0$.

The important point is that these deviations do not show any tendency to accumulate and increase indefinitely for higher and higher values of j. Of course, if this would be the case, the above assumption of an approximate Boltzmann distribution extending from $j = 0$ to $j = j_1$ would be meaningless. But on the other hand all the ϵ_j remain of the same order.

The formulation of

$$\eta = \frac{I_\gamma}{I_\gamma + I_{n\gamma}}$$

remains of course valid, and also:

$$I_\gamma = p(n_0 + n_1 + \ldots + n_{j_1})$$

$$I_{n\gamma} = s n_{j_1}$$

If the values for the ϵ_j's are introduced in these formulas, rather intricate results are obtained and we shall not reproduce them. As an approximation, I_γ does not suffer any important change from its preceeding expression,

$$I_\gamma = p n_0 \frac{1 - e^{-j_1 h\nu_e/kT}}{1 - e^{-h\nu_e/kT}}$$

but $I_{n\gamma}$ is slightly enhanced,

$$I_{n\gamma} = s\,(n_0\, e^{-j_1 h\nu_e/kT} + \epsilon_{j_1})$$

One obtains thus:

$$(2)\quad \eta = \left(1 + \frac{s}{a}\right) \frac{p \dfrac{1 - e^{-W/kT}}{1 - e^{-h\nu_e/kT}}}{p \dfrac{1 - e^{-W/kT}}{1 - e^{-h\nu_e/kT}} + s e^{-W/kT} + p\,\dfrac{s}{a}\,\dfrac{1}{1 - e^{-h\nu_e/kT}}}$$

(2) reduces to the above formula (1) in the limiting case $s \ll a$. Then the deviations from the Boltzmann equilibrium may be neglected.

3. COMPARISON BETWEEN OUR FORMULA

$$(1)\quad \eta = \frac{p \dfrac{1 - e^{-W/kT}}{1 - e^{-h\nu_e/kT}}}{p \dfrac{1 - e^{-W/kT}}{1 - e^{-h\nu_e/kT}} + s e^{-W/kT}}$$

AND THE USUAL MOTT FORMULA

$$(3)\quad \eta = \frac{p}{p + s e^{-W/kT}}$$

We performed this comparison in the case of the 3050 Å emission of KCl (4.10^{-5} Tl) ($^3P_1 \rightarrow {}^1S_0$ transition), using the experimental results described by P. Johnson and F. E. Williams.[1] For KCl (Tl), $h\nu_e$ is not an adjustable parameter, and is rather accurately known from spectral emission studies:

$$h\nu_e \approx 0.011 \text{ eV}$$

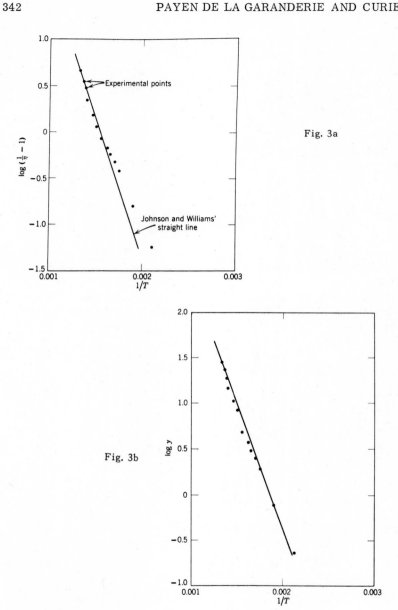

Fig. 3a

Fig. 3b

Fig. 3 — Comparison between formulas (1) and (3) and the experimental results. In order for formula (3) to be valid, $\log((\frac{1}{\eta} - 1)$ would be a linear function of $1/T$. In order for formula (1) to be valid, $\log y$ must be computed as a linear function of $1/T$, where

$$y = (\frac{1}{\eta} - 1) \cdot \frac{1}{1 - e^{-h\nu_e/kT}}$$

Figure 3A shows that the agreement between (3) and the experimental results is not perfectly satisfactory. Williams and Johnson succeeded in giving a value of W:

$W \approx 0.60$ eV

by using the high quenching region. The low quenching region would lead to a smaller value of W, $W \approx 0.47$ eV.

Figure 3B shows that with formula (1) the fit is better. We have used:

$W = 0.53$ eV $\qquad h\nu_e = 0.011$ eV $\qquad \dfrac{s}{p} = 92{,}300$

The difference between our value 0.53 eV and the Johnson William's value of 0.60 eV lies in the scope of the probable error ($\approx 10\%$) which was expected by these authors of their own results.

REFERENCE

[1]P. D. Johnson and F. E. Williams, J. Chem. Phys., 20, 124, (1952).

TRANSFORMATION OF COPPER CENTERS AND CENTER CHEMISTRY IN ZINC SULFIDE PHOSPHORS

N. Riehl and R. Sizmann

Technische Hochschule, München, Germany

ABSTRACT

Addition of Cu to ZnS may cause the appearance of two different kinds of luminescence centers: the well known green emitting and the blue emitting centers. The blue emitting Cu-centers arise by increasing the ratio: Cu-concentration/concentration of the charge compensating constituents. This indicates that the blue emitting centers are formed by the addition of Cu to the green emitting centers. The blue emitting centers can be transformed into green emitting centers by heat treatment at surprisingly low temperatures (200°C and lower). The green $\rightleftharpoons$ blue transformation occurs with observable velocity even at room temperature. To each temperature between 20° and 350°C belongs a definite equilibrium ratio of green and blue emitting centers. By fast cooling down to room temperature, this equilibrium ratio can be frozen in, so that measurements of the different ratios can be made at room temperature. It takes several weeks before the ratio again reaches the room temperature equilibrium value.

The green $\rightleftharpoons$ blue transformation can be considered as an association or a dissociation of an interstitial Cu^+ ion with an Cu^+ ion on a lattice site depending upon the duration of the transformation. The question of what happens with the charge compensating constituents ("coactivators", S^{2-} vacancies, etc.) when these transformations take place is discussed.

There exist two types of transformations: a quite reversible and an irreversible one. The first can be considered to be a dissociation of the blue emitting centers, where the removed interstitial Cu^+ ion diffuses to a position from which it can return to its original position close to the lattice site Cu^+ ion (and form again a "blue center") if the original temperature is

344

restored. The irreversible transformation (which can go only in the direction blue →green) is connected with deeper changes of the whole system and appears only under experimental conditions which permit some chemical reactions on the surface of the crystal.

Some results are described which prove the existence of these two transformation effects and which clarify the conditions for the prevalence of one or the other. Moreover, the work delivers a verified value for the reaction enthalpy of the green ⇌ blue transformation (0.76 ev).

1. INTRODUCTION

Addition of Cu to ZnS may cause the appearance of two different kinds of luminescence centers: the well known green emitting and the blue emitting centers.[1]

It seems almost certain that the green emitting center consists of a Cu^+ ion replacing a Zn^{2+} ion of the host lattice. The lack of positive charge must be compensated in some way. Different possibilities can be imagined for this charge compensation:

1) Substitution of a further Zn^{2+} ion by a trivalent positive ion (Al^{3+}, Ga^{3+});
2) Substitution of a halide ion for a S^2 ion;
3) Appearance of S^2 vacancies (one S^2 vacancy compensating two Cu^+ centers);
4) Appearance of interstitial Zn^{2+} ions (one interstitial Zn^{2+} ion compensating two Cu^+ centers).

The absence of paramagnetic configurations in unexcited ZnS seems to rule out other possibilities of charge compensation.

The blue emitting Cu centers arise when the ratio (Cu concentration)/(concentration of the charge-compensating constituents) is increased. This indicates that the blue-emitting centers are formed by addition of Cu to the green-emitting centers.

As we reported earlier[2] blue-emitting centers can be transformed into green-emitting centers by heat treatment at surprisingly low temperatures (200°C and lower). Later we found that the green ⇌ blue transformation occurs with observable speed even at room temperature.[3] At quite definite equilibrium ratio of green and blue emitting centers is associated with each temperature between 20° and 350°C. By rapid cooling to room temperature this equilibrium ratio can be frozen in so that measurements of the different ratios can be made at room temperature. It takes several weeks for the ratio to attain the room-temperature equilibrium value once more. From the fact that all these transformations are possible at such low temperatures we concluded that they are due only to displacements of interstitial particles and not of atoms on lattice sites. This led us to a model of the blue emitting Cu centers shown in Fig. 1. This model is very similar to the picture proposed by us[2] and by Kröger[4] several years earlier, the only difference lying in the absence of any paramagnetic constituents in the new model.

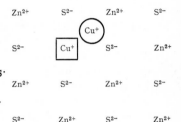

Fig. 1 — Scheme of a blue-emitting center (Cu^+ ion on an interstitial site adjacent to a Cu^+ ion on an lattice site).

Therefore the green $\rightleftharpoons$ blue trans·formation can be considered as a dissociation and association respectively of an interstitial Cu^+ ion with a Cu^+ ion on a lattice site. The question arises what happens to the charge compensating constituents ("coactivators", S^{2-} vacancies, etc.) when these transformations take place. If an interstitial Cu^+ ion is associated with a lattice site Cu^+ ion the whole structure has a double positive charge. The interstitial Cu^+ ion now plays the role of a "charge compensator" and further charge compensating constituents are no longer necessary. If they were present earlier they must now disappear to maintain electroneutrality. Since, on the other hand, these transformations take place at very low temperatures, a diffusion and disappearance of coactivators (e.g. Cl^- or S^{2-} vacancies cannot be assumed, we were led to the conclusion that in the green emitting ZnS(Cu) phosphors under consideration charge compensation is managed by easily moveable interstitial Zn^{2+} ions. If a surplus of Cu enters the crystal and forms blue-emitting Cu centers ("associates") interstitial Zn^{2+} leaves the crystal so that the immigrating Cu^+ ions replace interstitial Zn^{2+} ions in their function as charge-compensators.

To the extent that the blue-emitting phosphor is formed we can observe the green $\rightleftharpoons$ blue transformation caused by four variations of temperature as mentioned above. There exist two types of transformation: a quite reversible and an irreversible

one. The first can be considered as a dissociation of the blue-
emitting centers where the removed interstitial Cu^+ ion diffuses
to a position from which it can return to its original position
near the lattice site Cu^+ ion (and once again form a blue center)
when the original temperature is restored. The irreversible
transformation (which can only occur in the direction blue $\rightarrow$
green) is connected with more fundamental changes of the whole
system and appears only under experimental conditions which
enable some chemical reactions to take place on the surface
of the crystal.

In the present paper some results are described which prove
the existence of these two transformation effects and clarify
the conditions for the prevalence of the one or other of them.
Moreover the work results in a verified value for the reaction
enthalpy of the green $\rightleftharpoons$ blue transformation.

2. METHODS AND MATERIALS

It is well known that in phosphors of the group under consideration the ratio of the intensities of two different emission
bands depends strongly on the temperature at which the observation is made and on the intensity (density) of excitation. As we
were interested only in the changes of the concentrations of the
blue-or green-emitting centers we used the same conditions of
excitation, i.e., the same temperature and the same intensity
of the exciting radiation (366 mμ) in every set of experiments.
The observations were mostly made at room temperature or
at $-180°C$. As will be seen below, the reaction enthalpy of the
blue green-transformation is quite independent of the conditions
of excitation and also of the technique of separating the two
emission bands.

Two different arrangements were used for heating the phosphors (in the region $20° - 350°C$).

A) The sample was distributed as a thin sheet on a metallic
plate which could be heated and cooled to definite temperatures
and placed in a 1 l glass bulb (which was not heated). The bulb
was evacuated or filled with an inert gas. After heating to the
desired temperature the sample was cooled to room temperature and removed from the bulb.

B) The sample was placed in a small quartz tube and the tube
closed by fusing under vacuum. The filled tube was heated to
the desired temperature and then cooled to room temperature.

These two methods of heating give distinctly different effects because evaporation of volatile constituents or reaction products is possible in case A but not in case B.

The initially used phosphor was a ZnS(Cu) with a strongly blue and a weakly green emission (when observed at room temperature). The details of preparation were previously described.[2,3] This phosphor will be designated "Preparation I". (With other, similar phosphors we obtained essentially the same results).

The total Cl content of the phosphor was 1 atom Cl per 1700 molecules ZnS. (Determined in a very accurate manner by neutron activation analysis).

Another phosphor ("Preparation II") was also used, namely a mixture of "Preparation I" with 5% NH_4Cl. If heated to temperatures above 100°C this mixture undergoes some chemical reactions (especially in presence of air), which are discussed below. Thus the effect of heating this preparation is essentially different from the effect on the pure phosphor ("Preparation I").

3. RESULTS

a) Difference between reversible and irreversible blue-green transformations.

When heated in closed quartz tubes at a definite temperature (20° − 350°C) the phosphor soon reaches a state with a definite equilibrium between the concentrations of blue and green emitting centers. To each temperature there belongs a definite ratio between these two concentrations (if the total initial Cu-content is fixed). Prolongation of heating at the same temperature does not change the ratio. This ratio can be frozen in and measured at room-temperature or at −180°C. The equilibrium state can be reached from both sides: it is insignificant whether the temperature is reached coming from higher temperatures (i.e. starting with a prevailing green emitting phosphor) or from deeper temperatures (i.e. starting with a prevailing blue emitting phosphor). Fig. 2 shows the ratio blue emission/green emission (measured at room-temperature) depending on the temperature of heating.

If method A is used (a thin sheet of phosphor heated in a large evacuated bulb) transformation can be obtained only in the

direction blue → green but not in the opposite direction. The
heating under these conditions causes some irreversible processes. These are connected with the evaporation of some constituents and reaction products. This evaporation is extremely
strong if NH_4Cl is admixed to the phosphor ("Preparation II").
A yellowish deposit (sulphur) can be observed on the cold parts

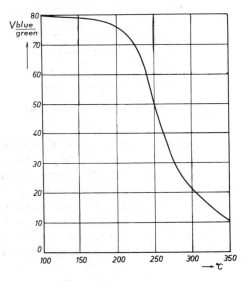

Fig. 2 — Equilibrium values of the blue/green
ratio as a function of the heating temperature.

of the bulb. There is no doubt that this reaction is due to the
action of chlorine. Similar effects occur if the sulfide is heated
in an atmosphere of HCl: in addition to the simple exchange
reaction resulting in the formation of H_2S and $ZnCl_2$, another
process occurs which leads to the appearance of a sulfur deposit
in the cold parts of the apparatus and of free zinc in the treated
ZnS sample. The clarification of this peculiar effect may be
of great importance for the elucidation of the role of chlorine
in the formation of ZnS phosphors.

   Although the reversible blue ⇌ green transformation is better
suited to theoretical analysis than the irreversible transformation, we shall first report some observations concerning the
latter.

   As can be seen from Fig. 3 the presence of a chlorinating
agent (NH_4Cl) has a strong influence on the blue → green trans-

formation. The curve in Fig. 3 shows the time dependence of

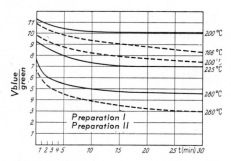

Fig. 3 — Dependence of the blue/green ratio
on heating time.

the blue-green transformation at different temperatures for the
initially blue-emitting ZnS(Cu) without NH_4Cl ("Preparation I")
and for the same phosphor plus NH_4Cl ("Preparation II"). In
both cases method A was used so that an irreversible evaporation of reaction products was possible. The curves show that in
the absence of NH_4Cl a stationary blue/green ratio is reached
after about 20 minutes, whereas in the case of the phosphor
containing NH_4Cl this ratio is shifted more and more toward
green emission.

If the heating is performed in such a way that the evaporated
reaction products can return to the phosphor as it is cooled,
("method B"), the reverse reaction (green → blue—transformation) occurs even in the case of preparation II. (The reverse
reaction is accompanied by a disappearance of the yellowish
deposit). But the reverse reaction does not occur when the
evaporated reaction products (the yellowish sulphur-deposit)
are mechanically removed before cooling.

When the preparation was used no visually perceptible evaporation of any products could be observed. But since after heating this phosphor in vacuum ("Method A") no green → blue reverse reaction occurs, we must conclude that some constituents
or reaction products do evaporate from this phosphor. This
leads to irreversible changes in the phosphor. Probably the
effect is due to small quantities of chlorine which are present
in the phosphor (see Cl analysis in Section 2). But if the heating
was carried out in a closed quartz tube and the disappearance of
any volatile products prevented, we always observed a complete

reversibility of the blue $\rightleftharpoons$ green transformation and the transformation could be repeated in both directions many times.

We shall now consider in more detail and quantitatively the reversible blue $\rightleftharpoons$ transformation which is independent of the presence of external chemical agents.

Special experiments have shown that the blue $\rightleftharpoons$ green transformation is not due to migration of Cu towards the macroscopic crystal surface. If, after a blue-green transformation, the outer parts of the grains are removed by dissolving in HCl, the reverse reaction (green $\rightarrow$ blue) is not inhibited. Therefore the Cu atoms which leave the centers during the blue $\rightarrow$ green transformation do not migrate to the crystal surface but rather become stored within the crystal.

b) Determination of the reaction enthalpy of the reversible blue $\rightleftharpoons$ green transformation.

Let us assume that the blue $\rightleftharpoons$ green transformation can be considered as a reaction of the type

$$A B \rightleftharpoons A + B \tag{1}$$

in which AB = the blue-emitting "associate" between a Cu^+ ion on a lattice site and an interstitial Cu^+ ion;

A = the green-emitting center, i.e. a Cu^+ ion on a lattice site without a Cu^+ ion on a neighboring interstitial site;

B = a Cu^+ ion which is removed from the interstitial position in the neighborhood of a lattice Cu^+ ion (it can be situated at an interstitial position far from a lattice Cu^+ ion or at any anomalous structures in the crystal, e.g. at dislocations; or it can be chemically bound in some way, e.g. as CuCl or Cu_2S.)

In the equilibrium state

$$\frac{d[AB]}{dt} = k_1[A] \cdot [B] - k_2[AB] = 0 \tag{2}$$

where k_1 and k_2 are the reaction rate constants for the formation and desintegration of AB.

It further holds that

$$\frac{k_1}{k_2} = \left(\frac{Z_1}{Z_2}\right) \cdot e^{-\frac{\Delta Q}{RT}} \tag{3}$$

or, with regard to (2)

$$ln \frac{[AB]}{[A][B]} = \text{const.} - \frac{\Delta Q}{RT} \tag{4}$$

The expression $[AB]/[A]$ can be set equal (or at least proportional) to the ratio of the intensities of the blue and green emission band, but the value of B cannot be measured directly. Since in our phosphor the ratio of the two emission bands is almost unchanged at temperatures below 100°C (Fig. 2), we must assume that at 20°C the reactant B is completely associated with the Cu^+ lattice ions forming blue-emitting centers. Therefore:

$$[B] \approx [AB]_{20°} - [AB] \tag{5}$$

From (5) and (4) we have

$$ln \left\{ \frac{[AB]}{[A]} \cdot \frac{1}{[AB]_{20°} - [AB]} \right\} = \text{const.} - \frac{\Delta Q}{RT} \tag{6}$$

The factor $1/[AB]_{20°} - [AB]$ can be evaluated from the intensity of the blue band for an equilibrium state at a sufficient low temperature (*e.g.* 20°C) and its intensity for the equilibrium state at the temperature under consideration.

Plotting $ln \{\}$ from (6) versus $1/T$ we obtain a straight line (Fig. 4). From its slope the value of the reaction enthalpy ΔQ can be calculated. We obtain $\Delta Q = 0.76$ eV for temperatures between 120° and 350°C. This value is quite independent of the special conditions of measuring the ratio blue emission/green emission. The value of ΔQ does not change even if the observed ratio of the emission intensities is changed by varying the conditions of excitation (varied temperature or varied intensity of excitation).

c) Discussion of the reaction mechanism.

Hitherto we have used only the assumption that the transformation blue → green is based on a dissociation of the interstitial Cu^+ ion from a lattice site Cu^+ ion. We have not suggested any hypothesis concerning the later fate of the interstitial Cu^+ ions after dissociation. It is imaginable that the interstitial Cu^+ ions

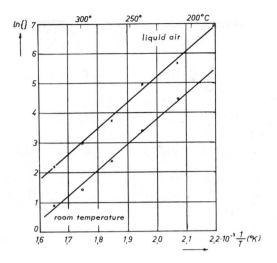

Fig. 4 — In $\{\}$ from eq. (6) plotted vs. $\frac{1}{T}$.

remain in the interstitial space but at sites far from the lattice site Cu^+ ions. It also seems possible that they are "trapped" at some irregular regions of the crystal, e.g. at dislocations. (As shown in Sec. 3a, they do not diffuse to the macroscopic outer surface of the crystal). Finally it can be supposed that the Cu^+ ions are at dislocations or in a foreign compound located at the dislocation (e.g., by the reaction: $2\ Cu^+ + ZnCl_2 \rightleftharpoons 2\ CuCl + Zn^{2+}$). The latter mechanism would explain the maintenance of electroneutrality after the emigration of the Cu^+ ion: the im-migrating Zn^{2+} ions take over the function of the emigrating in-terstitial Cu^+ ions as charge compensators.

To the extent that further experiments were carried out, they seem to rule out the first mentioned possibility (random distri-bution of Cu^+ ions in the interstitial space). If this hypothesis were correct reaction (1) must be a so-called "homogenous re-action". New experiments (not described here) seem to indicate that the reaction is not a homogenous one. We are testing this alternative by means of an improved experimental technique.

REFERENCES

[1] Rotschild S.: Trans Faraday Soc. <u>42</u>, 635 (1946).
Riehl N., <s>J</s>. H. Ortmann: Dokl. Akad. Nau SSSR <u>66</u>, 613, 841 (1949).
Kröger F. A., J. E. Hellingman u. N.W. Smit: Physica, Haag <u>25</u>, 990 (1949).
Riehl N., u.H. Ortmann: J. Allg. Chem. <u>25</u>, 1693 (1955) (russ.).
[2] Monographie Nr. 72 zu Angewandte Chemie, S. 47, Weinheim: Verlag Chemie 1957.
Ortmann H.: Tagungsband "Halbleiter und Phosphore", Garmisch, 1956, S. 220.
[3] Riehl N., u. H. Ortmann: Ann. d. Phys. VII. F. <u>4</u>, 1 (1959).
[4] Kröger F.A., J. E. Hellingman und N. W. Smit: Physica, Haag <u>25</u>, 990 (1949).

SOME STUDIES ON THE LUMINESCENCE CENTERS IN ZINC SULFIDE TYPE PHOSPHORS

Shigeo Shionoya, Takao Koda, Koh Era and Hiroko Fujiwara

The Institute for Solid State Physics
The University of Tokyo, Japan

ABSTRACT

In the investigation of the luminescence of zinc sulfide type phosphors, the nature of the centers and the electronic transitions responsible for the luminescence are two of the most interesting and fundamental problems. Some results concerning these problems will be reported.

1) Nature of the lead center.

Photoconductivity due to excitation in the absorption range of lead decreases with decreasing temperature, almost disappearing at 130°K. The rise of emission due to lead excitation is very fast at 77°K, the time constant being 50 μsec, whereas it is a slow process at higher temperatures, since electrons are raised to the conduction band and are trapped. It is concluded from these results that lead in zinc sulfide creates a localized center and that the excited state of the lead center is located at 0.36 ev below the bottom of the conduction band.

2) Energy transfer from the lead to the manganese center.

In lead and manganese activated zinc sulfide phosphors the manganese emission is sensitized by lead. The rise of manganese emission due to lead excitation is quite similar to that of lead emission: that is, it is very fast at 77°K whereas it is a slow process at higher temperatures. It is concluded that excitation energy absorbed by lead can be transferred directly to manganese by resonance.

3) Nature of the copper red center.

Copper incorporated in zinc sulfide as an activator in the ab-

355

sence of coactivators shows a red luminescence. The temperature dependence of the half-width of the red band was measured
at temperatures down to 4°K. The results suggest that the red
center is localized. It is tentatively suggested that the red
center is formed by the association of copper with a sulfur
vacancy, and that the luminescence transition is from a
donor-like sulfur vacancy level to an acceptor-like copper
level.

In the investigations on the luminescence of zinc sulfide
type phosphors, the nature of the various centers as well as
the nature of the electronic transitions responsible for the
luminescence are the most fundamental and interesting problems. Some results concerning these problems obtained in
this laboratory will be mentioned. The present paper is concerned with three problems, (I) the nature of the lead center,
(II) energy transfer from the lead to the manganese center,
and (III) the nature of the copper red center.

(I) NATURE OF THE LEAD CENTER

1. Introduction

A lead-activated zinc sulfide phosphor emits a yellow-green
luminescence. A remarkable feature of this phosphor is that
it exhibits a very strong infrared stimulability.[1.1,1.2]
Recently, Shionoya, Kallmann and Kramer[1.3] found very
interesting phenomena with this phosphor. The rise of the
fluorescence with the 4360 Å excitation from a high pressure
mercury discharge lamp is a slow process, of the order of
minutes at room temperature, whereas it is a very fast process with a time constant of less than one second at liquid nitrogen temperature. According to Shionoya et al[1.4] lead incorporated in zinc sulfide produces an absorption band in the wavelength region just beyond the absorption edge of the host crystal
with a maximum at around 4000 Å. Therefore the 4360 Å line
gives rise only to excitation of the lead center, but does not
excite the host lattice at all. With excitation by the 2537 Å line
from a low pressure mercury discharge lamp as well as β-rays
from a 14 mC $Sr^{90} - Y^{90}$ source, the rise of the fluorescence

is always a slow process, even at liquid nitrogen temperature.

These results then led to the suggestion[1,3] that lead creates a luminescence center localized within the forbidden band of the zinc sulfide lattice, and that at liquid nitrogen temperature electrons raised to the excited state of the lead center by the absorption of 4360 Å return immediately to the ground state, exhibiting the very fast rise, while, at room temperature, excited electrons are raised to the conduction band by thermal energy and then enter into traps, thereby producing the slow rise.

Shionoya et al[1,3] attempted to make glow curve measurements on this phosphor with 4360Å excitation at liquid nitrogen temperature. One would imagine, if one accepts the suggestion presented above, that there would be no glow emission. However it was found that this is not really the case. If the 4360 Å excitation was maintained at liquid nitrogen temperature for more than one minute, appreciable glow emission was observed. The area of the glow curves increased with increase of excitation time, although the intensity of fluorescence during excitation remained quite constant after the initial fast rise. The positions of three glow peaks were the same as those which were obtained after excitation by the 2537 Å line and β-rays.

These somewhat peculiar results can be understood by the following argument. Since glow emission is really observed, a very small part of electrons in the excited state of the lead center must enter into traps. The number of these electrons is so small compared with the total number of excited electrons that the variation of fluorescence intensity during excitation, which should be observed if trap filling is taking place, cannot be observed experimentally.

In this paper a further investigation of the luminescence characteristics of the ZnS:Pb phosphor is discussed so as to elucidate the nature of the lead center more in detail.

2. Experimental

a) Sample

Luminescent grade zinc sulfide powder mixed with a small amount of $Pb(NO_3)_2$ and with NaCl as flux (8% by weight) was fired at 1100°C for 30 min in air. The content of Pb remaining in the fired product was found to be 0.198% by weight by chemical analysis. What had been added was 0.3%.

b) Emission and excitation

The emission spectrum was measured with a Kipp and Zonen double monochromator and an RCA 1P22 photomultiplier connected to a dc amplifier and a millivolt recorder. The results are shown in Fig. 1.1 for room and liquid nitrogen temperatures. The emission peak is located at 4880 Å at room temperature, and is shifted 60 Å towards the shorter wavelengths at 77°K.

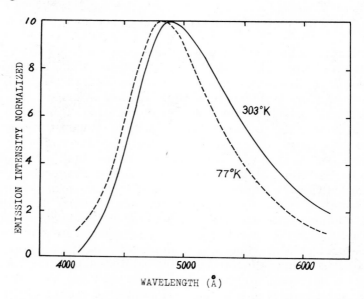

Fig. 1.1 — Emission spectra of ZnS:Pb with excitation from the 3650Å mercury line at 303 and 77°K.

The excitation spectrum for the ZnS:Pb phosphor had already been measured by Shionoya et al.[1,4] It has a peak at around 4000 Å due to the lead absorption as well as one at around 3400 Å due to the host crystal absorption.

c) Rise of fluorescence

The rise of fluorescence was measured with the photoelectric apparatus mentioned above, but with a 1P21 photomultiplier when it was the slow process. Rise curves taken under the 4360 Å irradiation of 6.7 μW/cm², which is used for the excitation of the lead center, are shown in Fig. 1.2 for various temperatures. As was mentioned already, at 77°K the rise is a very fast process, whereas at room temperature it is a slow process. At an intermediate temperature of 203°K the fast rise at the instant the excitation is put on is accompanied by the

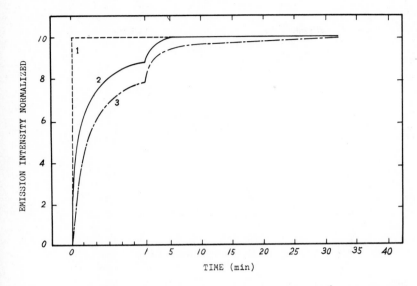

Fig. 1.2 — Rise curves of the fluorescence of ZnS:Pb under 4360Å irradiation of 6.7 μW/cm^2 at (1) 77, (2) 203, and (3) 303°K.

subsequent slow process; in other words the rise is a mixture of the fast and slow processes. The slow component of the rise becomes slower with a decrease in intensity of the 4360 Å irradiation. The character of decay is exactly the same as that of rise, namely slow at room temperature but very fast at 77°K.

Under the 2537 Å irradiation used for the host lattice excitation, the rise is always the slow process, as was mentioned above. Under 3650 Å irradiation the rise is a mixture of fast and slow processes at 77°K, quite similar to that at the intermediate temperature under the 4360 Å irradiation.

The time constant of the fast rise at low temperature was measured in the following way. The 4360 Å light was focused at a point where it was chopped by a rotating sector to make pulses. The light which was emitted because of excitation by the pulsed light was detected by a photomultiplier, the output of which was fed to a Tektronix oscilloscope. The patterns of the rise and decay were recorded photographically.

The results are shown in Fig. 1.3. The time constant was found to be approximately 50 μsec for the fast rise as well as for the fast decay at low temperature.

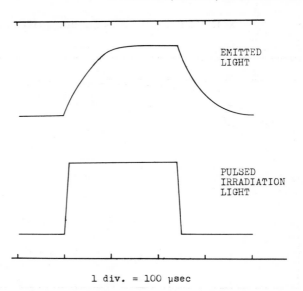

1 div. = 100 μsec

Fig. 1.3 — Fast rise and decay of the emission of ZnS:
Pb under 4360Å irradiation at 77°K, measured by means
of a pulsed light method.

d) Photoconductivity

Photoconductivity was measured with an ac impedance
method.[1,5] A sandwich type cell was made by inserting the
powder sample between a conductive glass and a thick copper
plate. The cell was made to be one arm of an impedance
bridge. The ac voltage supplied to the bridge was 1 kc/sec and
28 V.

After the bridge was balanced in the dark, the 4360 Å line
was used to irradiate the cell. It was found that the greatest
change induced by the irradiation was on the capacitance. To
measure very small changes of capacitance, the unbalanced
current produced by the irradiation was amplified and recorded.
The dependence of the capacitance change induced by the irradiation on the temperature was obtained in this way. Results are
shown in Fig. 1.4.

Kallmann et all[1,6] stated that the electron density in the conduction band is proportional to $(\Delta C/C_0)(1/D)$, where ΔC is
the change in capacitance induced by the irradiation and D is
the dissipation factor. Therefore Fig. 1.4 shows that the photoconductivity decreases with decrease in temperature and almost
disappears at 170°K.

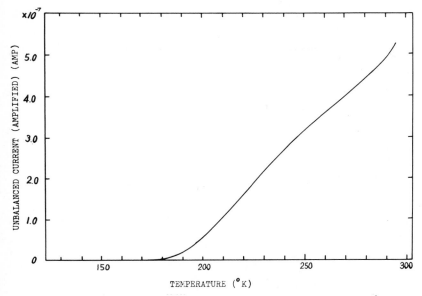

Fig. 1.4 — Temperature dependence of the unbalanced current induced by 4360Å in the measurement of the photoconductivity of ZnS:Pb by an ac impedance method.

In Fig. 1.5 the logarithm of the unbalanced current is plotted against the reciprocal of temperature. It gives a straight line in the low unbalanced current region. The unbalanced current is not exactly proportional to the photoconductivity, but may be assumed to be approximately proportional to it. The deviation from a straight line at the high current region is considered caused by the nonproportionality. The slope of the straight line gives 0.36 eV as the activation energy for the appearance of photoconductivity.

e) Glow curve

Glow curves were measured with the usual method. The phosphor was excited at 77°K with the 4360 Å line after having been completely deexcited by irradiation with strong infrared light at room temperature, and then was heated at a rate of 10°K/min.

As was mentioned already in Sec. 1, glow emission is observed with 4360 Å excitation if the excitation is continued for some time, in spite of the fact that very few electrons are raised to the conduction band by this excitation at 77°K. The results are shown in Fig. 1.6. With prolongation of the duration of excitation at 77°K, the glow emission becomes stronger. The glow area plotted against the time of excitation is shown in Fig. 1.7. The glow area becomes saturated at about 20 min of excitation, indicating that the traps are filled to saturation.

The glow curves always show three peaks at about 140, 205, and 290°K. The depths of the traps associated with these peaks were calculated by the usual method,[1.7] making three assumptions: that the thermoluminescence obeys monomolecular kinetics, that the frequency constant for trapped electrons to escape from the traps is $10^8 \sec^{-1}$, and that the retrapping of released electrons is negligible. The results were 0.21, 0.31 and 0.43 eV, respectively, for the 140, 205 and 290°K peaks. It is possible that the shallowest trap originates from the chlorine coactivator while the two deeper traps are associated with oxygen as an impurity.[1.8]

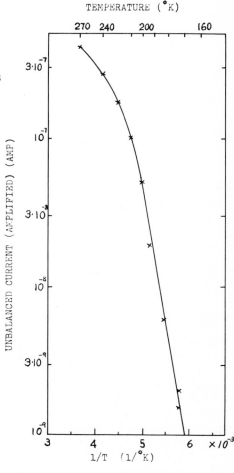

Fig. 1.5 — Replotting of Fig. 1.4 as the logarithm of unbalanced current versus 1/T.

3. Discussion

The results on the rise and decay of fluorescence and on the photoconductivity definitely indicate, as was suggested already,[1.3] that the lead center is a localized one within the forbidden band. The temperature dependence of the photoconductivity shows that the excited state of the center lies 0.36 eV below the bottom of the conduction band. Adding the fact that the excitation and emission peaks are located at 4000 Å (3.10 eV) and 4880 Å (2.54 eV), respectively, leads to the energy levels

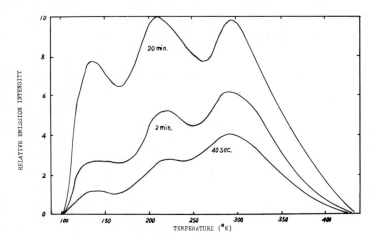

Fig. 1.6 — Glow curves for ZnS:Pb after excitation with 4360Å. The duration of excitation at 77°K is given in the figure.

of the lead center which are shown in Fig. 1.8. The levels shown by the solid line are those of the states when occupied by electrons. The location of the ground state is not certain,

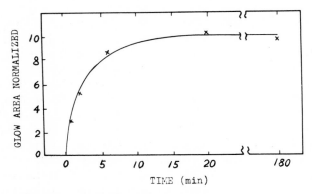

Fig. 1.7 — Glow curve area plotted against the duration of 4360Å excitation at 77°K for ZnS:Pb.

but it is probably approximately 0.4 eV above the top of the filled band.

The probability for electrons in the excited state of the lead center to be raised to the conduction band is given by $\gamma \exp(-\epsilon/kT)$, where ϵ is 0.36 eV. Assuming γ to be 10^{12} sec^{-1}, it is the order of 10^{-10} sec^{-1} at 77°K. On the other hand, the probability for electrons in the excited state to return to the ground state, emitting light is the order of 10^5 sec^{-1} according to the time constant measurement, which is 10^{15} times larger than the probability of going into the conduction band. Therefore, in the case of lead excitation trap filling requires considerable time. It is not unreasonable then that the glow emission is observed only after prolonged excitation although the change in the fluorescence intensity during excitation can not be detected experimentally.

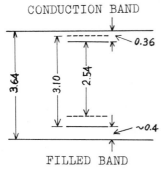

Fig. 1.8 — Energy levels of the lead center in a zinc sulfide crystal. The values given are in electron volts.

(II) ENERGY TRANSFER FROM THE LEAD TO THE MAN-GANESE CENTER

1. Introduction

Transfer of the excitation energy from one luminescence center to another, so-called sensitized luminescence, is one of the interesting problems in the luminescence processes of zinc sulfide type phosphors. Sensitized luminescence in photoconductive inorganic phosphors such as zinc sulfide is thought to be caused by either or both of the following two processes: 1) the excitation energy absorbed by the sensitizing center is transferred non-radiatively to the emitting center by quantum-mechanical resonance,[2.1] 2) photo-excited electrons and holes created at the sensitizing center are transferred to the emitting center via the conduction and filled band.[2.2,2.3] In the case where the luminescence of the emitting center is due to a forbidden transition, sensitization by a cascade process need not be taken into consideration.

Divalent manganese shows a bright orange luminescence due to a d-d transition when introduced into a zinc sulfide crystal.

Since this transition is forbidden, the luminescence appears strongly only with excitation of the host lattice.

One of the present authors, S. S.,[2.4],[1.4] found that the luminescence of manganese in zinc sulfide is sensitized by copper and lead behaving as sensitizing centers. These heavy metal impurities introduced into zinc sulfide create absorption bands of their own in the wavelength region just beyond the host absorption edge, and by photo-absorption in these bands they give rise to photoconductivity as well as luminescence of their own. The occurrence of the sensitzation of manganese was verified by the measurement of the excitation spectra. Shionoya[2.5] further studied extensively the luminescence characteristics of ZnS:Cu+Mn, and concluded tentatively that resonance transfer rather than photo-electron and hole transfer is the predominant mechanism in sensitization. Definite evidence for this conclusion, however, could not be obtained.

As was mentioned in detail in Part (I), lead introduced into zinc sulfide creates a localized center. Direct excitation of the lead center does not yield photoconductivity at liquid nitrogen temperature while it yields appreciable photoconductivity at room temperature. Combining this with the fact that in ZnS:Pb+Mn manganese emission is sensitized by lead, one might anticipate that the investigation of the luminescence properties of ZnS:Pb+Mn would present useful clues with which to examine and confirm the above mentioned tentative conclusion.

2. Experimental

a) Sample

Luminescent grade zinc sulfide powder mixed with small amounts of $Pb(NO_3)_2$ and $MnSO_4$ and with NaCl as flux (8% by weight) was fired at 1100°C for 30 min in air. A series of samples was prepared, in which the added amount of Pb was kept constant at 0.3% by weight while that of Mn was varied from 0.03 to 1%. The sample most extensively investigated contained the added amount of 0.06% Mn. All the data given in this paper are for this sample. The amount of activator remaining in the fired products was determined by chemical analysis. With the extensively investigated sample the activator content was found to be 0.201% Pb and 0.0534% Mn. Before firing, 0.3% Pb and 0.06% Mn had been added to the zinc sulfide.

b) Excitation and emission

ZnS:Pb+Mn phosphors emit a yellow green luminescence
due to lead as well as an orange luminescence due to manganese. In a series of samples containing a constant amount of
lead and varying amounts of manganese, the manganese emission becomes stronger with increase in manganese content, the
lead emission simultaneously decreasing and almost disappearing at higher manganese contents.

The excitation spectra for lead and manganese emission in
ZnS:Pb+Mn phosphors had been already reported by Shionoya
et al.[1,4] The spectra for these two emissions are quite similar
to one another, namely, both have a peak at around 4000 Å due
to the lead absorption as well as one at 3400 Å due to the host
crystal absorption. Since the ZnS:Mn phosphor (not containing
lead) does not have the 4000 Å excitation band, these results
led to the definite conclusion that the manganese emission is
sensitized by lead.

The emission spectra of the present ZnS:Pb+Mn phosphor
were measured under excitation by various monochromatic
beams ranging from 3300 to 4000 Å. The experimental method
was already mentioned in Part (I) Sec. 2.b. The excitation lines
used here were obtained by making the light from a 500W xenon
discharge lamp monochromatic by means of a Bausch and Lomb
grating monochromator.

The emission spectra obtained by excitation with 4000 and
3400 Å are shown in Fig. 2.1 and 2.2. The ratio of the emission
intensity of manganese to that of lead was found to depend remarkably on whether the excitation is due to absorption by the
lead center or by the host lattice. The ratios resulting from
different excitation wavelengths are shown in Table 2.1. The
results indicate that the ratio I_{Mn}/I_{Pb} is smaller with lead
excitation than with host excitation. Excitation by 4000 Å and
by 3300 Å may correspond to absorption by the lead center and
by the host lattice, respectively. With excitation by intermediate wavelengths both kinds of absorption seem to be present.
The peak of manganese emission is located at room temperature at about 5860 Å with 4000 Å excitation and at about 5920 Å
with 3400 Å excitation. It appears that the peak when the lead
is excited is located at a slightly shorter wavelength than when
the host crystal is excited. This phenomenon might be correlated with the sensitization effect. At liquid nitrogen temperature the peak is always shifted a little towards shorter wavelengths, and is accompanied with a remarkable decrease in
band width.

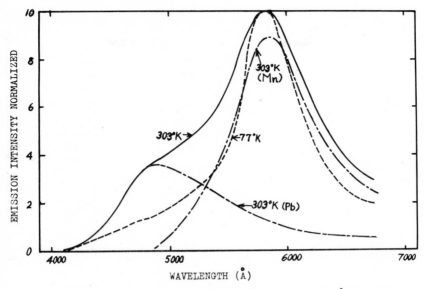

Fig. 2.1 — Emission spectra of ZnS:Pb+Mn with excitation by the 4000Å line at 303 and 77°K. The spectrum at 303°K is graphically separated into those of Pb and Mn.

Table 2.1

The ratio of the emission intensity of manganese, I_{Mn}, to that of lead, I_{Pb}, in ZnS:Pb+Mn when subjected to various excitation wavelengths. I is the intensity at the emission peak.

Excitation (Å)	I_{Mn}/I_{Pb}	
	Room Temperature	77°K
4000	2.5	7.4
3650	5.5	9.7
3400	15	45
3300	20	100

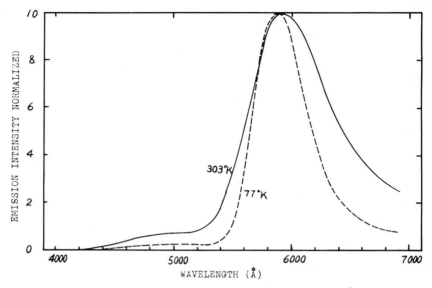

Fig. 2.2 – Emission spectra of ZnS:Pb+Mn due to excitation by 3400Å at 303 and 77°K.

c) Rise and decay of fluorescence

The rise characteristics of the lead and manganese fluorescences in the ZnS:Pb+Mn phosphor were measured with the same method as was mentioned in Part (I) Sec. 2.c. The emissions of lead and manganese were separated by the use of appropriate Matsuda color filters. The source used for excitation of the lead was the 4360 Å mercury line at an intensity of 6.7 μW/cm^2.

The rise characteristics of the lead emission in ZnS:Pb+Mn were exactly the same as those in ZnS:Pb which were already mentioned in Part (I) Sec. 2.c. The rise curves for the manganese emission under the 4360 Å irradiation are shown in Fig. 2.3 for various temperatures. It is immediately evident that the rise of the manganese emission behaves in a manner similar to that of the lead emission and consists mainly of the fast process at 77°K. This is a very important and remarkable feature of the rise of the manganese emission, and presents definite evidence, as will be discussed in detail in Sec. 3, for the idea that the sensitization of the manganese emission due to resonance transfer takes place at low temperatures. The

difference between the rise of the lead and that of the manganese
emission is that at 77°K the manganese rise consists of a fast

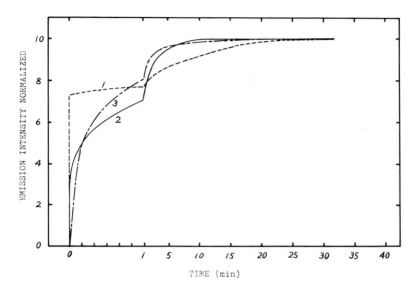

Fig. 2.3 — Rise curves of the manganese emission of ZnS:Pb+Mn under 4360Å irradiation of 6.7 μ W/cm^2 at (1) 77, (2) 203, and (3) 303°K.

component in the main accompanied by a small amount of slow
component, whereas the lead rise contains only the fast process.
At room temperature both the manganese and lead rises are
slow, and at an intermediate temperature of 203°K they consist
of mixtures of the fast and slow processes. One would expect
that if the manganese rise were to be measured at temperatures
considerably less than 77°K it would consist of only the fast
process. The decay of the manganese emission under 4360 Å
irradiation is precisely the same as the rise, namely, it is a
slow process at room temperature while at 77°K it consists
mainly of the fast process.

The time constants of the fast process involved in the manganese rise and decay at low temperature under 4360 Å irradiation was measured by the pulsed light method mentioned in
Part (I) Sec. 2.c. The results are shown in Fig. 2.4. The time
constants were found to be approximately 1 msec for the fast
rise and 2 msec for the fast decay. The decay characteristic
is nearly exponential.

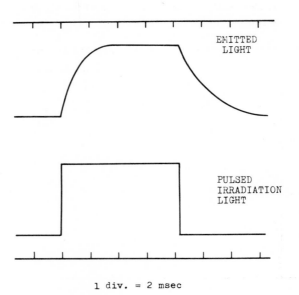

1 div. = 2 msec

Fig. 2.4 — Fast processes involved in the rise and decay of the manganese emission of ZnS:Pb+Mn under
4360Å irradiation at 77°K, measured by means of a pulsed
light method.

d) Temperature dependence of the emission

The temperature dependence of the emission intensities
of both manganese and lead under 4360 Å excitation is shown
in Fig. 2.5. The unit of emission intensity in the ordinate of
the figure was chosen so as to make possible the comparison
of the manganese and lead emission intensities. In the figure
the change of the ratio of the emission intensity of manganese
to that of lead, I_{Mn}/I_{Pb}, is also given.

e) Glow curve

Glow curves for the manganese and lead emissions of
ZnS:Pb+Mn after excitation with 4360 Å were taken in the way
which was mentioned in Part (I) Sec. 2.c. Results are shown in
Fig. 2.6.

The glow characteristics of the lead emission in ZnS:Pb+Mn
were exactly the same as in ZnS:Pb (See Part (I) Sec. 2.e). The
glow characteristics of the manganese emission were quite
similar to those of the lead emission. The manganese glow

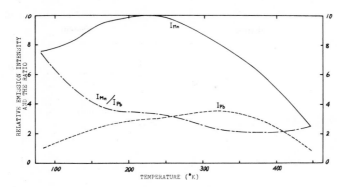

Fig. 2.5 — Dependence of the emission intensities of manganese (I_{Mn}) and lead (I_{Pb}) in ZnS:Pb+Mn, and dependence of the ratio I_{Mn}/I_{Pb} on the temperature under 4360Å excitation.

emission was also increased by prolongation of the duration of excitation at 77°K. The glow area plotted against the duration of excitation is shown in Fig. 2.7 for both the lead and manga-

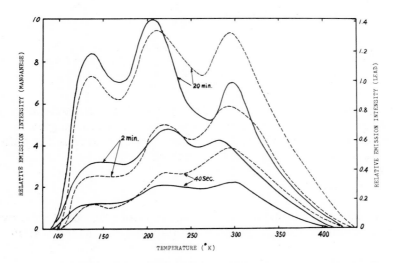

Fig. 2.6 — Glow curves for the manganese (solid line) and lead (dotted line) emission of ZnS:Pb+Mn after 4360Å excitation. The duration of excitation at 77°K is given in the figure.

nese emissions. In the figure the ratio of the glow area of manganese to that of lead, G_{Mn}/G_{Pb} is also plotted. The ratio is approximately eight, and is independent of the duration of

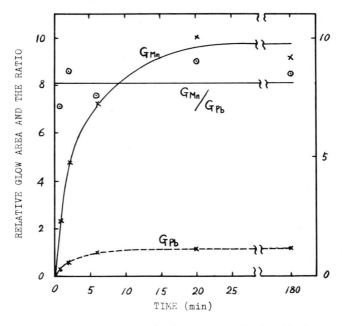

Fig. 2.7 – Glow curve areas for the manganese (G_{Mn}) and lead (G_{Pb}) emission in ZnS:Pb+Mn, and the ratio G_{Mn}/G_{Pb} against the duration of excitation by 4360 Å at 77°K.

excitation. The three peaks which appear in the manganese glow curves are exactly the same as those in the lead glow curves, indicating that the same traps are responsible for both the manganese and lead glow emissions.

3. Discussion

As was already mentioned in Sec. 1, either or both of the two mechanisms of energy transfer, namely the resonance transfer and the photo-electron and hole transfer, are responsible for the sensitized luminescence in photoconductive phosphors. To solve the problem of which mechanism holds for the sensitized luminescence in the ZnS:Pb+Mn phosphor, the rise characteristics of the manganese and lead emissions present a very useful key.

The lead center in zinc sulfide is a localized one within the forbidden band (See, Part (I) Sec. 3). At liquid nitrogen temperature little photoconductivity is produced by absorption in the lead center. This causes the very fast rise of fluorescence at low temperature, which gives directly the probability of the transition within the lead center. In spite of this fact the manganese emission is sensitized strongly by the absorption due to the lead center even at liquid nitrogen temperature. The rise of the manganese emission at 77°K due to the lead excitation is composed mainly of the very fast process. This fast rise of the manganese emission appears simultaneously with the appearance of the fast rise of the lead emission. These facts indicate that the excitation energy absorbed by the lead center is transferred directly to the manganese center without the assistance of the production of free electrons and holes. Therefore one can conclude without doubt that the sensitization of the manganese emission due to resonance transfer actually takes place at low temperatures. However the possibility of sensitization due to photoelectron transfer cannot be abandoned. This will be discussed later.

Bube[2,6] measured the excitation spectrum for the manganese emission of ZnS:Mn, and found, in addition to the host excitation band, four weak excitation peaks due to the forbidden transitions within the Mn center, i.e., 3980, 4320, 4770 and 5060 Å peaks. These peaks were not found in the measurements discussed here. This is probably due to the effect of impurities, oxygen in particular.

The energy levels of the Mn^{2+} ion in solids have been given as ^6S, ^4G, ^4P, ^4D and ^4F states starting with the lowest term, and it has been suggested that the luminescence corresponds to the $^4G \rightarrow {}^6S$ transition.[2,7] Then the four excitation peaks are considered to correspond to the transition from the ^6S ground state to the ^4G, ^4P, ^4D and ^4F excited states, respectively. Combining these considerations with the fact that the lead emission has a peak at around 4900 Å, it is suggested that the energy absorbed by the lead center is transferred to the ^4G or ^4P excited state of the divalent manganese center.

A simple theoretical treatment has been attempted to explain the characteristics of the manganese fast rise at low temperatures, based on the assumption that the manganese emission is caused by sensitization due to resonance transfer. According to preliminary results, both the rise and the decay of the manganese emission should involve the same two kinds of time con-

stant, and the final stage of the curves should be governed by
the time constant for the luminescence transition within the
divalent manganese center, while the initial stage should be
governed by the time constant which is very close to or slightly
larger than that for the luminescence transition within the lead
center. The former time constant will be about two orders of
magnitude larger than the latter. If the experimentally obtained rise and decay curves shown in Fig. 2.4 are replotted
in terms of the logarithm of the emission intensity versus time,
the rise curve gives two straight lines with the larger slope at
the initial stage, whereas the decay curve gives a simple
straight line. The characteristics of the rise curve seem to
agree with the theory, supporting the idea of resonance transfer. The characteristics of the decay curve, however, do not
agree with the theory. The discrepancy is not yet understood.

Finally we have to discuss the possibility of sensitization
due to photoelectron transfer. According to the theory of sensitized luminescence due to the resonance transfer, the probability of the transfer is almost temperature independent.[2.1]
Therefore sensitization due to resonance which has been confirmed at low temperatures should take place at higher temperatures also. The probability of resonance transfer should
be almost equal to or larger than that of the luminescence
transition in the lead center, which is estimated to be of the
order of 10^5 sec^{-1} from the experimental results on the fast
rise and decay processes shown in Fig. 1.3 in Part (I). The
probability that photoelectrons are created by the absorption
due to the lead center increases pronouncedly with temperature, and reaches a value of the order of 10^6 sec^{-1} at room
temperature, which is almost the same as the probability of
resonance transfer. Therefore, if sensitization due to photoelectron transfer were possible, it would become appreciable
at higher temperatures.

There is no experimental evidence which can present a
definite answer to this problem. However the following experimental results appear to imply that photoelectron transfer
contributes partly to the sensitization especially at higher temperatures. The ratio of emission intensities, I_{Mn}/I_{Pb}, shown
in Table 2.1, is much larger with host excitation than with lead
excitation. The rise of the emission in ZnS:Pb+Mn with lead
excitation involves both fast and slow processes. At liquid nitrogen temperature the slow process is entirely absent from
the lead rise, while it is still present in the manganese rise.

The ratio of the glow area of the manganese emission to that of the lead emission after lead excitation is approximately eight, whereas the ratio of the fluorescence intensity of manganese to that of lead is about three if it is averaged over the temperature range from 77° to 400°K; in other words the glow area ratio is much larger than the fluorescence intensity ratio. These results can be understood if it is assumed that photoelectron transfer also takes place and the capture cross section for free electrons and holes of the manganese center is larger than that of the lead center. Therefore, we would like to conclude that the photoelectron transfer mechanism also contributes, but only partially, to the sensitization process in ZnS:Pb+Mn phosphors.

(III) NATURE OF THE COPPER RED CENTER

1. Introduction

Copper impurity introduced into zinc sulfide crystal as an activator creates the green, blue and red luminescence centers, depending on the kind and amount of coactivator as well as on the firing conditions. The green center, which is the most well-known, appears when the amount of copper introduced is not very great (of the order of $10^{-6} \sim 10^{-4}$ mole/mole) and is comparable to or less than that of the coactivators which are group IIIb or VIIb elements. The blue center appears when the amount of copper is considerably larger (of the order of $10^{-4} \sim 10^{-3}$) and is more than that of the coactivators. The red center was recently discovered by Froelich[3.1]. It is created when zinc sulfide containing a small amount of copper is fired in an atmosphere of hydrogen sulfide and no coactivators are added.

The purpose of the work reported here was to investigate the atomic nature of the red center and to ascertain which electronic transition is responsible for the red luminescence. The work is still in progress, and the final conclusion has not yet been reached. Some experimental results obtained up to the present will be discussed.

2. Experimental

a) Sample

Luminescent grade zinc sulfide powder and specially purified cupric sulfide powder were used as starting materials.

Before mixing these materials, the zinc sulfide powder was
prefired in a hydrogen sulfide atmosphere at 600°C for 1 hr so
as to remove all traces of sulfate. Chlorine and aluminum were
selected to be coactivators, in order to examine their effects
on the red luminescence. Chlorine was introduced either by
firing in an atmosphere containing hydrogen chloride or by
adding sodium chloride to the starting materials. Aluminum
was introduced by adding aluminum sulfate to the starting materials. The different firing atmospheres were hydrogen sulfide, nitrogen, hydrogen, sulfur vapor and vacuum. Some samples were prepared by the refiring of some finished phosphors
in order to investigate the effect of successive firings on the
red luminescence. Details of the preparation conditions of
samples for which some experimental data are presented are
summarized in Table 3.1.

Table 3.1

Preparation Conditions of Samples for Which Some Experimental
Data are Presented in this Paper

A. Samples Prepared by a Single Firing

No.	Activator (mole/mole)	Coactivator (mole/mole)	Firing Conditions
O-1	Cu, 10^{-3}	None	1200°C, 40 min, in H_2S
O-2	Cu, 10^{-4}	None	1200°C, 1 hr, in H_2S
G-3	Cu, $7 \cdot 10^{-3}$	None	1050°C, 1 hr, in H_2S
I-1	Cu, 10^{-3}	Al, 10^{-5}	1200°C, 40 min, in H_2S

B. Samples Prepared by the Refiring of Finished Phosphors

No.	Finished Phosphor	Coactivator (mole/mole)	Firing Conditions
I-3	O-1	Al, 10^{-5}	850°C, 1 hr, in H_2S
I-4	O-1	Al, $6 \cdot 10^{-5}$	850°C, 1 hr, in H_2S
II-1	O-2	in HCl	1200°C, 1 hr, in H_2S
G-3S	G-3	None	950°C, 1 hr, in S_2, 9 atm

For measurements of the polarization of the red luminescence and photoconductivity a zinc sulfide single crystal containing copper, which gives red luminescence, was used. This
was prepared in the following way. A zinc sulfide single

crystal* grown by a sublimation method with no additives, which emits a weak green and blue luminescence, was prefired in a hydrogen sulfide atmosphere at 700°C for 1 hr after being imbedded in zinc sulfide powder. Then the crystal was imbedded in zinc sulfide powder mixed with 10^{-4} mole/mole of cupric sulfide and fired in a hydrogen sulfide atmosphere at 1200°C for 1 hr. This firing was repeated twice. The fired crystal showed a fairly bright red luminescence.

b) Emission spectra

With regard to the spectrum of the red luminescence the following was known from investigations made by Froelich[3.1] and also by Aven and Potter.[3.2] The shape of the emission spectrum fits exactly the Gaussian distribution. The peak of the emission spectrum is located at around 6700 Å at room temperature. It is shifted towards longer wavelengths with a decrease in temperature, and the half-width is decreased considerably.

The first step of this work was to investigate the temperature dependence of the spectrum of the red luminescence in a range down to liquid helium temperature. The method of measurement was the same as that mentioned in Part I Sec 2.b. The source of excitation was the 3650 Å mercury line. Some of the results obtained with sample G-3 are shown in Fig. 3.1.

The wavelengths of the peaks and half-widths were determined by fitting to a Gaussian distribution and are given in Table 3.2. One can notice the pronounced decrease of the half-width with a decrease in temperature. This will be discussed in detail in Sec. 3.

Table 3.2

The peak wavelengths and half-widths for the spectra of the red luminescence in ZnS:Cu (sample G-3) under 3650 Å excitation.

Temperature (°K)	Emission Peak (Å)	(eV)	Half-width (eV)
293	6520	1.90	0.68
252	6520	1.90	0.62
196	6600	1.88	0.56
77	6700	1.85	0.44
4	6730	1.84	0.40

*Kindly supplied by Mr. Tomoya Ogawa at the Institute of Physical and Chemical Research, Tokyo.

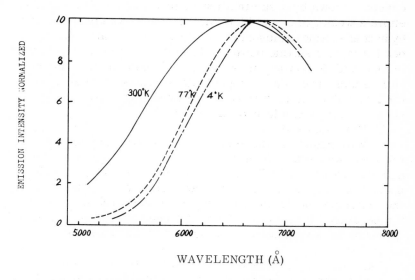

Fig. 3.1 — Emission spectra of sample G-3 (see Table 3.1) at 300, 77 and 4°K under 3650Å excitation.

The effect of the introduction of coactivators and that of the firing atmospheres on the formation and destruction of the red center were next investigated. The red luminescence usually appears when zinc sulfide mixed with cupric sulfide of $10^{-5} \sim 10^{-3}$ mole/mole is fired at $1000 \sim 1200°C$ in a hydrogen sulfide atmosphere. In the case of the 1050°C firing, the red luminescence is accompanied by a weak blue emission which peaks at about 4600 Å at room temperature (see the spectrum of sample G-3 shown in Fig. 3.5). In the case of the 1200°C firing this blue emission is completely removed (see the spectrum of sample O-2 shown in Fig. 3.4). This blue emission is regarded as the so-called copper blue luminescence, rather than the luminescence of the so-called self-activated zinc sulfide phosphor, since the emission peak shifts towards shorter wavelengths at low temperatures.[3.3]

An investigation was performed to determine whether the red center is formed by using similar firing conditions to those mentioned above but using atmospheres other than hydrogen sulfide. Nitrogen, hydrogen, sulfur vapor at 15 atm and a vacuum were tested as atmospheres. The result was that the red luminescence never appeared with any atmosphere other than hydrogen sulfide. Hydrogen sulfide seems necessary for the formation of the red center.

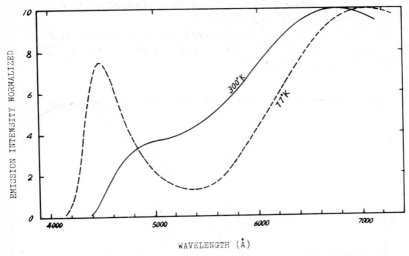

Fig. 3.2 — Emission spectra of sample I-1 (see Table 3.1) at 300 and 77°K under 3650Å excitation.

If coactivators in amounts less than that of the copper ac-tivator are added in the standard firing process which produces the red luminescent phosphor, weak blue and green lumines-cene appears in addition to the strong red luminescence. The addition of aluminum coactivator yields both the blue and green luminescence, while the addition of chlorine coactivator seems to yield only the blue luminescence. As an example the emis-sion spectra of sample I-1 (ZnS:Cu, Al) are shown in Fig. 3.2. At low temperatures the intensity of the blue luminescence is much stronger than that of the green luminescence, a well-known feature of the blue and green luminescence due to the copper activator.

If finished red luminescent phosphors are refired with the introduction of coactivators, the intensity of the red lumines-cence is diminished. This is accompanied by the appearance of weak blue and green luminescence. Also in this case alu-minum favors the appearance of both the blue and the green luminescence, while chlorine favors the appearance of only the blue. The case of aluminum is shown in Fig. 3.3 with samples

I-3 and I-4 (ZnS:Cu, Al). These samples were prepared by re-firing sample O-1 (ZnS:Cu) which emits in the red and not at all in the blue. The case of chlorine is shown in Fig. 3.4 with sample II-1. Chlorine was introduced by the firing in an atmo-sphere containing hydrogen chloride.

The refiring of finished phosphors in a sulfur atmosphere causes a similar effect to that of the chlorine refiring. The result is shown in Fig. 3.5.

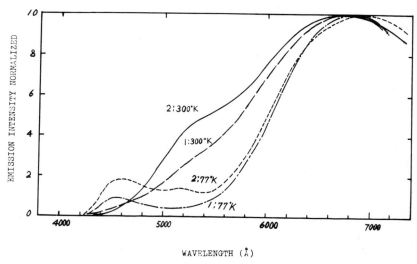

WAVELENGTH (Å)

Fig. 3.3 — Emission spectra of (1) sample I-3 and (2) sample I-4 (see Table 3.1) at 300 and 77°K under 3650Å excitation.

It is evident that with the refiring treatment the red centers are partly destroyed and the blue and green centers are cre-ated instead, or, it might be said that the red centers are partly converted to blue and green centers. If this consideration is right, the results indicate that the conversion to the blue cen-ter is effected more easily than to the green center.

c) Excitation spectra

The measurement of the excitation spectra was per-formed with a Kipp and Zonen double monochromator and a 500W xenon discharge lamp as the excitation source. As an example the result for sample I-1 (ZnS:Cu,Al) is shown in Fig. 3.6. The excitation spectra for the red as well as for the blue and green luminescence are given (for emission spectra,

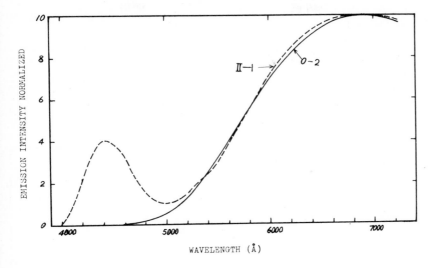

Fig. 3.4 — Emission spectra of sample O-2 and II-1 (see Table 3.1) at 300°K under 3650Å excitation.

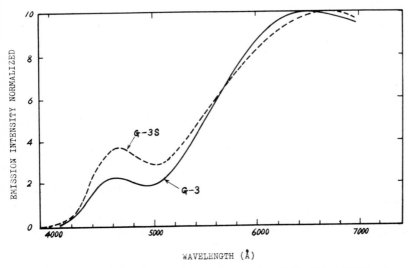

Fig. 3.5 — Emission spectra of sample G-3 and G-3S (see Table 3.1) at 300°K under 3650Å excitation.

see Fig. 3.2). Careful measurements were performed in the
visible range up to 6000 Å, and it was ascertained that no other
excitation bands exist in long wavelength region.

The excitation spectra for the blue and green luminescence
have a peak at about 3900 Å and a plateau at about 3600 Å. The
former seems responsible for the green luminescence, and the
latter for the blue luminescence.[3,4] The spectra for the red
luminescence seem to resemble the spectra for the blue luminescence rather than those for the green luminescence.

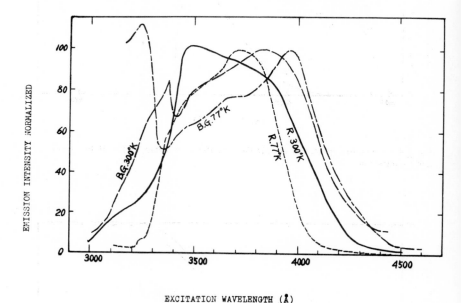

EMISSION INTENSITY NORMALIZED

EXCITATION WAVELENGTH (Å)

Fig. 3.6 — Excitation spectra for the red luminescence (R) and for the blue and green
luminescence (B.G.) of sample I-1 (see Table 3.1) at 300 and 77°K.

d) Polarization of luminescence

The polarization of the red and blue luminescence was
measured with the single crystal described in Sec. 2.a. The
single crystal emits, in addition to a bright red luminescence,
a weak blue and a very weak green luminescence. The ratios
of the intensity of the blue luminescence to that of the red
luminescence are 0.31, 0.25 and 0.25 at 300, 77 and 4°K, respectively, under 3650 Å excitation. The temperature characteristics of the emission spectra clearly indicate that the red

and blue centers in the single crystal are identical to those in powder phosphors.

The single crystal was the flake type. Observations with an interference microscope indicated that the crystal structure was a hexagonal type involving some stacking faults, and that the c-axis was parallel to the plane of the flake.

The polarization was measured with a common sheet polarizer and with RCA 7102 and 6199 photomultipliers, which were used for the red and the blue luminescence, respectively. The excitation source was the 3650 Å mercury line which was not made polarized.

The degree of polarization of the luminescence is expressed by $I_{\parallel c}/I_{\perp c}$, where $I_{\parallel c}$ and $I_{\perp c}$ are the intensities of luminescence polarized in the directions parallel and perpendicular to the c-axis of the crystal, respectively. The results are given in Table 3.3. Both the red and the blue luminescence are polarized in the direction perpendicular to the c-axis, but at $4°K$ the polarization of the red luminescence is considerably smaller than that of the blue. The polarization characteristics of the blue luminescence observed here coincide with the results of Lempicki.[3.5] These results seem to show that the polarization of the blue luminescence is quenched by some thermal process, while this is not the case for the red luminescence. In addition the red luminescence seems to be polarized very little.

Table 3.3

Degree of polarization, $I_{\parallel c}/I_{\perp c}$, for the red and the blue luminescence in a ZnS:Cu single crystal

Luminescence	Temperature ($°K$)		
	300	77	4
red	0.955	0.943	0.927
blue	0.965	0.921	0.862

e) Photoconductivity

The spectral sensitivity of the photoconductivity and its temperature change were measured with the single crystal. The photocurrent was measured with a vibrating reed electrometer. A monochromatic source of excitation was obtained by means of a 500W xenon discharge lamp and a Bausch and Lomb grating monochromator.

The results on the spectral sensitivity are shown in Fig. 3.7.
Comparing these results with the excitation spectra of powder
phosphors shown in Fig. 3.6, one will immediately notice that
at room temperature the spectral sensitivity of the photoconductivity is very similar to the excitation spectrum for the red
luminescence, while at low temperatures it is similar to the
excitation spectrum for the blue and green, rather than the
red, luminescence. The photoconductivity diminishes markedly
with decrease in temperature. The magnitude of the photoconductivity at 130°K is about one fortieth of that at room temperature. Combining these two facts the conclusion may be drawn
that the photoconductivity associated with the red center decreases with decrease in temperature much more rapidly than
does that associated with the blue and green center.

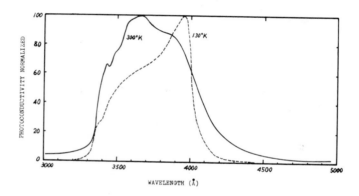

Fig. 3.7 — Spectral sensitivity of photoconductivity for a ZnS:Cu single
crystal with bright red and weak blue and green luminescence (see text
Sec. 2.a and 2.e) at 300 and 130°K.

f) Glow emission

Attempts were made to measure the glow curve for the
red luminescence. Careful measurements revealed, however,
that red luminescent phosphors fired at 1050°C (for instance
sample G-3) do not exhibit red glow emission, while phosphors
fired at 1200°C (for instance sample O-1) exhibit a fairly weak
red glow emission which peaks at 135°K at a heating rate of
10°K/min. The position of the peak of this weak glow emission is exactly the same as that observed usually with green
luminescent ZnS:Cu,Al phosphors prepared by firing in a hydrogen sulfide atmosphere after almost equal amounts of copper and

aluminum have been added. The depth of the trap associated with this glow peak is estimated to be about 0.21 eV, which is the same as a well-known value for the trap created by the introduction of halogen or aluminum coactivators.[1,8] The area of the red glow curve is about one fourth that of the green glow curve, which gives one an idea of the weakness of the red glow emission.

3. Discussion

First of all we would like to point out that based on the following facts the copper red center is considered to be localized within the forbidden band of the zinc sulfide crystal. The shape of the emission spectra fits the Gaussian distribution, and the half-widths of the spectra decrease markedly with decrease in temperature. These can be explained, as will be described later, by the above suggestion. The photoconductivity associated with the red center is diminished greatly with decrease in temperature. The peak of the emission spectrum shifts to longer wavelengths through lowering the temperature. If the transition responsible for the red luminescence were that between a localized level and the conduction or filled band, the peak would shift to shorter wavelengths, since the band gap increases with a decrease in temperature. The fact, found by Aven and Potter,[3,2] that the position of the peak is independent of the crystal structure of zinc sulfide, also presents the same kind of evidence, since the band gap in a hexagonal type crystal is slightly larger than that in a cubic crystal.

The temperature dependence of the half-width of the emission spectrum can be accounted for if a simplified configurational coordinate model frequently used for the localized centers is applied to the red center. If the configurational coordinate curves for both the ground and excited states of a localized center are assumed to be parabolas, the dependence of the half-width of an emission spectrum, W_E, on temperature is given by the following equation,[3,6] taking into account the fact that the contribution of the zero-point vibration becomes essential at very low temperatures.

$$W_E = (2K_g X_0)\left(\frac{1.386 k}{K_e}\right)^{1/2}\left(\frac{h\nu_e}{2k}\ \coth\ \frac{h\nu_e}{2kT}\right)^{1/2} \tag{3.1}$$

where K_e and K_g are the force constants for the excited and ground states, X_0 is the displacement of the minimum of the excited state from that of the ground state along the coordinate axis, and ν_e is the frequency of vibration associated with the excited state.

The value of ν_e can be estimated using the experimental data given in Table 3.2, and is found to be $(4.3 \pm 0.1) \times 10^{12}$ sec^{-1}. With the same data, Eq. (3.1) can be rewritten as,

$$W_E = (0.395 \pm 0.005) \left(\coth \frac{h\nu_e}{2kT} \right)^{1/2} \qquad (3.2)$$

where W_E is in electron volts.

The graph of this equation is shown in Fig. 3.8. The agree-

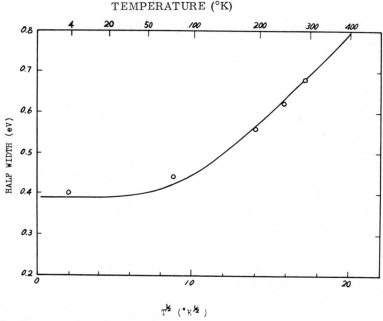

Fig. 3.8 — Half-widths of the spectra of the red luminescence versus temperature. The circles are the experimental points given in Table 3.2. The solid line is the plot of the theoretical equation, Eq. (3.2).

ment with experiment is fairly good. This gives clear evidence that the red center is a localized one.

The frequency for the optical mode of the lattice vibration in a zinc sulfide crystal is known [3.7] to be ν_t (transverse mode) =

= 9.0×10^{12} sec^{-1} and ν_l (longitudinal mode) = 1.1×10^{13} sec^{-1}. The value for ν_e is much smaller than these, indicating that the excited red center is more loosely associated with the surrounding atoms than the normal atoms of the lattice are.

The shape of the configurational coordinate curves cannot be determined with only the experimental data presently available. Some inferences, however, can be made. If one assumes that $K_e = K_g$, one obtains 3.43 eV for E_0, the difference between the minimum of the excited state and that of the ground state. This value is of course an over-estimate, since K_g is usually larger than or at least equal to K_e. This value, then, gives the upper limit of E_0. If one assumes that the peak energy of absorption is 3.35 eV (3700 Å) according to the excitation spectra shown in Fig. 3.6, one obtains E_0 = 2.99 eV and ν_e / ν_g = 0.31, where ν_g is the frequency of vibration associated with the ground state. The value for ν_e / ν_g may be too small. This gives 1.3 $\sim 1.4 \times 10^{13}$ sec^{-1} for ν_g, which is slightly larger than the experimental value for ν_l.

The shift of the emission peak towards longer wavelengths cannot be explained with this simplified configurational coordinate model, which predicts no shift of the peak with temperature. To account for the shift we have to assume an asymmetric configurational coordinate curve for the excited state. Since the shift is toward longer wavelengths, the assumptions should be that the minimum of the excited state is displaced towards the origin of the coordinate axis, and the shape of the curve for the excited state is steeper for the side close to the origin than for the other side.

The experimental results which would enable one to discuss the atomic nature of the localized red center are rather poor at the present time. We would like, however, to present a tentative atomic model for the red center. Usually, to introduce copper into the zinc sulfide lattice, charge compensation is required, which in most cases is effected by the introduction of coactivators. If it is assumed that copper is introduced substitutionally, an acceptor-like level should be created. This level is usually in the form of a compensated acceptor. Since in the red emitting phosphors no coactivators are introduced, it is likely that some lattice imperfection has performed the function of the coactivators. The most probable kind of imperfection would be a sulfur vacancy, since if a sulfur atom is removed from the lattice two electrons remain, which are available for charge compensation with copper. The sulfur vacancy should create a donor-like level. Thus we would like to assume that the red center is formed when a substitutionally introduced copper ion and a sulfur vacancy are closely associated in the lattice making a pair with the character of a molecule imbedded in the crystal, and further that the ground state of the center is the acceptor-like copper level and the excited state is the donor-like sulfur vacancy level.

This model was proposed by taking the following facts into account. The red center is formed only when the firing is performed in a hydrogen sulfide atmosphere.[3·8] Hydrogen sulfide decomposes appreciably at higher temperatures. A thermodynamical calculation using the equilibrium constant[3·9] for the reaction $H_2 S = H_2 + 1/2 S_2$ (g) shows that the partial pressure of the resulting hydrogen reaches about 0.3 atm at 1200°C. Hydrogen sulfide, therefore, should be regarded as a reducing, rather than a sulfurdizing, atmosphere. This effect may be important even if the red center is not formed in the hydrogen atmosphere. Apple and Prener[3·10] have found that if the red emitting phosphors are fired in an atmosphere of high pressure sulfur vapor, the infrared emission, which is attributed to the transition between the copper acceptor level and the filled band, results. This kind of phosphor exhibits p-type semiconductivity. These facts mean that because of the sulfur treatment the compensated copper acceptor level is converted to a non compensated one. The fact that the red emitting phosphor does not show a glow emission or shows only a weak one, is important in assuming this model. Since the sulfur vacancy level is regarded as the excited state of the center, electrons falling down to this level from the conduction band return immediately to the ground state. Therefore the sulfur vacancy level cannot act as a trap. Further, no coactivators are introduced. Then no traps will be present in the crystal. The appearance of the weak glow emission in phosphors fired at higher temperatures might be attributed to the formation of sulfur vacancies which are not associated with copper.

Either the introduction of coactivators or the refiring in the sulfur atmosphere of the finished red emitting phosphors partly destroys the red center. These facts support the model, since by these procedures the sulfur vacancy will be destroyed or replaced by the coactivator. A fact that the red luminescence is polarized very slightly seems also to support the model. Since the hexagonal structure of zinc sulfide is very close to the ideal hexagonal closed packing structure, the molecule-like red centers will be distributed in the lattice isotropically as a whole, causing little polarization. The fact that the emission spectrum is independent of the crystal structure,[3.2] also supports the model of the molecule-like center.

The authors would like to express their appreciation to Professor Shoji Makishima of this laboratory for his suggestions and discussions.

REFERENCES

[1.1] S. Makishima, Doctoral Thesis, Faculty of Engineering, University of Tokyo, 1944.
See also: N. Kameyama, "Theory and Applications of Luminescent Materials", p. 37 (1960), Maruzen, Tokyo.

[1.2] G. R. Fonda, J. Opt. Soc. Am. 36, 382 (1946)

[1.3] See: "Progress Report 3 on Solid State Radiation-Induced Phenomena", submitted by H. Kallmann, Physics Department, New York University, to United States Signal Corps, 1959.

[1.4] S. Shionoya and K. Amano, J. Chem. Phys. 25, 380 (1956).

[1.5] H. Kallmann, B. Kramer and A. Perlmutter, Phys. Rev. 89, 700 (1953).

[1.6] H. Kallmann, B. Kramer and P. Mark, J. Phys. Chem. Solids 10, 59 (1959).

[1.7] C. H. Haake, J. Opt. Soc. Am. 41, 649 (1957).

[1.8] W. Hoogenstraaten, J. Electrochem. Soc. 100, 356 (1953).

[2.1] D. L. Dexter, J. Chem. Phys. 21, 836 (1953).

[2.2] N. F. Mott and R. W. Gurney, "Electronic Processes in Ionic Crystals", p. 207 (1940).

[2.3] M. Schön, Z. Phys. 119, 436 (1942).

[2.4] S. Shionoya, J. Chem. Phys. 23, 1173 (1955).

[2.5] S. Shionoya, Bull. Chem. Soc. Japan 29, 935 (1956).

[2.6] R. H. Bube, Phys. Rev. 90, 70 (1953).

[2.7] C.C. Klick and J. H. Schulman, J. Opt. Soc. Am. 42, 910 (1952).

[3.1] H. C. Froelich, J. Electrochem. Soc. 100, 280 (1953).

[3.2] M. H. Aven and R. M. Potter, ibid., 105, 134 (1958).

[3.3] R. E. Shrader and S. Larach, Phys. Rev. 103, 1899 (1958).

[3.4] N. T. Melamed, J. Phys. Chem. Solids 7, 146 (1958).

[3.5] A. Lempicki, J. Electrochem. Soc. 107, 404 (1960).

[3.6] C. C. Klick and J. H. Schulman, "Solid State Physics", Vol. 5, p.110 (1957).

3. 7 H. Yoshinaga et al, J. Phys. Soc. Japan 13, 1235 (1958).

3. 8 W. van Gool and A.P.D.M. Cleiren, J. Electrochem. Soc. 106, 672 (1959).

3. 9 G. N. Lewis and M. Randall, "Thermodynamics and the Free Energy of Chemical Substances", p.299 (1922).

3.10 E. F. Apple and J. S. Prener, J. Phys. Chem. Solids 13, 81 (1960).

ASSOCIATION OF CENTERS IN ZINC SULFIDE

W. v. Gool and G. Diemer

Philips Research Laboratories
N. V. Philips' Gloeilampenfabrieken
Eindhoven, Netherlands

ABSTRACT

The interaction of lattice defects in ZnS is discussed. Special attention is paid to the situation where there are equal concentrations of activator (Ag, Cu, Au) and coactivator (Al, Sc, Ga and In) incorporated into ZnS. With increasing but equal concentrations changes take place in the fluorescence, the glow curves and the temperature dependence of the fluorescence. It is shown that calculations reported in the literature are not in accordance with the experimental results. Some suggestions are made as to the cause of this discrepancy.

1. INTRODUCTION

The fluorescence of ZnS is caused by the presence of local disturbances of the host lattice. These lattice defects can be impurities, either intentionally added or unintentionally present, and native defects. The latter are defects that can already be formed in ZnS consisting of zinc and sulphur only, for example vacant lattice sites, misplaced atoms (zinc on sulfur sites, etc.) and interstitial atoms.

Of the added impurities we shall discuss here the elements Ag, Cu, Au (generally A) and Cl, Al, Sc, Ga, In (generally C). The activators A, under special preparative conditions, are thought to occupy normal zinc sites having an effectively negative charge (Ag_{Zn}', Cu_{Zn}', Au_{Zn}'). The coactivators can have a positive charge. They will be present on zinc sites ($Al_{Zn}^{\cdot}$, $Sc_{Zn}^{\cdot}$, $Ga_{Zn}^{\cdot}$, $In_{Zn}^{\cdot}$) or on sulfur sites ($Cl_S^{\cdot}$). In an ionic description this corresponds to the presence of Ag^+, Al^{3+}, Cl^- ions etc. When the impurities are present in the form mentioned, they must be accompanied by some other defect in order to maintain the electroneutrality of the lattice. The incorporation of 10^{-4} gram atom of copper in ZnS, without the addition of an equal amount of coactivator, can provoke the occurrence of 10^{-4} "gram atom" of some single positively charged native defect, for example a sulfur vacancy ($V_S^{\cdot}$) or interstitial Zn ($Zn_i^{\cdot}$). Other situations are also possible. For example the copper could be incorporated as a neutral defect (Cu_{Zn}^{x}) and then no compensation is needed. The properties of ZnS containing Cu are not in accordance with this simple assumption. Even more complications arise from the possible association of Cu_{Zn}' and some positive compensation defect, for example $V_S^{\cdot}$. It is not yet possible to predict the effective charge of the association center ($Cu_{Zn}V_S$). The neutral associate can exist as such, but the negative form would have to be compensated (*e.g.* $[(Cu_{Zn}V_S)'] \approx [V_S^{\cdot}]$). When charged positively, compensation by Cu_{Zn}' or by negatively charged native defects is possible, thus $[(Cu_{Zn}V_S)^{\cdot}] \approx [Cu_{Zn}']$ or for example $(Cu_{Zn}V_S)^{\cdot} \approx [V_{Zn}']$. The situations described by the equations are called <u>incorporation mechanisms.</u> They are approximations of the complete neutrality condition, containing all possible charged centers. Even when some limiting assumptions are made, about one hundred incorporation mechanisms can still be written down for the case of one activator incorporated in ZnS, many of them containing association centers. The same situation arises when a coactivator is incorporated in ZnS. When both an activator and a coactivator are present, with one of them in excess, similar difficulties are encountered, because the excess will have to be compensated in some way.

The fluorescence of ZnS corresponding to the situations described above is not unimportant from a practical point of view. The so-called self-activated (SA-) emission, the "blue" copper-emission and the "red" copper-emission are obtained when the concentrations of activator and coactivator are unequal. Many articles deal with these emissions, but the experiments were not designed with a view to distinguishing between the possible incorporation mechanisms, and in fact no definite conclusions are reached. The experiments do, however, reveal that association of lattice defects is important in at least some of the fluorescence mentioned.

The numerous possible incorporation mechanisms are due to our lack of knowledge of the native defects. The situation can be compared with the study of an ionic solution in, say, water, in which one kind of ion is known, but where several other kinds of ions with unknown properties are present. For a better understanding of the defect chemistry of ZnS the primary task remains to increase our knowledge of the native defects, especially of the free energy of formation and the energy scheme of vacancies and interstitials. The same applies of course to many other compounds. We mention here only CdS: the decrease of its photoconductivity when the concentration ratio $[Cu]/[Ga]$ becomes greater than unity, and the slowness of the photoconductive response, are probably due to native defects or to association centers.

The theory and the experimental facts mentioned in this section, and also the relevant literature, have been more extensively discussed elsewhere.[1]

When an activator and a coactivator are present in equal concentrations the possibility exists that the native defects are present only in negligible concentrations. The incorporation mechanism $[A'] \approx [C^{\cdot}]$ may be predominant. This situation can occur when the concentrations of the native defects in pure ZnS (*i. e.* without foreign atoms) are low compared to those of the incorporated impurities. Some of the centers A' and $C^{\cdot}$ will be so close together that we can call them associated. In that case it is still possible to neglect the native defects in comparison to the added impurities. The remainder of this paper will be devoted to this situation.

2. CHANGE OF ASSOCIATION

The formation of the association center (AC) can be described by

$$A' + C^{\cdot} \rightarrow (AC)^{x} \tag{1}$$

The cross indicates that the center (AC) is effectively neutral. According to thermodynamics the temperature dependence of the equilibrium constant K

$$K = \frac{[(AC)^x]}{[A'][C']} \tag{2}$$

is given by

$$\frac{d \ln K}{dT} = \frac{\Delta H^0}{RT^2} \tag{3}$$

Here it is assumed that only a limited temperature range is considered, so that the enthalpy change ΔH^0 and the entropy change ΔS^0 will be constant. No exact calculations of ΔH^0 in ZnS are yet available, and it is not certain whether an important shift of the equilibrium will be found when the temperature is changed.

The change in the concentrations of the added impurities was used in the experiments in order to study association phenomena. When the amount of associate (AC) is low, then the following approximations hold:

$$[A'] = [C'] = c - [(AC)] \approx c \tag{4}$$

$$[(AC)] = K\left\{c - [(AC)]\right\}^2 \approx Kc^2 \tag{5}$$

The relative importance of the association center will increase with increasing concentrations c.

3. LITTLE ASSOCIATION: THE SINGLE CENTERS

At low activator and coactivator concentrations the experimental results can be summarized as follows. With the activators Ag, Cu and Au the well-known blue, green and yellow-green emissions are found. They are independent of the coactivator used.[1,2] These emissions will be indicated as high-photon-energy emissions (HPE-emissions), to distinguish them from other emissions encountered at longer wavelengths (Sect. 4). The glow curves are characteristic of the coactivator used[3] and will be referred to as high temperature glow peaks.

In this situation the interaction of the two kinds of centers can be neglected. According to Klasens[4] the nature of the single centers should be described as follows: the ionization energy of the activator ions Ag^+, Cu^+ and Au^+ is too large to allow any direct ionization by excitation with the usual ultra-violet radiation. Therefore it is assumed that the effectively

negative ions influence the surrounding sulfur ions. After excitation the center should be described as an activator ion,
e.g. Ag^+ with a bound hole on the neighboring sulfur ions. This
hydrogen model is also used for the coactivator centers.[3]
Hoogenstraaten[3] has shown that the approximation used holds
rather well for semiconductors such as Ge and Si, but not for
ZnS (especially with respect to the activators). The deviation
from the model is in such a direction that the orbit of the bound
hole is smaller than corresponds to the atomic distances.
Therefore it may be possible that some properties of the excited
activator center—e.g. the interaction with lattice defects separated a few atomic distances from the activator considered--
should be described in terms of Cu^{2+} rather than of Cu^+ + hole.

4. ASSOCIATION EFFECTS

When the concentrations of activator and coactivator are
increased a striking indication of association effects is the occurrence of new emission bands at longer wavelengths. These
low-photon-energy bands (LPE-emissions) depend on the nature
of both activator and coactivator. The LPE-emission bands are
sometimes broad and extend into the infrared region. They seem
to be of a composite nature. The subbands which compose them
could not be obtained as separate bands by changing the preparation conditions. The peak value of the LPE-emission shifts
sometimes to a lower energy when the concentrations of activator and coactivator are increased. Figures 1 and 2 show
the spectral distribution of the emitted light in the Cu-Sc series.
Details of the preparation and measurement have been reported
elsewhere[1,2] (concentrations are expressed as gram atoms/mole
ZnS).

In Figure 3 the glow curves and the temperature dependence
of the emission bands are shown. In addition to the peak due to
the single coactivator centers the glow curves have a second
peak at a lower temperature. The visually observed color during
glow, together with the plate voltage of the photomultiplier are
mentioned; the latter gives a qualitative indication of the emitted
intensity. As can be seen from Figure 3 the low-temperature
glow has the same color as the LPE-emission, whereas during
the high-temperature peak the activator emission (HPE) predominates. The temperature dependences of the emitted light
show some interesting features. At liquid nitrogen temperature

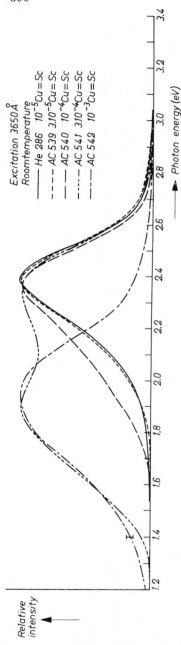

Fig. 1 – Fluorescence of ZnS
with equal molar amounts of Cu
and Sc (room temperature).

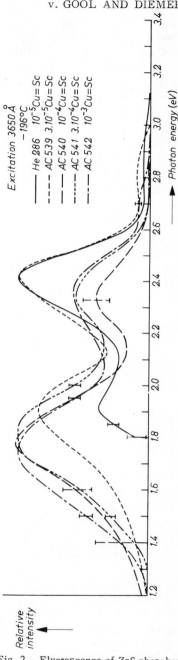

Fig. 2 – Fluorescence of ZnS phosphors
with equal molar amounts of Cu and Sc
(liquid nitrogen temperature).

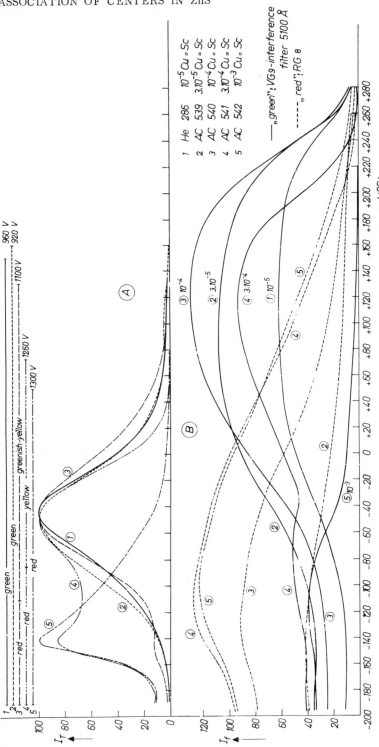

Fig. 3 – Glow curves (A) and temperature (B) of the Cu = Sc series.

the activator emission is rather weak and the emission of the
associate is rather strong. When the temperature is increased
both LPE-emission and HPE-emission pass through a maximum.
Since the maximum of the LPE-emission is reached earlier
than that of the HPE-emission, the HPE-emission predominates
at room temperature or higher. The quantitative behavior of
the phosphors depends on the concentrations of the activator
and coactivator.

A description of the properties of the associated defects can
be obtained by starting with the single defects. When an electron
during glow is transferred from an isolated coactivator center
to an isolated activator center through the conduction band it
gives rise to conduction. When the activator and the coactivator
center are closer together, the same transition can still occur
via an excited state, but now it is possible that the electron remains connected to the associate center. No conduction should
be expected during the transition and the behavior of the center
can be described with three energy levels, as indicated by p_1,
p_2, and p_3 in Fig. 4. The transitions within the association

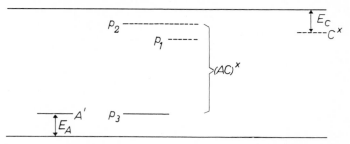

Fig. 4 – Energy levels of activator (A!), coactivator (C^x) and association
center $(AC)^x$.

center are indicated in Fig. 5. They are: the excitation G, the
fluorescing transition F_{AC}, the transition R to the metastable
state, the thermal excitation S of the metastable state and the
radiationless transition Q to the ground state. This model can
explain the occurrence of the low-temperature glow peak, the
color of the light emitted during the glow, and the initial increase
in intensity of the LPE-emission when the temperature is increased above – 196°C. The radiationless transition Q has been
introduced in order to explain the presence of the LPE-emission
even in the case where the temperature has been decreased to
– 196°C. If no return of the electrons to the ground state in
some way or another were assumed, all association centers
would come to the situation p_1 and no fluorescence would be

observed. Other interpretations of this fact are possible however. The presence of subbands in the LPE-emission can be
explained by the assumption that several kinds of association
centers exist, for example nearest neighbors, next-nearest
neighbors, etc. The concentration of each kind of association
center depends on the total amount of impurities added. The
position of the energy levels and the values of the transition
constants will cary with the distance between activator and
coactivator in the association center.

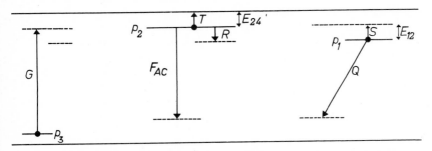

Fig. 5 — Three different states and some transitions of the neutral association center.

When the temperature is increased electrons and holes can
be released from the association centers and they can interact
with the non-associated activator and coactivator centers. Although we have for the moment not aimed at a quantitative interpretation, it can be understood at least qualitatively that the
HPE-emission (activator-emission) has only a low intensity at
– 196°C and shows a maximum when the temperature is increased.

5. COMPARISON WITH OTHER DESCRIPTIONS

The association effects in ZnS have been studied by several
other workers. Apple has described the fluorescence of ZnS
activated with Ag or Cu and coactivated with Ga or In.[5] Prener[6]
has interpreted the theory of Reiss[7] for strong electrolytes in
terms of solid state interactions. Apple and Williams[8] discussed the experiments of Apple, making use of Prener's calculations. The interpretation given in Section 4 resembles that
of Apple and Williams insofar as the LPE-emission is ascribed
to a nearby association of activator and coactivator. The HPE-
emission is assumed by the other authors to be caused by the
transition of an electron from the coactivator to the activator

via an excited state. We assumed that the electron is free
during this transition, because we did not find any coactivator
influence on the HPE-emission. Photoconductivity measurements during glow with well defined single crystals should
settle this question.

A more severe objection can be made to the calculations of
Hoogenstraaten[3] and Williams[9] about the energy value of the
associate emissions. According to these calculations this
energy should increase with increasing concentration of impurities and should even approach the band distance. Our experiments show, however, that when any shift is present, it is
in the direction of lower photon energies, and that the association emission is at lower energy values than the activator
emissions.

This result and the fact that no doubtful approximations
were made in the calculations mentioned indicates that the
starting point of these calculations is probably not quite right.
This starting point is essentially a four-particle system: hole,
electron, donor and acceptor. In the limiting case of nearby
association the system corresponds to a hole and an electron
in the field of a dipole formed by both nuclei. It is to be expected
that the excitation energy of this system approaches the formation energy of an exciton or the band gap energy of ZnS.

In Section 3 it was mentioned that in ZnS the excited copper
center should be looked upon as Cu^{2+} instead of Cu^+ + hole. In
that case the excitation of the association center should be considered as a transition from e.g. $Cu^+Sc^{3+}(S^{2-})_2$ to $Cu^{2+}Sc^{2+}$
$(S^{2-})_2$ or to $Cu^{2+}Sc^{3+}(S^{2-})_2$ + electron. The excitation energy of
the association center can then perhaps better be compared
with the band gap of $CuInS_2$ than with that of ZnS. In fact it may
be possible that the excitation energy of the fluorescence energy
of associated defects of the kind discussed can give information
about the approximation to be used in the calculations.

REFERENCES

[1] W. van Gool, Thesis (1961).
(Will be published as a supplement to Philips Research
Reports).
[2] W. van Gool, A. P. Cleiren and H. J. M. Heijligers, Philips
Res. Reports 15, 254, (1960).
[3] W. Hoogenstraaten, Philips Res. Reports 13, 515, (1958).
(Thesis 1958).
[4] H. A. Klasens, J. Electrochem. Soc. 100, 72, (1953).

[5] E. F. Apple, J. Electrochem. Soc. 105, 251, (1958).
[6] J. S. Prener, J. Chem. Phys. 25, 1294, (1956).
[7] H. Reiss, J. Chem. Phys. 25, 400, (1956)
[8] E. F. Apple and F. E. Williams, J. Electrochem. Soc. 106, 224, (1959).
[9] F. E. Williams, Phys. Chem. Solids 12, 265, (1960).

ANTI-STOKES LUMINESCENCE OF ZINC SULFIDE TYPE PHOSPHORS

I. Broser and R. Broser-Warminsky
Institut für Elektronenmikroskopie am Fritz-Haber-Institut
der Max-Planck-Gesellschaft, Berlin-Dahlem

ABSTRACT

Single crystals of ZnS, CdS, ZnSe, and CdSe have been investigated with regard to their property to luminesce with wavelengths shorter than that of the exciting radiation (anti-stokes luminescence). It has been found that at low temperatures almost every crystal possesses anti-stokes emission bands of a more or less strong intensity.

In order to fully investigate the two-step mechanism of excitation (Halsted, Apple, Prener, 1959) quantitative measurements were performed with copper activated crystals of ZnS and CdS in most cases at the temperature of liquid helium. Effects studied include the action of additional red and infra-red radiation on the form of the emission spectrum, the intensity dependence of Stokes and anti-stokes emission, the excitation spectra and the rise and decay curves of luminescence and photoconductivity. The results of the investigations can be explained with the aid of the two energy level system for the copper activator used thus far in connection with quenching and infrared luminescence of ZnS type phosphors. This system allows the transfer of an electron from the valence band to the conduction band by a two step process, creating an electron hole pair, which may recombine over the copper activator itself or over any luminescence center in the vicinity.

The existence of "anti-stokes" luminescence, i.e. of luminescence which can be continuously generated by radiation whose wavelength is longer than that of the emission, has been demonstrated for ZnS by Potter[1] and for CdS by Halsted, Apple and

Prener.[2] The latter authors could show that the green edge
emission of CdS with a photon energy of 2.4 eV is excited by
"red" photons of an energy down to 1.5 eV. They explained
the effect of anti-stokes emission by means of a two step
optical excitation process, in which an electron can be transferred from the valence band via an acceptor level to the conduction band. A more detailed description of the various processes involved in the generation of anti-stokes luminescence
in sulfide phosphors has been given by Halsted, Apple, Prener
and Piper[3] and by Broser, Broser-Warminsky and Schulz.[4]
The incorporation of copper has been found to be necessary
to create energy levels allowing transitions of holes and electrons terminating in both valence and conduction bands. Furthermore, connections with other optical properties and with
photoconductivity have been established, and it has been shown
that the centers for anti-stokes luminescence are identical
with the well known centers for infrared luminescence and
quenching in the investigated crystals.[5-10] There is a certain
difference in the energy level schemes presented in both
papers,[3,4] especially in connection with the absorption and
emission mechanism for the infrared emission, but, nevertheless, the main principle of anti-stokes emission in crystal
phosphors seems to be explained in a satisfactory manner.

There is, however, a distinct lack of experimental results
for quantitative considerations and for the discussion of details
of the excitation and emission of anti-stokes luminescence.
The purpose of this paper is to add to the available material
on this new and exciting topic of solid state physics. The investigations discussed below deal first of all with the proof of
anti-stokes luminescence in substances other than CdS. Single
crystals of ZnS, CdSe, and ZnSe were examined, generally at
the temperature of liquid helium. Quantitative measurements
were made with two single crystals of CdS and ZnS. It can be
concluded from the emission and excitation spectra measured
at different temperatures that the proposed mechanism[4] explains anti-stokes luminescence in detail.

APPARATUS

One of the main difficulties encountered in measuring anti-
stokes luminescence is that the emitted radiation cannot easily
be separated from the incident exciting radiation. In most cases,

the energy of photons generating anti-stokes emission is not much smaller than the energy of the emitted quanta; a published example[2] of exciting edge emission of CdS with 1.5 eV is a relatively rare exception. If we take the Franck-Condon shift between emission and absorption to be of the order of 0.5 eV,[10] it is even probable to observe anti-stokes luminescence, if the wavelengths of the exciting and the emitted light are equal. It is therefore obvious that the use of filters will not solve our problem. However, the separation of the two radiations is possible if one measures the luminescence shortly after excitation, i.e. if one investigates the emission characteristics of the afterglow. If the time between excitation and observation is short enough, no remarkable difference in contrast to the direct measurement of luminescence will appear.

A suitable apparatus for such investigations has been described elsewhere.[11] It consists of two discs, one in front and one in back of the crystal. In each disc there are holes which are radially displaced with respect to each other. The discs are connected by a common axis and can be rotated at high speed. The exciting radiation is incident on one side of the crystal, and the luminescence is observed with a photomultiplier from the other side. Thus, only the luminescent light, which is emitted directly after the incident light has impinged on the crystal, will be measured. The separation of the two radiations is complete. Most of the emission and excitation spectra mentioned in the following chapters were obtained with the aid of this apparatus.

An important condition for the detection of anti-stokes luminescence is that one works at relatively low temperatures. Anti-stokes luminescence is observed mostly on low temperature emission bands lying in a wavelength region not far from that of the band edge, since measurable absorption of light will only occur in the long wavelength tail of the absorption edge. Our measurements were therefore carried out in most cases at the temperature of liquid helium. The crystal was mounted within a metal cryostat, which had two quartz windows on two opposite sides.[12] A mixture of indium and mercury was used to cement the crystal to a metal holder, which was cooled from the interior with liquid helium. The substance investigated thus had a temperature slightly higher than 4.2°K but could be held in a vacuum.

Because of the low intensity of anti-stokes luminescence most of the emission and excitation spectra have been measured with the aid of interference filters. The resolving power of these instruments is relatively poor and therefore smaller details of the spectra such as the splitting of the edge emission by phonon interaction[13] have been lost. The important optical properties of the investigated ZnS-type phosphors are, however, shown quite well with such filters.

ANTI-STOKES LUMINESCENCE OF VARIOUS II-VI COMPOUNDS

At low temperatures anti-stokes emission could be observed with nearly every ZnS-type phosphor which was investigated. The efficiency, however, was, in most cases, very small compared with that of the "normally" excited luminescence. Only specimens which were doped with copper showed in some instances a relatively bright anti-stokes luminescence. Such crystals were used for the measurements reported here.

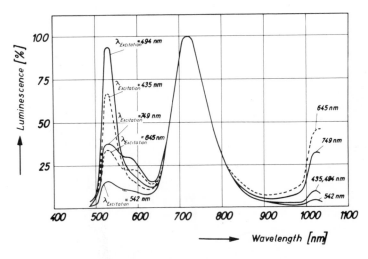

Fig. 1 — Emission spectra of a CdS:Cu crystal at 4°K under different excitations.

Figure 1 shows the emission spectrum of a CdS single crystal at the temperature of liquid helium for different wavelengths of monochromatic exciting radiation. Three main bands

can be observed: the green edge emission at about 520nm,* the
red band at 720nm, and the well known infrared copper band of
CdS at 1020nm. First of all, it can be seen that these three
bands occur at every wavelength of excitation whether there is
anti-stokes emission or not. The intensity ratio of the bands
varies by a factor 1:8 from the condition in which all bands are
excited with short wavelength light, to that in which one band is
excited anti-stokes (λ_{Exc} = 542 nm) and the other two Stokes.
This ratio is even better if one compares only the edge emission with the infrared copper emission being connected with
each other according to the picture of two-step excitation.[3,4]
This shows clearly that the low intensity of anti-stokes luminescence is due simply to the relatively small absorption coefficient for light of longer wavelength. In order to demonstrate
this, the excitation spectrum of the edge emission was compared
with the amount of radiation which was absorbed by the crystal
(Fig. 2). By dividing the luminescence by the absorbed energy one

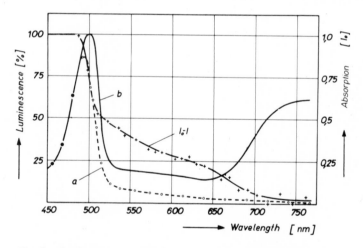

Fig. 2 — Excitation spectrum of a CdS crystal at 4°K for equal excitation energy I_0 (observed, curve a) and for equal absorbed energy I_0-I
(calculated, curve b).

obtains the light yield of the edge emission in units relative to
the highest yield near the absorption edge. The result is very

---

*Following standard German practice, the units of length used in this
paper are: 1 nm = 10^{-9} m = 1 mμ
                    1 μm = 10^{-6} m = 1 μ

striking: The drop in efficiency in the region in which one-step
excitation changes to two-step excitation is only 2.5 times
higher than that expected in the ideal case where nothing happens other than the creation of a free electron and a free hole
by two instead of one absorption processes. But, in reality,
the excitation of the red and infrared emission is preferred as
long as these emissions are excited by one-step processes. At
about 700nm the red luminescence is no longer a Stokes emission,
and the absorption coefficient for the excitation of the infrared
copper band becomes small. The distribution of the excitation
energy over the three bands is now the same as that for absorption near the absorption edge, and the efficiency of edge emission is 50% of that of the maximum.

Anti-stokes emission could also be observed with ZnS:Cu
crystals. Figure 3 represents emission spectra at 77°K excited

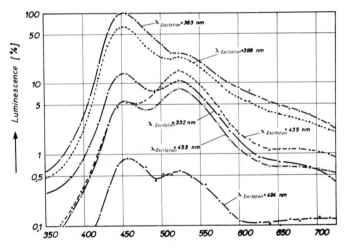

Fig. 3 — Emission spectra of a ZnS:Cu crystal at 77°K under different
excitations.

by light of different wavelengths. In this case no edge emission
was found, and the ratio of absorption and emission wavelength
is nearly one. Two main bands exist at 455 and 525 nm as is
known to be the case when copper is the activating substance.
The intensity ratio of these bands does not change considerably
with Stokes and anti-stokes excitation, although the absolute
brightness decreases very rapidly if the wavelength of the incident radiation crosses 450 nm. The influence of the Franck-

Condon shift can be seen from the curves. Between 400 and 450 nm the blue band ceases to be excited with a one-step process, and therefore a much stronger decrease in intensity is observed than is the case for the green band, which first drops down between 450 and 500 nm. Thus, it is obvious that the blue emission is already anti-stokes with excitation by radiation of 435 nm and the green emission with excitation of 494 nm. With the latter wavelength both emissions can only be generated by a two-step process, and the intensity ratio is very nearly the same as that with excitation in the lattice absorption region at 332 nm.

Emission generated with longer wavelength irradiation is not limited to sulfide phosphors. The investigation of ZnSe and CdSe crystals, which were not intentionally doped, showed the existence of anti-stokes emission for most of the specimens. Figure 4, for example, shows emission spectra of a ZnSe

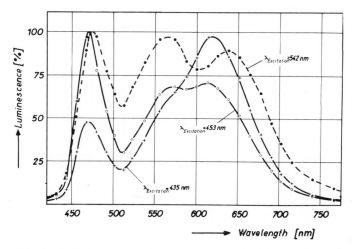

Fig. 4 — Emission spectra of a ZnSe crystal at 4°K under different excitations.

crystal at 4°K for three different excitation wavelengths. Edge emission ($\lambda_{max} \approx 470$ nm) and two other luminescent bands have been found. Excitation of the whole spectrum is possible even with radiation of 540 nm, which lies in the middle of the investigated wavelength region. With a CdSe crystal an excitation spectrum of the 716 nm band[12] extending up to more than 1000

nm (Figure 5) could be obtained. The efficiency of anti-stokes
emission was about 7% of the maximum at 670 nm, a value

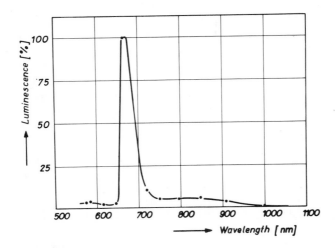

Fig. 5 — Excitation spectrum of the 716 nm emission band of
a CdSe crystal at 4°K.

which would increase considerably if divided by the absorbed
energy in a manner similar to that shown in Figure 3. The
selenides were not especially prepared for the generation of
anti-stokes luminescence, and therefore a much higher luminescent brightness can be expected if the substances are better
doped. In any case, our measurements show that anti-stokes
luminescence is not a rare exception of Stoke's law, but is
quite common for ZnS-type phosphors. It can be expected that
other luminescent solids also exhibit radiation, which can only
be excited by multiple-step processes.

TWO-STEP EXCITATION IN CdS:Cu AND ZnS:Cu

It has been demonstrated that anti-stokes luminescence can
be understood by the assumption of two optical absorption
processes, by which an electron is transferred from the valence
band via an empty acceptor level to the conduction band.[3,4] The
main supposition that such a mechanism works with a reasonable
efficiency is that optical transitions from the acceptor are
allowed with high probability to both valence and conduction

bands. If this is true, the efficiency depends very markedly on the state of occupation of the acceptor levels during the illumination. In order to have a large number of electrons transferred from the valence band to the conduction band, the number of empty and filled acceptors ought not to be very different from each other. Maximum efficiency would be achieved if the product of the transition probability of a hole into the valence band and the number of acceptors which are occupied by a hole were equal to the product of the transition probability of an electron into the conduction band and the number of acceptors not occupied by a hole. In this case an equal number of free electrons and holes would be excited and these can recombine over any luminescence center in the same manner as if they were generated by a one-step band-band transition. In any other case, a part of the excitation energy will not be used for anti-stokes emission, but will cause other effects, such as infrared emission, quenching, or stimulation.

Acceptor levels which meet the above mentioned conditions are generated by the incorporation of copper into ZnS-type phosphors. It is well known[6,7] that these levels can have interactions with both valence and conduction bands and that it is possible to prepare a phosphor with the Fermi-level lying near the position of these levels (p-type ZnS[6,14,15]). Thus, two sorts of centers exist even in the non-excited state, those which are occupied by a hole and those which are not occupied. Absorption of radiation can take place at the same time and with the same energy of the photon with both sorts of centers. The level system of these luminescence centers has already been described in connection with infrared emission, with quenching, and with the measurement of absorption spectra of ZnS and CdS[4,10] (Figure 6). It consists mainly of two levels within the forbidden gap, which can be occupied by two holes or by one hole, or which can remain empty. Radiation of long wavelength can be absorbed according to transition A_5 giving rise to infrared luminescence. Transition A_4 creates free holes and is the cause of quenching of photoconductivity and visible luminescence. Excitation of free electrons is explained by transitions A_3 and A_2 for the non-occupied and the singly-occupied center respectively. Luminescence transitions connected with the singly-occupied center are E_2, corresponding to the green band in ZnS (λ_{max} = 525 nm) and the infrared band (λ_{max} = 1020 nm) in CdS, and E_4 corresponding to the infrared emission of nearly equal wavelengths in both substances. The

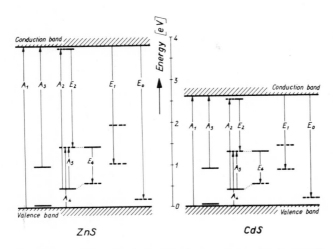

Fig. 6 — Energy level system of the luminescent centers in ZnS:Cu
and CdS:Cu at low temperature.

two-step process for the generation of anti-stokes luminescence
is composed of transitions A_4 and A_3. A good yield will be
achieved if the singly occupied center is present in the non-
irradiated state, i.e. if p-type ZnS or CdS is investigated. Besides the excitation of free holes and the electrons, other luminescence transitions are possible, for example E_0, edge
emission, or E_1, the short wavelength copper band.

The above mentioned rule that there is a maximum efficiency
for two-step excitation for a certain ratio of occupied and non-
occupied centers can be demonstrated by using a second light
beam, which causes transitions A_4, but not transitions A_3,
thus changing a certain number of singly occupied centers into
non-occupied ones. Figure 7 shows the emission spectra of the
ZnS:Cu crystal at three different temperatures with and without
additional irradiation in the range between 0.55 and 2.5 μm.*)
The primary radiation has a wavelength of 435 nm so that the
blue emission is already anti-stokes, whereas the green band
and the red band which exists especially at low temperatures
are excited by one-step processes. At the temperature of
liquid helium an equally strong enhancement of about a factor
of two for all three bands can be observed. At this temperature,
the number of non-occupied centers will be small, as the number

of traps, which can be filled with electrons from the acceptors is high. Therefore, transitions A_3 in Figure 6 are rare and the whole luminescence, which can be excited with excitation

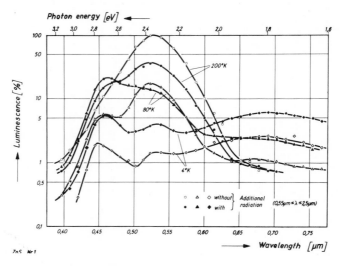

Fig. 7 — Effect of additional long wavelength radiation on the emission spectrum of a ZnS:Cu crystal at different temperatures (λ_{Exc} = 435 nm)

of a wavelength of 435 nm, is small compared with that at higher temperatures. If the crystal is irradiated with long-wavelength light, causing transitions A_4, a certain number of singly occupied centers will lose their holes and change into the non-occupied state. Thus, process A_3 increases and so does the brightness of the luminescence for all bands. The fact that there is no difference in the behavior of Stokes and anti-stokes luminescence can be explained by the assumption that many more transitions A_4 than A_3 are generated even without additional radiation, so that the increase of hole concentration in the valence band does not play a role for the anti-stokes luminescence.

At higher temperatures, the ratio of occupied to non-occupied centers becomes smaller, and the effect of additional radiation acts in a different way on the three bands. The blue anti-stokes emission will still be strengthened, as the number of transitions A_3 is increased and the additional number of holes at higher free electron concentrations is needed for the recombination over blue centers. For the green center two effects work one against another: the increase in transitions A_3 causes an increase in the number of free holes, but the marked decrease in the number of singly occupied centers reduces the probability for the luminescent process E_2. With increasing temperature the latter effect will be the more effective the greater the change in the singly occupied centers caused by the additional radiation is. Thus, the green emission will be quenched beginning with a certain temperature instead of being enhanced, as can be seen from Figure 7. The red emission of ZnS:Cu, which is not connected with the singly occupied center, is strengthened by the additional long wavelength light, because of the higher absorption rate for 435 nm radiation.

The absorption transition A_4 can be caused only by photons with an energy of more than about 1.5 eV according to our level scheme of Figure 6, and therefore the enhancement effect of the blue emission should disappear for radiation with a wavelength higher than about 0.8 μm. In Figure 8 the dependence

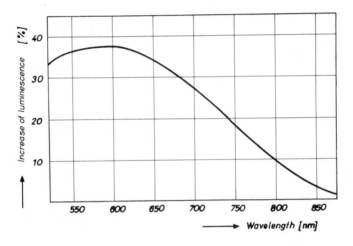

Fig. 8 — Enhancement of 450 nm emission by additional radiation of various wavelengths at 77°K (λ_{exc} = 435 nm)

of the increase of anti-stokes luminescence on the wavelength of the exciting radiation at 77°K is shown. It confirms our assumption that the centers for two-step processes are identical with those for quenching and infrared luminescence of copper activated ZnS and CdS.

The intensity dependence of luminescence, which is excited
by two-step processes, should be different from that of "normal" emission. Assuming in the first approximation that the
luminescence intensity is proportional to the product of free
holes and free electrons, then if the same number of holes and
electrons is generated, the intensity dependence should obey
in the anti-stokes case a quadratic, in the Stokes case a linear
law. This behavior can be observed up to a certain degree
(Figure 9) in a CdS crystal. For excitation in the lattice absorption range the three observed bands (see Figure 1) have

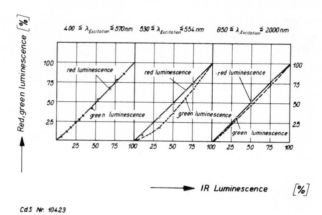

CdS Nr. 10423

Fig. 9 — Intensity of red and green luminescence, plotted
against the intensity of infrared luminescence of a CdS crystal at 4°K.

the same intensity dependence. Excitation in a region where
the green edge emission is anti-stokes, and where the red and
infrared emission are not anti-stokes, gives the expected law
for edge emission with an exponent lying between 1 and 2. However, if one uses an even longer wavelength for the excitation,
the intensity dependence for all three bands becomes again the
same. In this case, the number of transitions A_3 (Figure 6)
is much smaller than the number of transitions A_4, and thus
only the change of free electrons with the intensity of the exciting radiation will change the intensity of anti-stokes emission
(green and red) as is also the case for the infrared stokes emission.

The proposed mechanism of anti-stokes luminescence in-

cludes the assumption that only the excitation process is different from that of normal luminescence. The recombination
of holes and electrons via luminescence centers follows the
same law as for the normal case. This can be seen especially
clearly when one compares decay and rise curves of anti-
stokes and Stokes emission with the non-stationary behavior of
photoconductivity (Figures 10a and 10b). At 60°K the green
edge emission of CdS decays in each case much faster than the
infrared copper emission band at 1020 nm and the photoconductivity, since the acceptor levels of edge emission are situated so close to the valence band that the temperature empties
the acceptors of holes in a very short time.[16] The rise curve
of edge emission, however, is proportional to the increase of
free electrons with time, and equals therefore the rise curve
of photoconductivity. This is true for two-step and one-step
excitation as well. At 4°K, electrons of the valence band can
reach neither the levels of edge emission nor the levels of infrared emission. Now, all bands should decay in the same way
if the number of electrons in the conduction band is the same.
Figure 10b shows this for Stokes and anti-stokes edge emission
and for the infrared copper band. The fact that there is a big
difference in the decay constants of luminescence and photoconductivity is not typical for all crystals.[12] It may be that the
investigated crystal is somewhat inhomogeneous, so that the
region with the smallest conductivity, which determines the
photocurrent, is not the same as that which emits the brightest
luminescence.

CONCLUSION

   The measurements described have shown that anti-stokes
emission is a rather common phenomenon in ZnS-type phosphors. The basic ideas of Halsted, Apple and Prener[2] of its
generation by two-step optical transitions via special acceptor
levels have been confirmed. An energy level scheme which
explains a variety of experiments could be outlined. It consists
of two energy levels lying within the forbidden band, which can
be occupied in the excited state by holes. Transitions terminating in the valence and the conduction band as well are possible,
thus allowing the transfer of an electron to the conduction band
by a two-step process. The energy level scheme is identical
with that proposed for the explanation of infrared emission and

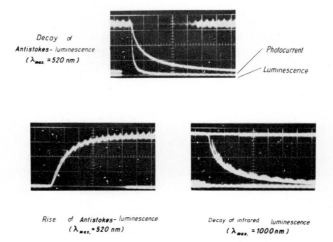

Decay of
Antistokes- luminescence
($\lambda_{max.}$ = 520 nm)

Photocurrent

Luminescence

Rise   of   Antistokes- luminescence
($\lambda_{max.}$ = 520 nm)

Decay of infrared   luminescence
($\lambda_{max.}$ = 1000 nm)

Fig. 10a — Rise and decay of luminescence and photoconductivity of a CdS
crystal at 60°K.

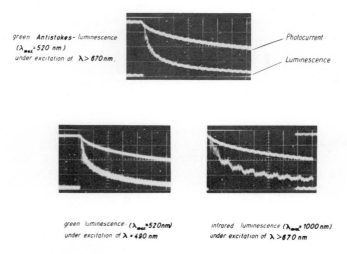

green Antistokes- luminescence
($\lambda_{max.}$ = 520 nm)
under excitation of λ > 670 nm.

Photocurrent

Luminescence

green luminescence ($\lambda_{max.}$ = 520 nm)
under excitation of λ = 490 nm

infrared   luminescence ($\lambda_{max.}$ = 1000 nm)
under excitation of λ > 670 nm

Fig. 10b — Decay of luminescence and photoconductivity of a CdS crystal at
4°K.

quenching of photoconductivity and visible luminescence in ZnS and CdS crystals. These phenomena seem to be connected with the incorporation of copper into the phosphor. Two-step excitation processes are not restricted to the generation of anti-stokes luminescence, but are also expected to play an important role in other optical and electrical effects in II-VI compounds.

REFERENCES

[1] R. M. Potter, J. Electrochem. Soc. 106, 58C (1959).
[2] R. E. Halsted, E. F. Apple, and J. S. Prener: Phys. Rev. Let. 2, 420 (1959).
[3] R. E. Halsted, E. F. Apple, J. S. Prener, and W. W. Piper, Proc. Internat. Conf. on Semiconductor Physics, Prague 1960, p. 776, Publishing House of the Czech. Acad. Sci., Prague 1961.
[4] I. Broser, R. Broser-Warminsky, and H. -J. Schulz: Proc. Internat. Conf. on Semiconductor Physics, Prague 1960, p. 771, Publishing House of the Czech. Acad. Sci., Prague 1961.
[5] R. Bube: Proc. IRE 43, 1836 (1955).
[6] I. Broser and R. Broser-Warminsky: J. Physique Radium 17, 791 (1956).
[7] P. F. Browne: J. Electronics 2, 1 (1956).
[8] G. Meijer: J. Phys. Chem. Solids 7, 153 (1958).
[9] E. F. Apple and J. S. Prener: J. Phys. Chem. Solids 13, 81 (1960).
[10] I. Broser and H. -J. Schulz: J. Electrochem. Soc. 108, 545 (1961).
[11] I. Broser and R. Broser-Warminsky: Z. Elektrochem. 61, 209 (1957).
[12] I. Broser, R. Broser-Warminsky, G. Klipping, R. Rass, and H. -J. Schulz: J. Phys. Chem. Solids (to be published).
[13] C. C. Klick: J. Opt. Soc. Am. 41, 816 (1951).
[14] F. G. Ullman and J. J. Dropkin: J. Electrochem. Soc. 105, 46 C (1958), J. Electrochem. Soc. 108, 154 (1961).
[15] R. M. Potter and M. H. Aven: Bull. Am. Phys. Soc. II 4, 227 (1959).
[16] I. Broser and R. Broser-Warminsky: Solid State Physics in Electronics and Telecommunications 4, 680, Academic Press, London 1960 (Proc. Internat. Conf., Brussels 1958).

SOME CURIOUS PROPERTIES OF A SERIES OF ZINC CADMIUM SULFIDE PHOSPHORS

A. Crosnier and G. Curie

Laboratoire de Luminescence
Faculte des Sciences de Paris (France)

ABSTRACT

In Zinc sulfide phosphors activated with copper, the green band occurs at the most usual concentrations in copper, and the blue copper band at higher concentrations. A short review of the theories leading to these results is given. In the same way there exists in CdS (Cu) a 0.80μ band analogous to the blue band and a 1.02μ band analogous to the green band.

With most commercial zinc and cadmium sulfides, a concentration of 1.4×10^{-4} g Cu/g phosphor, which is near the optimum for ZnS, leads to the green band for ZnS and to the short wavelength band for CdS.

Thus a series of mixed ZnS + CdS (1.4×10^{-4} g Cu) phosphors have been prepared, in which the growing of the short wavelength band leads to a non-monotonic variation of the emission color. These results have been made quantitative by means of the chromaticity diagrams and the dominant wavelength of the emission color has been plotted simultaneously with the peaks of the emission bands.

An analogous study has been performed on ZnS + CdS (Ag) phosphors, but here no anomalous color change is observed within the series.

I. INTRODUCTION

The phosphors of the ZnS(Cu) type show two main emission bands, which are ascribed to the Cu^+ activator. The following table gives the position of the peaks of these bands.

Position of the Emission Peaks for the Zinc-cadmium sulfides		
Phosphor	Short Wavelength Band	Long Wavelength Band
ZnS(Cu) wurtzite	4450 Å	5230 Å
ZnS(Cu) blende	4600 Å	5350 Å
ZnS(Ag) wurtzite	4370 Å	4800 Å
ZnS(Ag) blende	4500 Å	4950 Å
ZnS(Au) wurtzite	4700 Å	5300 Å
ZnS(Au) blende	4800 Å	5500 Å
CdS(Cu) wurtzite	8200 Å	10200 Å
CdS(Ag) wurtzite	7160 Å	7800 Å
CdS(Au) wurtzite	8000 Å	11500 Å

Different models have been advanced for describing the energy levels which are involved inside these centers. All of them may be distributed into three classes:

a) the classical Riehl-Schön-Klasens model, which takes into account a photon-radiative transition between the conduction band and a localized level situated above but in the vicinity of the valence band.

b) the Lambe and Klick model, in which the radiative transition occurs between the valence band and a localized level situated slightly below the conduction band.

c) the Prener and Williams "associated donor-acceptor" model.

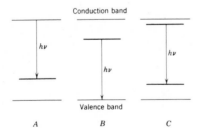

Fig. 1 — The three classes of models proposed for the light centers.
A. The Riehl-Schön-Klasens model.
B. The Lambe and Klick model.
C. The Prener-Williams model.

In the present state of things, it is difficult to choose between these theories, but they all have to explain the following experimental facts, which seem to be generally accepted:

1) Copper is introduced as a monovalent Cu^+ ion in both
blue and green centers of ZnS(Cu) [Bowers and Melamed experiments, relying on magnetic susceptibility measurements].

2) When the respective amounts of activator and coactivator are of the same order, the long wavelength band dominates;
if, on the other hand, the activator concentration is much
larger than the coactivator concentration, then the short wavelength band dominates.

This appears most strikingly in diagrams recently described
in van Gool's thesis.

D. Curie and G. Curie have made the following suggestion,
which takes these facts into account and is derived from the
donor-acceptor model:

In both blue and green centers of ZnS(Cu), Cu^+ produces a
localized acceptor level above the valence band. In the blue
emission band, the radiative transition comes from the bottom
of the conduction band or rather from a shallow level related
to a physical defect in the lattice (this is in agreement with a
suggestion made by van Gool). In the green band, the radiative
transitions come from a deeper donor level associated with
the coactivator (chlorine, bromine, iodine or oxygen according
to Grillot).

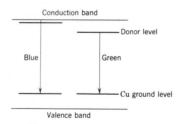

Fig. 2 — A model for blue and green
emission from ZnS(Cu).

We emphasize that the above model gives a simple picture
explaining these results, and many other evidences may be advanced for supporting it, but the present communication rests
only on the experimental fact (2) and does not depend on any
theory for its interpretation.

In addition, other emission bands exist in the zinc sulfide
type phosphors, for example the blue emission of "self-

activated" ZnS samples, which may be ascribed to S$^-$ vacancies (Melamed) acting as centers of the Lambe and Klick class (van Gool). Other examples are the red emission of highly doped ZnS (Cu) phosphors (Froelich), which may be ascribed to Cu ion pairs, possibly associated with an S vacancy, and the emission of samples containing as an activator an element of the 5th column substituted for sulfur and as a coactivator an element of the 3rd column substituted for zinc or cadmium. We are not concerned with these emission bands in the present communication, but possibly some anomalous color changes may be found in them, analogous to the phenomena which will be described below.

II. EMISSION SPECTRA OF A SERIES OF ZnS + CdS (Cu) PHOSPHORS

We have prepared a series of mixed crystals of ZnS + CdS, all of them containing 1.4×10^{-4} g Cu/g phosphor, and baked for half an hour at 1050°C in a nitrogen atmosphere. This activator concentration gives the optimum luminescence for ZnS(Cu) under 3650 Å U.V. excitation (A. Guntz).

We used for this purpose different samples of commercial "pure" zinc sulfide: Auer, Massiot, Osram, Riedel de Haen, and no matter what their origin the results were in reasonable agreement. Large differences were observed in the intensity of the blue luminescence of the "self-activated" sulfide, but this emission disappears when copper is added and then the emission from the different samples is approximately identical (color and intensity). Our different ZnS (1.4×10^{-4} g Cu) phosphors all show a green emission and the intensity of the blue band is small. Thus it seems that no significant differences exist in the amount of chlorine or oxygen in most commerical "pure" zinc sulfides.

The same is true for cadmium sulfide phosphors. We used CdS samples from Auer and also some products prepared by Grillot in the laboratory. It may be seen in Fig. 3 that the concentration 1.4×10^{-4} g Cu, which gives mostly the green (long wavelength) emission band in our zinc sulfides, leads on the other hand mostly to the 0.8 μ (short wavelength) emission band in our cadmium sulfides.

The ZnS + CdS (Cu) series described below was prepared by using Osram zinc sulfide and Auer cadmium sulfide. The

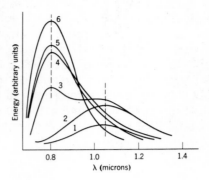

Fig. 3 — Spectral distribution of the emitted radiation from different samples of CdS
(Cu), all baked at 900°C. From Grillot.
Curve 1: 5.10^{-6}gCu; curve 2: 10^{-5}gCu;
curve 3:2.5×10^{-5}gCu; curve 4:5.10^{-5} gCu;
curve 5:7.5×10^{-5}gCu and curve 6:10^{-4}
gCu.

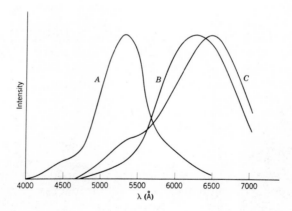

Fig. 4 — Emission spectra of three samples in the series
ZnS + CdS (Cu).

    A. 100% ZnS (Cu).

    B. 70% ZnS, 30% CdS (Cu).

    C. 65% ZnS, 35% CdS (Cu).

emission spectra were obtained under 3650 Å excitation by means of a Desvignes monochromator; the detector was a photomultiplier from Lallemand.

Fig. 4 shows some of these emission spectra. Of course the position of the peaks of the short wavelength and long wavelength emission bands (Fig. 7) is in agreement with the well-known results of previous authors (Guntz, Rotschild, Henderson, etc.). The interesting point is the respective intensity of these bands. As was said above, the short wavelength band is much smaller than the long wavelength band in our ZnS(Cu), and the same is true as long as the amount of CdS remains below 35 pct in weight.

For the (65 pct ZnS, 35 pct CdS) $(1.4 \times 10^{-4}$ g Cu) samples, the short wavelength band peaks in the green at 5400 Å and the long wavelength band in the red at 6450 Å. For this sample the intensity of the short wavelength band rises suddenly and the result is a nonmonotonic variation of the emission color, as observed with the eye, within the series. The following table gives these colors:

Phosphor	Emission Color
100% ZnS	green
90% ZnS, 10% CdS	yellow-green
80% ZnS, 20% CdS	yellow
75% ZnS, 25% CdS	orange-yellow
70% ZnS, 30% CdS	orange
65% ZnS, 35% CdS	orange-yellow
60% ZnS, 40% CdS	orange
50% ZnS, 50% CdS	orange
40% ZnS, 60% CdS	orange-red
30% ZnS, 70% CdS	red
20% ZnS, 80% CdS	deep red

The chromaticity diagram and the dominant wavelength of the above phosphors:

Let E be the spectral distribution of the emitted radiation. The C.I.E. chromaticity coordinates x, y, z are defined by:

$$X = \int x_\lambda E_\lambda \, d\lambda \qquad Y = \int y_\lambda E_\lambda \, d\lambda \qquad Z = \int z_\lambda E_\lambda \, d\lambda$$

$$x = \frac{X}{X + Y + Z} \qquad y = \frac{Y}{X + Y + Z} \qquad z = \frac{Z}{X + Y + Z}$$

$$x + y + z = 1$$

x_λ, y_λ, z_λ are the standard C.I.E. distribution coefficients (Fig. 5).

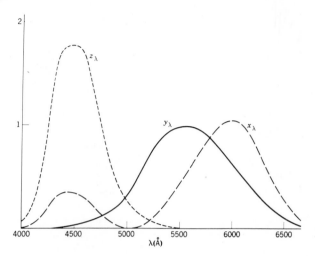

Fig. 5 — The C.I.E. distribution coefficients. y_λ is identical with the relative luminous efficiencies of the monochromatic radiation, for scotopic vision by the photometric standard observer.

In order to make quantitative the preceeding results, we performed these calculations for the above series of phosphors. The color inversion for the phosphor with 35 pct CdS corresponds to a coming back of the representative point on the chromaticity diagram.

The dominant wavelength and excitation purity have been computed from Fig. 6. The dominant wavelength is shown in Fig. 7, together with the peaks of both emission bands.

We prepared other series of ZnS + CdS (Cu), for instance, with a smaller concentration of copper; then the long wavelength emission band dominates in all the phosphors, and such series do not show any color inversion.

III. EMISSION SPECTRA OF A SERIES OF ZnS + CdS (Ag) PHOSPHORS

In all ZnS(Ag) samples which have been prepared until now,

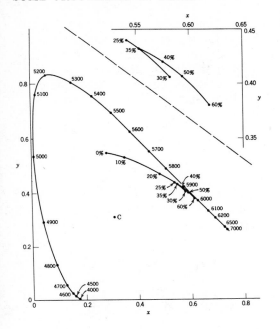

Fig. 6 — Description on the chromaticity diagram of our series ZnS + CdS (Cu).

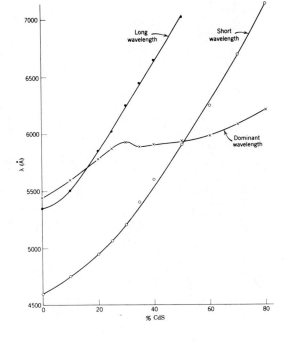

Fig. 7 — The dominant wavelength and the peaks of the short wavelength and long wavelength emission bands from ZnS + CdS(Cu).

the short wavelength emission band (blue 4500 Å) is by far the most important one. Evidence for the occurrence of a blue-green emission band (4800—4950 Å) has been given by Henderson, Ranby and Halstead, and confirmed by H. Payen de la Garanderie and D. Curie. However the height of this second band may reach 10—15 pct of the main band, but not more.

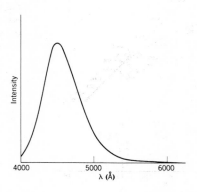

Fig. 8 — Emission spectrum of a ZnS(Ag).

In CdS(Ag), the band peaking at 7160 Å or the band peaking at 7800 Å may be the highest, depending upon the baking temperature. In agreement with Grillot, we prepared red-emitting CdS(Ag) phosphors by baking at a low temperature, 650°C, while the emission is mostly in the infrared when one bakes at 1000°C.

Thus chromaticity diagrams from a series of ZnS + CdS(Ag) phosphors may be observed, in which the dominant wavelength increases more or less rapidly with the cadmium content. But in no case does this phenomena result in a color inversion.

Figs. 9 and 10 show the chromaticity diagrams and dominant wavelength of a series of ZnS + CdS(Ag), baked at 650°C in a nitrogen atmosphere and using the same base materials ZnS and CdS as in the preceeding copper-activated series.

Note added in proof:

A crystallographic study of our mixed crystals ZnS+CdS (Cu) has been kindly made in the *Institut de Chimie-Physique* of the Faculty of Science, Paris (Prof. Y. Cauchois) by Drs. Renaud and Bonnel. X-ray and electron diffraction studies were performed. Preliminary results are as follows:

The 100 pct ZnS, baked at 1050° for half an hour, was indeed a mixture of both blende and wurtzite forms, the blende
proportion being the largest. The mixed crystals ZnS+CdS
were also mixtures of blende and wurtzite; the wurtzite proportion was the largest and increased regularly as the amount of
CdS increased. No inversion in these proportions was detected
for the 35 pct amount of CdS, which gives the color inversion
in luminescence spectra.

In addition, X-ray diffraction shows that the lattice constant
increases regularly as the CdS content increases; thus we have
really to deal with mixed ZnCdS crystals. Electron diffraction
gives evidence for the heterogeneity of the material: we observed separately some crystals of ZnCdS with blende form
and other crystals of ZnCdS with wurtzite form. The wurtzite
crystals are the largest in size.

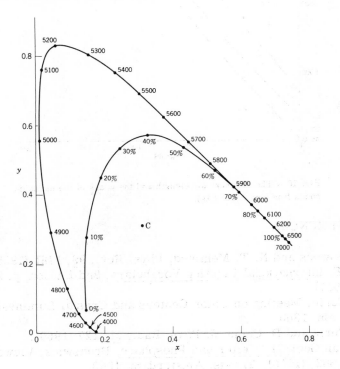

Fig. 9 — Description on the chromaticity diagram of our series ZnS +
CdS (Ag).

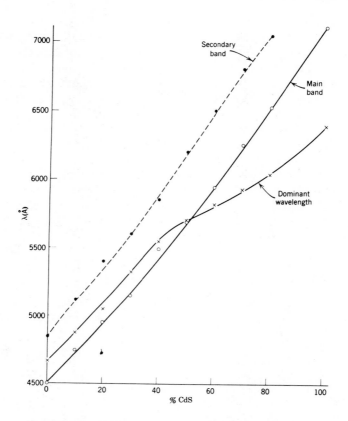

Fig. 10 — The dominant wavelength and the peaks of the emission
bands from ZnS + CdS (Ag).

REFERENCES

R. Bowers and N. T. Melamed, Phys. Rev., 99, 1781 (1955).
C.I.E. International Lighting Vocabulary, 2nd Edition, p. 29
    (1957).
D. Curie, Meeting on Color Centers and Crystal Luminescence,
    Turin, 1960.
G. Curie and D. Curie, J. Phys. Rad., 21, 127 (1960).
W. van Gool, Halbleiter und Phosphore, Brunswick, Vieweg,
    p. 602, (1958). Thesis, Amsterdam, 1960.
E. Grillot,J. Phys. Rad.,17, 624 (1956).
A. Guntz, Thesis, Paris, 1923.
S. T. Henderson, P. W. Ranby, M. B. Halstead, J. Electrochem.
    Soc., 106, 27 (1959).

J. Lambe and C. C. Klick, Phys. Rev., 98, 909 (1955); 100, 1586 (1955); J. Phys. Rad., 17, 663 (1956).

H. Payen de la Garanderie, J. Phys. Rad., 22, 428 (1961).

S. Rotschild, Trans. Faraday Soc., 42, 635 (1946).

F. E. Williams and J. S. Prener, Phys. Rev., 101, 1427 (1956); J. Electrochem. Soc., 103, 342 (1956); J. Phys. Rad., 17, 667 (1956).

PHOTOCONDUCTIVITY OF ZINC CADMIUM SULFIDE

B. Kramer* and H. Kallmann
New York University

ABSTRACT

The luminescent and photoconducting processes of some in-organic phosphors, such as ZnS activated with Cu or Ag, show marked similarities. The Schön-Klassens model assumes that this similarity arises because free electrons are the main con-tributors to the conductivity, while the recombination of these free electrons gives rise to the luminescent process. It is therefore of interest in the field of luminescence to investigate the free electron concentration under various conditions of ex-citation.

It is not easy, however, to determine the true conductivity of a phosphor, especially in powder form. This form is impor-tant in luminescent work since controlled activation and specific mixtures (i.e., Zn:Cd) can be produced. Some of the difficulties arising in dc measurements are due to polarization, as well as grain-grain and grain-electrode junctions. Using ac impedance measurements, much better values of the conductivity can be obtained and a number of different ac techniques, both with powdered phosphors and single or poly-crystals will be dis-cussed.

The second part of this paper will deal with some of the results obtained using these techniques, and their relation to the light emission process. It will be shown that, in the light of these experiments, certain modifications of the simple band model picture must be made.

INTRODUCTION

The relationship between the light emission and photoconduc-tivity processes in ZnCdS type phosphors has been investigated

---

*Also at Physics Department, Hunter College, New York, New York.

intensively by many laboratories to determine the electron transitions in such solids. The knowledge of the photoconductive behavior is necessary for a complete understanding of the elementary processes. However, the measurement of photoconductivity, especially in powdered phosphors, is extremely difficult because of barrier and polarization effects. The use of single crystals, which would at least partially diminish these difficulties, is limited because many activation experiments and impurities cannot be obtained as easily with single crystals as with powdered material.

A. AC PHOTOCONDUCTIVITY MEASUREMENTS

Ac impedance measurements are more fruitful in determining photoconductivity than dc measurements, since the effect of barrier layers can be separated from the bulk conductivity. Whether the capacitance change observed when ZnCdS type phosphors are excited is due to free to trapped carriers has been raised by a number of investigators.[1] We feel that the experimental data strongly support the free carrier assumption for the following reasons:

1. It is known (from dc measurements) that these materials evidence photoconductivity.
2. The observed variations of C (capacitance) and D (dissipation factor) in insulated illuminated phosphors under ac measurements can be correlated in detail to the dc photoconductivity observations.
3. If the capacitance change depends on trapped electrons, it should go up strongly as the temperature is lowered and remain for an appreciable time after excitation is removed. Neither of these effects is observed. The capacitance change decreases to close to its zero value, after excitation has ceased at liquid nitrogen temperatures. If this capacitance change is due to trapped electrons, this would indicate that all trapped electrons have been released. However, the consecutive release of trapped electrons by heat (glow curve) shows that this is by no means the case, since light emission and capacitance changes become very large with increasing temperature.

Two figures (1 and 2) are shown here to compare the theoretically predicted change of impedance with experimental results.[2] It is clear that best measurements can be made at the peak of the dissipation curve (minimum of Q curve); by varying the frequency, this peak can be shifted to any desired excitation range. It can be shown[3] that for uniform excitation the conductivity σ is given by $\sigma = \omega\epsilon\,(\Delta C/C_0)(1/D)$ where ΔC is the increase in capacitance, C_0 is the dark capacitance, and D is the dissipation factor of the phosphor capacitor. For inhomogeneous excitation, these

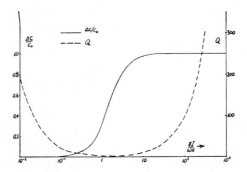

Fig. 1 — Theoretical curves showing capacitance change ($\Delta C/C_0$) and Q (reciprocal of dissipation factor) versus intensity for homogeneous excitation. Phosphor thickness assumed equal to insulator thickness.

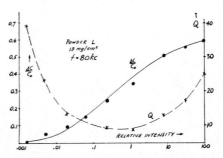

Fig. 2 — Experimental capacitance change and Q for a ZnCdS phosphor inhomogeneously excited by UV. Maximum intensity $\sim$ 100 μw/cm².

curves spread out over a larger intensity range, and the above relation cannot be used.

If, rather than plotting $\Delta C/C_0$ and D versus intensity, one plots D ($\Delta C/C_0$) against $\Delta C/C_0$ (essentially the imaginary versus the real part of the dielectric constant), one obtains (for uniform excitation and a single conductivity) a Cole-Cole diagram which is a semicircle with a maximum corresponding to the peak in D. Increasing the conductivity (or decreasing the frequency) moves a point on this curve in a clockwise direction. In some cases such a plot may be more conducive to interpretation than the $\Delta C/C_0$ and D curves.[4]

Using the ac method, the conductivity can be obtained, not only during equilibrium conditions but also during the rise and decay periods as well as in the glow curve, and the values of the conductivity calculated from such measurements may be compared with the corresponding luminescence. The relationship between light and conductivity will be discussed below.

One might assume that photoconductivity measurements with single crystals would be more straightforward and that simple dc techniques could be used, but surface layers and contact difficulties leading to non-ohmic behavior and problems of injection and ejection arise. Conductivity measurements on CdS crystals were, therefore, carried out using ac methods. The first series of measurements are done with crystals on which transparent gold electrodes are directly deposited on the flat surfaces. Investigating a large number of such crystals under carying conditions of excitation and measuring frequency[5] show that they fall into two groups; one where the equivalent parallel crystal capacitance remains relatively unchanged over large variations in exciting intensity; the other where this capacitance shows very large increases with increasing excitation (Table 1). The first group we called "non-barrier crystals", the second group "barrier crystals," because it is the shorting out of the bulk of the crystal leaving only the barrier that gives rise to the large capacitance increase observed with the second group of the crystals. The physical difference between these two groups accounting for this behavior is probably the ionic cleaning undergone by the first group prior to electrode evaporation but lacking with the second group.

The two crystals shown in the table are A, which is typical of the "non-barrier" group, and B, typical of the "barrier" group. The column at the left gives the excitation in terms of electrons excited per sec per cm^3. At every frequency the large increase in capacitance of the "barrier" crystal can be observed, while the capacitance of the "non-barrier" crystal shows a much

TABLE 1

Effective Parallel Resistance (in Ohms) and Capacitance[a] (in $\mu\mu f$) at Various Frequencies.

Excitation[b] ($\mathrm{Electrons/sec\text{-}cm^3}$)	0.1 KC		1 KC		10 KC		100 KC	
	C	R	C	R	C	R	C	R
Crystal A								
1.5×10^{14}	0-900	2.9×10^{3}	0-400	2.9×10^{3}	19	2.9×10^{3}	15	2.9×10^{3}
1.5×10^{13}	0-400	2.3×10^{4}	29	2.3×10^{4}	18	2.3×10^{4}	16	2.3×10^{4}
1.5×10^{12}	53	2.4×10^{5}	22	2.3×10^{5}	13	2.4×10^{5}	11	2.4×10^{5}
1.5×10^{11}	38	1.5×10^{6}	15	1.6×10^{6}	9	1.6×10^{6}	8	1.2×10^{6}
1.5×10^{10}	14	1.5×10^{7}	10	1.6×10^{7}	6	5.0×10^{6}	2	2.9×10^{6}
Crystal B								
2.2×10^{14}	–	1.1×10^{3}	4.2×10^{4}	1.7×10^{3}	3000	8.5×10^{2}	156	6.3×10^{2}
2.2×10^{13}	–	7.7×10^{3}	2.7×10^{3}	7.1×10^{3}	121	6.7×10^{3}	19	6.3×10^{3}
2.2×10^{12}	269	8.5×10^{4}	103	7.7×10^{4}	31	7.7×10^{4}	23	6.3×10^{4}
2.2×10^{11}	84	5.6×10^{5}	35	5.6×10^{5}	18	5.3×10^{5}	17	5.9×10^{5}
2.2×10^{10}	33	5.3×10^{6}	19	5.0×10^{6}	17	5.9×10^{6}	18	$\sim 10^{7}$

[a] The data for C have a tolerance of several micromicrofarads. A calculation based upon the geometry of crystal gives a value of about 6 $\mu\mu f$.

[b] Tungsten source; Corning filters 1-56 plus 3-67; 5400 A $< \lambda <$ 8000 A.

smaller change. In all cases the resistance goes approximately inverse to the excitation, as would be expected when the traps are saturated. The frequency dependence of the capacitance change is explained by the fact that the barrier layer acts as a high capacitance in series with the bulk of the crystal which can be assumed to consist of a parallel combination of a capacitor and a resistor, the latter being determined by the excitation. At low frequencies or high excitations this resistor effectively shorts out the crystal capacitance, and only the high "barrier" capacitance is observed. Accurate determinations of the "non-barrier" crystal capacitance at low frequencies and high excitation values are difficult because of the high dissipation factor of the combination.

These ac photoconductivity measurements allow the determination of both the barrier layer and, at the same time, the resistance of the bulk crystal. Dc measurements would result in a non-ohmic behavior with breakdowns leading to nonreproducible results.

One can artificially introduce a barrier in the form of an insulating layer between the electrode and the CdS crystal surface; a one mil thickness of mylar with one side coated with a semi-transparent electrode was used.[6] Thus, we again have a photo-resistor insulated from the electrodes, and the $\Delta C/C_0$ and D curves follow the same behavior as predicted (Fig. 3) for

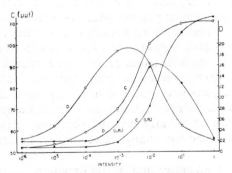

Fig. 3 — Capacitance and dissipation factor versus intensity of CdS crystal with mylar insulators with and without simultaneous infrared. Measuring frequency: 1000 cps; maximum intensity: $\sim 5\ \mu w/cm^2$.

phosphor powders where the spaces between the grains serve as insulating barriers. In the case of an insulated crystal, however, the relative change in capacitance is much larger than for a powdered sample, because the ratio of photoconductor thickness to insulator thickness is much larger. Table 2 gives the values (calculated from experimental data) of the parallel

TABLE 2

Intensity (μw/cm^2)	Parallel Capacitance ($\mu\mu$f)	Parallel Resistance (Ω)
5	–	6×10^4
5×10^{-1}	158	2×10^5
5×10^{-2}	80.6	1×10^6
5×10^{-3}	32.9	5×10^6
5×10^{-4}	20.1	1.6×10^7
5×10^{-5}	14.2	5×10^7
0 (Dark)	12.3	5×10^8

Parallel capacitance and resistance of a CdS crystal as a function of exciting intensity (uniform illumination, $\lambda > 5200$ Å).

capacitance and the parallel resistance of the crystal itself. It is seen that this parallel capacitance increases with increasing excitation, whereas it would be expected to remain constant assuming the simple model of a capacity with parallel resistor for the conductive crystal. This result underlines the inherent difficulty in considering photoconductive material as homogeneous resistors. The blocking layer prevents injection or ejection of electrons and, thereby, causes a non-uniform charge distribution with the electrons more concentrated in the region close to the positive electrode. However, such inhomogeneous charge distributions are inherent to the problem and may be present even with "direct" contacts. The ac measurements, particularly with artifically induced blocking, give a new possibility of examining the charge distribution inside the photoconductor.

A theoretical investigation of the problem[7] leads (at slowly varying fields) to the following:

1. At some point in the interior of the crystal the concentrations of free electrons, trapped electrons, and ionized activators are exactly what they would be, if no field was applied.

2. In the region closer to the electrodes these concentrations are altered; a net positive charge (ionized activators) appears

near the negative electrode, and a net negative charge (free and trapped electrons) appears near the positive electrode.

3. With increasing applied voltage and excitation these "depletion" and "accumulation" regions of relatively high field strength shrink, and a large portion of the crystal becomes field free.

4. The effective capacitance of this crystal-mylar combination can be measured and the interior concentration of free electrons calculated.

Figure 4 shows some of these theoretical results, and the curve shown is calculated assuming that equilibrium conditions exist between free and trapped electrons, but that the positively charged activators cannot follow the field. In this case increasing voltage results in decreasing capacitance change, as observed experimentally.[6] The abscissa in Figure 4 is the Debye length which is proportional to $n^{-1/2}$ where n is the density of free electrons.

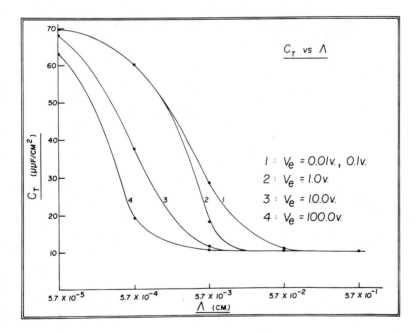

Fig. 4 — Capacitance change of a CdS crystal with mylar blocking layers as a function of the Debye length. Curves 1, 2, 3, and 4 are calculated using various external voltages.

B. RELATION BETWEEN LUMINESCENCE AND PHOTO-CONDUCTIVITY

On the Schon-Klassens model the conductivity σ depends predominantly on the concentration of free electrons (n), $\sigma = ne\mu$. The light emission process is given by βnp_t, where β is a recombination constant and p_t is the number of ionized activators. Since n_t electrons are trapped, one has

$$p_t = n + n_t$$

(where we have neglected the concentration of free holes) as a condition of charge neutrality. For $n_t \gg n$ (which holds for most cases), $p_t = n_t$, and the light emission term L can be written as $L = \beta n \, n_t$.

Consequently, the equilibrium values of L and n should depend differently on intensity. If one can neglect quenching, L is always proportional to the intensity, but n is proportional to the square root of the intensity in the intensity range, when n_t is not saturated $(n_t < n_0)$, and is proportional to the intensity for $n_t \simeq n_0$. At higher excitation intensities, where $n > n_0$, n again becomes proportional to the square root of the intensity.

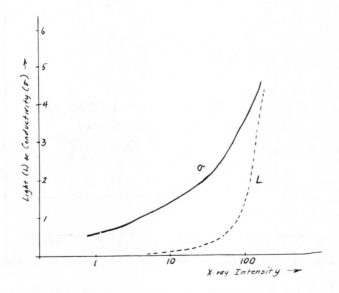

Fig. 5 — Light emission L and conductivity δ as a function of X-ray intensity for a ZnS:Ag phosphor at room temperature.

Figures 5 and 6 show the relation between σ and light emission for a ZnS:Ag phosphor at room and liquid nitrogen temperatures.[8] They go parallel (and proportional to the intensity) in the low temperature case, but the conductivity goes only as $I^{1/2}$ for most of the intensity range at room temperature. The sample was irradiated by X-rays to obtain uniform excitation throughout the phosphor.

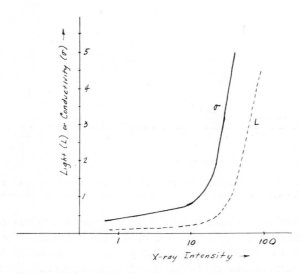

Fig. 6 — Light emission L and conductivity σ as a function of X-ray intensity for a ZnS:Ag phosphor at liquid nitrogen temperature.

Figure 7 shows the light emission and conductivity obtained when a phosphor is heated from liquid nitrogen temperature after X-ray excitation. The luminescence and conductivity peaks are easily observed; the luminescence peak is always shifted to lower temperatures because it depends on the product of n and p_t, while the conductivity depends only on n. As the temperature increases, various levels of traps empty, but p_t, the number of ionized activators, constantly decreases. There is one conductivity peak (at 130°K) without a corresponding light peak. This may be due to hole conductivity.

The relationship between light and conductivity under UV excitation plus additional IR is given in Table 3.[9] The actual conductivity cannot be obtained by the relation for uniform

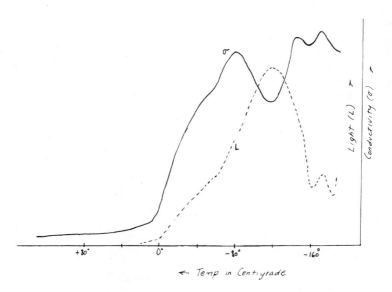

Fig. 7 — Light emission L and conductivity σ obtained when heating a ZnS:Ag phosphor after X-ray excitation at liquid nitrogen temperature.

excitation $[\sigma = \omega\epsilon\,(\Delta C/C_0)\,(1/D)]$, since the illuminated side is more strongly excited than the rear side because of scattering. However, the relative conductivity can be obtained as follows: Equilibrium values of $\Delta C/C_0$ and D are taken for a wide range of known exciting intensities. Then, a decrease in $\Delta C/C_0$ due to infrared quenching can be compared to a decrease in $\Delta C/C_0$ due to lower exciting intensity. Since the conductivity for these phosphors varies between a dependence on I or $I^{1/2}$ (I is the excitation intensity), we have the two extremes of conductivity decrease listed in Table 3. It is seen that the quenching of conductivity is greater than the quenching of light for most of the cases. Since it is known from other investigations that the trap density is decreased by infrared,[10] the product of n_t and n, that is the light emission, should be quenched more than n alone. This, however, is not usually observed. It may mean that infrared has, in addition to its quenching properties, an enhancing effect on luminescence. Some mechanisms for this have already been discussed.[10,11]

The data of the ZnS:Mn phosphor are quite different from that observed with copper or silver activators. They show that in this case the light emitting processes and the photoconductivity

TABLE 3

Light and Conductivity Quenching.

Phosphor	Compound	ND-0		ND-1[a]		IR Filter [b]
		$\frac{L_{UV+IR}}{L_{UV}}$	$\frac{\sigma_{UV+IR}}{\sigma_{UV}}$	$\frac{L_{UV+IR}}{L_{UV}}$	$\frac{\sigma_{UV+IR}}{\sigma_{UV}}$	
A	ZnS:Cu	0.88 0.85	0.60-0.36 0.41-0.17	0.64 0.50	0.45-0.20 0.27-0.072	7-56 7-69
B	ZnS:Cu	0.92 0.89	0.49-0.24 0.42-0.18	0.53 0.37	0.23-0.053 0.12-0.015	7-56 7-69
C	ZnS:Cu	0.89 0.72	0.55-0.30 0.29-0.085	0.51 0.21	0.28-0.078 0.12-0.015	7-56 7-69
D	ZnS:Cu	0.73 ----	0.46-0.21 --------	0.46 0.34	0.25-0.063 0.36-0.13	7-56 7-69
E	ZnS:Ag	0.95 0.90	0.60-0.36 0.67-0.50	0.78 0.64	0.58-0.27 0.50-0.25	7-56 7-69
F	ZnS:Ag	0.79 0.88	0.68-0.46 0.77-0.60	0.31 0.60	0.69-0.47 0.75-0.56	7-56 7-69
G	ZnS:Mn	1.0 1.0	0.81-0.65 0.61-0.37	1.02 1.02	0.49-0.24 0.43-0.19	7-56 7-69

(a) The exciting intensity with ND-1 is approximately 30 times less than for ND-0.

(b) 7-69 passes wavelengths between 7000 Å and 10,000 Å; 7-56 passes wavelengths greater than 8000 Å.

processes must be quite different from the other phosphors: infrared has a quenching effect on the photoconductivity, but almost no effect (except for a slight enhancement in some cases) on the corresponding light emission.

REFERENCES

[1] For a general reference see C. F. Garlick, Handbuch d. Physik, Vol. 19, p. 391.

[2] H. Kallmann, B. Kramer and A. Perlmutter, Phys. Rev. 89, 700 (1953).

[3] H. Kallmann, B. Kramer and P. Mark, J. Phys. Chem. Solids 10, 59 (1959).

[4] H. Kallmann, P. Mark; to be published in J. Phys. Chem. Solids.

[5] S. Jaffe (at this laboratory); submitted for publication.

[6] H. Kallmann, B. Kramer and G. M. Spruch, Phys. Rev. 116, 628 (1959).

[7] B. Jaffe, Ph.D. Thesis, New York University, 1962.

[8] P. Wachter (at this laboratory); unpublished.

[9] B. Kramer, A. Turner, (Hunter College); unpublished.

[10] B. Kramer, M. Schon, Zeits, f. Physik 160, 145 (1960).

[11] H. Kallmann, K. M. Luchner, Phys. Rev. 123, 2013 (1961)

INVESTIGATIONS ON THE LUMINESCENCE OF INORGANIC SOLIDS AT THE INSTITUTE FOR SOLID STATE PHYSICS, THE UNIVERSITY OF TOKYO

Shoji Makishima, Takeshi Tomotsu, Masao Hirata, Sohachiro Hayakawa*
Katsue Hasegawa**, Ryozo Kambe***, and Shigeo Shionoya

The Institute for Solid State Physics
The University of Tokyo
Minato-ku, Tokyo, Japan

ABSTRACT

Recent results of investigations of the luminescence of inorganic solids at this laboratory will be reviewed briefly. The paper consists of three parts.
I) Luminescence of NO_2-containing systems.

Alkali nitrites emit blue luminescence with a fine structure due to the NO_2^- ion at liquid nitrogen temperature. Luminescence characteristics including polarization were studied. Influences on the luminescence of the hydrogen bond formed between the NO_2^- ion and the matrix were also studied. If the Tl^+ ion is added to the nitrite crystal, a red luminescence appears. From the polarization characteristics of this luminescence it is suggested that the origin of this luminescence is the weak coordination bond formed between the thallium and nitrogen atom.
II) Luminescence of Sm^{3+} in $BaTiO_3$ matrix.

The Sm^{3+} ion embedded in inorganic solids usually shows a luminescence of line-like spectra composed of six groups. The emission spectrum of Sm^{3+} in $BaTiO_3$ was analyzed in detail, and it was found that the whole spectrum consists of the overlap of two kinds of Sm^{3+} emission. It is suggested that Sm^{3+} can occupy both Ba^{2+} and Ti^{4+} sites, and that each group in the

---

*Presently at Tokyo Institute of Technology, Tokyo.
**Sent from Matsushita Communication Industrial Co., Yokohama, to this Institute as a member of the research staff.
***Presently at The Faculty of Technology, The Tokyo Metropolitan University, Tokyo.

emission spectrum of Sm^{3+} at Ti^{4+} sites is located at longer
wavelengths than that of Sm^{3+} at Ba^{2+} sites.

III) Luminescence of thallous complex ions.

If a thallous ion is put into alkali or alkaline earth halide
solution, thallous complex ions are formed. Their absorption
and emission spectra were studied. It was found that $(TlCl_2)^-$
ion has an absorption peak at 243mμ and an emission peak at
430mμ.

Part I

Luminescence of NO_2-Containing Systems

Introduction

Luminescence phenomena in most crystalline phosphors are
much more complicated than in liquid and gaseous phases and
the true nature and structure of the luminescence centers in
inorganic phosphors are not yet clearly understood, except in
the case of some simple centers created with such activators
as rare earths, manganese and UO_2^{2+}. For the purpose of
investigating the luminescence mechanism in the solid state,
it is advantageous to study systems in which the electronic
structure of the luminescence center is fairly well understood
and the excitation is localized within the center. Further if the
spectra of photo-absorption and emission are associated with a
fine structure which can be used as a mark, it is even more
advantageous, since by using such a structure as a clue it is
possible to obtain some information on the structure of the
luminescence center and on the dynamic process taking place
there.

Nitrite salts and related NO_2-containing systems are especially advantageous for the purpose mentioned above. This is summarized in the following three points.

(1) The NO_2^- ion is one of the best examples of a luminescence
system in which the excitation is localized. This ion involves
a rather simple π-electron system and has an absorption band
with a peak near 350mμ. At low temperatures it emits a strong
blue fluorescence as the reverse process of 350mμ absorption.

The low temperature luminescence of alkali nitrites was first reported by Sidman.[1] Prior to his report some of the present authors[2] reported that silver nitrite and silver-containing sodium nitrite emit yellow fluorescence. In the continuation of this work they found the low temperature luminescence of sodium nitrite independently of Sidman.

(2) The luminescence of the NO_2^- ion involves a fine structure which is useful as a mark. It was reported by some of the authors[2] and also by Sidman[1] that this structure is composed of several sharp peaks with distance of about 830 cm^{-1} between them, which can be assigned to the bending vibration frequency of the NO_2^- ion. This is quite remarkable in that this seems to be the only example for which the origin of fine structure associated with luminescence in solids can be clearly explained.

(3) The NO_2^- ion forms complex ions with many kinds of heavy metal ions like Tl^+, Pb^{2+}, Ag^+, Zn^{2+}, etc. As will be mentioned below a new luminescence band appears when a complex ion is formed between the NO_2^- and a heavy metal ion. This suggests that the luminescence center is composed of a coordination bond, and will provide an important clue with which to solve the problems of the luminescence centers in some inorganic phosphors.

I. ALKALI NITRITES AND RELATED NO_2-CONTAINING SYSTEMS

1. Samples

Single crystals of sodium nitrite were prepared by the Bridgman method. With regard to other alkali nitrites the preparation of single crystals was not possible with this method. Their luminescence properties were investigated using powders.

The sodium nitrite crystal belongs to the orthorhombic system. Its structure is shown in Fig. 1. The lengths of the a, b and c axes in the unit cell are 3.55, 5.56 and 5.38Å, respectively. The N-O distance is 1.23Å and the N-O-N angle is 116°.[3] The single crystal has cleavage planes at (101) and (10$\bar{1}$), and the angle between these two planes is 67°. The b axis is the intersection of these two planes, the c axis is the bisector of the angle between the two planes and the a axis is perpendicular to the b and c axes. Sample crystals cut in this manner were examined by means of the X-ray Laue method, and the orientations of the axes were confirmed.

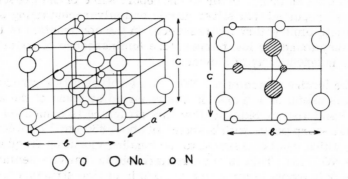

Fig. 1 — Crystal structure of Na NO_2. Atoms shown by hatched
areas are at $1/2\,a$.

2. Absorption and Its Polarization

The absorption spectrum and its polarization of the $NaNO_2$
single crystal were investigated in detail. The measurements
were carried out with a Cary Model 14 spectrophotometer. To
eliminate the fluorescence at low temperatures a Corning No.
9863 filter was inserted before the photomultiplier. The thickness of the samples was made less than 0.1 mm, since the absorption is fairly strong.

The results are shown in Fig. $2(a)-2(f)$. The orientation of
the sample crystals and the polarization of the incident light are
shown in the figures. Marks like

mean that the direction of the incident light was perpendicular
to the crystal plane indicated. The symbol E shows the direction of the electric vector of the incident light.

$NaNO_2$ has an absorption band at around 350 mμ. This is due
to a transition within the NO_2^- ion. This absorption is polarized
in the direction of the a axis, $i.e.$ perpendicular to the plane of
the NO_2^- ion, and has been assigned[1,4] to a transition in which
one of the unshared electrons of the nitrogen atom is raised to
an antibonding π orbital of the NO_2^- ion ($n_N \rightarrow \pi^*$). Another feature of this absorption is that it is associated with a fine struc-
ture. The distances between peaks in the fine structure are
about 670 cm^{-1}, which agrees with the bending vibration frequency of the excited NO_2^- ion.

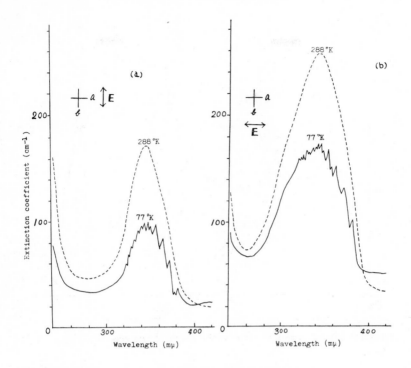

Fig. 2 — (a),(b) Absorption spectra of the NaNO$_2$ single crystal.

It is shown from Fig. 2(c) that there exists another weaker absorption band with a peak at around 300 mμ which is polarized in the direction of the c axis. The origin of this band has not yet been analyzed.

3. Luminescence and Its Polarization

Alkali nitrites emit blue fluorescence associated with a fine structure at temperatures less than −100°C with 365 mμ excitation. This fluorescence is due to the NO$_2^-$ ion. Nitrites of lithium, sodium, potassium and rubidium were tested. A nitrite other than those of the alkali metals, tetraethyl nitro amine N(C$_2$H$_5$)$_4$NO$_2$ was tested.

The emission spectra of sodium and potassium nitrite at 77°K and 4°K under 365 mμ excitation are shown in Fig. 3. The spectrum of the sodium salt is composed of about six sharp peaks accompanied by several small sub-peaks on the longer wavelength side. The distances between the peaks are almost

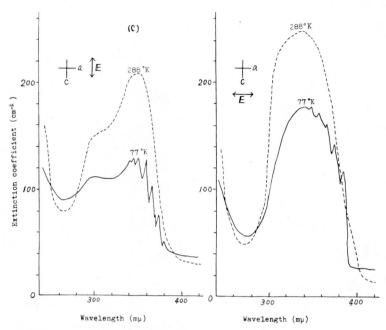

Fig. 2 (c), (d) — Absorption spectra of the NaNO₂ single crystal.

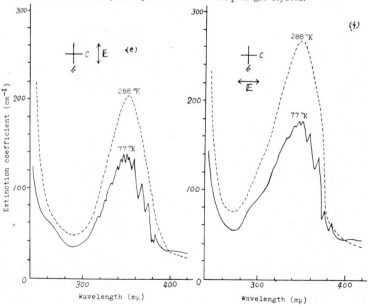

Fig. 2 (e), (f) — Absorption spectra of the NaNO₂ single crystal.

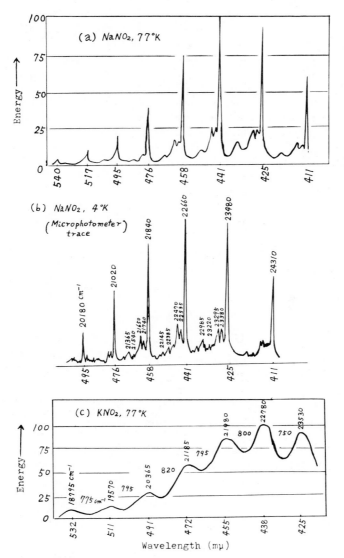

Fig. 3 — Emission spectra of sodium and potassium nitrites at 77°K and 4°K with 365 mμ excitation.

equal and are about 830 cm⁻¹. This value agrees with the bending vibration frequency of the NO_2^- ion. The fine structure in the spectrum of the potassium salt is diffuse compared with that of the sodium salt, and the distances between peaks are slightly smaller than those for the sodium salt.

The spectrum of rubidium salt is a broad band with a peak at around 450 mμ and contains no fine structure. This may be due to the low Debye temperature of the lattice. With regard to a lithium salt, $LiNO_2 \cdot H_2O$ was tested, since an anhydrous salt could not be prepared because of the difficulty of removing the water of crystallization. This material shows a broad band blue fluorescence, and fine structure was not observed. $N(C_2H_5)_4NO_2$ also shows a broad blue band.

The polarization of the fluorescence was measured in $NaNO_2$ single crystals at 77°K. The re-sults are shown in Fig. 4. The ex-citation was directed perpendicu-lar to the crystal plane indicated by marks beside each curve like

$$\underline{\quad\overset{a}{\overline{}\Big|}_{b}\quad}$$

and the lumines-cence was observed in the same direction. The ordinate gives the degree of polarization, P, of the lu-minescence in formula [1], where $I_{\|}$ and $I_{\perp}$ are the luminescence in-tensities, corresponding to the cases where the polarizer and the analyzer are parallel or perpen-dicular to each other, respectively. The abscissa, θ, is the angle be-tween the electric vector of the exciting light and the crystal axis shown as the horizontal line in the mark. The results show that the luminescence is polarized in the a direction. Since this blue luminescence represents the reverse process of the 350mμ absorption, which is polarized in the a direction, the result is quite reasonable.

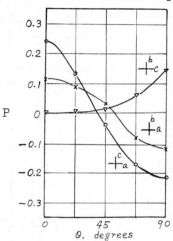

Fig. 4 — Degree of polarization P of the luminescence from the $NaNO_2$ single crystal at 77°K with 365 mμ excitation.

$$P(\theta) = [(I_{\|} - I_{\perp})/(I_{\|} + I_{\perp})]_\theta \qquad [1]$$

4. Excitation Spectra

Excitation spectra were measured with a powder of sodium nitrite. The same measurements with single crystals are now under way. The results for the powder are shown in Fig. 5. The excitation spectrum is somewhat different from the absorption spectrum shown in Fig. 2. It involves two peaks at 370 and at 330 mμ. If they are compared with those in the absorption spec-trum at 350 and 300 mμ, they are both shifted towards longer wavelengths. This difference suggests that the vibrational levels in the excited state with large numbers of vibrational quanta have lower luminescence efficiencies than those with small numbers of vibrational quanta. Further it seems that there is a fairly strong anisotropy in the excitation spectra.

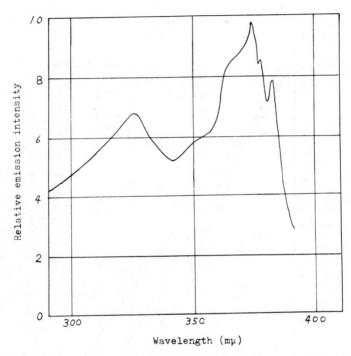

Fig. 5 — Excitation spectrum for the blue luminescence of NaNO$_2$ powder at 77°K.

5. Temperature Effect on the Luminescence

The intensity of the blue luminescence of alkali nitrites decreases with increasing temperature, and the luminescence almost disappears at about −80°C. The dependence of the luminescence intensity on temperature is given by the following equation in the case of a simple luminescence center.

$$I = \frac{I_0}{1 + \gamma \exp\left(- \Delta E / R T\right)} \qquad [2]$$

Here $\gamma \exp(-\Delta E/RT)$ is the probability of a non-radiative transition and I_0 is the luminescence intensity at extremely low temperatures where non-radiative transitions are negligible. In Fig. 6, $\log\{(I_0 - I)/I\}$ is plotted against $1/T$. The activation energies for temperature quenching ΔE calculated from these curves are shown in the figure.

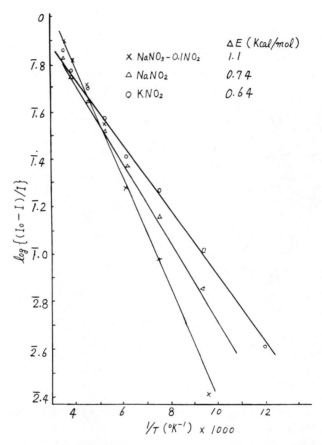

Fig. 6 — Temperature dependence of the luminescence intensity of some alkali nitrites.

The fine structure in the emission spectra becomes diffuse with increasing temperature. As an example of this phenomenon the variation of the shape of the 425 mμ peak in the emission spectrum of NaNO$_2$ with temperature is shown in Fig. 7. The fine structure almost disappears at 183°K.

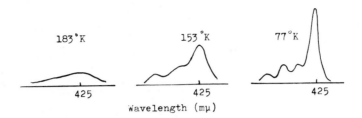

Fig. 7 — Effect of temperature on the 425 mμ peak in the emission spectrum of NaNO$_2$ under 365 mμ excitation (microphotometer trace).

6. Effects of the Hydrogen Bond Formed between the NO$_2^-$ ion and the Surrounding Matrix

It is of interest to investigate how the luminescence of the NO$_2^-$ ion is affected if it is imbedded in a matrix. If a hydrogen bond is formed between the NO$_2^-$ ion and the surrounding matrix, its effect will be most interesting. The matrix most suitable for this purpose is urea, because it has a low melting point and because urea and alkali nitrites mix well and a strong hydrogen bond is formed between them.

If NaNO$_2$ is introduced into urea, with a concentration of more than 0.01 mole/mole, a blue luminescence due to the NO$_2^-$ ion appears, as is shown in Fig. 8. Comparing these spectra with that of the NaNO$_2$ crystal, it is clear that the spectrum in Fig. 8(b) is the overlap of that of pure NaNO$_2$ with that of the NaNO$_2$-urea system, $i.e.$ the series of sharp peaks is due to pure NaNO$_2$ and the series of diffuse peaks due to the NaNO$_2$-urea system. In the case of smaller amounts of NaNO$_2$ shown in Fig. 8(a) only the spectrum of the NaNO$_2$-urea system appears.

The distance between the diffuse peaks in the spectrum of the NaNO$_2$-urea system is about 785 cm^{-1}, which is slightly smaller than the corresponding value in pure NaNO$_2$ of 830 cm^{-1}. If the positions of the corresponding peaks in the spectra of pure NaNO$_2$ and the NaNO$_2$-urea system at the shortest wavelength region are compared with each other, the peak of the latter is shifted about 490 cm^{-1} towards longer wavelengths.

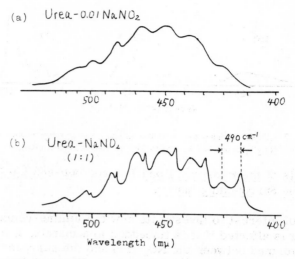

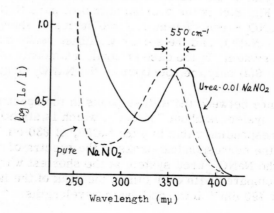

Fig. 8 — Microphotometer traces of emission spectra of a
NaNO$_2$ —urea system at 77°K with 365 mμ excitation.

The absorption spectra of NaNO$_2$-urea systems were measured in the molten state at 100°C, since single crystals of this
system could not be prepared. The results are shown in Fig. 9.
The absorption peak of the NaNO$_2$-urea system is shifted
550 cm^{-1} towards longer wavelengths.

Fig. 9 — Absorption spectrum of a molten NaNO$_2$— urea system
at 100°C.

It is quite certain that in the $NaNO_2$-urea system a fairly strong hydrogen bond is formed between the NO_2^- ion and urea as expressed below.

$$-N \begin{array}{c} \diagup O^- \dots\dots H \diagdown \\ \diagdown O \ \dots\dots H \diagup \end{array} N-$$

The formation of this hydrogen bond may make the electronic energy state of the NO_2^- ion somewhat stable. The electronic transition responsible for the 350 mμ absorption and the blue luminescence is $n_N \leftrightarrow \pi^*$ as was mentioned above. The stabilization due to the hydrogen bond formation may be much stronger with the π^* state than with the n_N state. Therefore the shift of the absorption and emission of the NO_2^- ion in the $NaNO_2$-urea system towards longer wavelengths is quite reasonable. The hydrogen bond formation may also make the bending vibration frequency of the NO_2^- ion somewhat smaller, since it increases the effective mass of the oxygen atoms in the NO_2^- ion. The decrease in the distance between peaks in the emission spectra from 830 cm^{-1} to 785 cm^{-1} is also explained by these considerations.

II. HEAVY METAL NITRITES AND HEAVY METAL-NO$_2$ COMPLEX SYSTEMS

As was mentioned above, some of the present authors[2] reported that pure silver nitrite and silver-containing sodium nitrite crystals show a yellow luminescence associated with a fine structure, and concluded that the origin of this yellow luminescence lies in the bond between the silver and the NO_2 group which has a covalent nature. In the continuation of this work the luminescence of heavy metal nitrites and heavy metal-NO_2 complexes has been extensively investigated.

A. Heavy Metal-NO₂ Complex Systems

1. Samples

Alkali nitrites containing Ag^+, Tl^+ and Pb^{2+} were investigated. The preparation of single crystals of these materials was tested, but success was achieved only for Tl^+-containing $NaNO_2$. Other materials which were investigated were in powder form.

The single crystals of Tl$^+$-containing NaNO$_2$ were prepared by means of Bridgman method. Thallium salt was added to molten sodium nitrite with content of 0.1 mol percent. Single crystals containing more than this content could not be made by this method.

2. Absorption

The absorption spectrum of the Tl$^+$-containing NaNO$_2$ single crystal was measured. The character of the 350 mμ absorption band due to the NO$_2^-$ ion is exactly the same as that of the pure NaNO$_2$ single crystal. The color of Tl$^+$-containing NaNO$_2$ is slightly yellowish. Therefore this crystal should have an absorption band in the blue region, which is probably due to the thallium-NO$_2$ complex. With the single crystal made by us this absorption was too weak to be measured by the usual methods, since the content of Tl$^+$ was very low. It is possible to measure this band with Tl$^+$-containing NaNO$_2$ solutions. A new absorption band with a peak at 460 mμ was produced by the addition of Tl$^+$ salt to a NaNO$_2$ solution.

3. Luminescence

If heavy metals of Ag$^+$, Tl$^+$ and Pb^{2+} are added to alkali nitrites, new yellow or red luminescence appears. The emission spectra of these materials in powder form with 365 mμ excitation are shown in Fig. 10, 11, and 12.

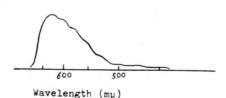

Wavelength (mμ)

Fig. 10 — Microphotometer trace of the emission spectrum of Ag$^+$—containing NaNO$_2$ (1 mole percent silver) at 77°K with 365 mμ excitation.

The structures of the emission spectra due to silver and lead are diffuse. The distances between peaks are about 750 cm^{-1} for the silver-containing salt and 810-840 cm^{-1} for the lead-containing salt. These values can be assigned to the bending vibration frequency of the NO_2 group within $AgNO_2$ and $Pb(NO_2)_2$ which is imbedded in the $NaNO_2$ crystal in the form of a localized molecule. The emission spectrum due to thallium is a broad band with a peak at around $680m\mu$ and does not have fine structure even at $4°K$.

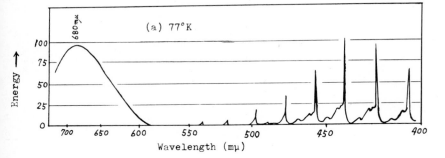

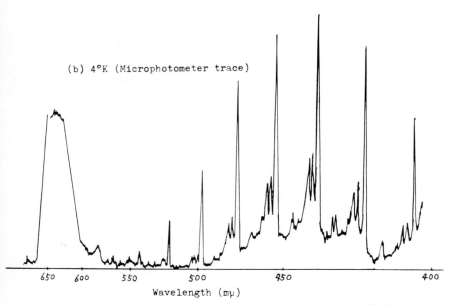

Fig. 11 — Emission spectrum of Tl^+—containing $NaNO_2$ (01 mole percent thallium) at 77°K and 4°K with 365 mμ excitation.

The polarization of the luminescence of heavy metal-NO_2 complex systems was studied by measurements on a Tl^+-containing $NaNO_2$ single crystal at 77°K with 365mμ excitation. The results

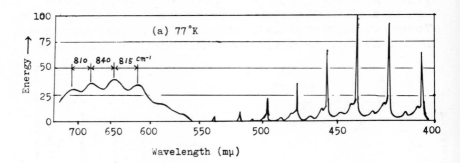

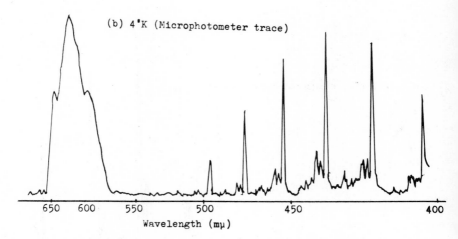

Fig. 12 — Emission spectrum of Pb^{2+}—containing $NaNO_2$ (0.1 mole percent lead) at 77°K and 4°K with 365 mµ excitation.

are shown in Fig. 13. The method of measurement and the notation are the same as was described above (See Sec. I.3). The results show that the red luminescence due to thallium is polarized mainly in the *b* direction. If it is assumed that thallium replaces Na^+ in the crystal, this direction of polarization is that which connects the thallium and nitrogen atoms (See Fig. 1).

The excitation spectrum of the luminescence of this type of

system was measured with Tl^+-containing $NaNO_2$ powder at 77°K. The results are shown in Fig. 14. The ordinate gives only the relative emission intensity and is not calibrated for the amount of absorption of the exciting light. Since the absorption coefficient in the blue region is several hundredths of that in the ultraviolet region, the emission efficiency in the blue region of excitation will be at least one order of magnitude larger than that in the ultraviolet region.

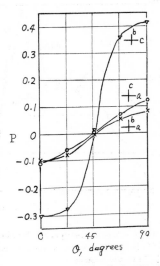

Fig. 13 – Degree of polarization P of the red luminescence due to thallium from a thallium-containing $NaNO_2$ single crystal at 77°K with 365 mμ excitation.

This excitation spectrum has fine structure in both the blue and the ultraviolet region. The origin of this structure is not yet understood. The shape of the spectrum in the ultraviolet region is considerably different from that for the blue luminescence due to the NO_2^- ion. As will be mentioned below, the excitation of the red luminescence due to ultraviolet absorption should involve a process of energy transfer. Then this difference might be attributed to the spectral dependence of the probability of this energy transfer. Further it seems that there exists an anisotropy of the excitation spectrum. Measurements with single crystals are now under way, and these problems will be solved in the future.

From the above results, the following ideas can be put forth concerning the luminescence of heavy metal-NO_2 complex systems. It is suggested that if thallium or other heavy metals replace Na^+, a weak coordination bond is formed between the heavy metal and the nitrogen atom because of the unshared electrons of the latter. Then the red luminescence due to heavy metals may be assigned to a transition between the excited and ground levels of this bond. This seems to explain reasonably well the results on the polarization of the red luminescence. The following explanation is also possible. The assumption may be made that the red luminescence is due to the reverse of a transition in which one of the unshared electrons of the nitrogen

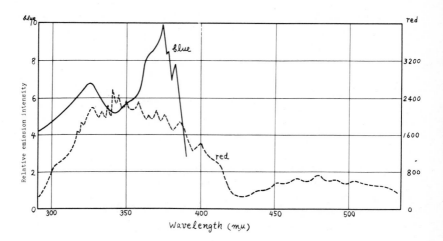

Fig. 14 — Excitation spectra for the luminescence of Tl$^+$—containing NaNO$_2$ powder at 77°K. Both the red luminescence due to thallium and the blue luminescence due to the NO$_2$$^-$ion are shown.

atom is raised to the empty orbital of the heavy metal, the $6p$ orbital in the case of thallium. The experimental results can be understood by this assumption. If these considerations are correct, then it is suggested that in the case where the red luminescence is produced by excitation in the near ultraviolet region some kind of intermolecular transfer of excitation energy takes place, since the near ultraviolet absorption causes a $n_N \rightarrow \pi^*$ transition within the NO$_2$$^-$ ion.

B. Heavy Metal Nitrites

The luminescence of AgNO$_2$ and TlNO$_2$ were investigated. These nitrites show yellow or red luminescence at low temperatures with 365 mμ excitation. The luminescence of AgNO$_2$ persists towards higher temperatures up to 90°C.

The emission spectra of AgNO$_2$ at various temperatures are shown in Fig. 15. This material shows a quite peculiar phenomenon. The spectral distribution of the emission is almost the same in the whole temperature range. At room temperature the emission spectrum shows no structure. At 77°K a diffuse structure appears, but it disappears again at 4°K. We thought this phenomenon very curious and repeated the measurement carefully. There was a reproducibility of the disappearance of the structure at 4°K. The reason for this phenomenon is not quite

understood yet. It might be due to a change in the crystal structure below 77°K.

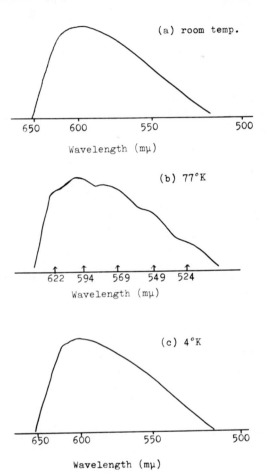

Fig. 15 — Microphotometer trace of emission spectra
of AgNO$_2$ at room temperature, 77°K and 4°K with
365 mμ excitation.

The emission spectrum of AgNO$_2$ at 77°K is almost the same
as that of Ag$^+$-containing NaNO$_2$. Then it may be concluded from
the considerations mentioned above that the origin of the yellow
luminescence of AgNO$_2$ is the coordination bond between the
silver and the nitrogen atom. That the silver and nitrogen-con-
necting bond in AgNO$_2$ has a partially covalent character is

supported by the fact that nitro-paraffins are formed together
with nitrite ester if alkyl halides react with $AgNO_2$. Therefore
this conclusion seems quite reasonable.

The emission spectrum of $TlNO_2$
at 4°K is shown in Fig. 16. This has
a fine structure whereas the emission spectrum of Tl^+-containing
$NaNO_2$ does not. However, since
the spectral distribution of these
two emissions are almost the
same, the origin of the luminescence may be the same, namely
the coordination bond between thallium and nitrogen as was mentioned above. The distances between peaks in the fine structure
are 1000-1100 cm^{-1}, which are
considerably larger than those for
$AgNO_2$ and Ag^+ or Pb^{2+}-contain-
ing $NaNO_2$. It is not certain yet
whether this structure can be as-
cribed to the bending vibration of the NO_2 group.

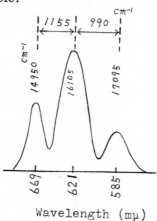

Fig. 16 — Microphotometer trace of
the emission spectrum of $TlNO_2$ at
4°K with 365 mμ excitation.

REFERENCES (Part I)

[1] J. W. Sidman, J. Am. Chem. Soc., 78, 2911 (1956); 79, 2669
   (1957).
[2] S. Makishima and T. Tomotsu, Bull. Chem. Soc. Japan, 27,
   476 (1954).
[3] G. B. Carpenter, Acta Cryst. 5, 132 (1952).
[4] W. G. Trawick and W. H. Eberhardt, J. Chem. Phys. 22,
   1462 (1954).

Part II

Luminescence of Sm^{3+} in $BaTiO_3$

1. Introduction

The trivalent samarium ion shows usually a bright orange luminescence with a complicated line-like spectrum due to an f-f electronic transition, when imbedded in crystalline matrices.

The luminescence characteristics of Sm^{3+} in solids were most extensively investigated with CaS:Sm by one of the present authors, S. Makishima.[1] He found that the line-like emission spectrum lies in the range from 550 to 980 mμ, and that it is composed of six groups each including several sharp lines. It was concluded that the emission of these groups is due to the transition from a certain excited state, probably ^6F, to the sextet ground state, $i.\,e.\ ^6H_{5/2}$, $^6H_{7/2}$, $\cdots$, and $^6H_{15/2}$. The fine structures in the spectrum of each group were thought to be caused by either or both of (1) the Stark effect caused by the crystalline field surrounding the Sm^{3+} and (2) the interaction between the electronic state of Sm^{3+} and the phonon of the host lattice.

In this paper results of investigations on the luminescence and its characteristics of Sm^{3+} imbedded in a $BaTiO_3$ matrix are presented. The state of the Sm^{3+} luminescence center and the origin of fine structure in the emission spectra are the main subjects.

As is well known, $BaTiO_3$ is a typical ferroelectric material. The investigation of the luminescence of $BaTiO_3$ containing Sm^{3+} may provide some information about the influence of ferroelectricity on the luminescence of solids, as well as about the mechanism of ferroelectricity in $BaTiO_3$ type materials.

The luminescence of $BaTiO_3$ containing Sm^{3+} had been already studied by Oshima et al[2] and by Keller et al.[3] However these two groups of authors reported some contradictory results. One of the purposes of this work is to resolve this contradiction.

2. Experimental

a) Samples

Specially purified $BaTiO_3$ containing Sm^{3+} was prepared in the following way. Barium-titanyl oxalate [4], $BaTiO(C_2O_4)_2 \cdot 4H_2O$, was used as the starting material. To introduce Sm^{3+} the solution of its nitrate was mixed with barium-titanyl oxalate. Then the mixture was fired in a quartz crucible at 1100°C for four hours to obtain $BaTiO_3$. The identification of the fired products was made with an X-ray diffraction method, and it was confirmed that barium-titanyl oxalate was completely converted into $BaTiO_3$, and that no other forms of the double oxides of barium and titanium were present.

b) Emission Spectra

All samples containing Sm^{3+} showed a fairly bright orange luminescence with 365mμ excitation. The intensity of the luminescence is strong at liquid nitrogen temperature, but decreases rather rapidly with increasing temperature.

Microphotometer curves of the photographs for the emission spectra of samples containing 1.0 mole percent samarium at low temperature are shown in Fig. 1. The calibration of the ordinates of the curves, which would give accurate intensities

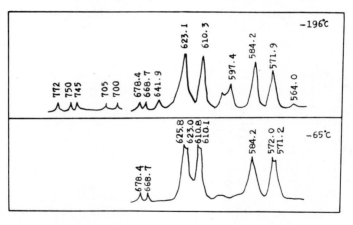

Wavelength (mμ)

Fig. 1 — Microphotometer curves of emission spectra.
Sample — $BaTiO_3$: Sm (1 m%)

of the emission lines, was not made. In Fig. 2 accurate intensities, obtained by the photoelectric method, are given for the visible region. In Fig. 1 the emission at −65°C was so weak that photographs in the infrared region could not be taken.

It can be noticed by looking at these two spectra that the emission lines at 564.0, 597.4, and 641.9 mμ almost disappear at −65°C. To investigate this phenomenon in detail the temperature changes of the intensities of these emission lines were measured with the photoelectric method. It was found that the intensities of the lines at 564.0, 597.4, and 641.9 mμ decrease with increasing temperature much more rapidly than do those of the other lines.

Emission spectra of samples containing samarium in various concentrations, which were obtained by the photoelectric method, are shown in Fig. 2. The ordinate gives the emission intensity expressed in arbitrary units. The figure shows the change in intensity with samarium concentration. The emission inten-

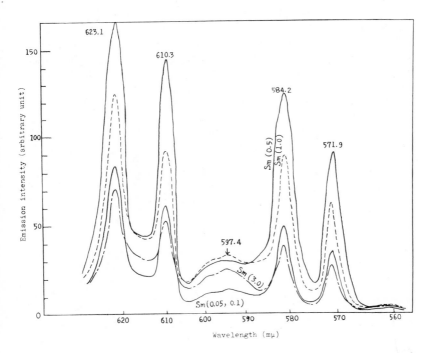

Fig. 2 — Emission spectra of BaTiO$_3$ containing samarium in various concentrations at −196°C. The concentrations are expressed by mole percent.

sity increases with an increase in samarium concentration, goes through a maximum at a concentration of about 0.5 mole percent and then decreases. However, it should be noticed that the intensity of the four distinct lines shown in the figure is a maximum at 0.5 mol percent, whereas the intensity of the relatively weak 597.4 mμ line is a maximum at 1.0 mole percent. Thus the dependence of the intensities on the samarium concentration of the four distinct lines is different from that of the 597.4 mμ line. This is made clear by calculating the ratios (R) of the intensity of the 584.2 mμ line, which is selected to be the representative of the four distinct lines, to that of the 597.4mμ line. The ratios are given in Table 1. They decrease with increase in samarium concentration.

As was mentioned in the Introduction, the emission spectrum of Sm^{3+} is composed of six groups which arise from the transition to the sextet ground state. The above results show that the whole emission spectrum is divided into two parts, one represented by 584.2mμ and the other represented by 597.4mμ, and that these two parts have different dependences on temperature and on samarium concentration. To make these facts consistent with the designation of the transition which produces Sm^{3+} emission, we would like to make the assumption that there exist two kinds of Sm^{3+} center in the matrix, and that the whole spectrum consists of the overlap of those emitted from the two centers. If only one kind of Sm^{3+} center were involved in the

Table 1

Sm^{3+} concentration (mole %)	(R) $I_{584.2}/I_{597.4}$	$I_{584.2}$ (arbitrary units)
0.05 and 0.1	4.1	49
0.5	4.0	123
1.0	2.7	88
3.0	1.5	38

Dependence of the emission intensity of the 584.2 and 597.4 mμ lines on the concentrations of Sm^{3+} in the BaTiO$_3$ matrix.

matrix, all the lines in the spectrum would show the same characteristics and one could not account for the above experimental facts.

Under this assumption, the emission lines at 571.9 and 584.2 mμ, 610.3 and 623.1 mμ, and 668.7 and 678.4 mμ, are assigned to the first, second and third groups in the spectrum from one of the two Sm^{3+} centers, and that at 564.0 to the first, 597.4 to the second, and 700 and 705 mμ to the third group from the other center. The former center will be called hereafter center A and the latter center B.

c) Influence of Foreign Cations

One of the probable explanations of the two kinds of Sm^{3+} center is that Sm^{3+} in the matrix might occupy different cation sites. The ionic radii* of Sm^{3+}, Ba^{2+} and Ti^{4+} are 0.95, 1.35 and 0.68Å, respectively. Therefore it is not unreasonable to consider the possibility that Sm^{3+} can occupy both Ba^{2+} and Ti^{4+} sites, though not with equal probability. To examine this consideration the following experiment was attempted. Some foreign cations were introduced into the matrix in such a way as to change the probability for Sm^{3+} to occupy either of the two cation sites. If some trivalent cations with larger ionic radii than that of Sm^{3+} are introduced into the matrix, those cations may occupy preferentially the Ba^{2+} site and drive Sm^{3+} into the Ti^{4+} site. On the other hand, if some tri- or penta- valent cations with ionic radii nearly equal to that of Ti^{4+} are introduced, those cations may occupy preferentially the Ti^{4+} site and drive Sm^{3+} into the Ba^{2+} site. Further, some monovalent cations with larger ionic radii than Sm^{3+} may draw Sm^{3+} to the Ba^{2+} site. La^{3+}, V^{5+}, and K^+ were selected to be the cations used for these purposes. Since the ionic radii of La^{3+}, V^{5+}, and K^+ are 1.15, 0.68, and 1.33Å, respectively, it may occur that in the case of La^{3+} the number of Sm^{3+} ions at Ti^{4+} sites is increased, while in the case of V^{5+} or K^+ it is decreased.

It was found that the wavelengths of the emission lines do not change but their relative intensities change with the introduction of foreign cations. The variation of the ratio (R) of the intensity of the 584.2 mμ line to that of the 597.4 mμ line caused by the introduction of various foreign cations is given in Table 2. This clearly expresses the importance of the effects of foreign cations, namely, La^{3+} favors the formation of center A, while V^{5+} and K^+ that of center B. If the ideas expressed above on the effect of foreign cations are correct, then these results lead to the suggestion that center A is Sm^{3+} at Ti^{4+} sites and center B Sm^{3+} at Ba^{2+} sites.

---

*Pauling's value.

Table 2

X	(R) $I_{584.2}/I_{597.4}$	$I_{584.2}$ (arbitrary units)
—	4.0	97
La^{3+}	4.3	112
V^{5+}	2.3	47
K^+	0.8	22

Dependence of emission intensity of the 584.2 and 597.4 mμ lines on the foreign cation X(1.5 mole %) in BaTiO$_3$: Sm(0.5 mole %).

3. Discussion

As was mentioned in Sec. 2.b there is strong experimental evidence for the fact that there exist two kinds of Sm^{3+} center, called center A and center B, in the BaTiO$_3$ matrix. The line spectra emitted from both center A and center B seem to be composed of six groups, and the spectrum of center A is shifted slightly towards longer wavelengths. Usually the intensity of emission from center A is stronger than that from center B.

The results on the effect of the introduction of some foreign cations lead to the suggestion that centers A and B are Sm^{3+} at Ti^{4+} and Ba^{2+} sites, respectively. This suggestion is strongly supported by the following considerations. It is well known that the emission of Sm^{3+} in a series of alkaline earth oxides and sulfides has a tendency to shift towards shorter wavelengths with an increase in the nearest distance between cation and anion in the matrix.[5] This seems to mean that the decrease in the interaction between Sm^{3+} and O^{2-} or S^{2-} increases the energy differences between the excited and ground states of Sm^{3+}.

The crystal structure of BaTiO$_3$ is the perovskite type. The nearest distance between Ti^{4+} and O^{2-} is 2.00Å and that between Ba^{2+} and O^{2-} is 2.83Å. Therefore, Sm^{3+} at a Ti^{4+} site may have a stronger interaction with the nearest oxygens than when at a Ba^{2+} site, if it can occupy both Ti^{4+} and Ba^{2+} sites. If one considers the emission spectra observed with alkaline earth oxides and sulfides, it is quite reasonable to expect that each of the six groups in the emission spectrum of Sm^{3+} at Ti^{4+} sites is located in the longer wavelength region than those of Sm^{3+} at Ba^{2+} sites. This expectation agrees well with the suggestion concerning the A and B centers.

Thus it may be fairly unambiguously concluded that Sm^{3+} introduced into the $BaTiO_3$ matrix occupies both of the two cation sites, *i. e.* Ti^{4+} and Ba^{2+} sites, that these two kinds of Sm^{3+} emit different spectra each of which is composed of six groups of lines, and that each group in the spectrum of the Sm^{3+} center at Ti^{4+} sites (called center A) is shifted towards longer wavelengths than the corresponding one of the Sm^{3+} center at Ba^{2+} sites (center B). Another possibility which can be offered to explain these experimental facts is to assume that the two kinds of centers are a single Sm^{3+}, and two Sm^{3+} ions in association. However, since the result of adding foreign cations can be reasonably explained by the above considerations, that result seems to be strong enough to reject this second possibility.

The line spectrum shown in Fig. 1 was arranged in accordance with the above considerations, and is shown in Fig. 3 and Table 3.

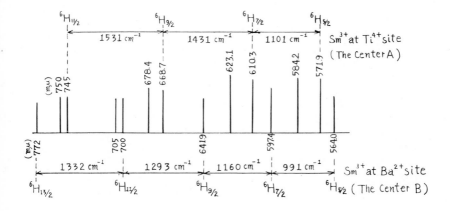

Fig. 3 — Diagram of the emission spectrum of Sm^{3+} in a $BaTiO_3$ matrix at $-196°C$.

The ratios of the intervals between the six levels of the ground state can be calculated for a free ion on the basis of a theory on the break-down of Russel-Saunders coupling.[6] The values are shown in the last column of Table 3. Taking into consideration the fact that the theoretical ratio may not be strictly accurate for Sm^{3+} in crystalline matricies, the disagreement of

Table 3

Kind of Sm^{3+}	Sm^{3+} in BaTiO$_3$				Expected ratio from a theory on the break-down of Russel-Saunders coupling for free Sm^{3+}
	Sm^{3+} at Ti^{4+} sites		Sm^{3+} at Ba^{2+} sites		
Interval	cm^{-1}	ratio	cm^{-1}	ratio	
Energy Term					
$^6H_{5/2}$ —— $^6H_{7/2}$	1101	7	991	7	7
$^6H_{7/2}$ —— $^6H_{9/2}$	1431	9.1	1160	8.2	8.5
$^6H_{9/2}$ —— $^6H_{11/2}$	1531	9.8	1293	9.1	9.5
$^6H_{11/2}$ —— $^6H_{13/2}$	—	—	1332	9.5	10.1
$^6H_{13/2}$ —— $^6H_{15/2}$	—	—	—	—	10.1

Energy term intervals between the six levels of the ground state of Sm^{3+}.

the experimental ratio with the theoretical one seems to be rather small.

If the emission spectra observed by us are compared with those by Oshima et al.[2] and those by Keller et al.,[3] a very interesting thing is found. It is quite clear that the spectra observed by the former authors are those of Sm^{3+} at Ti^{4+} sites while those by the latter authors are those of Sm^{3+} at Ba^{2+} sites. This may have occurred due to a difference in preparation of the samples. The problem of the discrepancy between the results by these two groups of authors is thus completely solved.

The emission spectrum of Sm^{3+} at Ti^{4+} sites is shifted towards longer wavelengths than that of Sm^{3+} at Ba^{2+} sites. If the energy of this red shift is calculated from the group of lines for the two centers at the shortest wavelength region, it is about 610 cm^{-1}. Similarly, the red shift between Sm^{3+} in TiO_2 and in BaO is calculated from the data by Tomaschek et al[5] to be 290 cm^{-1}. The nearest distances between the cations and O^{2-} in $BaTiO_3$ are very close to those in BaO and TiO_2, i.e. d(Ba–O) = 2.77Å and d(Ti–O) = 1.97Å. Therefore it may be assumed that the chemical binding in $BaTiO_3$ has almost the same character as that in BaO and TiO_2. If so, the red shift between the two kinds of Sm^{3+} in $BaTiO_3$ should be expected to show almost the same value as that between Sm^{3+} in BaO and in TiO_2. However the experimental value of the former shift, 610 cm^{-1}, is much larger than that of the latter shift, 290 cm^{-1}. This fact may indicate that the interaction between Ti^{4+} and O^{2-} in $BaTiO_3$ is much stronger than in TiO_2 and may be connected with the ferroelectricity of $BaTiO_3$ due to the coupling of Ti^{4+} with O^{2-}.

The origin of the fine structure in each of the six groups of the Sm^{3+} emission spectra was investigated briefly. To do this the emission spectrum of Eu^{3+} in $BaTiO_3$ was examined. From a comparison of the spectrum of Sm^{3+} with that of Eu^{3+}, a tentative conclusion was drawn that the fine structure in the spectrum of each group is caused mainly by the Stark effect due to the crystalline field. From an analysis of the details of this Stark splitting some information might be derived on the internal field strength around the Ti^{4+} ion which plays an important role in the occurrence of ferroelectricity.

REFERENCES   (Part II)

[1] S. Makishima, Doctral Thesis, Faculty of Engineering, University of Tokyo, 1944. See also, N. Kameyama, "Theory and Applications of Luminescent Materials" (written in Japanese) Maruzen Co., Ltd., Tokyo, (1960) p. 37.
[2] K. Oshima, S. Hayakawa, and H. Nagano, J. Chem. Phys. 24, 903 (1956).
[3] S. P. Keller, and G. D. Pettit, J. Chem. Phys. 31, 1272 (1959).
[4] W. S. Clabaugh, E. M. Swiggard, and R. Gilchrist, J. Res. Nat. Bur. Stand. 56,289 (1956).
[5] R. Tomaschek, Phys. Z. 33, 878 (1932).
[6] B. R. Judd, Proc. Phys. Soc. A69, 157 (1956).

Part III

Luminescence of Thallous Complex Ions

1. Introduction

If a small amount of thallous halide is added to alkali halide solutions, they are made to emit a blue luminescence. This is accompanied by the appearance of a new absorption band. Investigations by Fromherz and Lih[1,2] and also by Pringsheim and Vogels[3] clearly indicated that the luminescence and the absorption are due to the formation of the thallous complex ion.

A fact of great interest concerning this phenomenon is that the luminescence and absorption spectra of the thallous complex ion are remarkably similar to those of the corresponding thallium-activated alkali halide crystal phosphors. This led to the suggestion that the luminescence and absorption of the crystal phosphors are also due to complex centers.[4]

On the other hand, Seitz[5] presented another suggestion: that thallium in the crystal phosphors behaves as a simple thallous ion and the electronic transition within the thallous ion is responsible for the luminescence as well as the absorption. Williams[6,7] developed, on the basis of this suggestion, an absolute theory on the luminescence center in KCl:Tl type phosphors, and calculated quantitatively the configurational coordinate model of the center. Recently, however, a critique of this theory was made by Dexter and Knox,[8] and further, Knox[9] has shown that the coupling between an excited activator state and an electron transfer state should be included in the theory. Williams and his coworkers[10,11,12] improved upon their own theoretical calculations and revised somewhat the model of the center, which, however, basically is the same as their first model.

Consequently, the problem of the luminescence centers in thallium and other heavy metal-activated alkali halide phosphors still involves some ambiguities, and the true nature of the centers is considered to be not yet completely explained. The purpose of this work is to present some useful information on this problem through further investigation of the luminescence properties of the solutions of thallous-halogen complex ions.

2. Experimental and Discussion

a) Absorption

Absorption spectra of solutions were measured with a Cary Model 14 spectrophotometer. The thickness of liquid in a quartz cell was 1mm.

Absorption spectra of TlCl solution and of TlCl-containing KCl solutions are shown in Fig. 1. TlCl solution has an absorption peak at 214 mμ. In the measurement of TlCl-KCl solutions, pure KCl solutions of the same concentrations were used as references. Therefore the figure shows only the spectra which appear with the introduction of thallous ion, and the absorption due to the hydrated chlorine ion is absent.

The results show that the absorption peak shifts towards longer wavelengths with increase in chlorine ion concentration. This shift, as well as the simultaneous change of the absorption peak height and band width, indicates the formation of thallous-chlorine complex ions. To measure the absorption at higher chlorine concentrations $CaCl_2$ was used instead of KCl. The wavelengths of the absorption peaks were plotted against the chlorine concentrations in Fig. 2. The shift of the peak towards longer wavelengths ceases at a chlorine concentration of about 8 Mol/L, indicating that the form of the complex ion does not change beyond this concentration.

The absorption characteristics of TlBr-KBr solutions are very similar to those of TlCl-KCl solutions. However TlF-KF solutions behave quite differently. TlF solution has an absorp-

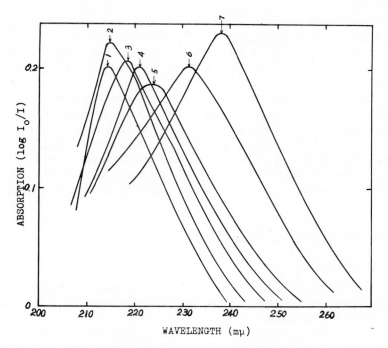

Fig. 1 — Absorption spectra of TlCl solution and of TlCl-containing KCl solutions. The thickness of the solution layer is 1 mm. The TlCl concentration is constant $(6.7 \times 10^{-4}$ Mol /L $)$ for all the spectra. The KCl concentrations are 1 : 0, 2 : 0.0606, 3 : 0.1515, 4 : 0.303, 5 : 0.606, 6 : 1.515, 7 : 3.03 Mol /L

tion peak at 213 mμ, the same as that of TlCl and TlBr. This peak wavelength as well as the band width, however, does not change at all with increase of the fluorine ion concentration. This fact is clear evidence that the thallous ion never forms complex ions with the fluorine ion.

The absorption peak at around 213 mμ is also observed with Tl_2CO_3, Tl_2SO_4 and $TlNO_3$ solutions. This absorption is due to the thallous ion which is not coordinated with halogen ions but hydrated with water molecules.

Scott and Hu[13] have shown from solubility measurements that in TlCl-KCl solutions complex ions which are present in the region of appreciable chlorine concentration are neutral (TlCl) and monovalent $(TlCl_2)^-$. They[14] further analyzed the absorption spectra with the assistance of dissociation constants for (TlCl) and $(TlCl_2)^-$, and indicated that the absorption peaks for these two complexes are located at around 225 and 245 mμ,

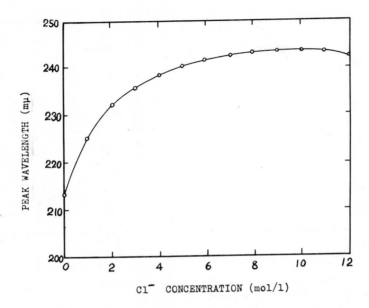

Fig. 2 — The peak wavelengths of the absorption spectra of $CaCl_2$ solutions containing TlCl (6.7×10^{-4} Mol /L) against Cl^- concentration.

respectively. The results given in Fig. 2 show that the absorption peak does not exceed 243 mμ even at very high chlorine concentrations. Then it may be said that even at higher concentrations complex ions which are involved are mostly $(TlCl_2)^-$, although there is an indication that complex ions involving more than two chlorine ions are present with concentrations much lower than that of $(TlCl_2)^-$.[13]

b) Luminescence

Solutions of thallous-chlorine (or bromine) complex ions emit a blue luminescence. The spectrum was measured with a Kipp and Zonen double monochromator and an RCA 1P21 photomultiplier. The excitation source was the 253.7 mμ mercury line. The results are shown in Fig. 3. Careful measurements were performed to see whether another luminescence band appears in the ultraviolet region. However, no luminescence other than the blue was observed, even when excitation of shorter wavelength, down to 220 mμ, was used. Further, investigations on whether the thallous ion which is not coordinated with a halogen ion in solutions emits luminescence, were also made. No luminescence was found.

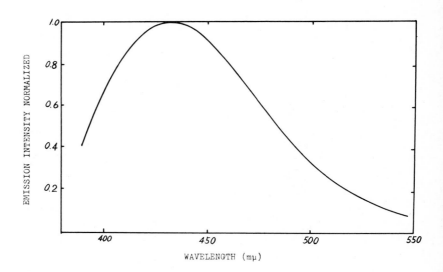

Fig. 3 — The emission spectrum of CaCl$_2$ solution (4 Mol /L) containing TlCl
(0.001 Mol /L) with 253.7 mμ excitation.

    The relation between the intensity of the blue luminescence
and the chlorine concentration is shown in Fig. 4. Since the absorption coefficient for the 253.7 mμ excitation line varies with
the chlorine concentration, precautions were taken to insure
that the layer of solution was made thick enough for the 253.7
mμ line to be absorbed completely by the layer. In the figure
the molecular absorption coefficients at 243 mμ, $i.\,e.$ the absorption peak due to the $(TlCl_2)^-$ ion, are also plotted against
chlorine concentration. There is a remarkable proportionality
between the emission intensity and the absorption coefficient.
This leads to the conclusion that the emission band which peaks
at 430 mμ is due to the $(TlCl_2)^-$ ion.
    The KCl:Tl crystal phosphor has two main absorption bands
which peak at 196 and 247 mμ and two main emission bands
which peak at 305 and 475 mμ. Some other minor bands are
also involved in the absorption as well as the emission.
    The above investigation on the solutions of thallous complex
ions indicates that only the complex ion involving two halogen
ions is luminescent and that the absorption and emission bands
of this complex ion correspond to the 247 mμ absorption and
475 mμ emission bands in the crystal phosphor, respectively.

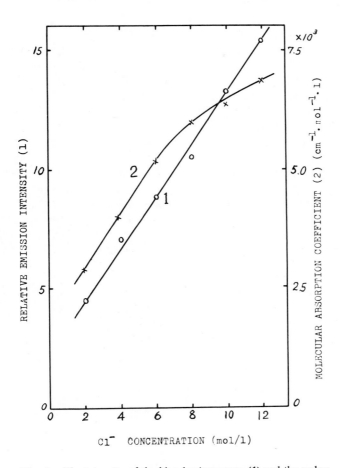

Fig. 4 — The intensity of the blue luminescence (1) and the molec-
cular absorption coefficients at 243 mμ (2) for CaCl$_2$ solutions containing TlCl (6.7 × 10^{-4} Mol /L) against Cl$^-$ concentration.

These facts suggest that the formation of the coordination bond
plays an important role in the appearance of the luminescence
in KCl:Tl type crystal phosphors, and that the 247 mμ absorption and 475 mμ emission bands are directly coupled to each
other, and both originate from a luminescence center the
atomic configuration of which is similar to that of the (TlCl$_2$)$^-$
type complex ion. The fact that TlF-KF solutions, in which no
complex ions are formed, show no luminescence, supports
this suggestion.

REFERENCES   (Part III)

[1] H. Fromherz, Z. Phys. 68, 233 (1931).
[2] H. Fromherz and K. H. Lih, Z. Phys. Chem. A153, 321 (1931).
[3] P. Pringsheim and H. Vogels, Physica 7, 225 (1940).
[4] R. Hilsch, Proc. Phys. Soc. (London) 49, 40 (1937).
[5] F. Seitz, J. Chem. Phys. 6, 150 (1938).
[6] F. E. Williams, ibid., 19, 457 (1951).
[7] F. E. Williams, J. Opt. Soc. Am. 10, 869 (1957).
[8] D. L. Dexter and R. S. Knox, Phys. Rev. 104, 1245 (1956).
[9] R. S. Knox, ibid., 115, 1095 (1959).
[10] F. E. Williams, B. Segall and P. D. Johnson, ibid., 108, 46 (1957).
[11] F. E. Williams and P. D. Johnson, ibid., 113, 97 (1959).
[12] P. D. Johnson and F. E. Williams, ibid., 117, 964 (1960).
[13] K. H. Hu and A. B. Scott, J. Am. Chem. Soc. 77, 1380 (1955).
[14] A. B. Scott and K. H. Hu, J. Chem. Phys. 23, 1830 (1955).

ABSOLUTE EFFICIENCIES OF PHOSPHORS WITH ULTRA-VIOLET AND CATHODE-RAY EXCITATION

A. Bril
Philips Research Laboratories
N.V. Philips' Gloeilampenfabrieken
Eindhoven-Netherlands

ABSTRACT

The methods used for measuring the absolute radiant efficiencies of phosphors for ultraviolet and cathode-ray excitation are compared. In the case of cathode-ray excitation the energy of the electrons was 20 kV, the beam current $3\,\mu A$. Both the emitted fluorescent power and the power of the electron beam have to be determined absolutely. For ultra-violet excitation the phosphors were irradiated with a high-pressure mercury lamp with suitable filters thus isolating a wavelength region of 2500-2700 Å and obtaining a strong irradiation. The efficiency can be measured directly as a single quantity (ratio of the emitted fluorescent power to the power absorbed from the exciting radiation).

In both cases the radiation was measured with a fast thermopile having a constant spectral power response.

Measurements were carried out for the standard phosphor samples issued by the National Bureau of Standards (Washington). For $MgWO_4$, to which frequent reference is made in the literature, we found with U.V. excitation a radiant efficiency of 44% (corresponding to a quantum efficiency of 84% and a luminous efficiency of 115 lm/W). For C.R. excitation Zn_2SiO_4 – Mn is often used as a standard; we found for sample No. 1021 a radiant efficiency of 8% (corresponding to a luminous efficiency of 41 lm/W).

INTRODUCTION

We will first discuss the various definitions of the efficiency of fluorescent substances; then we will compare the methods of measurement for ultraviolet excitation and for cathode-ray excitation.

For ultraviolet (U.V.) excitation we distinguish the radiant, the quantum and the luminous efficiency.

The *radiant efficiency* η is defined as the ratio of the emitted fluorescent power to the power absorbed by the phosphor from the exciting radiation (both powers to be expressed, for instance, in Watts). The *quantum efficiency* q is the ratio of the number of emitted fluorescent quanta to the number of the absorbed quanta. Finally the *luminous efficiency* L is the ratio of the luminous flux emitted by the phosphor (*e.g.* in lumens) to the absorbed power (*e.g.* in Watts).

For *cathode-ray* (C.R.) excitation the term quantum efficiency is irrelevant. The *radiant efficiency* is defined as the ratio of the emitted power to the power of the electron beam falling on the phosphor. In this case the efficiency does not refer to the power *absorbed* by the phosphor but to the total power incident on the phosphor. The power lost by the emission of slow secondary electrons is, in our case, negligible. The power loss by primary electrons which are elastically reflected or whose energy is only partly absorbed by the phosphor, is not taken into account. This reflection coefficient is only well known for metals. For high atomic number the correction for reflected primaries might be considerable. The *luminous efficiency* for C.R. excitation is again defined as the ratio of the emitted luminous flux and the power of the C.R. beam.

We have measured only the radiant efficiency. From this quantity the quantum and lumen efficiencies can be calculated. In the case of U.V. excitation the quantum efficiency is

$$q = \eta \, \frac{\int \lambda p\,(\lambda)\,d\lambda}{\lambda_0 \int p\,(\lambda)\,d\lambda}$$

where $p\,(\lambda)$ is the power emitted by the phosphor at wavelength λ and λ_0 is the exciting wavelength. The integration is taken over the whole range of emission.

The luminous efficiency is

$$L = \eta\, K_m \, \frac{\int p\,(\lambda)\,\overline{Y}\,(\lambda)\,d\lambda}{\int p\,(\lambda)\,d\lambda}$$

where $\overline{Y}\,(\lambda)$ denotes the eye-sensitivity as a function of wavelength and K_m is the maximum value of the luminous flux per Watt of radiant power (683 lm/W at 555 mμ).

For measuring the absolute efficiency with C.R. excitation two quantities have to be determined in an absolute way, namely the power of the emitted radiation and the electrical power falling on the phosphor.

For U.V. excitation no absolute determination is required. The ratio of the power emitted by the phosphor and the power falling on the phosphor can be determined directly as a relative quantity. This ratio can be converted to the radiant efficiency by applying some corrections as will be discussed below.

In order to see for what quantitites the knowledge of the absolute values is required we will now discuss the methods of efficiency measurement which are used by us.

a) <u>C.R. excitation</u>. To determine the electrical power falling on the phosphor care must be taken that the total current measured is really incident on the phosphor, i.e. the irradiated area of the phosphor must be smaller than the total area covered with the phosphor layer. A schematic diagram of the demountable cathode-ray tube used for the experiments is given in Fig. 1. A beam of electrons from the gun g with filament f is

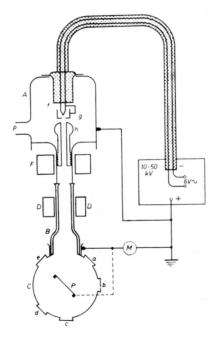

Fig. 1 — Schematic drawing of the demountable cathode-ray tube used for the efficiency measurements. A metal chamber, h anode, f filament, g cap, p pump connection, F focusing coil, D deflection coils, B glass tube, C metal cylinder, P target plate, a, b, c, and d quartz windows, M microammeter.

accelerated by a high voltage applied between g and the anode h. The electron beam strikes the plate P to which several phosphor samples can be applied. By moving this plate magnetically from the outside (without opening the tube) along the axis of the cylinder C each sample can be brought successively under the electron beam. A more detailed description of the tube has been given by Bril and Klasens.[1]

The secondary electrons emitted by the phosphor are collected by the metal plate P on which the phosphors are applied and by the cylindrical tube C surrounding that plate with phosphors. The sum of these currents is equal to the primary current provided that no charging up of the phosphor takes place. We may assume this to be true because the phosphor grains are in contact with the metal plate.

To prevent low energy secondary electrons from escaping e.g. to the middle part B of the tube, B is given a potential of about 100 V negative with respect to C and P. In this way the primary current is measured by the meter M of Fig. 1. Care is taken that the incident beam does not penetrate through the phosphor layer. No anode voltages higher than 20 kV are used, so that the depth of penetration of the primary electrons, being $\approx 2\,\mu$, is even smaller than the size of the grains of most phosphors.[2] The layer of the phosphor has been chosen thick enough to reflect all the fluorescent radiation which is generated in the layer (for the absorption of the emitted radiation by the layer a correction can be applied.[1]

In most investigations the radiation emitted by the phosphors has been measured with a photocell or photomultiplier whose response changes rapidly with wavelength. In these cases it is necessary to determine accurately the spectral response of the cell used and the spectral energy distribution (S.E.D.) curves of the phosphors.

In our measurements the emitted radiation was determined with the aid of a thermopile having a constant power response as a function of wavelength. Therefore no corrections had to be applied and the knowledge of the S.E.D. curve is not necessary for radiant efficiency measurements. This method of measurement has been made possible at least in part by the marked improvement in the construction of infrared spectrophotometers by many firms, so that small, fast and sensitive thermopiles and thermocouples are available together with low-noise tuned A.C. amplifiers suitable for these detectors.

In most cases a water filter was placed in front of the

thermopile to absorb long wavelength infrared radiation. The amount of radiation from the filament of the gun falling on the thermopile was negligible.

The output of the phosphor was compared with the radiation of a tungsten ribbon lamp which was diffusely reflected by a magnesium oxide layer. For this comparison the plate P was not positioned as is shown in Fig. 1, but was perpendicular to the electron beam falling on it. The thermopile and the tungsten ribbon lamp were then placed in front of the quartz windows a and e respectively.

It can thus be seen that the absolute determination of the efficiency of phosphors with cathode-ray excitation depends on the knowledge of:

1) The absolute reflection coefficient of the MgO in the wavelength range considered.
2) The relative response of the thermopile as a function of wavelength in the wavelength region of the emission.
3) The absolute output of a standard lamp.
4) The absolute value of the primary voltage.
5) The absolute value of the primary current.

b) U.V. excitation. The measurement of efficiencies with short wavelength ultraviolet excitation will be described in more detail in a forthcoming paper by Bril and Hoekstra.[3] The phosphors were excited by a high-pressure mercury lamp with suitable filters to isolate the short wavelength U.V. in the region of 2500-2700 Å. In Fig. 2 the transmission curves of these filters are given, and Fig. 3 shows the spectral energy distribution of the exciting radiation. As in the case of C.R. excitation here too use is made of a plate with various samples of phosphors and MgO which are successively irradiated by moving the plate. The U.V. radiation reflected by the MgO, the sum of the radiation emitted by the phosphor and the U.V. radiation reflected by the phosphor, and in some cases the radiation emitted by the phosphor only, are again measured with the aid of a thermopile. From these data the radiant efficiency can be calculated as will be described in the next section.

The latter efficiency measurement depnds on the knowledge of:

1) the absolute reflection coefficient of MgO
2) the relative response of the thermopile in the wavelength region of excitation and emission.

A comparison of these points for U.V. excitation with those given above for C.R. excitation makes it evident that efficiency measurements with U.V. excitation can be done more accurately than those with C.R. excitation.

We have based the values for the reflection coefficient of MgO on careful measurements carried out by Middleton and Sanders.[4]

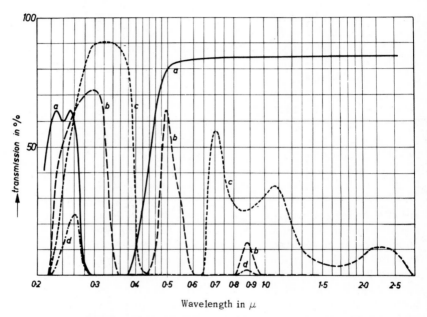

Wavelength in μ

Fig. 2. — Transmission curves of the filters used in front of the mercury discharge lamp.
————— a. chlorine, 1 atm. thickness 4 cm.
— — — — b. $NiSO_4$–$6H_2O$, 500 g/l, thickness 1 cm.
----------- c. Schott UG5 glass filter, thickness 0.2 cm.
.-.-.-.-.-.- d. Combination of the filters mentioned in a, b and c.

We checked the response of the fast Hilger and Watts FT1 thermopile as a function of λ in the ultraviolet and visible region. It proved to be constant within an error of 3 pct.

The luminous intensity of the standard lamp was measured with a flicker-photometer by the optical department of our laboratory. This measurement was in accordance with the intensity measurement of a 100 W inside frosted lamp calibrated by the National Bureau of Standards.

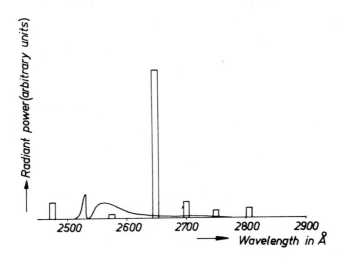

Fig. 3 — Spectral energy distribution of the exciting radiation. (High-pressure mercury discharge + filter combination d given in Fig. 2.) Spectral lines are shown as bands of 10 Å in width.

MEASUREMENTS

a) Cathode-ray Excitation. Efficiency measurements were carried out on the standard samples issued by the National Bureau of Standards (Washington). Samples 1020 to 1025 were selected from among commercial cathode-ray tube phosphors; samples 1026 to 1033 from among phosphors used in fluorescent lamps.[5] An absolute measurement was carried out on a willemite sample (Zn_2SiO_4-Mn) by the method mentioned in the previous section. The efficiency of the other phosphors was measured relative to this willemite sample. When measured with the aid of a thermopile having a constant response the efficiencies of the phosphors are directly proportional to the thermal emf's, when self absorption of the emitted radiation is not considered. The accuracy of each efficiency is about ± 15 pct of its value i.e. No. 1021 has an efficiency of 8(± 1) pct. The results of the measurements are given in Table I. The S.E.D. curves of the phosphors have been given in Fig. 4 and Fig. 6.

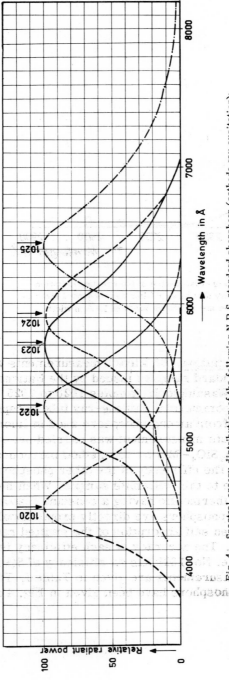

Fig. 4 – Spectral energy distribution of the following N.B.S. standard phosphors (cathode-ray excitation):

No. 1020 ZnS-Ag
No. 1022 ZnS-Cu
No. 1023 (ZnCd) S-Ag
No. 1024 (ZnCd) S-Ag
No. 1025 $Zn_3(PO_4)_2$-Mn.

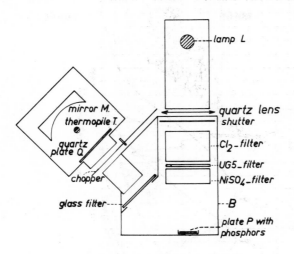

Fig. 5 — Schematic diagram of the apparatus for efficiency
measurements with U.V.-excitation.

Table I

Number	Sample	Radiant efficiency in pct	Luminous efficiency in lm/W
1020	ZnS-Ag	21	22
1021	$Zn_2 SiO_4$ - Mn	8	41
1028	$Zn_2 SiO_4$ - Mn	6	33
1022	ZnS-Cu	11	46
1023	(ZnCd) S-Ag	19	90
1024	(ZnCd) S-Ag	12	48
1025	$Zn_3(PO_4)_2$ - Mn	6	9
1026	$CaWO_4$ - Pb	3	5
1027	$MgWO_4$	2.5	7
1032	$BaSi_2 O_5$ - Pb	4	
1033	$Ca_3(PO_4)_2$ - Tl	0.2	

b) Ultraviolet Excitation. As mentioned in the introduction
the phosphors are excited with short wavelength U.V. radiation
in the region of 2500-2700Å (to obtain a high irradiation density), while the emitted and reflected radiation is detected with
the aid of a thermopile. A schematic drawing of the apparatus
is given in Fig. 5.

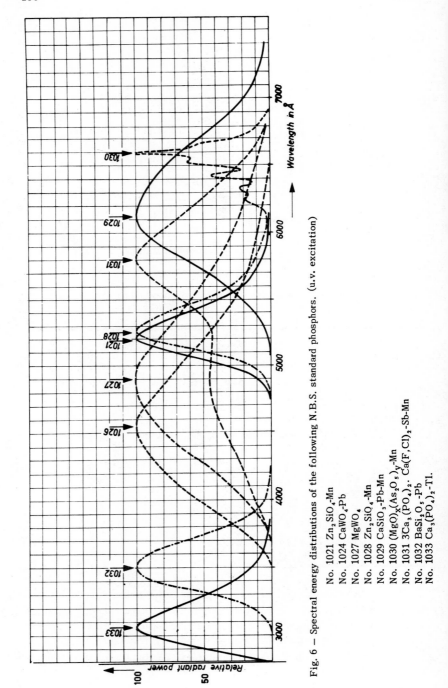

Fig. 6 – Spectral energy distributions of the following N.B.S. standard phosphors. (u.v. excitation)

No. 1021 Zn_2SiO_4-Mn
No. 1024 $CaWO_4$-Pb
No. 1027 $MgWO_4$
No. 1028 Zn_2SiO_4-Mn
No. 1029 $CaSiO_3$-Pb-Mn
No. 1030 $(MgO)_x(As_2O_5)_y$-Mn
No. 1031 $3Ca_3(PO_4)_2 \cdot Ca(F,Cl)_2$-Sb-Mn
No. 1032 $BaSi_2O_5$-Pb
No. 1033 $Ca_3(PO_4)_2$-Tl.

When the reflection coefficient r of the phosphor for the exciting radiation is known, the radiant efficiency can be calculated from two thermal emf's V_M and V_A, where V_M is due to the U.V. radiation reflected by the magnesium oxide and V_A is the thermal emf due to the fluorescence from the phosphor plus the U.V. radiation reflected by the phosphor. The reflection coefficient ρ of the MgO powder used by us was 0.91.

The exciting U.V. power is CV_M/ρ, C being a proportionality factor. The absorbed energy is thus $C(1-r)V_M/\rho$. The emitted fluorescence is $C(V_A - r V_M/\rho)$. Thus we find for the radiant efficiency

$$\eta = \frac{\rho \dfrac{V_A}{V_M} - r}{1 - r} \tag{3}$$

When, however, the reflection coefficient r of the phosphor is not known, one additional measurement is performed. A filter, absorbing the exciting radiation completely is placed in front of the thermopile so that only the fluorescence is measured. The resulting thermal emf is V_B. A glass filter may be used in the case of the short wavelength U.V. excitation. When the transmission of the filter for the fluorescent radiation is τ, we find

$$r = \frac{V_A - V_B/\tau}{V_M/\rho} = \rho \frac{V_A - V_B/\tau}{V_M} \tag{4}$$

and

$$\eta = \frac{\rho}{\tau(1 - r)} \frac{V_B}{V_M} \tag{5}$$

The first method (when r is known) is especially useful for U.V.-emitting phosphors where the fluorescence cannot easily be separated from the exciting radiation with a suitable filter.

An important check on the possible influence of stray radiation is found in the thermal emf due to MgO when the glass filter is placed in front of the thermopile. This should be zero because no reflected U.V. radiation is transmitted through the glass filter. In all our measurements this thermal emf was less than 1 pct of V_M.

The results for the standard phosphors of the N.B.S. are given in Table II.

Table II

Number	Sample	Reflection coeff. r in pct.	radiant efficiency η in pct.	quantum efficiency q in pct.	luminous efficiency L in lm/W
		Excitation wavelength region 250-270 mμ			
1026	$CaWO_4$-Pb	5	42	75	65
1027	$MgWO_4$	7	44	84	115
1028	Zn_2SiO_4-Mn	8	33	68	180
1021	Zn_2SiO_4-Mn	36	35	70	175
1029	$CaSiO_3$-Pb-Mn	17	29	68	80
1030	$(MgO)_x(As_2O_5)_y$-Mn	5	29	73	23
1031	$3Ca_3(PO_4)_2 \cdot$ $Ca(F,Cl)_2$-Sb-Mn	23	34	71	125
1032	$BaSi_2O_5$-Pb	35	55	75	
1033	$Ca_3(PO_4)_2$-Tl	15	49	56	

The spectral energy distributions of the fluorescence of the phosphors are shown in Fig. 6.

In low pressure mercury fluorescent lamps the phosphors are mainly excited by 2537 Å monochromatic radiation. For phosphors whose efficiency does not vary much with wavelength, the efficiency values of Table II are also approximately valid for this monochromatic excitation. For $CaWO_4$ (No. 1026), $MgWO_4$ (No. 1027) and the Zn_2SiO_4 with high concentration (No. 1028) the efficiency values are nearly unchanged, while for Mg arsenate-Mn (No. 1030) a 5 pct higher value is found in the latter case. For the other phosphors the reflection and excitation spectra are not sufficiently constant to give their values for 2537 Å excitation. Thus this is also the case for the halophosphate which is generally used in fluorescent lamps. Measurements by Johnson[7] of this type of phosphor show that the maximum efficiency might be reached at a much shorter excitation wavelength.

RELATIVE MEASUREMENTS

Because of all the factors to be considered it would take a lot of time if absolute measurements had to be carried out for every phosphor. Therefore in practice it is easier to perform relative measurements with help of a suitable standard phosphor. As was already mentioned in the previous section we generally used Zn_2SiO_4-Mn as a standard for C.R. excitation because of its good secondary emission characteristics, reasonably high efficiency, good temperature dependance, good stability. For ultraviolet excitation $MgWO_4$ is generally chosen as a standard because of its high efficiency, easy and reproducible manufacturing process (no activator) and because it has been used as a standard for a very long time. When the efficiency and reflection of $MgWO_4$ are η' and r' respectively, the efficiency of η_p of another phosphor is

$$\eta_p = \frac{1 - r'}{1 - r} \; \frac{V_B}{V_{B'}} \; \eta'$$

r can be determined in the normal way with the aid of Eq. 4.

EFFICIENCY MEASUREMENTS OF ULTRAVIOLET AND INFRARED EMITTING PHOSPHORS

The measurement of U.V. fluorescent phosphors both with C.R. and U.V. excitation has already been discussed. Standard sample No. 1032, $BaSi_2O_5$-Pb has a maximum emission at about 3500 Å, No. 1033, $Ca_3(PO_4)_2$-Tl at about 3000 Å (see Tables I and II).

For measurements of infrared fluorescent phosphors only a quartz window was used in front of the thermocouple (thus no water filter). In this way efficiencies of emission up to 5μ can be measured. The amount of radiation of the filament reflected to the thermopile was negligible. Examples of infrared emitting phosphors are ZnS-Ag-V, ZnS-Cu-V, CdSe-Cu-Ga and CdSe-Au-In[7] with maxima of emission between 1 and 2.5μ. The results of the measurements for C.R. excitation and excitation with 365 mμ, 436 mμ and 546 mμ radiation are given in Table III.

ACKNOWLEDGMENT

The author wishes to express his thanks to Mrs. W. van Meurs-Hoekstra and Mr. Th. J. Westerhof for the careful performance of the measurements.

Table III

Efficiencies of infrared emitting phosphors

Number	Sample	maxima of emission	cathode-ray excitation, radiant efficiency		excitation by		
					365mμ	436mμ	546mμ
70859/1	ZnS-5x10^{-5}Ag-V	2.0μ	2.5%	reflection	25%	43%	75%
				radiant eff.	9%	6%	1%
				quantum eff.	49%	27%	4%
110559/2	ZnS-2x10^{-4}Cu-V	2.0μ	0.5%	reflection	5%	14%	28%
				radiant eff.	1.5%	1.5%	1.5%
				quantum eff.	7%	8%	6%
170859/3	CdSe-2x10^{-4}Cu-Ga	1.2μ	0.7%	reflection	6%	6%	6%
				radiant eff.	1%	1.5%	2.5%
				quantum eff.	3%	4%	5%
110859/5	CdSe-2x10^{-4}Au-In	1.4μ	0.6%	reflection	7%	6%	6%
				radiant eff.	1.5%	1.5%	2%
				quantum eff.	5%	5%	6%

REFERENCES

[1] A. Bril and H. A. Klasens, Philips Res. Rep., 7, 401 (1952).
[2] W. Ehrenberg and J. Franks, Proc. Phys. Soc. B64, 1057 (1953).
[3] A. Bril and W. Hoekstra, Philips Res. Rep., 16, 356 (1961).
[4] W. E. K. Middleton and C. L. Sanders, J. Opt. Soc. Am., 41, 419 (1951).
[5] Nat. Bur. of Stand. Techn. News Bull., 42, 145 (1958).
[6] P. D. Johnson, J. Electrochem. Soc., 108, 159 (1961).
[7] M. Avinor and G. Meijer, Phys. Chem. Sol., 12, 211 (1960).
M. Avinor and G. Meijer, J. Chem. Phys., 32, 1456 (1960).
G. Meijer and M. Avinor, Philips Res. Rep., 15, 225 (1960).

CATHODO-, PHOTO-, AND D.C.-ELECTROLUMINESCENCE

IN ZINC SULFIDE LAYERS

D. A. Cusano

General Electric Research Laboratory
Schenectady, New York

ABSTRACT

A number of electro-optical effects can be observed by applying electrodes to vapor-reacted phosphor layers and subjecting them to high d.c. fields while irradiating with ultraviolet, visible light, x-rays, or cathode rays. These effects are manifestations of nonohmic contact and extrinsic semiconduction in zinc sulfide. Certain aspects of cathodoelectroluminescence (CEL) and photoelectroluminescence (PEL) are discussed in detail. For manganese-activated phosphors containing chlorine, the similarities between CEL and PEL support the interpretation that incident radiation controls electroluminescence by affecting changes in field distribution and conduction electron density. Arguments are extended to d.c. EL produced in the same phosphors by prior Cu_2S coating to show, in all these d.c. cases, that the highly localized manganese center is collision-excited in high fields by fast electrons. For PEL and d.c. EL of other phosphors, collision-ionization and recombination processes in high fields are necessary. Finally, the experimental results on variously doped films offer very little support for the suggestion that electroluminescence in conventionally prepared zinc sulfide powders, single crystals, or films occurs by minority carrier injection at p-n junctions.

INTRODUCTION

No single interpretation of zinc sulfide electroluminescence (*i.e.*, EL) seems yet to be unanimously accepted. In the opinion of some investigators, it is still not clear whether the phenomenon is dominated by high fields and majority carriers on the one hand or forward-biased p-n junctions and minority carriers on the other. That this situation exists after over a decade of concentrated experimental and interpretive work in many laboratories is testimony largely to the fact that electroluminescence is observed most easily, most often, and with highest efficiency in the experimental arrangement shown typically in Fig. 1. This arrangement includes a specially-prepared zinc sulfide powder suspended in a dielectric between planar electrodes. Neither the geometry of the structure nor the chemical and physical identity of the phosphor powder is sufficiently well-defined to make interpretation an easy task. Although the work on single crystals has contributed a great deal to the understanding of various EL features, the effort has been small in comparison to powder work. In spite of a simpler physical and electrical nature, there are frequently many uncertainties in impurity introduction, incorporation, and structural uniformity.

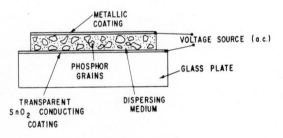

Fig. 1 — Conventional Granular EL Cell

The work to be described in this paper is concerned with the luminescence of vapor-reacted zinc sulfide phosphor films subjected to the combined influence of incident radiation and applied voltage,[1,2] (see Fig. 2),--primarily photoelectroluminescence (PEL)[3,4] and cathodoelectroluminescence (CEL),[5] $i. e.$, the photon and cathode ray control of electroluminescence respectively. Although the use of films in itself is a simplification for studying electroluminescence--providing the structural and chemical nature of the phosphors are reasonably well known—the primary significance of the work on PEL and CEL is that the ability to show d.c. EL is brought about not by special chemical processing but by the effect of incident radiation on otherwise homogeneous phosphor films, save for a requirement that they have non-ohmic cathode contacts.[1]

The existence of this radiation-controlled EL is dependent on the presence of high fields,[6] these fields extending well into the phosphor from the cathode side. Two somewhat related d.c. mechanisms can be differentiated on the basis of the kinds

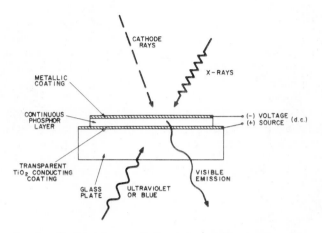

Fig. 2 — Continuous Layer Cell and Means of Irradiation

of impurity centers present.[1,5b] In manganese-activated phosphors, the experimental results indicate that fast electrons excite (but do not ionize) the manganese activator system by direct collision. Emission occurs by subsequent spontaneous de-excitation. In phosphorus, arsenic, or antimony activated phosphors, the data support a mechanism of activator center ionization by direct collision with fast electrons and recombination with light emission via capture of slow electrons. The doubly-activated nature of all these phosphors seems to be a considerable asset for strong PEL or CEL.

Similarities will be drawn between radiation-controlled EL and d.c. EL produced in identical films by chemical formation of cuprous sulfide (Cu_2S) surfaces prior to cathode electroding.[1] Basically, the same mechanism operates,—electrons are injected from the cathode into a high field zinc sulfide region, neither the continuous injection nor the establishment of the high field being dependent in d.c. EL on incident radiation. In contrast to recent suggestions[7,8] that zinc sulfide EL (both a.c. and d.c.) is actually forward-biased p-n junction luminescence, the accumulation of evidence in this film work favors the earlier interpretations[9-12] that high fields and fast carriers are necessary. In fact, it appears that anything resembling a *p-n* junction which may be considered present at external surfaces in films or both external and internal surfaces in powders, is actually operating with a reverse bias, *i.e.* majority, rather than minority, carrier injection and barrier field intensification, rather than barrier elimination, are dominating the EL behavior.[13-17]

The PEL and CEL phenomena* are basically d.c. in mechanism, their voltage "in-phase" nature easily demonstrated at low frequencies. The enchancement observations reported first by Destriau[18] in zinc-cadmium sulfides activated by sufficient manganese, and later by Gobrecht and Gumlich[19] for zinc sulfides activated likewise, will be seen to be basically a.c. in mechanism,—involving not radiation controlled d.c. EL, but instead an a.c. field control of the luminescence excited by ultraviolet, x-rays, or cathode rays. The terms already suggested,[20] electrophotoluminescence (EPL) or electrocathodoluminescence (ECL) would be applicable here. Where the mechanism is in doubt,[21-24] the in-phase or out-of-phase nature of the light emission is the best guide. Other observations of enhancement reported for electroluminescent phosphors which are simultaneously photoconducting[25,26] are most likely understood in the same way as are the intentionally prepared EL + PC intensifiers.[27,28]

Electronic Structure

The vapor reaction process for the formation of phosphor films and the chemical and structural nature of these deposits are described in Apprendix A. The characteristic and defining features of the films in the experimental arrangement of Fig. 2 are discussed in Appendix B. From analysis of these and other data,[1] the various films studied which exhibited enhancement can be grouped into two classes for discussion, the electronic structure of each represented schematically in Fig. 3. The theoretical bases for these models are found in donor-acceptor theory as extended to large band gap semiconductors.[29,30]

---

*The practical aspects of the work on PEL and CEL which pertain to light amplification, fluoroscopic intensification, cathode ray intensification and storage, etc. are described elsewhere [2,5] and will not be discussed in this paper.

The class I phosphors are characterized by an ionizeable type of impurity center and a highly localized center due to manganese,[31] namely the inner $3d$ level system. Partial substitution of cadmium for zinc is well known to reduce the band gap, shift the self-activated 4500Å emission to longer wavelengths, but leave the manganese emission relatively unaffected. In agreement with other authors,[32] excitation of the manganese by long wavelength ultraviolet is assumed to arise from a resonance transfer[33,34] of recombination energy at ionizeable type centers. When both a short wavelength recombination emission and the manganese emission are in evidence, it seems reasonable to suppose that the ionizeable centers nearest to the manganese sites are primarily responsible for the manganese excitation. (Resonance transfer is markedly distance dependent.)

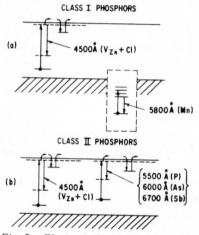

CLASS I PHOSPHORS

(a)   4500Å $(V_{Zn} + Cl)$

5800Å (Mn)

CLASS II PHOSPHORS

(b)   4500Å $\begin{Bmatrix} 5500\ \text{Å (P)} \\ 6000\ \text{Å (As)} \\ 6700\ \text{Å (Sb)} \end{Bmatrix}$
$(V_{Zn} + Cl)$

Fig. 3 — Electronic Structure of ZnS Phosphors and Electronic Transitions
(a) Class I phosphors — ZnS:Mn,Cl, Zns:Mn, Cu,Cl, and ZnS:Mn,X,Cl
(b) Class II phosphors — ZnS:X,Cl and, in some cases, ZnS:Cu,Cl
Note: $(V_{Zn} + Cl)$ denotes self-activation and X denotes P, As, or Sb

Since manganese dominates the properties of these class I phosphors, the same classification here can include phosphors of the ZnS:Mn, X, Cl type, where X = P, As, Sb, or Cu.

Class II phosphors are characterized by two different ionizeable impurity systems, for example, one center resulting from self-activation and the other attributed to one of the group

VB activator elements P, As, or Sb. It will be evident that the electron capture cross section of the longer wavelength centers is much smaller than that of the short wavelength centers.[1,5b] This is important for strong PEL. Phosphors with only one ionizeable type center, such as some ZnS:Ag,Cl preparations, show negligible effects. The common ZnS:Cu,Cl phosphors show some PEL only when both "blue" and "green" centers are present, as for example, at low copper concentrations. These can hence be included in the class II category. Preparations exhibiting only the strong green emission band do not PEL.[1]

Photoelectroluminescent and Cathodoelectroluminescent Properties

Of special significance is the absence of EL (d.c. or a.c.) in unirradiated samples, and similarly the absence of transient or steady state luminescent effects when voltage is applied or removed from irradiated samples, if these samples possess low resistive or truly ohmic contact at both electrodes. Such is the case even if average field strengths approach breakdown values (5×10^4 V/cm), or the current density is high. These results can be compared with those of Alfrey and Cooke who observed that low resistance contacts failed to produce EL in zinc sulfide single crystals, whereas barrier-like contacts did.[35]

If at least one electrode is rectifying or high-resistive, the situation is quite different. For d.c. operation with that electrode as cathode, the manganese or class I phosphors show a small, sometimes spotty, and generally unsteady EL yellow emission, the current through the cell similarly noisy. This EL output has a markedly super-linear voltage dependence. Upon illumination with near ultraviolet, visible, x-rays, or cathode rays—as long as essentially the entire phosphor thickness is exposed, though not necessarily uniformily with depth— the yellow light output builds up considerably beyond the photoluminescent or EL level (or the sum of these) and attains an equilibrium value dependent on the intensity of illumination and the applied voltage. The light emission, at all but very low irradiation intensity, is now very uniform and steady. The total current, which consists of a dark plus photoconductive, or dark plus cathodoconductive part, whichever the case may be, is also very steady.

The same comments can be made generally for class II

phosphors, the EL in the unirradiated case, however, being much weaker than it is in manganese samples.

The primary evidence that this d.c. enhancement involves a radiation control of electroluminescence rather than a voltage, electric field, or current control of photoluminescence has already been reported.[3,4] At low to moderate irradiation levels there is more than an order of magnitude greater intensity in PEL emission than there is in the ultraviolet or visible irradiating beam. The dependence of the steady state PEL output on incident 3650Å intensity is shown for several samples in Fig. 4.

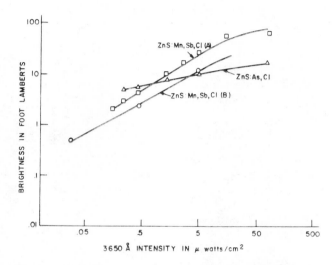

Fig. 4 — PEL Light Output Dependence on Incident 3650Å Intensity.

The energy gain for the lower ZnS:Mn, Sb,Cl sample shown runs from 30 at the lowest intensity to about 4 at the highest intensity. At much lower intensities, the emission is spotty, unsteady, and approaches the weak EL background already mentioned. At much higher intensities, the PEL emission starts showing saturation and can be eventually swamped by the increasing photoluminescence of the samples.

To the above evidence of PEL with gains greater than unity for both class I and class II phosphors can be added a similar situation for bombardment with cathode rays.[2] Fig. 5 illustrates the dependence of steady state CEL emission on current density for a Zns:Mn,As,Cl sample bombarded with 15 kilovolt electrons.

The negative electrode was a 0.1 micron thick evaporated aluminum film. For comparison, the emission from a good powder phosphor with 10% energy efficiency is also shown. The behavior appears to be in gross respects quite similar to that of PEL, see Fig. 4. Yet cathode ray absorption differs considerably from near ultraviolet absorption in that the local absorption density is much higher and band gap excitation occurs.

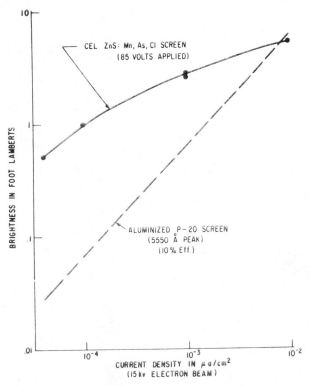

Fig. 5 — CEL Light Output Dependence on Incident Electron Beam Current Density

In the region of $5 \times 10^{-4} \mu a / \mathrm{cm}^2$, there is only twice as much energy in CEL emission than there is in the cathode ray beam. This gain may seem low by comparison to the ultraviolet case. Operationally, however, the performances of PEL and CEL are quite comparable when judged by the ratio of visible emission to the ionized activator centers created directly by radiation. Some 13 ev are required in the cathode ray case [36] where only

3.4 ev are required for 3650Å. Incidentally, the performance of x-ray PEL[1] should be comparable to that of CEL.

If cathodoluminescent (no applied voltage) emission is subtracted from CEL emission, (see Fig. 6), one can observe CEL saturation similar to that for PEL. There exists saturation at

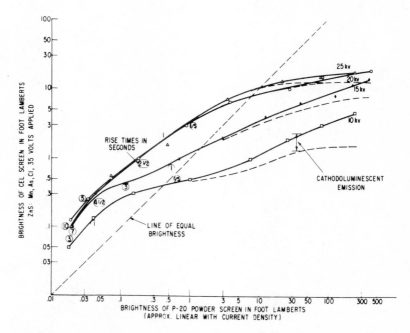

Fig. 6 — CEL Light Output versus P-20 Screen Light Output under the Same Bombardment Conditions. (The P-20 Light Output is Linearly Proportional to Beam Intensity in this Range. Cathodoluminescent Emission is Subtracted from CEL Light Emission to Obtain Dotted Line Portions.)

each bombarding voltage, the saturation value increasing with beam voltage but then approaching an optimum of its own when the range of the electrons is comparable to sample thickness.[2] For each bombarding voltage, briefly, there is a certain value of d.c. electroluminescence which can be "turned on," in any fraction or in full, by proper choice of incident electron intensity. Saturation values for PEL or CEL lie in the tens to hundreds of foot lamberts.

PEL response spectra are essentially the same as those of photoconductivity. The main difference between class I and class II phosphors (see Appendix B) is that the latter have

broader, double-band response. This means simply that both
of the ionizeable type centers are photoconductive. However,
the PEL and CEL emission spectra are considerably more informative regarding the radiation-controlled EL mechanisms
involved in the two phosphor types. Fig. 7 compares the PEL
and CEL emissions of several phosphors with their respective
cathodoluminescent spectra.

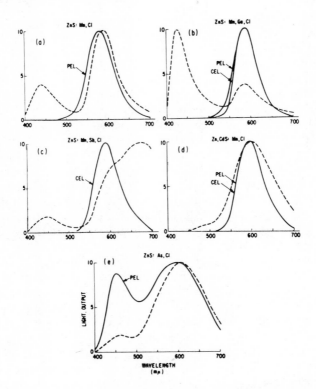

Fig. 7 — CEL and PEL Emission Spectra of Various Phosphor
Layers Compared to their Cathodoluminescent Emission Spectra
(dotted lines.)

The complete dominance of the manganese yellow band is
observed for manganese activated samples. This is so regardless of whether 1) a blue or green band is dominant without
applied voltage, 2) nickel is present as an impurity to give visible and infrared PEL response, 3) cadmium sulfide is present
in solid solution to about 25% or 4) simultaneous activation in
part by phosphorus, arsenic, or antimony is utilized. In addition,

the PEL and CEL spectral results are relatively insensitive as to whether 1) extrinsic radiation in the ultraviolet, visible, and near infrared is used, or 2) intrinsic radiation such as cathode rays or x-rays are employed. Furthermore, there is also an insensitivity of spectra to voltage polarity in samples prepared to PEL strongly on both polarities. See appendix B. In some cases there is also a shift of the yellow band with applied voltage.[6]

The phosphorus, arsenic, and antimony phosphors show contrastingly different spectral behavior. Although their two emission bands are evident in both PEL and cathodoluminescence, the blue band is much stronger in the PEL case. Incidentally, these class II phosphors usually require more specialized electroding since considerably higher currents than those for manganese are necessary to observe a given light output.

The transient behavior of luminescence upon application and removal of voltage during irradiation is about the same for all films, up to average fields of about 10^4 V/cm. This is even true for films with only one type of activator system.[1] Quenching occurs upon field application, the magnitude increasing with decreasing irradiation intensity. In some cases a smaller, but finite, quenching occurs during the steady state. Upon field removal, transient stimulation often occurs. Both transient effects get slower with decrease in irradiation intensity. Generally stimulation involves shorter times than quenching. Note: An important point with regard to the class II phosphors is the dominance of the long wavelength emission in the transient stimulation at voltage removal. This is just the opposite from what was recently described for the steady state spectra—there, the short wavelength emission dominated.

The steady state PEL or CEL light emission, along with the accompanying d.c. photoconductivity or cathodoconductivity, builds up gradually with time after voltage application from zero volts, that is, for average fields greater than about 5×10^3 V/cm (up to 10^5 V/cm or so). If, however, a bias field of about 10^4 V/cm is applied, given sufficient time for equilibrium to occur, the application of further voltage leads to transient stimulation connected with PEL emission itself.[1] Finally, although rise times are similar for class I and II phosphors, the presence of P,As, or Sb in either type of phosphors gives very long PEL or CEL decay upon removal of irradiation. This is apparently the result of very low electron capture crossection for ionized P, As, or Sb centers.

It is now informative to compare the maximum observed "electrical energy to visible light" conversion efficiency of samples exhibiting strong PEL with x-rays, PEL with near ultraviolet, and CEL with cathode rays,—all at roughly the same d.c. voltage. The small photoluminescence or cathodoluminescence part of the emissions can be ignored under these conditions. Fig. 8 illustrates a number of efficiency values for different

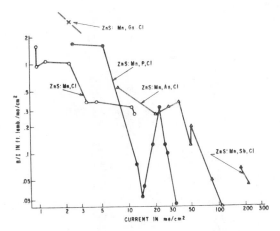

Fig. 8 — Brightness per Unit Current Density versus Current Density for Various PEL and CEL Samples Activated by Manganese. (40 to 80 volts applied.)

samples of manganese phosphors in terms of brightness per unit current density versus current density. The efficiency is lower for more highly photo- or cathodo-conducting samples. It is found that the maximum efficiency of a given sample is dependent only on the applied voltage and steady-state current density. Whether it is illuminated by ultraviolet, x-rays, cathode rays, or other volume-penetrating radiation is a secondary matter. The highest energy conversion efficiency found to-date is about 3×10^{-4} for manganese phosphors, but significantly much lower for class II phosphors (about 7×10^{-6} for ZnS:As,Cl).

D.C. Electroluminescence

It has been possible to make manganese-activated films electroluminesce strongly with d.c. voltage by treating the exposed zinc sulfide surface in a dilute aqueous solution of a

copper salt prior to final electroding. (Such treatment, with
similar behavior, has been studied extensively in powders.[12])
The net result of this surface treatment is the conversion of a
thin outer phosphor region into a copper sulfide phase.* Apart
from a short electrical "forming" which occurs usually at the
first voltage application, the sample exhibits very superlinear
d.c. brightness and current voltage characteristics—the brightness invariably steeper. A plot of brightness per unit current
density versus applied voltage is shown in Fig. 9.

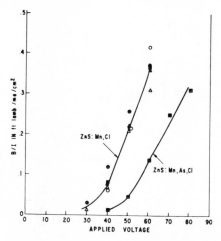

Fig. 9 — Brightness per Unit Current Density
versus Applied Voltage for Two Manganese
Activated Phosphors Made Electroluminescent
by Cu_2S Formation on the Cathode Side of the
Layer.

There are several very obvious similarities between this
d.c. EL and PEL (or CEL). The first is that no matter what the
spectral nature of the luminescence under cathode rays or ultraviolet, the EL emission is entirely in the narrow manganese
yellow band, just as was described for PEL and CEL. Secondly,
the highest d.c. EL energy efficiency found to-date is about
2×10^{-4}, very comparable to the maximum value for PEL or
(CEL). Over 100 foot lamberts have been observed with d.c.,
and up to 1100 foot lamberts "in-phase" at 6000 cycles. (At
liquid nitrogen temperature, the efficiencies decrease about a

*This phase has been examined in considerable detail. It was found to
be primarily Cu_2S (Also some Cu_9S_5), p-type, and with resistivity as
low as 0.2 ohm-cm in some cases.

factor of two.[1]) Thirdly, the EL occurs only when the metal
contacting the Cu_2S side is negative, that is, when the polarity
is such that electrons are being injected into the phosphor from
the Cu_2S or cathode contact. As in PEL or CEL, the nature of
the contact itself is quite important, for the EL emission can
be alternately eliminated or introduced by alternately washing
in potassium cyanide to remove Cu_2S or washing in aqueous
copper salt solution to redeposit it.

Although class II phosphors can be made only weakly d.c.
electroluminescent through the use of Cu_2S, the d.c. EL efficiency was measured to be about 3 or 5×10^{-6}, only somewhat
lower than that realized in PEL for the same materials. Significantly, values for d.c. EL or low frequency "in-phase" EL
of single crystals (activated by copper) are only somewhat
better, averaging approximately 10^{-5}.[37]

A.C. Behavior

Under a.c. operation, the PEL and CEL phenomena are still
"d.c.-like" in mechanism—the light emission which occurs at
low frequencies being essentially in-phase with the voltage and
simply falling off in intensity with frequency. The form of the
decrease is determined by the irradiating conditions, and the
ability of a.c. to impede polarization build-up or actually de-
polarize the phosphor. Fig. 10 shows a typical oscillogram of
the light output under 3650Å irradiation and 40 cycle a.c.
voltage for a Zn, CdS:Mn,Cl sample. The upper trace depicts
the voltage wave—the lower ones the "brightness" waves for
average fields of 1.5, 3, and 6×10^4 V/cm. (The sample is
asymmetric in d.c. operation, one polarity exhibiting considerably stronger PEL, transient quenching, and field-off stimulation.) The horizontal dotted line for each trace displays the
photoluminescent (zero field) light level. Only quenching and
stimulation of photoluminescence are evident for fields up to
about 10^4 V/cm. Quenching begins shortly after the voltage increases from zero and is maintained throughout the major part
of the first cycle. Stimulation begins to appear in the latter
half of this cycle, well before the voltage swings through zero
and then continues smoothly into the second half cycle. Notice,
however, the strong PEL peaks which appear superimposed on
the quenched regions for higher fields. They are essentially
in-phase with the voltage, shifted slightly by the lag in internal

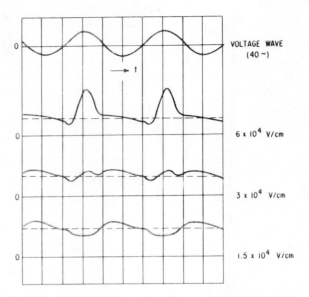

Fig. 10 — Waveforms for Applied Voltage and "Brightness" for
Several Values of the Average Field. (Sample is a Zn,CdS:Mn,
Cl one, the frequency is 40 cycles per second, and the irradiation is by 3650Å. The dotted horizontal lines display the zero
field photoluminescent light level.

field build-up. These peaks are much stronger if rectified a.c.
is employed, higher for full wave than for half wave. Similar
behavior occurs for symmetrical samples and for class II phosphors as well.

When band gap irradiation is employed, as in cathode ray
bombardment, there is either an absence, or only a small amount,
of the above manganese band quenching for class I phosphors.
However, the low field stimulation is still present and generally
has increased. Thus, a net out-of-phase luminescent enhancement
results which can be identified with that reported by authors[18,19]
who have worked with zinc and zinc-cadmium sulfide granular
phosphors having sufficient manganese content and which were
embedded in a good dielectric (See Fig. 1). This net enhancement results primarily from competition between recombination
centers which excite the internal manganese system via energy
transfer and other recombination centers present, whether the
latter lead to optical emission or radiationless transitions. Since
the enhanced emission occurs following the separation of elec-

trons from ionized centers, the phenomenon should be similar
to other time-separated excitation and emission phenomena
such as those of phosphorescence [31],[38] or thermoluminescence.[32],[38]
It is well known in the latter cases that, although both recombination and manganese emission are present during excitation, the
manganese emission strongly dominates in the delayed output.
Hence, either 1) the holes from various sites are thermally ex-
changed to the manganese transfer sites before most of the recombination occurs, or 2) some of the recombination sites
which are not effective for resonance transfer while the dense
electron cloud is building up and leaving the region of ionization,
do become effective when the conduction electrons are much
fewer in number and returning to this region. Incidentally, blue
or other recombination emission usually show a net quenching
in the case of band gap irradiation. However, Gobrecht and
Gumlich[19d] have recently observed blue enhancement and manganese yellow band suppression at low temperatures.

Discussion

It has been shown that PEL, CEL, and d.c. EL in a given
phosphor type involve the same mechanism for converting electrical energy into light. Furthermore, there must be a means
for localizing the applied voltage near the cathode and hence
substantially intensifying the electric field on the side from
which electrons enter the phosphor. In PEL and CEL, this localization of the applied voltage results from the steady-state
analogue of a Mott-Schottky exhaustion region.[39],[40],[41] This exhaustion and its build-up is evidenced by the requirement for
non-ohmic cathode contact, the suppression of luminescence
on field application, the transient stimulation of luminescence
upon field removal, the greater breakdown strength under irradiation, the intensity dependent build-up of both light emission
and d.c. photoconduction (or cathodoconduction), etc.[1] Such
modification of potential distribution and its associated increase
of conduction electrons via emission from the cathode can occur
for any zinc or zinc-cadmium sulfide phosphor containing ionizeable impurity centers. Whether or not a sample will show
PEL or CEL to any substantial degree depends on whether a
steady-state EL mechanism exists for utilizing the type of
luminescent centers that are present.

The mechanism which is consistent with all the data for
class I phosphors is that of direct collision-excitation of the

manganese[12,42,43] internal $3d$ levels by fast electrons in the high field region, with subsequent emission in the characteristic 5800Å manganese band. 1) The complete absence of other emissions in the steady state—providing manganese is not in extremely small concentration, 2) the field quenching of manganese photoluminescent emission and other recombination type emissions under long wavelength ultraviolet excitation, and 3) the insensitivity of d.c. maximum efficiency on phosphor composition together represent strong evidence against a resonant transfer process for this high-field EL mechanism, even though the latter process is dominant in the zero or low field cases. Although the data do not deny it unambiguously, the fact that no other recombination-type emissions are enhanced in the steady state for manganese phosphors —even though these emissions may dominate the cathodoluminescent spectra—indicates there is little likelihood of electron-hole pair formation by fast electron collision with valence electrons and hence little likelihood that their recombination energy is being used to excite the internal manganese system. In fact, there is qualitative evidence from this work that the introduction of manganese into zinc sulfide actually increases breakdown field strength and the general stability prior to breakdown, probably because fast electrons lose energy to the tightly bound, non-ionizeable manganese centers rather than, and prior to, losing this energy by collision with other activator centers or valence electrons. There is in films, likewise, very little evidence from thermoluminescent data (see Fig. B3) for a divalent electron trapping state due specifically to manganese[31] (except for very high manganese concentration) which state, after capturing an electron, would capture a free hole with then some sort of transfer of this recombination energy to the inner manganese $3d$ system. (Such a mechanism has been employed by Gobrecht and Gumlich[19] to account for the excitation of manganese in a.c. enhancement.) If one assumes this type of transfer process for PEL, it is difficult to see why nickel, which is presumed to be a divalent impurity and also produce such a trap, is effective only in extending PEL and photoconductive spectral response to the visible and infrared (see Fig. B2) rather than competing with manganese for electron-hole recombination energy. Adding nickel does not decrease the magnitude of 3650Å PEL.

The direct collision excitation of manganese by fast electrons quite naturally extends to the case of d.c. EL as produced by copper salt treatment. The function of the thin copper sulfide layer at the cathode is to provide a contact which is blocking to electrons entering from the cathode until a sufficient field is localized through substantial increase of applied voltage. It is believed, in agreement with other authors[13-17] working with single crystals and powders, that the p-type nature of this contact is an advantage for EL in that a built-in high field undoubtedly exists in the phosphor near the contact. (The present mechanism would apply as well to d.c. EL produced with cathode contacts of electrolyte solutions,[12] conducting organics,[43] fine copper powder,[15] etc.) Thus, any relationship of this EL to p-n junction phenomena is actually through the reverse bias characteristics, $i.e.$ the utilization and perhaps intensification of a reverse field in zinc sulfide and the field-sensitive tunnel-injection of majority carriers (electrons), not minority carriers, into the phosphor.* For PEL, CEL, or d.c. EL, the maximum energy efficiency of 3×10^{-4} would represent a production of about one quantum per 300 electrons traversing the layer under an applied 40 to 80 volts. There appears to be no need from the theoretical point of view, nor evidence from experiment, that carrier multiplication or electron avalanches, employed by various authors[9,10,12,44], are present. Similarly, there is no evidence, nor need, for direct field ionization of deep traps.

In the class II phosphors, where no field-stable activator center such as manganese is involved, the following d.c. EL mechanism seems to be operating. (Its efficiency, by comparison to the manganese case, however, is much lower. Much higher conduction electron density is involved in order to achieve a given brightness.) The long photoconductive decay and both the transient and steady state spectra showed that the electron capture cross sections of the ionized phosphorus, arsenic, or antimony activators are much smaller than that of the self-activated "blue" centers, especially in a high field. (The evidence from single crystal work[42] suggests a low capture cross section for ionized copper also.) In the steady state, more short wavelength centers are found in the ground state

---

*The present mechanism could be extended to Thornton's recent observations of d.c. EL at 2 volts in ZnS:Cu,Mn,Cl films.[7b] With about 0.5 volt in the form of a rectifying contact at the cathode (see Appendix B) sufficient potential drop may be available for direct excitations by those electrons from the cathode which surmount the cathode barrier. The internal manganese emission can be excited optically by ~ 2.5 ev quanta.[31,38]

while more long wavelength centers are found ionized.* The
latter centers are primarily responsible for the positive space
charge and the localized high field. Hence, the PEL light emission is due to recombination of slow electrons in the high field
region preferentially at blue centers, although some recombination is not excluded at long wavelength centers. The process of
ionization, consistent with this process of recombination, is
that of high field collision-ionization of blue centers by fast
electrons.[5b] Again, this does not deny some collision-ionization of long wavelength centers which may be occupied. For class
II, the high output-to-input PEL gains[4] can be understood on the
basis of the high electron-to-quantum (10^5 to 5×10^5) photoconductive gains. Only 1 electron out of 10^4 electrons passing
through the localized field region need be accelerated and col-
lision-ionize an activator center to enable this low-efficiency
d.c. EL to explain a PEL gain of 10 or so.

Conclusions

   Both the mechanisms given here for converting electrical
energy into light during strong PEL and CEL are consistent
with the present understanding of impurity systems and photo-
or cathodo-conduction processes in zinc sulfide. These EL
mechanisms could well have been deduced without a prior
knowledge that zinc sulfide is an important EL material. Given
non-ohmic (rectifying or high-resistance) cathode contacts to
allow field intensification and localization in irradiated zinc
sulfide, the d.c. emission in samples dominated by manganese
is an indication of the presence of fast electrons in high fields
while that in samples with ionizeable centers is an indication of
slow electron recombination processes as well as fast electrons
in high fields. Since the d.c. EL efficiency of class II phosphors
is the product of a high field recombination and a collision-ionization efficiency, whereas that of manganese activated phosphors
is solely a collision-excitation efficiency (emission is by spontaneous de-excitation), it is no surprise that manganese activated phosphors are considerably more efficient. Poor high field

---

   *Such a competition between two classes of "ground states" with con-
siderably different electron capture cross sections has already been
used by Rose[45] to account for the behavior of highly sensitive photoconductors. These P, As, or Sb and Cl doped phosphors are examples of
such photoconductors.

recombination is undoubtedly the cause of lower d.c. efficiency in phosphors with ionizeable type centers only.

There seems, finally, to be no report of a high d.c., or a high truly "in-phase", EL efficiency with powders, crystals, or films of zinc sulfide. Consequently, it is believed that the present high a.c. EL efficiency ($> 10^{-2}$), seen with zinc sulfide powdered phosphors (including manganese) dispersed in non-conducting dielectrics, is 1) the result of establishing conditions for recombination emission to occur <u>following</u> excitation, with relaxation of the field in the excitation region, whence one can then take advantage of the well known high recombination efficiency seen in photoluminescence and cathodoluminescence for most zinc sulfides (including manganese, via resonance transfer) and 2) the elimination of the high I^2R losses present with d.c., where carriers have to pass completely through both excited and unexcited regions of the phosphor. Until light emission can be unambiguously identified with minority carrier injection, it must be concluded that this process plays a minor role indeed in either a.c. or d.c. EL of present powders, crystals, or films of zinc sulfide. This, of course, does not preclude a strong process being found when suitable homo- or hetero-junctions are prepared. In addition, the remark is not to be extended to cadmium sulfide.

APPENDIX A

Phosphor Preparation, Constitution, and Structure

The vapor reaction method of growing zinc sulfide layers[46] can be regarded as an extension to large area coating of a well known method which is frequently used for growing single crystals.[47] The latter is that of bringing together those vapors or gases which contain the elemental constituents of a simple solid and allowing them to react together and produce that solid. Instead of adjusting conditions for growth to occur from a single seed, as is done when a single crystal is desired, the production of microcrystalline layers requires nucleation at many discrete sites of a substrate surface.

The method is a dynamic one and requires the continuous control of such variables as concentration of reactants, vapor pressure of each of these, freshness of the vapor mixture, (usually a competing reaction occurs in the vapor phase) etc.

The visual appearance, microcrystalline size, and degree of contact between crystallites are dependent in a complex way on such things as the nucleating surface, coating pressure and temperature. By trial and error it has been possible to arrive at optimum conditions for coating and to maintain these conditions sufficiently well for the reproduction of desirable samples,[1] even though a complete understanding of the kinetics is not yet available.

Many of the common sulfide impurities have been incorporated as the film grows by adding to the coating atmosphere the vapors of these impurity elements or their volatile salts. Fig. A1 schematically illustrates the coating arrangement. The

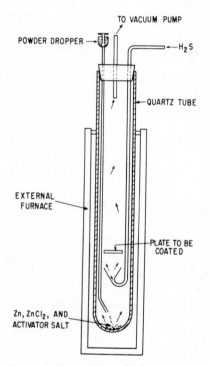

Fig. A1 — Vapor Reaction Coating Arrangement for ZnS Phosphor Layers

activators manganese, phosphorus, arsenic, antimony, and silver, and the coactivator chlorine, have been usually introduced in this manner. Alternate methods have been used for

small amounts of impurities which diffuse very readily into
zinc sulfide. Copper is the most important example. Either a
small amount of this activator is deposited on the surface to
be coated, from which it then diffuses into the layer as the sulfide grows, or the small amount is deposited on a completed
sulfide and diffused into the layer by subsequent heat treatment.
Further details on the preparation of specific films has been
published elsewhere.[1,46]

The thickness of the films studied has ranged from 1 to 50
microns, the majority from 5 to 15 microns. A film growth
rate of 1/2 to 1 microns per minutes has been most frequently
employed, with deposition temperature from 500-650°C and
hydrogen sulfide pressure about 500 microns of mercury. Film
adherence to pyrex and other glass, quartz, or ceramic bases
has been quite satisfactory. As the film grows in thickness, the
growth occurs non-uniformly on a microscopic scale and the
film develops a light-scattering or translucent character. This
scattering, a manifestation of the original nucleation, is primarily of surface origin and by subsequent polishing with conventional polishing compounds (such as fine particle alumina) can
be essentially eliminated. Polishing, however, has not been
used to any large extent for the present investigations, since
the crystallinity of the phosphor surfaces is adversely affected.

Chemical analyses of the phosphors have shown that manganese can be incorporated from less than 0.04% to 3% by
weight of zinc sulfide, phosphorus and arsenic from less than
0.001% to 0.02%, and chlorine from below 0.01% to 0.3%. Both
electron and x-ray diffraction examinations show that the films
have the hexagonal (or wurtzite) crystal structure. The "broken-
ring" patterns indicate a large crystallite size with considerable
preferred orientation of the c-axes perpendicular to the substrates.*

For the present electro-optical studies the zinc sulfide films
have been deposited on TiO_2-coated glass with very little ad-
verse effect on luminescent efficiency. (The process of applying TiO_2 on glass involves a vapor reaction between $TiCl_4$ and

---

*In more recent unpublished work the vapor reaction growth of zinc
sulfide on single crystals of cadmium sulfide has been seen to be both
single crystalline and epitaxial. The orientation of the overgrowth on
various single crystal faces is consistant with the tendency shown here
on amorphous substrates for the c-axes to be perpendicular to the substrate.

H_2O at about 250°C.) During the deposition of the zinc sulfide, providing zinc vapor is present as a reactant with the vapors of other salts and H_2S, the TiO_2 layer undergoes chemical reduction and its resistance is lowered considerably. Films about 0.3 microns thick change in resistance from more than 10^{10} ohms per square to 10^3 ohms per square and below. Both SnO_2 and In_2O_3 coated substrates have not been employed since they are adversely affected by the phosphor reactant vapors Zn, $ZnCl_2$, and H_2S at ~ 600°C. The top metallic coating shown in the experimental arrangement of Fig. 2 is put down via evaporation, spraying, or other common techniques.

APPENDIX B

Characteristic Features of Vapor-Reacted Phosphors and Cells

The following experimental data are helpful in understanding the nature of the impurity centers in these phosphor films, the simplicity of the arrangement of Fig. 2, and the single-crystalline nature of the phosphors for charge transport across the thin dimension.

The emission spectra under cathode ray excitation are shown for several films in Fig. B1. The narrow width of the manganese yellow band is indicative of de-excitation and emission from the internal $3d$ levels of manganese. The two-band nature of manganese and group V b activated phosphors is evident, although the two bands are not resolved for ZnS:P,Cl specimens as well as for the others. The relative peak heights in each phosphor are controlled by preparation temperature, pressure, and activator-coactivator ratio. The only difference of these spectra from those taken under 3650Å excitation is the relative intensity of the blue band. It is much lower for the latter at ordinary intensities because of the reduction in local excitation density. Spectra under 3650Å at liquid nitrogen temperature are quite similar to the spectra of Fig. B1.

The d.c. photoconductive response for several samples is shown in Fig. B2. An unresolved but obviously double-banded nature for phosphorus and arsenic activated samples is observed here, as it also is in the photoluminescent excitation spectra (not shown). ZnS:Mn, Cl and ZnS:Cu,Cl, by comparison, exhibit an appreciably more narrow and single band in both photocondutive response and photoluminescent excitation. The peak appears near 3700A.

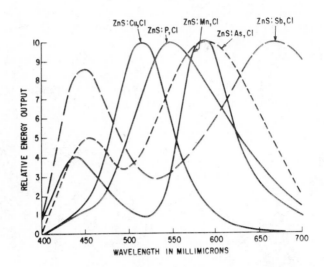

Fig. B1 — Cathodoluminescent Emission Spectra of ZnS Phosphor Layers (15kv and $1\mu a/cm^2$)

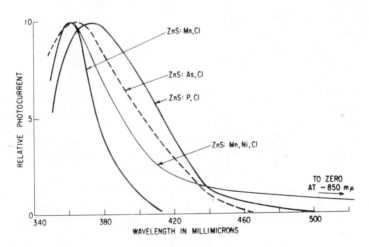

Fig. B2 — Photoconductive Response Spectra of ZnS Phosphor Layers

Typical thermoluminescent "glow" curves are shown in Fig. B3. The primary feature of these curves is simplicity, the same type of glow curves for high-temperature-fired granular phosphors being by comparison much more complex. An intense

peak occurs at roughly the same temperature for all films.
P. D. Johnson has attributed this peak to electron trapping
states in high concentration from 0.2 to 0.3 ev below the conduction band. A smaller secondary peak, indicating the presence of
deeper but fewer traps, shows up for srsenic and phosphorus
activated samples. Only for very high manganese doping is
there any evidence in the manganese cases for a subsidiary
peak near −30°C which could be attributed to electron trapping
states introduced specifically by manganese.[31]

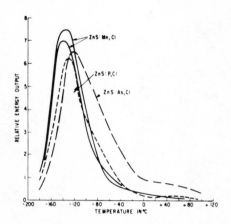

Fig. B3 − Thermoluminescent Spectra of
ZnS Phosphor Layers

Many phosphors exhibited high photoconductive gains in
terms of electrons per quantum for radiation in the long wavelength ultraviolet and blue regions of the spectrum and d.c.
fields greater than $5 \times 10^3 \mathrm{V/cm}$.[1] With irradiation intensity
around $0.1 \mu \mathrm{w/cm}^2$ and fields approaching $5 \times 10^4 \mathrm{V/cm}$, the
best gains were of the order of 10^6 for ZnS:As,Cl and 10^3 to
10^4 for ZnS:Mn,Cl respectively. (Cathodoconductive gains,
expressed as electrons per electron−hole pairs produced by the
incident cathode rays were similarly high,—around 10^4 for a
ZnS:Mn,As,Cl sample at 25 kilovolts and $10^{-4} \mu \mathrm{a/cm}^2$ bombardment.) These gains were observed despite the presence of rectifying or high resistance contacts resulting from conventional
electroding and easily detectable at low voltage and low illumination. Furthermore, with both high 3650Å intensity ($\sim 25 \mu \mathrm{w/}$
cm^2) and electric field ($\sim 5 \times 10^4 \mathrm{V/cm}$), the effect of electrode
contacts becomes negligible and high currents are transported

through the samples. Current densities from 10 to 100 ma/cm^2 can be observed in many cases. These currents seem to be space charge limited,[1] their magnitude reduced from that possible with trap-free zinc sulfide by the already mentioned shallow electron traps of high concentration.

The anomalous, high photovoltages reported by some experimenters for zinc sulfides [48,49] have not been observed in any of the zinc or zinc-cadmium sulfide films. This holds for single depositions up to 50 microns thick and for cadmium sulfide or other II-VI vapor-reacted samples. The maximum open-circuit photovoltage found for the arrangement shown in Fig. 2 was 0.8 V for zinc sulfides under 3650Å and 0.45 V for zinc-cadmium sulfides in the near ultraviolet or deep blue. These maximal values were obtained with gold and copper evaporated electrodes, the polarity developed being that of metal (+) and TiO_2 (−). Aluminum and indium electroding generally led to lower photovoltages. The photovoltaic results, in detail, varied with phosphor doping and the type of contact made at the TiO_2 interface during phosphor growth.

The n-type conductivity for most zinc and zinc-cadmium sulfides under irradiation has already been demonstrated.[50,51] Several differently activated films, all doped with chlorine, showed n-type behavior according to R. E. Halsted. No evidence for hole conduction has been found for irradiated samples.

In summary, the data given in both appendices effectively rule out—for transport through the films—the presence or importance of internal junctions or grain boundaries which would dominate the electro-optical behavior described in this paper. (It is understood, however, that for transport parallel to the plane of the films, intercrystalline barriers or junctions could play a role.) For the structures of Fig. 2, only the electrode contacts are really in evidence. Since a detailed knowledge of the nature of zinc sulfide contacts is not available, it will suffice to describe the contacts made by most metals to irradiated zinc sulfide or zinc-cadmium sulfide as "high-resistive" or "rectifying," metal to n-type semiconductor contacts. Generally, the TiO_2 - ZnS contact appears to be low-resistive for ZnS:Mn, Cl films but more rectifying or high-resistive for P, As, or Sb activated samples. The TiO_2 - ZnS contact can be intentionally made high-resistive or rectifying for any of the phosphors by pre-coating the TiO_2 with a thin, high-resistive film of SiO_2, undoped ZnS, or Al_2O_3 prior to vapor reaction of the phosphor. The thickness of this intermediate layer need be only 100Å or less. The difficulty, truly, lies in making ohmic contact to these several micron thick films, the wetting or soldering techniques which are frequently employed for electroding single crystals or making transistor contacts being relatively difficult to use here because of frequent "shorting" or "wetting-through."

Acknowledgments

The author 1s indebted to F. E. Williams for profitable theoretical discussion, interest, and encouragement, particularly in the early portions of this work. Many thanks are extended to F. J. Studer on various experimental aspects. Aknowledgement is also given to R. L. Sormberger and Miss G. P. Lloyd for the preparation of zinc sulfide layers and optical measurements thereon. Finally, we express our appreciation to H. B. Huntington, Rensselaer Polytechnic Institute, Troy, New York, for helpful discussions throughout the advanced study program concerning which a good deal of this work was performed.

BIBLIOGRAPHY

[1] D. A. Cusano, Doctoral Dissertation, Rensselaer Polytechnic Institute, Jan. 1959 (Listed in Dissertation Abstracts, XX, No. 2, 1959).
[2] D. A. Cusano, work on CEL, sponsored by U. S. Army Engineer Research and Development Laboratory, Fort Belvoir, on contract DA-44-009-ENG-4151, final report.
[3] a) D. A. Cusano, Phys. Rev. 98, 1169(A) and 546 (1955).
   b) F. E. Williams, Phys. Rev. 98, 547 (1955).
[4] D. A. Cusano, Phys. Rev. 106, 604 (1957).
[5] a) D. A. Cusano, IRE Trans. on Nucl. Sci. NS-3, 102 (1956).
   b) D. A. Cusano, Bound volumes of papers presented at "Image Intensifier Symposia" sponsored by U. S. Army Engineer Research and Development Laboratory, Fort Belvoir, Oct. 6, 7, 1958, and Oct. 24-26, 1961.
[6] D. A. Cusano and F. E. Williams, J. phys. et radium 17, 742 (1956).
[7] a) W. A. Thornton, Phys. Rev. 116, 893 (1959).
   b) W. A. Thornton, Phys. Rev. 122, 58 (1961).

[7] c) W. A. Thornton, J. Electrochem. Soc. 108, 636 (1961).

[8] D. W. G. Ballentyne, J. Electrochem. Soc. 107, 807 (1960).

[9] D. Curie, J. phys. et radium 13, 317 (1952); 14, 510 (1953).

[10] a) W. W. Piper and F. E. Williams, Phys. Rev. 81, 151 (1952).

b) W. W. Piper and F. E. Williams, British J. Appl. Phys. Suppl. 4 S39 (1955).

c) W. W. Piper and F. E. Williams, "Solid State Physics," 6, 95 (1958) Academic Press, New York and London.

[11] L. Burns, J. Electrochem. Soc. 100, 572 (1953).

[12] P. Zalm, Philips Res. Rept. 11, 353 (1956); 11, 417 (1956).

[13] J. F. Waymouth and F. Bitter, Phys. Rev. 95, 941 (1954).

[14] G. Diemer, Philips Res. Rept. 10, 194 (1955).

[15] W. Lehmann, J. Electrochem. Soc., 104, 45 (1957).

[16] S. Narita, J. Phys. Soc. (Japan) 15, 128 (1960).

[17] A. N. Georgobiani and M. V. Fok, Opt. i Spektr. 10, 188 (1961), Optics and Spectroscopy, 10, 95 (1961).

[18] a) G. Destriau, Meeting of the Electrochem. Soc., Chicago (May 1954).

b) M. Destriau, Compt. rend. 238, 2298 (1954).

c) G. Destriau, Compt. rend. 245, 1913 (1957).

[19] a) H. Gobrecht and H. E. Gumlich, J. Phys. et radium 17, 754 (1956).

b) H. Gobrecht, H. E. Gumlich, H. Nelkowski, and D. Langer, Z. Physik 149, 504 (1957).

c) H. E. Gumlich, Doctoral Dissertation, Berlin, D83 (1958).

d) H. Gobrecht, H. E. Gumlich, and J. zum Bruch, Z. Phys. 162, 169 (1961).

[20] F. E. Williams, Meeting of the Electrochem. Soc., Washington (May 1957).

[21] J. Mattler, J. Phys. et radium 17, 758 (1956).

[22] J. Woods, J. Electronics and Control 3, 531 (1957).

[23] P. M. Jaffe, J. Electrochem. Soc. 106, 667 (1959).

[24] a) G. Wendel, Z. Naturforsch. 15a, 1010 (1960).

b) H. Winkler, et. al., Z. Physik, 161, 330 (1961).

c) R. Henck and A. Coche, J. Phys. et radium 22, 59 and 98 (1961).

[25] a) W. A. Thornton, Bull. Am. Phys. 3, 273 (1958), Abstracts SP1 and VII.

b) H. F. Ivey, Paper at Internat. Conf. on Solid-State Physics, Brussels, June 2-7, 1958.

[26] K. Patek, Czechosl. J. Phys. 9, 161 (1959).

[27] B. Kazan and F. H. Nicoll, Proc. IRE 43, 1888 (1955).

[28] G. Diemer, H. A. Klasens, and J. G. van Santen, Philips Res. Rept. 10, 401 (1955).

[29] a) J. S. Prener and F. E. Williams, J. Electrochem. Soc. 103, 342 (1956).

b) J. S. Prener and F. E. Williams, J. Phys. et radium, 17, 667 (1956).

[30] R. Bowers and N. T. Melamed, Phys. Rev. 99, 1781 (1955).

[31] F. A. Kröger, "Luminescence of Solids," p. 234 (1948), Elsevier, (New York).

[32] a) V. L. Levshin and V. F. Tunitskaya, Opt. i Spektr. 8, 663 (1960), Optics and Spectroscopy, 8, 350 (1960).

b) V. L. Levshin and V. F. Tunitskaya, Opt. i Spektr. 9 223 (1960), Optics and Spectroscopy, 9, 118 (1960).

[33] T. Forster, Ann. Physik 2, 55 (1948).

[34] D. L. Dexter, J. Chem. Phys. 21, 836 (1953).

[35] G. F. Alfrey and I. Cooke, Proc. Phys. Soc., 70B, 1096 (1957).

[36] G. Gergely, Z. Phys. Chem. (Leipzig) 211, 274 (1959).

[37] D. R. Frankl, Phys. Rev. 100, 1105 (1955).

[38] R. H. Bube, Phys. Rev. 90, 70 (1953).

[39] M. Geller, Phys. Rev. 101, 1685 (1956).

[40] G. F. Alfrey and K. N. R. Taylor, J. Electronics and Control 4, 417 (1958); 4, 301 (1960).

[41] R. Williams, Paper at Internat. Conf. on Photoconductivity, Ithaca, N. Y., Aug. 21-24, 1961, Abstract C2.

[42] D. R. Frankl, Phys. Rev. 111, 1540 (1958).

[43] a) G. S. Kozina, V. N. Favorin, and I. D. Anisimova, Opt. i Spektr. 8, 218 (1960), Optics and Spectroscopy, 8, 112 (1960).

b) V. F. Favorin and G. S. Kozina, Opt. i Spektr. 10, 91 (1961), Optics and Spectroscopy, 10, 43 (1961).

[44] G. Neumark, Phys. Rev. 116, 1425 (1959).

[45] A. Rose, " Photoconductivity Conference," p. 23 (1954) John Wiley.

[46] a) F. J. Studer and D. A. Cusano, J. Opt. Soc. Amer. 45, 493 (1955).

b) D. A. Cusano and F. J. Studer, Enlarged Abstracts of the Electrochemical Society, Spring Meeting 63(A) May 1955.

c) D. A. Cusano and F. J. Studer, U. S. Patents 2,675,331; 2,685,530; 2,732,313.

[47] R. Frerichs, Phys. Rev. 72, 594 (1947).

[48] G. Cheroff and S. P. Keller, Phys. Rev. 111, 98 (1958).

[49] A. Lempicki, Phys. Rev. 113, 1204 (1959).

[50] E. E. Bukke, Opt. i Spektr. 3, 334 (1957).

[51] R. E. Halsted, Phys. Rev. 99, 1897 (1955).

ELECTROLUMINESCENCE OF CADMIUM SULFIDE SINGLE CRYSTALS

H. Komiya*, S. Ibuki** and H. Yamashita***

Research Laboratory, Mitsubishi Electric Mfg. Co., Ltd.
Amagasaki, Japan

ABSTRACT

Pure single crystals of cadmium sulfide to which low electric fields ($\sim 10^4$ volts·cm^{-1}) are applied emit green, orange, yellow, and red light. We believe that these emissions, except for the red, are due to recombinations of injected carriers, although intrinsic emissions cannot be observed. When a pulse voltage is applied to the sample, the rise of light emission lags a few hundred microseconds behind the pulse current and the decay time of the emission is tens of microseconds. The spectral distribution of the emission has two large peaks, *i.e.* 530mμ green and 600 mμ orange at room temperature. As the crystal temperature becomes lower, a 510mμ peak adds to the green emission and the intensity of the green emission increases, whereas that of the orange one decreases.

INTRODUCTION

Some electroluminescent phenomena in single crystals of cadmium sulfide were previously reported by G. Diemer[1] and R. W. Smith.[2] We will report our experimental results in this paper and attempt some interpretations. Pure non-conductive crystals in relatively low applied electric fields (10^4 volts.cm^{-1}) emit green, orange, yellow and red light. However, highly photosensitive crystals, for instance those doped with Cl, Ag or Cu, emit only red light at room temperature.

The samples used were in the form of flakes about 7mm in length, 2mm in width and 0.2mm in thickness; they are deemed pure crystals and show high resistivities above 10^7 Ω·cm under

* Now at Dept. of Physics, Purdue Univ., Lafayette, Ind.
** Now at Solid State Branch, Aeronautical Res. Lab., Wright-Patterson Air Force Base, Dayton, Ohio
*** Now at Engineering Dept. Associated Co. Div., Westinghouse Elect. International Co., East Pittsburgh, Pa.

illumination of 1000 lux from a tungsten filament lamp. Photo-conductivity, above the dark value, under illumination of 1000 lux varies from one to 10^4 depending on the sample, but the luminescent aspects and voltage-current characteristics seem to be independent of the photoconductivity of the sample. Photo-luminescence of the sample under 385mμ ultraviolet excitation from a conventional ultraviolet lamp cannot be observed except for red luminescence in some samples at room temperature.

We tried indium, silver paste and aquadag as electrodes. Since no difference was found among those as far as current-voltage characteristics and luminescent aspects of the sample were concerned, only indium was used as electrodes.

EXPERIMENTS

A. d.c. Current-Voltage Characteristics and Luminescent Aspects

We soldered In metal on both ends of the sample and used these In contacts as electrodes (about 2mm distance). We applied a d.c. voltage in darkness across the two electrodes through a large series resistance ($10^5 \sim 10^8 \Omega$), then measured the voltage across the electrodes and the current which flowed in the crystal. Fig. 1 shows typical current-voltage charac-teristics. First, despite the increase in applied voltage the cur-rent remains very small (less than 10^{-9} amperes). As the ap-plied voltage approaches 3.5 Kilovolts, the current becomes very noisy. At about 5 Kilovolts, the current suddenly begins to increase. Then the applied voltage is reduced to about 2 Kilo-volts. We call this phenomenon forming after the analogous one in silicon or germanium. Curve (1) in Fig. 1 shows the current-voltage characteristic after forming. A special feature of this curve is the negative characteristic of its latter half. Repeating this measurement, with successively lower series resistances the curve transfers from (1) to (4). Coming to point (g), the current increases abruptly, at which point the crystal is de-stroyed.

As the current is increased to point (a) on curve (1), orange, yellow and green spots appear near the edge of the anode. The number and intensity of these spots increases with increasing current. From point (b) on curve (2) spots the same as those on curve (1) appear. When the current gets to point (c), clear

green curtains appear which extend about 1mm from some of the
yellow or green spots toward the cathode. This curtain sways
gently at a swaying rate of about several cycles per second. In
addition, the green curtain has many stripes perpendicular to
the electric field which seem to flow into the end of the curtain.
The flow speed of these stripes is about 10cm/sec and rises

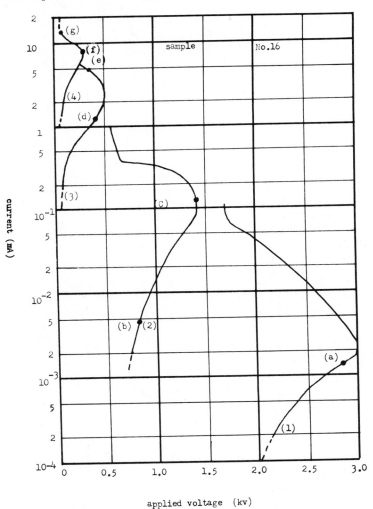

Fig. 1 — Typical Current-voltage Characteristics of a non-conductive Crystal. Series Resistance; (1) 50MΩ, (2) 10MΩ, (3) 350KΩ,
(4) 50KΩ.

with increase in current. Fig. 2 shows the above aspect of

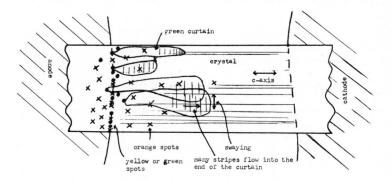

Fig. 2 — The appearance of the luminescence: orange, yellow, green spots, and green curtains.

luminescence. When curve (3) reaches point (d), the belt-like red emission appears in contact with the anode edge and the green curtain becomes belt-like, touching the cathode side of the red emission. A slight increase in the current moves this red-green belt to the cathode. Then yellow, green and orange spots in the zone of the anode side of the red-green belt vanish. At point (e) the red-green belt has arrived at the cathode and then has gone out. After this only a few red spots remain on the cathode edge and the crystal temperature rises locally about 400°C. However, we could not find any changes in the crystal by microscopic observation after the voltage was cut off. On curve (4) from point (f) red emissions appear locally and at point (g) breakdown of the crystal occurs, followed by scorching.

B. Pulse Characteristics

We applied a pulse voltage to the sample and observed the current and light emission wave forms. The crystal had been preformed only in one direction by d.c. voltage; then the pulse voltage was applied to the sample in the same direction as the preforming d.c. voltage. Fig. 3 shows the current wave forms

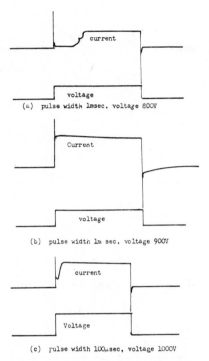

(a) pulse width 1msec. voltage 800V

(b) pulse width 1m sec. voltage 900V

(c) pulse width 100μsec, voltage 1000V

Fig. 3 — Current wave forms and pulse
voltage.

and corresponding pulse voltages. It seems in this figure that
the current is in phase and the capacitive current is small. This
differs from the case of zinc sulfide single crystals. At lower
voltage [(a) in Fig. 3] the current begins to flow after the voltage
to the crystals is applied. The current of (b) shows reversal at
voltage off. The delay of about 7 microseconds in the rise of the
current remains till the current value corresponding to point
(e) in Fig. 1. Fig. 4 shows the emission wave forms corresponding to the pulse current. The measurements were made by means
of a 1P22 or 931A photomultiplier without optical filters. The
results are scarcely different from the case of green or orange
only. It should be noticed in this figure that the rise of emission
is delayed several hundreds of microseconds with respect to
the current and the decay is delayed tens of microseconds.

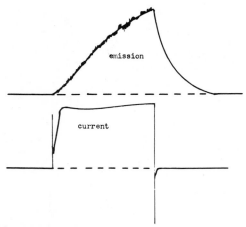

(a)   pulse width 100μsec,

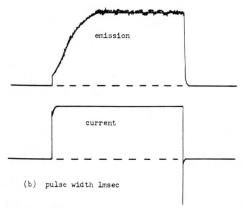

(b)   pulse width 1msec

Fig. 4 — Emission wave forms and pulse current without filters.

C. Potential Distribution

We measured d.c. electric potential distribution on the sur-face of the electrode side of the crystal by a null method with a Au probe when the crystal emits green, yellow or orange. Fig. 5 shows examples of the experimental results. The results de-pend on the samples and current values. However, the following

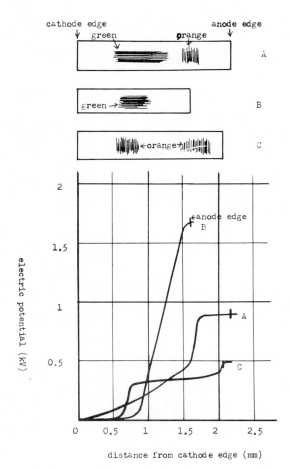

Fig. 5 — The electric potential distribution and appearance of emission.

has been observed.

1) There exists a steep change of potential at the anode edge for most cases, but for larger currents (above 300 microamperes) it does not always exist.

2) In the area of orange emission the electric potential has an abrupt drop, too.

3) At the cathode edge the electric potential is smooth but has no steep changes.

4) There certainly exist high field regions in the anode side of the green curtain and the green curtain extends about 1mm from the end of the high field region.

D. Capacitance of the Crystal

In order to study the nature of the above barriers we measured the capacitance of the crystal by the conventional bridge method. The dependence of capacitance on d.c. current and on measuring frequency is shown in Fig. 6 and 7, respectively. It seems from these figures that the measured capacitance is negative and its absolute value increases with increase in d.c. current or decrease in measuring frequency. The conductance of the crystal is independent of the measuring frequency (30cps ~10Kcps) and is nearly proportional to the d.c. current.

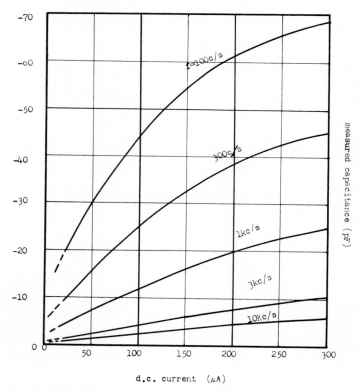

d.c. current (μA)

Fig. 6 – Capacitance-d.c. current characteristics the parameter is the measuring frequency.

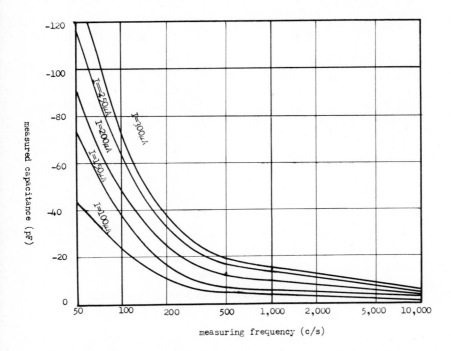

Fig. 7 — Capacitance-frequency characteristics the parameter is the d.c. current.

E. Spectral Distribution

The spectral distribution of emission was measured at room temperature. It is conjectured from the color of the crystal that the macroscopic temperature is below 50°C. Fig. 8 shows the spectral distribution of emission which has two main peaks at about 530 and 600mμ and three subpeaks at 550, 560, 575mμ. The three subpeaks vary in intensity and even slightly in their wavelengths, depending on the crystals. However, the two main peaks can be found in most crystals at about 530 and 600mμ. The resolution of the spectrometer is 10mμ and the detector used is a 1P28 or 931A photomultiplier. The value of the intensity in Fig. 8 has been corrected for the spectral sensitivity of the 1P28 or 931A. The fact that the peak at 530mμ is weak in the region of small current coincides with the fact in section A.

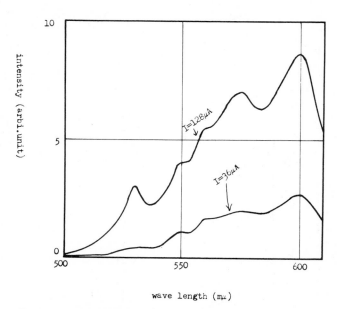

wave length (mμ)

Fig. 8 — Spectral distribution of emission at room temperature.

F. Dependency of Emission Intensity on d.c. Current

The total emission intensity and the green and orange intensities are almost proportional to the d.c. current below one
hundred microamperes. As the current further increases, the
emission intensity increases, but at a decreasing rate. Fig. 9
shows the emission intensity to d.c. current characteristics.
In this figure the intensity through the V-058 filter which cuts
off the emission under 580mμ is not proportional to the d.c.
current. But we assume that this is due to internal changes in
the crystal.

G. Temperature Dependence of Emission

We had intended to measure the temperature dependece of
the two main peaks. However, since we found another peak of
shorter wavelength than 530mμ at low temperature, we measured the temperature dependence of the two main peaks at about
530mμ and 600mμ and another peak at 507mμ at a temperature
of −145°C as is shown in Fig. 10. In this figure the broken curves

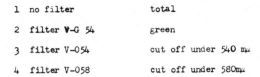

1	no filter	total
2	filter V-G 54	green
3	filter V-054	cut off under 540 mμ
4	filter V-058	cut off under 580mμ

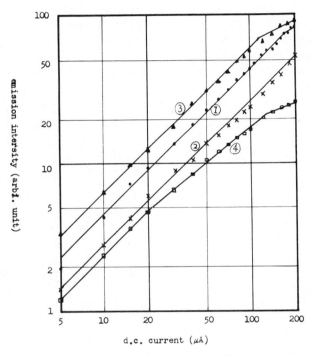

Fig. 9 — Emission intensity — d.c. current characteristics.

show rough intensity tendencies of wavelengths between the above three peaks. The wavelength of the first peak shifts to longer wavelength with increase in temperature. We believe that this is edge emission. The intensity of this peak increases at the beginning of the temperature range and has a maximum value at about −75°C; then it decreases. The positions of the two main peaks (at 530mμ and 600mμ) vary very little. The intensity of the 530mμ peak decreases with rise in temperature. On the other hand, the intensity of the 600mμ peak first increases then decreases during the rise in temperature from −145°C to 27°C.

DISCUSSION

The contact between the soldered In electrode and the non-conductive cadmium sulfide crystal is probably poor, so that a contact
barrier is made. The high electric field applied across the barrier
breaks this barrier locally and then the current suddenly increases. We call this phenomenon forming. After forming the
new barrier is made at the anode edge. We do not know as yet
what the new barrier is due to; however, the barrier is made
by applying voltage or by the flow of current, but not the formed
patch proposed by R. W. Smith.[2] If it were due to a formed

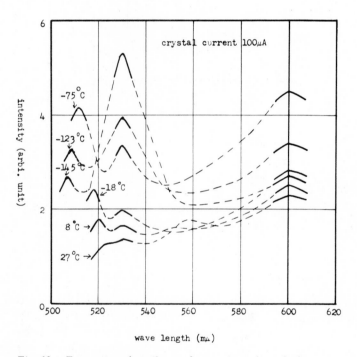

Fig. 10 — Temperature dependency of two main peaks and edge emission.

patch, there should exist a steep change of electric potential at
the original cathode edge when the electric field was reversed,
but we did not find such a steep change at the cathode edge. The
negative slope of the d.c. current-voltage characteristic probably arises from electron multiplication by electron avalanche

and from thermal destruction of the crystal in microscopic regions.

The pulse current (a) in Fig. 3 is unstable, namely, the rise point of the current moves back and forth at constant voltage. But the average point of rise shifts to the early one with increase of pulse voltage. This phenomenon occurs in a narrow range of voltage, $i.e.$ the range of several tens of volts. We surmise that it shows the start of an electron avalanche. A small number of samples shows a reverse current like (b) in Fig. 3 which is probably due to a decay of space charge. We suppose the delay of about $5\,\mu$ sec of (c) in Fig. 3 arises from the formation of space charge.

There exist higher fields ($\sim 5 \times 10^4$ volts/cm) in the orange emitting region. We believe that this is a concentration of microscopic high field ($10^5 \sim 10^6$ volts/cm) points at crystal defects, because the orange emitting region is made of groups of many orange spots. Free holes are perhaps generated preferencially by impact ionization in this high field region rather than by hole injection from the anode. The measurements of Fig. 6 and Fig. 7 contain considerable error ($20 \sim 30\%$); however, the fact is that the capacitance is negative. This must be investigated further.

The emissions are probably due to recombinations of electrons injected from the cathode or generated by avalanche-with holes generated by impact ionization. The two main peaks at $530m\mu$ and $600m\mu$ shift very little in position with variation of crystal temperature, so that these are due to the recombination of holes with electrons through recombination centers. The first peak varies its position with temperature. The energy corresponding to the wavelength of this peak nearly agrees with the width of the band gap at each temperature, so that this is probably edge emission. The intensity of the $530m\mu$ peak decreases with increase in temperature. This can be explained by assuming that the rate of carrier migration from shallow trapping states of recombination centers increases with rise in temperature. The change in intensity of the edge emission may be explained by the variation of the number of free holes, that is, the change in migration rate of holes from trapping states and in the rate of non-radiative recombination.

ACKNOWLEDGMENT

We would like to acknowledge various suggestions of Dr. J. Yamaguchi to our work, and the assitance of K. Nojima in our experiments.

REFERENCES

[1]G. Diemer; Philips Res. Rep. 9, 109 (1954).
[2]R. W. Smith; Phys. Rev. 93, 347 (1954).
            Phys. Rev. 105, 900 (1957).

ELECTROLUMINESCENCE OF TWO-BAND ZINC SULFIDE
VOLTAGE DEPENDENCE OF THE SPECTRAL DISTRIBUTION

J. Mattler and T. Ceva

Laboratoire de Luminescence, Faculté des Sciences de Paris

ABSTRACT

In the case of ZnS:Cu samples with blue and green emission, the electroluminescence spectrum is not modified appreciably by varying the voltage applied to the electroluminescent cells. On the contrary, the two bands behave differently with field variation for ZnS:Cu + Mn samples which emit blue and yellow, or which emit green and yellow bands.

We have shown that this is the case for a wide range of applied voltage by isolating the different spectral bands and studying their light output L as a function of V. Log L is proportional to $1/\sqrt{V}$, and parallel lines are obtained for the green and blue emissions of ZnS:Cu,Cl, while different slopes are observed for the blue and yellow or green and yellow bands of ZnS(Cu,Mn)

These results support the hypothesis formulated by G. and D. Curie to interpret the existence of two bands in ZnS:Cu, according to which the same fundamental Cu level plays a role in both the blue and green emissions.

For the electroluminescent sulfides with single band emission, it is generally assumed that the "threshold" for emission for ZnS:Mn is higher than that for ZnS:Cu, and the yellow emission, corresponding to the Mn, increases more rapidly with voltage. On the contrary, in ZnS:Cu + Mn with two bands, the yellow emission increases more slowly than the blue or green.

Nevertheless, for one of our ZnS:Cu + Mn samples a sudden rise in the angular coefficient of the graph log L versus $1/\sqrt{V}$ appears at high voltages. In other words, for this sample the yellow emission at high voltages behaves as usual and corresponds to the direct excitation of the Mn centers. On the other hand, the behavior of manganese at low voltages corresponds to the sensitization effect of Mn by Cu: copper is excited, then there is a transfer of excitation energy to the Mn centers. The study of brightness waves seems to support this point of view.

INTRODUCTION

Zinc sulfide activated with copper gives, for definite conditions of preparation, electroluminescent (EL) products which show distinct blue and green emissions. In addition, by incorporating copper and manganese activators in the same base lattice, it is also possible to obtain EL samples with two emission bands: either blue and yellow or green and yellow.

We have performed a general study of the EL of such sulfides having two-band emission; *i.e.*, of the spectral changes produced by modifying the frequency and the intensity of the exciting field. We also studied the action of temperature, the brightness waves for different spectral bands, etc. In the present paper we deal with the problem of the spectral changes resulting from variation of the voltage applied to the EL cells and with the evolution of the different bands with voltage.

Various authors have given some evidence[1,2,3,4] that no appreciable changes in the spectra of single-band EL sulfides occur when the intensity of the electric field is varied. (For one ZnS:Cu with green EL, we have observed a shift of 25Å in the emission peak towards higher wavelength when the voltage is changed from 65 volts to 650 volts).

The cells used in our experiments are of the following type: conducting mica sheet, sulfide embedded in araldite and deposited on the non-conducting face, silver layer as the second electrode.[5] All the spectral curves reported here have been corrected, taking into account the sensitivity of the detector for the different radiations and the dispersion of the spectrophotometer, in order to give the distribution in energy of the emitted radiation. For all the measurements an a.c. voltage of 50 cps was used.

In some of the spectral distribution curves the ordinates were multiplied by a constant in order to plot the different curves on the same graph.

EXPERIMENTAL RESULTS

Fig. 1 shows the spectral emission at three different voltages of a zinc sulfide activated with copper, with blue and green EL (sulfide No. 1). It can be seen that the spectrum remains unmodified although the voltage varies from 190 volts to 825 volts;

the ratio of the relative intensities of the blue (4600Å) and green (5200Å) peaks remains practically constant (1.25; 1.24; 1.23). We came to the same conclusion for another sample (No. 2) of copper-activated zinc sulfide of the same type with two bands located in the vicinity of 4450 and 5200Å.*

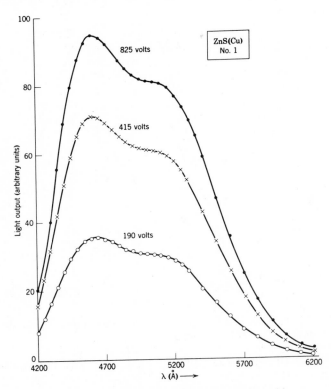

Fig. 1 – Spectral distribution of the radiation emitted by an electroluminescent ZnS(Cu) at different voltages.

On the contrary, in the case of zinc sulfides activated by copper and manganese (if the manganese concentration is not too high) variations in the applied voltage involve significant spectral changes as can be seen in Figs. 2 and 3. Fig. 2 gives the emission spectra of a ZnS (Cu,Mn) sample with green and yellow emission (sulfide No. 3) at 340 and 545 volts, while Fig.3

*This sample was prepared in our laboratory by Mlle. Lesage, while all the other phosphors studied were kindly furnished to us by the Research Laboratory of the Lamp Div., Westinghouse Elec. Corp. at Bloomfield, N.J.

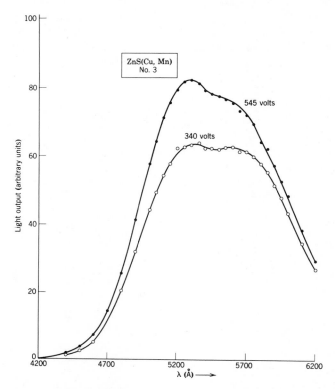

Fig. 2 — Spectral distribution for an electroluminescent ZnS(Cu,Mn) sample at two different voltages.

represents the spectral curves of a ZnS (Cu, Mn) phosphor with blue and yellow emission (sulfide No. 4) for 545, 700 and 820 volts.

In order to see if these conclusions are valid for a wide range of applied voltages, we isolated the different spectral bands by means of interference filters and studied the light output L in each band as a function of V. The emission is proportional to exp $(-b/E)$ with $E \sim V^{1/2}$; upon plotting log L as a function of $V^{-1/2}$, straight lines are obtained for the blue, green and yellow emissions for all the phosphors investigated.

In addition, it is found that the respective lines representing the blue and green emissions of ZnS(Cu) are almost parallel (Fig. 4) while this is not the case (Fig. 5) for the blue and yellow or green and yellow emissions of ZnS(Cu,Mn). Thus we have evidence that the intensities of the two bands due to the

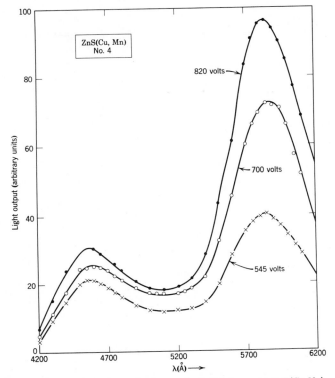

Fig. 3 — Spectral distribution for an electroluminescent ZnS(Cu,Mn) sample at different voltages.

copper activator change in the same way with voltage, while the contrary happens for the bands emitted by different activators such as Cu and Mn. The energy necessary to ionize the "blue centers" and the "green centers" in ZnS(Cu) is therefore the same.

INTERPRETATION OF THE RESULTS:

These results are not easily explained on the basis of the usual energy level scheme for ZnS(Cu) in which blue and green emission is assumed to occur at different centers. However they can be easily interpreted by the model recently proposed by G. Curie and D. Curie[6,7]. These authors assume that the same fundamental Cu-level (ground state) occurs in the blue emission and in the green emission. This level may lie at some

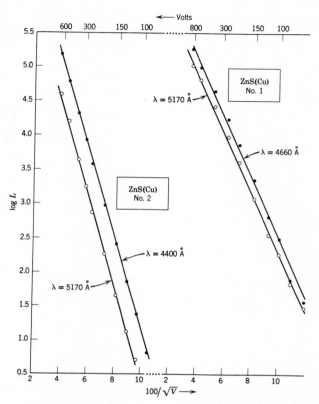

Fig. 4 — Light output versus voltage of the blue and green emission bands for two ZnS(Cu) samples.

tenths of eV ($\simeq 0.9$ eV) above the valence band (Fig. 6). The blue emission may be due to a direct recombination of an electron situated at the bottom of the conduction band (or at a level just below) with a hole in the fundamental state. The green emission, on the contrary, may be ascribed to a transition leading to the same fundamental copper level, starting from a deeper excited level; for example, this excited level may be an associated donor level in the sense of the associated donor-acceptor model of Prener and Williams; it may be introduced by a co-activator such as Cl or perhaps by O.

The emission law of electroluminescence $L \sim \exp(-b/E)$ can be put in a more explicit form $L \sim \exp(-W/ex_m E)$,

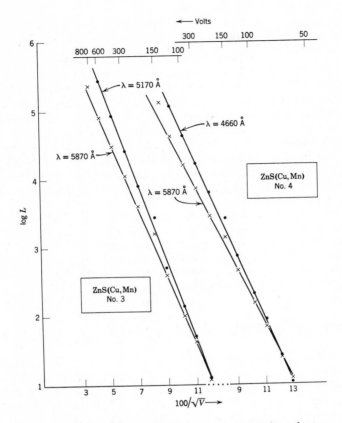

Fig. 5 — Light output in the different bands versus voltage for two ZnS(Cu,Mn) samples with blue and yellow or green and yellow emission.

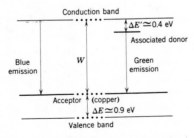

Fig. 6 — Light center model proposed by G. and D. Curie for ZnS(Cu), with blue and green emission.

e,   charge of the electron,

x_m, mean free path of the accelerated electrons,

W,   energy necessary to excite or ionize the luminescence center.

If we assume that W is equal to the emitted light quantum $h\nu$ and if the "blue centers" and "green centers" really exist with distinct fundamental levels, then the EL intensity of the blue band should rise more rapidly with the voltage than the intensity of the green band. This prediction does not agree with the experimental results. But if we identify W with the distance between the fundamental level of the center and the bottom of the conduction band, then the blue and green emissions will vary in the same way with the applied voltage, in agreement with the experiments.

Thus electroluminescence studies provide support for the center model proposed by G. and D. Curie on the basis of other arguments derived especially from photoluminescence. However we must add that this argument implies the validity of the mechanism of impact ionization of centers by the accelerated electrons in electroluminescence.

SENSITIZATION EFFECT OF MANGANESE BY COPPER

For ZnS(Cu, Mn) phosphors with green and yellow emission (sulfide No. 3), it is apparent from Figs. 2 and 5 that the intensity of the yellow band rises more slowly with the voltage than that of the green band. In the case of sulfide No. 4, there is an apparent contradiction between the results of Figs. 3 and 5. The spectral curves indicate that the yellow emission rises more rapidly with V than the blue band; in Fig. 5, on the contrary, the slope of the line log L versus $V^{-1/2}$ is smaller for the yellow than for the blue band. We have therefore studied the behavior of this phosphor in more detail.

The spectral curves of Fig. 3 were measured at relatively high voltage as a consequence of the weak transmission of the spectrophotometer used while the measurements with the filters were made at low voltages. If the same range of voltages is used, both methods of measurement give the same results. At low voltages the yellow emission rises more slowly than the blue (we have checked this by tracing the spectra at 205 and 375 volts); for higher voltages we observed just the contrary. Fig. 7 shows that the slope of the straight lines suffers a sudden change at a voltage of about 550 volts for the cell which was studied here. No similar effect has been observed for ZnS(Cu, Mn) with green and yellow emission.

We have attempted to explain this special behavior of the yellow emission.

It is generally assumed for single-band EL sulfides that the emission "threshold" of ZnS(Mn) is notably higher than the "threshold" of the green (or blue) emission of ZnS(Cu), but above it the yellow emission increases faster than the green or the blue.[5] With our ZnS(Cu, Mn) sample No. 4, yellow emission

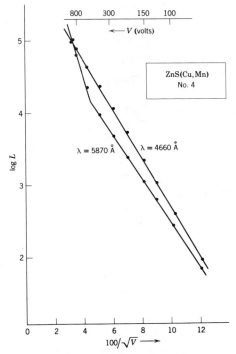

Fig. 7 — Light output versus voltage for the blue and yellow emission of a ZnS(Cu, Mn) sample.

at high voltages can therefore be considered as normal and due to the direct excitation of Mn centers, as explained in the scheme of Fig. 8. The Mn fundamental level is located in the valence band, therefore $W_{Mn} > W_{Cu}$ in spite of the fact that $h\nu_{Mn} < h\nu_{Cu}$ and this would explain the more rapid rise of normal yellow emission with voltage than the green (or the blue) emission.

The different behavior of the yellow band at low voltages would correspond to the sensitization effect of Mn by Cu: there

would be normal excitation of copper followed by a transfer of
excitation energy to the manganese centers.[8] This can occur

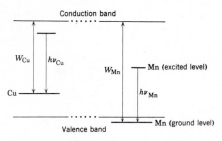

Fig. 8 – Light center model suggested to explain the yellow
emission compared with the blue or the green.

as explained in the scheme of Fig. 9. The copper ions are excited in the usual way; thermal activation can occur and excite
an electron from the filled band up to the Cu center, creating
a hole in the valence band (Process I). The hole then diffuses

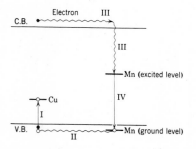

Fig. 9 – Emission process involving excitation energy transfer by hole motion from Cu
to Mn in electroluminescent ZnS(Cu,Mn). A resonance transfer process can occur too.

through the lattice and is captured by a Mn center (Process II),
followed by non-radiative capture of an electron by an excited
Mn level (III). Finally there occurs the light emitting transition
to the fundamental state of the Mn center (IV).

We attempted to see if the study of the brightness waves can
give some more information in order to support this interpretation of the behavior of the yellow emission. The brightness
waves of ZnS(Mn) are easily identified because they are very
regular and characterized by the absence of secondary peaks.[9,10]
For both samples of ZnS(Cu,Mn) we isolated the different emission bands by filters and obtained the corresponding brightness

waves. The applied voltages were 200 and 300 volts, respectively.

It is seen clearly on the oscillograms of Fig. 10 that at low
voltages the brightness wave for the yellow emission of sample
No. 3 is not characteristic of the activator Mn, but has the
form corresponding to the Cu activator (a well pronounced
secondary peak on the decreasing branch whose phase is slightly in advance of that of the secondary maximum given by copper). For the sulfide showing blue and yellow EL emission
(No. 4), the waves corresponding to both emission bands have

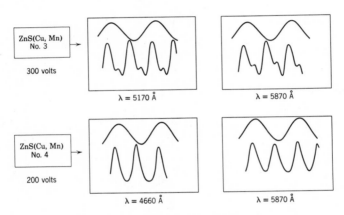

Fig. 10 — Brightness waves of the different emission bands for two
ZnS(Cu,Mn) samples.

the regular form given by ZnS(Mn) and also by ZnS(Cu) with
blue emission. It is therefore necessary to complete this study
in the future by investigating the effect of voltage and temperature on the brightness waves.

REFERENCES

[1] G. Destriau and P. Loudette, J. Phys. Radium, serie 8, Vol.
    1, p. 51, 1940.
[2] G. Destriau and H. F. Ivey, Proc. I.R.E., 43, No. 12, p. 1911,
    1955.
[3] W. Lehmann, J. Electrochem. Soc., 103, p. 667, 1956.
[4] P. Zalm, Brit. J. Appl. Phys. 54, p. 48, 1955.

[5] J. Mattler, J. Phys. Radium, 17, p. 42, 1956.
[6] G. Curie and D. Curie, J. Phys. Radium, 21, p. 127, 1960.
[7] D. Curie, Proceedings of the Intern. Conf. on Color Centers and Crystal Luminescence, Turin, Sept. 8-12, 1960.
[8] H. C. Froehlich, J. Opt. Soc. Am., 43, p. 320, 1953.
[9] J. Mattler, J. Phys. Radium, 17, p. 725, 1956.
[10] R. E. Halsted and L. R. Koller, Phys. Rev., 93, p. 349, 1954.

STORED ELECTROLUMINESCENCE

H. Kallmann, B. Kramer* and E. Weissman
Physics Department, New York University

ABSTRACT

It is shown that the electroluminescent capability of a sample can be stored for minutes after the preceding applied voltage pulse by choosing a suitable matrix, such as T.C.P. This storage decays only slowly and disappears after one hour. It can be destroyed by illuminating the sample during the voltage free intervals. This storage capability is due to an internal polarization, which persists for minutes after the applied voltage is removed and which is almost of the same order as the field of the applied voltage. Electron injecting sources, which have injected electrons under the influence of the original field, do not inject any more, even when exposed to a similar field but of opposite direction.

INTRODUCTION

The investigation reported in this paper originated in the well known observation[1] that the light flashes observed in ac electroluminescence in microcrystalline ZnS:Cu do not in general change their magnitudes appreciably when the ac voltage is biased in one or the other direction; that is, when a dc voltage is superimposed on the ac field. If the former equals half the peak to peak voltage of the latter, the interior of the sample sees twice the field strength with bias than without bias, if no internal polarization occurs. Since the described electroluminescence flashes (which are much shorter than the period of the applied field) depend essentially upon the local field strength, one concludes that they are brought about not so much by an

---

*Also at Physics Department, Hunter College, New York, New York,

exhaustion of an electron injecting source but by the polarization of such a source by an internal counter field.

In a single grain the applied field may produce injection of electrons at localized spots, and may further increase the number of charges by multiple impact excitation. Under the influence of the applied field, a separation of charges will occur, and charge layers will develop near the boundaries of the grain, if it is surrounded by a matrix into which electrons can enter only with difficulty; i.e., a barrier exists at the boundary.

These charge layers will screen the inside of the grain against the applied field, and, if enough charge is available, the field inside the grain is almost zero, and practically all the field lies across the boundary. When the external field is then removed, the inside of the grain suddenly sees an electric field of almost the same strength as the original applied field but of opposite direction.

If, immediately after the removal of the original field, a field of opposite direction is applied, then indeed the interior of the grain sees double the external field strength for an instant. Thus, internal polarization can produce almost double the field strength applied by an unbiased external field or square wave. The situation is similar for ac fields. If a grain has an electron injecting source on only one of its sides and a field is applied which could drive electrons into the interior, then, charges are produced and separated. Upon reversal of this field the interior of the grain may still see almost double the field strength, but the electron injection source may not see this full field strength since it is located close to one of the boundaries and, because of this, not as much free charge may be produced as with the original direction of the field. As a consequence of this, such a grain would emit smaller light flashes under an unbiased square wave voltage than with a biased one. Since this is not usually observed, one may conclude that these electron injecting sources are more or less distributed along the whole length of the grain.

One could, of course, also consider the situation in which the sample as a whole is polarized, so that the charge layers are close to the electrode boundaries. Then, the entire interior of the sample would see the polarization field, and upon reversal of the external voltage would see double the field strength, and consequently all the electron injecting sources would be subjected to such a field strength and would produce charges and

light accordingly. Such a polarization of the whole interior of
the sample probably does not occur in electroluminescence
experiments, since full electroluminescence flashes build up
in a fraction of a second, while, according to measurements of
internal polarization,[2] a complete polarization in such a sample takes longer build-up periods of time.

This general situation is fairly well known,[3,4] but very little
is known about the special polarization which is so essential
for the production of electroluminescence. The experiments
described below try to clarify this situation and demonstrate
directly that such polarization is essential for the bringing
about of the experimentally observed features.

METHOD

First, a square wave of a voltage V_0 between zero and maximum is applied to the sample and the "on" and "off" flashes
investigated. Then, this voltage is biased by a dc voltage V_0.
This is the equivalent to the application of a series of undirec-
tional pulses of voltage $2V_0$ with voltage free intervals in between of duration τ, which is also the duration of the voltage
application. The voltage diagrams are shown in Figure 1a, b.
The light flashes appearing at the turning on and off of the
voltage are measured as functions of V_0 and τ. Then, a series
of unidirectional pulses are applied, but this time in such a way
that each voltage pulse in one direction is followed by a pulse
in the opposite direction with voltage free intervals in between.
Measurements of this type have also been reported by Morehead.[4] Such a series is described in Figure 1d and is called a
delayed square wave, since the pulses of opposite polarity are
delayed by a time interval τ. For this series the "on" and "off"
flashes are again determined as functions of V_0 and τ. In this
series the influence of additional illumination on the electroluminescence flashes was also studied, and the peak heights of
the delayed square waves compared to unidirectional pulses of
various magnitudes and normal square waves.

In all the figures the heights of the light flashes are given,
which is a good measure of the total intensity emitted during
one flash since the width of the flashes did not change considerably for the various experiments undertaken. These measurements were carried out for samples without a special matrix, with castor wax, and with tricresyl phosphate as a matrix.

Castor wax, because of its high dielectric constant, increases electroluminescence. Tricresyl phosphate (T.C.P.) is a liquid with a noticeable conductivity; it produces rather high electroluminescent flashes.

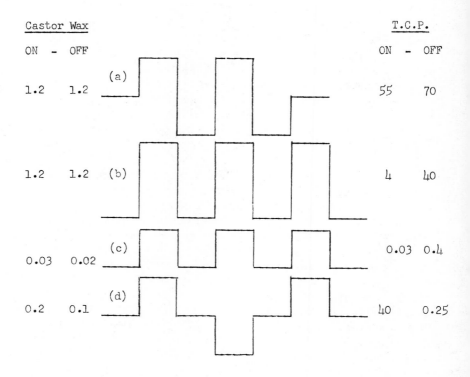

Fig. 1 – Equilibrium Values Obtained After Many Pulses

RESULTS

The results with castor wax and those using tricresyl phosphate as a matrix are shown in Figure 1. The shape of the applied external voltage is shown, and the heights of the light flashes (as measured with a photomultiplier) are shown in the columns to the left and right. The width of these light flashes, which did not depend markedly upon the method in which the voltage was applied, can be seen in Figure 2 for flashes with 60 cycle voltage.

Figure 1a shows the results with a square wave of 100 volt pulse height measured from the zero level. Figure 1b shows the results with the biased square wave, which is equivalent to a series of unidirectional pulses of 200 volts pulse height. The duration of the voltage free interval equals 1/2 min. It is seen that the heights of the "on" and "off" flashes are roughly the same. In all cases the first "on" flashes are much smaller than the "off" flashes and require several pulses in order to become of the same order of magnitude as the "off" flashes, whereas the "off" flashes set in with full magnitude after the first voltage pulse. There is little difference in flash height between the square wave and the unidirectional pulses of double the voltage. Figure 1c gives the results of a series of unidirectional voltage pulses of half the voltage as that of Figure 1b, 100 volts as compared with 200 volts. The flashes are smaller by almost two orders of magnitude. If a voltage pulse of opposite direction would be applied instead of the voltage free interval, one would be back to the square wave of Figure 1, and the flashes would be much larger. In Figure 1d, the voltage pulses of opposite polarity are delayed by the period τ, which is equal to the pulse duration, and larger "on" flashes than "off" flashes are obtained. One observes that the light flashes are much smaller than those of the corresponding square wave (Figure 1a). Thus, the delayed application of the opposite voltage has reduced the height of the flashes considerably. But comparing 1d with 1c, one notices that the light flashes of the delayed square wave are definitely larger than those of the unidirectional series. Thus, the delayed square wave yields light flashes whose magnitudes are between those of the square wave and those of the unidirectional pulses. The flashes produced by the opposite voltages are thus conditioned in their magnitude by the preceding pulse.

The situation is considerably different when the light flashes of a sample containing T.C.P. as a matrix instead of castor wax are studied. Figures 1a and 1b (use right hand column) present the results with unidirectional pulses of voltage $2V_0$ (biased square wave) and with a normal square wave of voltage V_0. Here, there is a very remarkable difference between the biased and unbiased waves. The latter has two flashes of about the same amplitude, while the unidirectional pulses display only one large flash per full period ("off") and one smaller flash ("on"). The number of large flashes is thus reduced to half when the square wave is biased by V_0. The relation between this "off" flash, and the flashes corresponding to the unidirectional pulses of 100 volts or 200 volts is the same as for castor wax.

Figure 2 is an oscilloscope picture of electroluminescent light flashes with 60 cycle ac unbiased voltage (lower row) and biased voltage (upper row). The sinusoidal curve presents the voltage trace, which in the upper row is shifted to the top of the picture. In this picture the reduction in height of one flash with the biased ac is quite obvious. This difference between the flashes of an electroluminescent sample in T.C.P. and in castor wax becomes much more pronounced when delayed square waves are applied, as shown in Figure 1d. Although these pulses have only a pulse height V_0, the ratio of "on" to "off" flashes is more than 100 for the T.C.P. sample, but only 2 for the castor wax sample, and the magnitude of the "on" flash is about 100 times that of the "off" flash of unidirectional pulses.

The following important feature should be emphasized. The "on" flashes of unidirectional pulses (1b, 1c) never reach the magnitude of the "off" flashes contrary to what was observed with castor wax matrices. The "off" flashes in Figure 1c are about 100 times smaller than those of Figure 1b due to the smaller voltage of the pulses in Figure 1c. This shows the strong dependence of the flashes upon voltage. In the delayed square wave series (1d), however, the "on" flashes are much larger than the "off" flashes of the unidirectional pulses of voltage V_0 and of the same magnitude as those of the "off" unidirectional pulses with double the voltage. The delayed square wave flashes ("on") are very similar to those obtained with the corresponding normal square wave of Figure 1a.

If one reduces the voltage free interval between two consecutive pulses of the delayed square wave to zero, one obtains the square wave of Figure 1a, but it is found that the flashes do not change appreciably in height as τ is reduced. This result means that the delaying of the pulses of opposite direction does not reduce the magnitude of the flashes considerably as long as the delay period is not extended over extremely long periods of time; one hour and more. This is demonstrated in the lower row of Figure 3, where the dependence of the heights of the flashes upon the duration τ of field free intervals is presented for a delayed square wave. It is seen that the height decreases only slowly with time for half a minute, and it is almost as high

for 30 seconds as for 1 second. After one hour it is still
slightly higher than the "off" flashes of the unidirectional
pulses with shorter intervals.

One has further to note that after 60 minutes these "on"
flashes are still much larger than the "on" flashes of a series
of unidirectional pulses. This means that these electroluminescent systems have a very remarkable memory. The difference

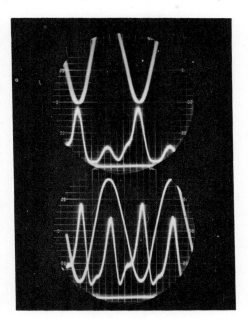

Fig. 2 —
Upper Picture: Light emission and voltage wave
form for 160 volts peak to peak 60 cps ac plus
80 volts dc.
Lower picture: Light emission and voltage wave
form for 160 volts peak to peak 60 cps ac only.

in magnitude of the "on" and "off" flashes for unidirectional
pulses in T.C.P. was already found by Morehead as was the fact
that the flash of the delayed square wave was considerably
larger than that for unidirectional pulses; but apparently he uses
much shorter intervals τ than were used in this investigation.

The upper row of Figure 3 shows how this memory can be

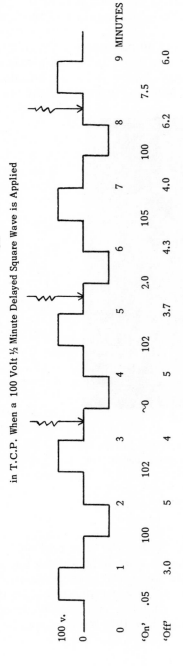

Destruction by Light of the Polarization in the 32 $\frac{MGM}{CM^2}$ EL-1 Sample

in T.C.P. When a 100 Volt ½ Minute Delayed Square Wave is Applied

	0	1	2	3	4	5	6	7	8	9 MINUTES
'On'		.05	100	102	~0	102	2.0	105	100	7.5
'Off'		3.0	5	4	4	5	3.7	4.3	4.0	6.2	6.0

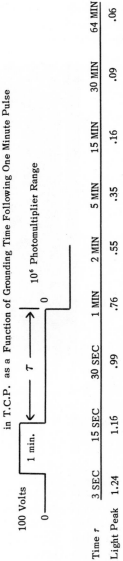

Light Peak Due to 100 Volt Reverse Field on 15 $\frac{MGM}{CM^2}$ EL-1 Sample

in T.C.P. as a Function of Grounding Time Following One Minute Pulse

10^6 Photomultiplier Range

Time τ	3 SEC	15 SEC	30 SEC	1 MIN	2 MIN	5 MIN	15 MIN	30 MIN	64 MIN
Light Peak	1.24	1.16	.99	.76	.55	.35	.16	.09	.06

Fig. 3

destroyed. In this series a delayed square wave is used with 1/2 min. voltage free intervals. During these intervals, however, the sample was illuminated with visible light or infrared light, as indicated in the figure. In the moment the sample is illuminated in this way, the strong "on" flash of the following voltage pulse disappears and is reduced to the much smaller, normal size of the "off" flashes of a unidirectional pulse series. This shows that the electroluminescent storage is destroyed by illumination. Now it is well known[2] that internal polarization caused by trapped charges is removed by illumination, since the free charge created in this way tends to cancel the internal polarization field. Thus, these experiments give strong credance to the idea that internal polarization plays a very important role in electroluminescence. This will be more fully discussed in the next section.

INTERPRETATION OF THE RESULTS

For the discussion of the results, described in the previous section, the picture described in the introduction will be used. It is assumed that a single electroluminescent grain becomes internally polarized under the influence of an external field because of the production of free charge inside the grain. One reason for assuming that the polarization is limited to a grain and not extended over the whole sample was already given above.

There is one other observation which points in the same direction. Experiments with electrophotoluminescence distinctly disclose two types of field influence. When the sample is excited by strongly absorbed light and the illuminated side is made positive, the "on" flash is large and the "off" flash weak or even negative (fluorescent emission reduced). With opposite polarity the role of the "on" and "off" flashes is reversed. This behavior is quite characteristic for this type of photoelectroluminescence.

This can be explained by the assumption that in one instance electrons are driven into the highly excited region, in the other instance they are driven out of this region into an area of little or no excitation. With T.C.P. as a matrix, however, this behavior is different. The reduction of light emission is much less pronounced. One can interpret this to mean that with this matrix electrons are not swept out of the excited areas, as though T.C.P. prevents electrons from going over from one grain to another.

If a voltage pulse is applied to an unilluminated sample,
free charges are produced by electron injecting sources, and
subsequently may be multiplied by impact excitation. These
charges find only a few positively charged activators in the
grain with which they can recombine. Thus, the "on" flash of
the first voltage pulse is small. If the voltage is turned off,
the polarization field drives the electrons back into a region
where positive activators reside, and recombination accompanied by light emission occurs, and a considerable "off" flash
is observed. However, only a fraction of the available charges
recombine; some remain trapped. If the internal polarization
decays quickly, the next voltage pulse in the same direction
will find no internal field, and again free charges are produced
in the same manner as before. This time, however, the grain
is not void of positively charged activators. Even if the polarization field has subsided, many positively charged activators
are still available from the first pulse, and thus the newly
created charges already find recombination centers. Thus, the
"on" flash is increased. This will continue until an equilibrium
is reached, and "on" and "off" flashes are roughly of the same
magnitude.

If, instead of a series of unidirectional pulses, a delayed
square wave is applied, the situation is very similar to that of
the unidirectional pulses as long as the internal polarization
field has almost fully subsided before the next voltage pulse is
applied. If this polarization field, however, has not yet completely disappeared when the next pulse is applied, then, when
a voltage of reversed polarity is applied, the interior of the
grain sees a larger field than in the case without polarization.
The applied field and the remaining polarization field add up,
and as a consequence the "on" flashes will now increase in
size, since more free charges are produced.

Such an increase in "on" flashes is already seen with castor
wax samples and delayed square wave application in Figure 1d.
If the reverse field application follows the turning off of the
preceding voltage pulse more closely, the light flash intensity
increases and eventually, when it follows instantly the preceding
pulse (square wave), the heights of the light flashes have reached
that of unidirectional pulses with double the voltage. The reverse applied field and the internal polarization field add up
almost completely.

In samples with castor wax matrix the internal polarization
field apparently decays rather quickly when the external voltage

is turned off. Thus, the grain experiences a strong field each time the external voltage is turned on or off. In the first case, it sees the applied field; in the second, the internal field. Both are of the same order of magnitude and decrease rather rapidly after each change of the applied voltage; the applied field by the buildup, the latter by the decay of the polarization field. Thus, turning on and off of unidirectional pulses always means the creation of a strong field inside the grain. Therefore, the "on" and "off" light flashes become equal after several pulses have been applied.

Somewhere along the line new charges are repeatedly produced to replace those which have recombined during the flashes. It should be remembered that only a fraction of all existing charges recombine. Otherwise not enough positively charged activators would be left for the next voltage pulse to produce an "on" flash. Probably new charges are produced immediately at the turning on of the applied voltage as well as at its turning off.

The only difference with the T.C.P. samples lies in the much slower decay of the internal polarization field. This still persists minutes after the preceding voltage pulse (see Figures 1d and 3). The applied reverse voltage and the internal polarization field add up to a much larger field than that corresponding to the applied voltage alone. This is borne out by the experiments described in Figures 1d and 3. The lower row (Figure 3) describes the decay of the flash height with increasing time interval τ between the original voltage pulse and the application of the reverse pulse. Even after one hour, the "on" flash is still somewhat larger than the normal "off" flash with unidirectional pulses. The importance of the polarization field is shown even more clearly by the experiments of the upper row of Figure 3. Illumination of the sample during the period without external voltage destroys the large "on" flash of the reversal voltage pulse and makes it equal to the "off" flash.

It is known from measurements of internal polarization that the creation of free charges by illumination destroys any internal charge polarization. The free charges move in such a way as to cancel the internal field, but many of the positive activators and trapped electrons have not yet recombined. Thus, when voltage is applied after illumination, the grain sees only the applied field, and charges are produced from the injecting sources. These give light emission by recombining with positively charged activators left from the preceding illumination. Because of the

persisting internal field (with T.C.P.) the grain or its interior
sees a strong field in the moment the external voltage is turned
off and a much smaller field in the moment the external voltage
is turned on. In the latter case it experienced only the small
difference between the external field and the internal field.
Thus, the turning on and off of the external field no longer produces the same field inside the grain as in the case of rapidly
decaying polarization field. As a consequence of this, the "on"
and "off" flashes are quite different from each other in cases
where the internal polarization decreases only slightly during
the period of no applied voltage. The instantaneous field the
grain sees, when the external voltage is turned on, is relatively
weak and, therefore, the "on" flashes are considerably smaller
than the "off" flashes. (See Figure 1c).

Somewhere during the turning on and off of the applied voltage, new charges are produced to compensate for those which
have recombined during the emission of light. They are probably produced mainly when the external voltage is turned off,
because the grain sees the largest field in this moment except
for the very first voltage pulse. Apparently, this production
of charges is not enough to destroy the polarization; otherwise
the polarization would disappear immediately. The fact that a
large polarization persists also indicates that the light emitted
in an "off" flash is actually produced only by the recombination
of a rather small fraction of the charges originally created.
Thus, in a series of applied voltage pulses, new charges are
produced at each voltage removal or application, but each of
them is much less than those produced in the very first voltage
pulse.

This is borne out by another observation. As described
above, the height of the light flashes in a T.C.P. matrix decays
only slowly with τ. This means that the internal polarization
field decays by a still smaller amount, since the height of the
flashes increases much faster than proportional to the applied
voltage. Consequently, in an off period of the applied voltage,
the grain sees a field which is almost as high as the originally
applied field. Nevertheless, the electron injecting sources
in the grain, which have supplied the electrons in the first place,
no longer inject electrons at the original rate although they are
exposed to a rather strong field. That this injection of electrons
is much reduced follows from the fact that the polarization
field decays so slowly. The electron injecting sources produce
charges only during a very short time, as seen when pulses or

ac voltages of a short period are applied. In the experiments with long intervals without applied voltage, these sources are exposed to a strong internal field for very long times, which are much longer than those during which they have produced charges.

One can account for this by assuming that the injecting sources, after they have given off electrons, do not inject electrons any more before electrons have been restored to them, even if they are exposed to the original field strength but in opposite direction; or by assuming that different injecting sources are present in the grains which inject electrons only after the field strengths in their neighborhood have surpassed certain values. Otherwise, it would be difficult to account for the long life of the polarization field and, thus, for the large increase in the height of the light flashes, when a reverse voltage is applied in T.C.P. samples.

One could conjecture that the large "on" flash in the delayed square wave is not so much brought about by the injection and production of new charges as a consequence of the doubling in field strength, but by a much stronger release of polarized charges as a consequence of the increase in field strength. This was the explanation Morehead has given for the increase in flash height for his delayed square wave. With this assumption one could not understand why the "on" flash of the delayed square wave with T.C.P. is just as large as the "off" flash of unidirectional pulse of twice the voltage. This would then only be fortuitous. In the latter case, one has unidirectional pulses of twice the voltage, and these higher voltages produce more charges and, thus, increase the flash height. That they should always be equal to the number of charges driven back by twice the field strength does not appear very likely.

The experiments described here certainly demonstrate the important role internal polarization fields play in ac electroluminescence. No reason can be given why T.C.P. increases the persistence of the internal polarization so strongly, whether this is due to a prevention of charge exchange between grains or to some other unknown reason. It was assumed for the special interpretation given here that the internal polarization resides inside the single grains. Very similar conclusions could be drawn if this would be the case, but the internal polarization would be due to charge layers which accumulate at the electrode boundaries of the sample. The internal field would not be limited to specific grains, but then to the whole sample. The reasons mentioned above seem, however, to indicate that one has to assume grain polarization.

REFERENCES

[1] F. Matossi and S. Nudelman, Phys. Rev. 98, 434 (1955).
[2] J. R. Freeman, H. Kallmann and M. Silver, Rev. Mod. Phys., 33, 553 (1961).
[3] P. Zalm, G. Diemer and H. A. Klasens, Philips Research Report 9, 81 (1954).
[4] F. F. Morehead, Jr., J. Electrochem. Soc. 105, 461 (1958).

IDENTIFICATION OF ACTIVATOR SITES IN HALOPHOSPHATE PHOSPHORS

Peter D. Johnson
General Electric Research Laboratory
Schenectady, New York

ABSTRACT

In the calcium halophosphate phosphors, $3[Ca_3(PO_4)_2] \cdot$ $\cdot Ca(F,Cl)_2 : Mn^{+2}, Sb^{+3}$, the activators are believed to substitute for calcium. The spontaneous polarization of luminescence of synthetic single crystals of these phosphors depends on which of the two different Ca^{+2} sites in the apatite structure are occupied by each of the activators and on the local symmetry of the two sites. In the fluorophosphate, Mn^{+2} luminescence is completely polarized with its electric vector parallel to the crystal c-axis; and the Sb^{+3} luminescence is partially polarized perpendicular to the c-axis. These orientations are reversed in the chlorophosphate; and the Sb^{+3} luminescence is more strongly polarized than the Mn^{+2} luminescence. Luminescence of Sb^{+3} in a mixed chloro-fluorophosphate crystal is polarized parallel to the c-axis, with the proportion of polarization varying with the heat treatment of the crystal. Symmetry arguments suggest that luminescent Mn^{+2} is in the CaI position in fluorophosphate and in the CaII position in chlorophosphate. Preliminary electron spin resonance studies confirm these conclusions. The position of Sb^{+3} in chlorophosphate is uncertain. In fluorophosphate it is probably in the CaII position.

Synthetic apatite, $3[Ca_3(PO_4)_2] \cdot Ca(F,Cl)_2$, activated with Sb^{+3} and Mn^{+2} is a widely used fluorescent lamp phosphor. There has been considerable interest for a number of years in the problem of where in the crystal lattice the activators are situated. It is generally believed that both manganese and an-

563

timony substitute for Ca^{+2} in one or the other of the two different non-equivalent Ca^{+2} sites.[1,2,3] Various indirect evidence
has been adduced in efforts to resolve the problem of which of
these calcium sites are occupied by each of the activators. The
local symmetry of the two sites is shown in Fig. 1. The CaI
site[4] is on a trigonal symmetry axis in the center of a slightly
twisted prism of six oxygen atoms (point group symmetry C_3),

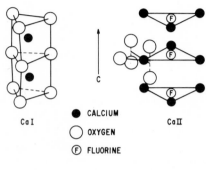

Fig. 1

and CaII is in a reflection plane containing an adjacent fluoride
ion also in the reflection plane (point group symmetry C_{1h}). In
the chlorophosphate the halide lies on the same hexagonal screw
axis as the fluoride but between the reflection planes.[5] The
positions of the halides in mixed chloro-fluoro phosphates depends on heat treatment.[6]

Butler and Jerome[1] cite the invariance of the antimony
emission with identity of the halide as evidence for assigning
Sb^{+3} to the CaI position. They propose that the Sb^{+3} ions replace Ca^{+2} in two adjacent CaI positions and that charge compensation is accomplished by the presence of an interstitial O^{-2}
near these two substituents. The shift in the emission of Mn^{+2}
with change in Cl^- and F^- composition ratio is considered evidence that Mn^{+2} is in the CaII position. Ouweltjes[2] concurs
with Butler and Jerome's reasoning with respect to manganese.
However he proposes that Sb^{+3} substitutes for CaII with charge
compensation by substituting O^{-2} for the adjacent halide. Prener
and Williams[3] are in accord with Ouweltjes in the assignment
of activator positions. They point out that substituting O^{-2} at the
F^- position in both chloro- and fluorophosphate leaves the Sb^{+3}
environment independent of halide thus explaining the independence of Sb^{+3} emission on halide composition.

Recently Narita[7] has calculated the effect of change in lattice constants on the emission spectrum of Mn^{+2} in halophosphates assuming the manganese to be in the CaI position. The calculated shift is in accord with the experimentally observed effect of changing $[Cl^-]/[F^-]$ ratio on the Mn^{+2} emission spectrum. The approximations and assumptions in the calculation are such that only qualitative agreement with experiment is to be expected, however.

The paramagnetic resonance of Mn^{+2} in powder synthetic apatite phosphors has been investigated by Kasai,[8] with the conclusion that most of the Mn^{+2} is at the CaI positions. In natural crystals of apatite Mn^{+2} is found by paramagnetic resonance to be in both positions.[9]

In the present work the spontaneous polarization of luminescence is described, and its relationship to the symmetry of the possible activator sites is discussed. Concurrently work on the spin resonance of Mn^{+2} and other paramagnetic impurities introduced into synthetic single crystals of apatite has been in progress. The preliminary results of this work will be cited in connection with the optical measurements, however a more complete exposition of the spin resonance results will appear in a separate publication. It is clear that when some Mn^{+2} is found in both Ca^{+2} positions, as is the case for natural crystals, one or the other or both types of sites may participate in luminescence. Thus luminescence measurements provide a more direct way of investigating luminescent, as opposed to inactive, centers. Since Sb^{+3} is not paramagnetic, optical measurements are the only way of studying Sb^{+3} centers. The correct interpretation of optical polarization measurements requires knowledge of the nature of the states involved in luminescence as well as the symmetry of the possible activator sites. In the present case comparison of absorption and emission spectra with those of simpler, better understood phosphor systems provides some information as to the electronic states involved in luminescence.[10] Neither spin resonance nor optical measurements alone permit completely unambiguous identification of the activator centers. In combination they may permit a reasonably certain assignment of sites.

EXPERIMENTAL

Fluorophosphate crystals were grown as previously described[10] by the Kyropoulos method from rf induction-heated iridium or rhodium crucibles. Chlorophosphate crystals have been made by quickly fusing the powder and cooling rapidly so as to form a skim of solid over the melt. The solid surface inhibits loss of $CaCl_2$. After formation of solid on the surface of the melt, the crucible is slowly cooled and heated alternately several times over a period of about 20 to 30 minutes. Crystals grow mainly from the surface down. Melting back eliminates small crystals, leaving only the largest ones which grow larger upon subsequent cooling. In this way single crystals up to $3 \times 5 \times 10$ mm in dimensions have been made. In contrast to fluorophosphate, which has conchoidal fracture, chlorophosphate crystals tend to cleave perpendicular to the c-axis. Although the chlorophosphate crystals are clear unstrained single crystals, chloride deficiencies detectable by chemical analysis are found in most of them.

All of the fluorophosphate crystals have at least a few parts per million of Mn^{+2} and Sb^{+3} which were present in the starting materials. These show predominantly the pink luminescence of Mn^{+2}. The chlorophosphate crystals show predominantly the blue emission band of Sb^{+3}. Mn^{+2} could be increased in concentration in fluorophosphate either by addition to the melt or by diffusion by immersing the crystal in Mn^{+2}-containing powder. Large amounts of Sb^{+3} could not be incorporated into a crystal by doping the melt because of its high segregation coefficient. Most of the doping was done by embedding the crystal in phosphor powder containing the desired impurity and heating in CO_2 at 1200°C for several hours.

Paramagnetic resonance measurements were done at liquid He temperature by Ludwig and Woodbury using the same apparatus employed for their work on transition metal doped semiconductors.[11]

The measurements of the spontaneous polarization of luminescence were made using the experimental arrangement shown in Fig. 2. In each case the crystals were cut out as thin rectangular slabs with the c-axis in the plane of the slab. Orientation was determined using the polarizing microscope.[12] For the polarization measurement the crystal was placed on the stage of a polarizing microscope with its polarizer and condenser replaced by a 4 watt mercury germicidal lamp and a Corning 9863 filter, giving predominantly 2537 Å radiation for excitation. In order to eliminate light scattered at the edges, the crystals were glued to a blackened disc with a round aperture through which excitation radiation passed. The field of view of the microscope was smaller than this aperture. Initial centering of the sample was done with a lower power eyepiece. Suitable filters were interposed between the sample and the 0.1 n.a. objective of the microscope to select the wavelength region of emission desired. Because of the overlap of the Mn^{+2} and Sb^{+3} emission bands, it is not possible with filters to isolate each completely from the other when they are present with comparable intensity. For this reason whenever possible the relative concentrations of the activators were adjusted to make one or the other band predominate. Measurements on crystals of different activator concentrations in the range of low concentrations up to a few hundredths of a mole percent showed no dependence of proportion of polarization on concentration. A pale yellow Corning 3387 filter was used above the sample to eliminate the small amount of blue, Hg 4046 Å, light from the excitation source transmitted by the 9863 filter and the sample. For observations of the antimony luminescence a blue Corning 5030 filter was used in addition. The efficacy of this filter was checked during the measurements on chlorophosphate crystals, where it was found difficult to make one band predominate over the other to the desired extent, by using a deeper blue Corning 5543 filter. The results agreed within the error of measurement. For Mn^{+2} luminescence in fluoro- and mixed chloro-fluorophosphate crystals a red Corning 2434 filter was used. For the chlorophosphate crystals a sequence of filters cutting off at successively longer wavelengths were employed. All of the measurements were obtained as point by point readings of current from the RCA 5819 photomultiplier attached to the eyepiece as a function of angle reading of the stage, with the analyzer in place.

Some preliminary experiments using polarized excitation have been performed. In these the dependence of intensity of Mn^{+2} luminescence on the angle between the crystal c-axis and the plane of polarization have been determined. The 2537 Å excitation was polarized by multiple reflections at Brewster's angle from a stack of fused quartz plates.

RESULTS AND DISCUSSION

The intensity of luminescence transmitted by the analyzer is shown for the emission of Sb^{+3} and Mn^{+2} in fluorophosphate in

Fig. 3. The proportion of polarization, given by $P = (I_{max} - I_{min})/(I_{max} + I_{min})$ is unity for the luminescence of manganese. Emission in this case is linearly polarized with the E-vector parallel to the crystal c-axis. The solid line is a $\cos^2 \theta$ curve, where θ is the angle between the crystal c-axis and

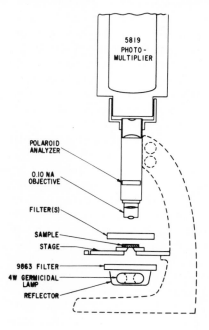

Fig. 2

the plane of polarization transmitted by the analyzer. This is the behavior to be expected from a uniaxial source. Antimony emission differs in two respects from manganese emission. First, it is only partially polarized, and second, the polarization is perpendicular to the c-axis of the crystal. Within experimental error the antimony results fit a $\sin^2 \theta$ + constant relationship as shown. The proportion of polarization of the antimony luminescence varies only slightly from crystal to crystal, the differences being probably due to differences in amount of luminescence scattered by small inclusions and crystal imperfections.

In chlorophosphate the orientations of polarization of the two activators are reversed. As seen in Table I antimony luminescence is strongly polarized with its electric vector par-

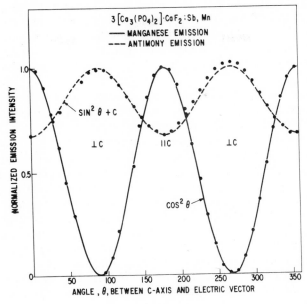

Fig. 3

allel to the crystal c-axis. Because of the difficulty mentioned above of isolating the antimony and manganese emission in the chlorophosphate accurate quantitative significance should not be attributed to the proportions of polarization given in Table I for chlorophosphate. Careful measurements with different crystals and different filters however make it certain that $P < 1$ for antimony.

Table I

Spontaneous Polarization of Luminescence
in Halophosphate Crystals

	Mn^{++}	Sb^{++}
Fluorophosphate	1.0 ‖C	0.19 ⊥C
Chlorophosphate	0.32 ⊥C	0.55 ‖C
0.7F, 0.3Cl	‖C	‖C

Manganese luminescence in chlorophosphate is partially polarized perpendicular to the crystal c-axis. The value given was obtained by extrapolating values of P obtained using filters transmitting at successively longer wavelengths. The proportion of polarization levels off when filters transmitting at wavelengths longer than the long wave length tail of the antimony luminescence are used. Again although it is not possible to arrive at a precise quantitative value, we can say with certainty that $P < 1$.

In mixed chloro-fluorophosphate both manganese and antimony luminescence are polarized parallel to the crystal c-axis. Values of P for this phosphor depend on heat treatment of the crystal. Preliminary measurements on the effect of quenching crystals of $3[Ca_3(PO_4)_2] \cdot Ca(F_{0.7}, Cl_{0.3})_2$:Sb, Mn show a decrease in $P"$C for Sb^{+3} emission upon quenching. This result is in accord with the findings of Apple[6] that quenching of mixed chlorofluorophosphates tends to freeze in the fluorophosphate structure. Further investigation of the effect of heat treatment on polarization would be of interest since the spectra and polarization of the quenched samples change over periods of several weeks when they are stored at room temperature.

The differences in spontaneous polarization of luminescence of each activator are in strong contrast to the similarity of the emission and absorption spectra of each in the two host lattices. Since the polarizations of both Mn^{+2} and Sb^{+3} are reversed in the two host lattices, there are two possibilities as to their positions. They may each be in different positions in the two host lattices, or alternatively one or both may be predominantly in the CaII position in both cases, with the difference in local symmetry at the CaII position depending on the halide present accounting for the differences in polarization. In the cases where polarization of emission is not complete the activator may be distributed between both positions.

For the interpretation of the polarization of luminescence in these phosphors it is necessary to consider only the local symmetry of the possible activator sites. It has been concluded previously[10] that the states of both activators involved in luminescence are at least several volts below the conduction band and are thus strongly localized.

In the case of Sb^{+3} the ground state is the $^1S_0$ of the $5s^2$ configuration and the emitting state is the $6sp$, $^3P_1$ mixed by spin orbit coupling with the $^1P_1$. In the CaI position the configuration of lowest energy for Sb^{+3} in the emitting state resulting from the crystal field splitting will be with the activator having its p-orbital directed along the trigonal symmetry axis due to the coulomb attraction of the two adjacent CaI ions on this axis. The six nearest neighbor oxygen atoms are predominantly co- valently bonded to phosphorus and so probably contribute only in a small way to the local field. Thus if Sb^{+3} occupies the CaI position we expect its luminescence to be polarized parallel to the crystal c-axis as is the case in chlorophosphate.

For the CaII position simple electrostatic arguments are not easily applicable. In addition to the single fluoride which may be replaced by oxide there are 5 oxygen atoms at three different distances from this site with a sixth oxygen still further away. Because of the mixed covalent and ionic nature of the atoms surrounding it and the low symmetry of this site the nature of the crystal field is difficult to understand even qualitatively. It is clear that an activator at this site is not likely to have its luminescence polarized parallel to the c-axis with $P = 1$. Par- tial polarization parallel to the c-axis is possible as is polari- zation perpendicular to c. Since the CaI site must lead to polarization parallel to the c-axis in the case of Sb^{+3} lumines- cence, the existence of antimony luminescence polarized per- pendicular to the c-axis as in fluorophosphate strongly suggests that Sb^{+3} is in the CaII position in this case. The partial polari- zation here may be due either to the symmetry of the CaII site or it may result from a distribution of Sb^{+3} between the two sites. The variation of P_{Sb} among different crystals is appreci- able but may result from varying amounts of scattering in the different crystals. We conclude that luminescent Sb^{+3} is pre- dominantly in the CaII position in the fluorophosphate. Only if $P_{Sb} = 1$ in the chlorophosphate could we be reasonably certain that Sb^{+3} is in the CaI position. There remains the possibility that this activator is in the CaII position in both host lattices with the difference in polarization resulting from the difference in crystal structure in the two lattices.

The unexcited state of Mn^{+2} is the $^6S_0$ of the $3d^5$ configura- tion. As in other manganese activated phosphors, the emitting state is probably one of the quartet states differing from the ground state only in electron spin.[13] As with antimony the crys- tal field splitting should result in the wavefunction of the non- spherically symmetrical emitting state having high values in the direction of the two adjacent Ca^{+2} sites on the trigonal axis when the Mn^{+2} is in the CaI position. Again this results in polarization parallel to the c-axis as occurs in the fluorophos- phate. For the same reasons cited for antimony in fluorophos- phate, we conclude that in the chlorophosphate luminescent

Mn^{+2} is predominantly in the CaII position. In addition to the difference in crystal field at the two sites, different distributions of the $3d$ electrons among the d-orbitals probably occur in the emitting state in the two different environments. It is not surprising then that there is a difference in Mn^{+2} emission spectra of fluoro- and chlorophosphate.

The conclusions as to the positions of Mn^{+2} are confirmed by electron spin resonance. In our synthetic luminescent crystals of fluorophosphate Mn^{+2} is preferentially in the CaI position, although a fraction of it is occasionally found at the CaII position in crystals with high Mn^{+2} concentration. In chlorophosphate Mn^{+2} has only been found in the CaII position. Resonance measurements on other transition element ions in the halophosphates are in progress. It is hoped that the resonance spectra of the trivalent ions will provide some correlation with the present results on Sb^{+3}.

The fact that Mn^{+2} is found at both Ca^{+2} sites in fluorophosphate and in natural apatite indicates that there is not a large energy difference between the two configurations. It is not surprising therefore that the identity of the halide with its accompanying effect on crystal structure has a large effect on the relative populations of Mn^{+2} in the two sites.

Because charge compensation of Sb^{+3} by substitution of F^- by $O^=$, as suggested by Ouweltjes[2] and Prener and Williams,[3] seems energetically more favorable than the interstitial compensation proposed by Butler and Jerome,[1] one would expect the CaII position to be preferred by Sb^{+3} in both chloro- and fluorophosphate. As mentioned before, the chlorophosphate crystals have a considerable deficiency of $CaCl_2$. It has been found for hydroxyapatites that in cation deficient crystals cation vacancies occur predominantly at the CaI positions.[14] The high concentration of CaI vacancies is probably the agency whereby Sb^{+3} is attracted to these positions in chlorophosphate. Further investigation of the effects of vacancy concentration, activator concentration and quenching on the polarization of Sb^{+3} luminescence should help to resolve some of the uncertainty as to the behavior of Sb^{+3} in chlorophosphate. It should be pointed out that the results reported here were obtained on crystals containing concentrations of Sb^{+3} and Mn^{+2} less than 10^{-2} to 10^{-4} times those usual in commercial phosphors. The value $P = 1$ for Mn^{+2} in fluorophosphate was obtained in crystals containing these activators in the concentration range of about 3×10^{15} to about 3×10^{17} atoms/cc. Commercial phosphors have of the order of 10^{20} atoms Mn^{+2} and Sb^{+3} per cc (about one mole percent). Interactions between nearby Mn^{+2} and Sb^{+3} may have considerable effect on the distribution of activators over the Ca^{+2} sites. In this connection it is interesting that the decay time to $1/e$ of initial brightness for manganese luminescence in both chloro- and fluorophosphate powders is about 12 millisec. Since one would expect quite different decay times due to differences in crystal field at the two sites, the distribution of manganese at high concentrations may be similar in chloro- and fluorophosphate in contrast to the behavior at low concentrations. The decays of both powder phosphors are however simple exponential down to a few percent of initial brightness.

Another factor which could affect the distribution of activators over cation sites in the synthetic crystals is the considerable departure from the stoichiometric composition. In addition to Ca^{+2} and halide vacancies resulting from evolution of calcium halide during crystal growth, some halide is replaced by oxygen, since an oxidizing atmosphere is used to avoid reducing phosphate. Such departures from stoichiometry may affect the distribution of activators over cation sites as well as affecting the value of P when a large fraction of activators is near enough to vacancies or oxygen replacing halide to change the crystal field at the activator position from the normal field for the host lattice at that position. That such effects are probably actually occurring is evidenced by the fact that the decay rate of Mn^{+2} luminescence in both synthetic chloro- and fluorophosphate is faster than $10^3 \, sec^{-1}$.

Our interest in this work has been principally in the positions of the luminescent impurities. Other problems which may be susceptible to study using optical polarization measurements are the energy, distance and directional relationships between Sb^{+3} sensitizers and the Mn^{+2} ions to which they transfer energy. We have found when using polarized 2537 Å excitation, which is absorbed only by Sb^{+3}, there is an orientation dependence of Mn^{+2} luminescent intensity in fluorophosphate. The intensity is approximately 30% greater when the crystal c-axis is parallel to the plane of excitation than when it is perpendicular. Thus the orientational specificity of the excitation is preserved to at least some extent during the energy transfer process. Further work on this effect on crystals with different Sb^{+3} and Mn^{+2} concentration and with different halide compositions is in progress.

CONCLUSIONS

Both the polarization of luminescence and electron spin resonance of synthetic single crystals indicate that luminescent Mn^{+2} is in the CaI position in fluorophosphate and in the CaII position in chlorophosphate. From the polarization of luminescence Sb^{+3} is believed to be predominantly in the CaII position in fluorophosphate. The position of Sb^{+3} in chlorophosphate is uncertain, but is probably mainly in the CaI position. The distributions of activators in commercial phosphors with high activator concentration may differ from those in low concentration synthetic crystals. The mechanisms of luminescence in the halophosphates may be better understood from the results of quenching and annealing experiments on the mixed chloro fluorophosphates and measurements of luminescent properties under polarized excitation.

ACKNOWLEDGMENTS

The author is indebted to F. C. Mostek for assistance in preparing the halophosphate crystals.

REFERENCES

[1] K. H. Butler and C. W. Jerome, J. Electrochem. Soc. 97, 265 (1950).
[2] J. L. Ouweltjes, Philips Tech. Rev. 13, 346 (1951).
[3] J. S. Prener and F. E. Williams, Electrochem Soc. Extended Abstracts, May 1-4, pg 31 (1955).
[4] St. Naray-Szabo, Zeit. Krist. 75, 387 (1930).
[5] S. B. Hendriks, M. E. Jefferson and V. M. Moseley, Zeit Krist. 81, 352 (1932).
[6] E. F. Apple, this conference
[7] K. Narita, J. Phys. Soc. Japan 16, 99 (1961).
[8] P. H. Kasai, Paper presented at Japanese Physical Society Meeting, Osaka (Oct. 1960) (private communication).
[9] John H. Mackey, private communication.
[10] Peter D. Johnson, J. Electrochem. Soc. 108, 159 (1960).
[11] G. W. Ludwig and H. H. Woodbury, Phys. Rev. 113, 1014 (1959).
[12] N. H. Hartshorne and A. Stuart, "Crystals and the Polarizing Microscope," Arnold, London 1950.

[13] P. D. Johnson & F. E. Williams, J. Chem. Phys. $\underline{17}$, 435 (1949).

[14] A. S. Posner and A. Perloff, J. Res. Nat. Bur. Stds. $\underline{58}$, 279 (1957).

EFFECTS OF COOLING RATE ON CALCIUM
HALOPHOSPHATE PHOSPHORS

E. F. Apple and W. E. Ishler
General Electric Company
Cleveland, Ohio

ABSTRACT

The effects of very rapid cooling (from $600-1200°C$ to room temperature) of (1) $Ca_5(PO_4)_3F$, (2) $Ca_5(PO_4)_3Cl$ and (3) Ca_5 $(PO_4)_3(Cl, F)$ containing Sb and Mn activators have been studied. With (1), the spectral distributions of the emission bands (Sb blue, Mn yellow) do not change as a result of rapid cooling. When either (2) or (3) is cooled rapidly (i. e., "quenched"), the spectral distribution of the Mn emission shifts to shorter wavelengths (toward that of $Ca_5(PO_4)_3F:Mn_7Sb$) while that of the Sb emission does not seem to change. The effects of quenching are reversible in a slow-cool, quench, slow-cool cycle.

It is thought that the only major difference between the location of atoms in calcium fluorophosphate and chlorophosphate is in the positions of F $(00\frac{1}{4}, 00\frac{3}{4})$ and Cl $(000, 00\frac{1}{2})$.[4,5] It is proposed that the effect of quenching (2) or (3) is to randomize the Cl atoms over both normal F sites and Cl sites thus effecting a change in luminescence and structure toward those of calcium fluorophosphate. X-ray diffraction data thus far obtained are consistent with the proposed change in structure obtained on rapid cooling.

INTRODUCTION

The technique of rapidly quenching experimental samples from elevated temperatures to room temperature has been used extensively in the studies of high temperature phase equilibria, diffusion, order-disorder phenomena, etc., but it has received less attention in the study of luminescence and related phenomena.

Since the object of quenching is to "freeze in" for room temperature observation the equilibrium configuration found at the firing temperature, it is sometimes possible to produce a different structure of the base lattice and/or different configurations of the activator atoms or defects than those observed in slowly-cooled or annealed samples. For example, Lorenz and Prener were able to correlate changes in the emission spectra and phosphorescence in Li_2TiO_3:Mn to the change in structure from an ordered to a disordered (with respect to cation arrangement) state. The ordered samples were annealed at 900°C while the disordered material was prepared by quenching from 1200°C to room temperature.[1]

Koelmans has shown that efficient ZnS:In phosphors can be prepared by firing in H_2S at 1200°C and quick cooling to room temperature. Refiring the phosphor to 600°C kills the luminescence at room temperature. He attributes this effect to association of the activators at the lower temperature.[2] The foregoing examples demonstrate both structural and activator configurational effects produced by quenching.

This paper will concern the effects of quenching on the luminescence and structure of calcium halophosphate phosphors, approximately $Ca_5(PO_4)_3(F,Cl)$, activated with Sb and Mn. Part of this work was presented in an earlier paper.[3] These phosphors have the same structure as the mineral apatite, $Ca_5(PO_4)_3F$, with a slight difference in the position of the chloride and fluoride which will be discussed later.[4,5] Johnson has reviewed the literature and presented new data on the nature of the luminescent centers in calcium halophosphates.[6] We have observed differences in spectral distribution (of the Mn emission) and structure (with respect to halogen positions) in chlorophosphates and chlorofluorophosphates between samples slowly cooled from or quenched from 800−1200°C to room temperature. The quenched samples of the above approach more closely the structure and spectral distribution of fluorophosphates. The changes observed are reversible in a slow-cool, quench, slow-cool, quench sequence. The structure and spectral distribution of emission in calcium fluorophosphates are not affected by quenching but the intensity of emission is dependent on rate of cooling.

It is thought that both structure (with respect to halogen

positions) and distribution of Mn activator between the two
types of Ca sites are different in quenched and slow-cooled samples. These differences lead to the reversible changes in spectral distribution of emission that are observed.

In addition, preliminary measurements of damage caused by
UV, X-ray, and cathode rays show that the quenched samples
are less susceptible to radiation damage.

EXPERIMENTAL METHOD

Prefired halophosphates were used in all experiments to obviate the effects of evolution of gases which occurs during phosphor formation and to more nearly ensure the existence of
equilibrium conditions.

In one set of experiments the phosphors were fired at the
desired temperature in tightly covered quartz beakers for $1-2$
hours duration. To ensure slow cooling, the beakers were either
allowed to cool overnight in the furnace or were cooled more
rapidly in an insulated but unheated chamber. To quench, the
beakers were removed from the furnace at the desired temperature and the phosphor was quickly dumped into a beaker of
water. Although seemingly crude, this method provided very
rapid quenching and surprisingly did not damage the phosphor.

Most of the experiments, however, were carried out in cylindrical, Dewar-type, thin wall quartz tubes (holding about 50 gram
charges) which were plugged with quartz wool or sealed off.
The phosphors were heated for periods of 0.5 to 3 hours and
were cooled at three different rates: very fast ("quenched") by
immersion of the tube in water, moderately fast by air cooling,
and slowly by oven cooling. (The times to reach 500°C from
about 1100° were roughly 20, 200, and 9000 seconds, respectively, as determined with a thermocouple imbedded in the 4mm
thick phosphor sample.)

Although most of the work was performed on halophosphate
phosphors containing Sb, or Mn, or Sb and Mn, some quench,
slow-cool experiments were carried out on halophosphates with
no added activators.

The phosphor brightness under 2537Å excitation was measured through a filter whose transmission approximates the
normal eye sensitivity curve with selenium photocells connected
to a sensitive galvanometer. Spectral distributions of emissions
under either 2537Å or cathode ray excitation were measured on

several automatic recording spectroradiometers over the range
4000–7000Å. Diffuse reflectance (vs. MgO) was measured over
the 2500–7000Å range on a Beckman DK spectrometer with reflectance attachment. X-ray diffraction patterns were obtained
with a General Electric XRD-5 unit.

Radiation damage experiments were carried out on plaques
of one-inch diameter using either X-ray or 1850Å radiation or
the discharge from a high frequency coil (Tesla type) in vacuum.
Diffuse reflectivities before and after irradiation were measured. The difference in reflectivities is proportional to the absorption introduced by the irradiation.

EXPERIMENTAL RESULTS

a. Calcium Fluorophosphate

The spectral distribution of calcium fluorophosphate with
Sb activator, which was fired at 1150°C and slowly cooled* to
room temperature, is shown in Figure I-A. Sensitivity of measurements decreases rapidly below 4300Å. The plateau in the 4100-
4300 Å region of the spectral distribution curves is instrumental
in origin. The spectral distribution of the quenched sample
is nearly identical to that shown. This is evident from
Figure I-B which plots the difference of relative intensity
(quench minus slow-cool) vs. wavelength. The absolute
intensity of the blue emission was about the same in
quenched and slowly-cooled samples. We conclude that neither
the spectral distribution nor emission intensity of this phosphor
is affected by quenching.

The spectral distribution (under 2547Å excitation) of slowly
cooled calcium fluorophosphate activated with Sb and Mn is
shown in Figure II-A. Figure II-B plots ΔI (quench minus slow-
cool) vs. wavelength and shows about a three percent general
increase in the overall intensity of the blue emission band. This
means that the ratio of the relative intensities of the blue Sb to
the yellow Mn emission is greater in the quenched than in the
slowly-cooled sample. Note that the spectral distribution of the
Mn emission is about the same in the two types of samples and
peaks at about 5720Å. The brightness of the quenched sample
was about three percent greater than the slowly-cooled phosphor.
We conclude that the brightness increases, the ratio of Sb to Mn

---

*The data reported throughout as "slowly cooled" will pertain to fur-
nace-cooled samples.

emission increases, but the spectral distributions of the Sb and Mn emissions remain the same on quenching a fluorophosphate with Sb or Mn activators.

b. Calcium Chlorofluorophosphate

In these samples, about ten percent of the fluorine has been replaced with chlorine. Figure III shows the spectral distributions of the quenched and slowly-cooled samples, both fired at 1150°C. Similar results are obtained in samples quenched from 600—1200°C to room temperature. The spectral distribution of

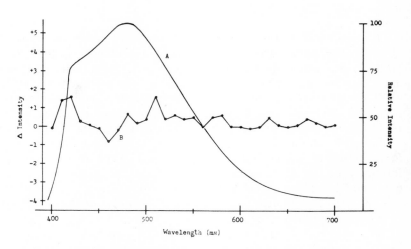

Fig. I — Spectral properties of calcium fluorophosphate with Sb
A — Spectral distribution of emission (2537Å excitation).
B — Difference in relative intensity, ΔI (quench minus slow-cool) vs. wavelength.

the Mn emission lies in a slightly shorter wavelength region in the quenched sample than in the slowly-cooled phosphor. In addition, the brightness of the former is 2—3% higher which increase may be due in whole or part to the shift of spectral distribution toward the maximum transmission region of the normal eye sensitivity filter.

In addition to the difference in spectral distribution of the Mn emission, the diffuse reflectances (vs. MgO) as shown on

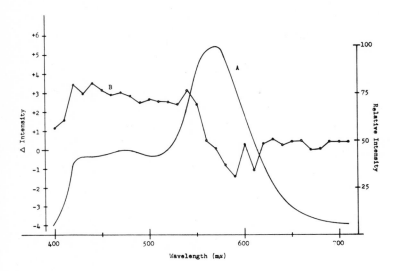

Fig. II — Spectral properties of calcium fluorosphosphate with Sb and Mn
A — Spectral distribution of emission
B — Difference in relative intensity, ΔI (quench minus slow-cool) vs wavelength.

Figure IV are slightly different in the 3000—4000Å region with the quenched sample exhibiting the higher reflectance.

One difficulty sometimes encountered in calcium halophosphate phosphors is the loss of chlorine on long-term heating which may change the optical properties. However, since the slowly-cooled samples would actually be at elevated temperatures for a longer period of time, it seemed unlikely that loss of chlorine was involved at all. In fact, it was demonstrated that the change in spectral distribution of Mn emission is entirely reversible since a slow-cool, quench, slow-cool sequence for a given sample showed the spectral shifts expected. This is clearly shown in Figure V which plots the difference in relative intensities (ΔI) between (A) slowly-cooled then quenched, and (B) quenched then slowly-cooled samples. The two curves exhibit almost opposite symmetry which would be expected in the case of reversibility.

Table I shows the X-ray diffraction data on three portions of the samples listed in Figures III and V. The changes in the intensities of certain diffraction lines are reversible in a sample which is subjected to the sequence slow-cool, quench, slow-cool.

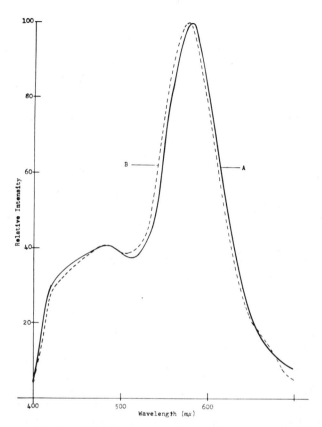

Fig. III — Spectral distribution of emission of calcium chlorofluorophosphate with Sb and Mn

A — —————— Slowly-cooled
B — ------------ Quenched

The X-ray data of a calcium fluorophosphate phosphor are given
for comparison. The "d" spacings are precise to 0.01Å.

Similar differences in spectral distribution of the Mn emission between quenched and slowly-cooled samples are observed
in calcium chlorofluorophosphate with Mn activator but no Sb.
In these cases, cathode ray excitation was used since the Mn
does not respond directly to 2537Å radiation. Figure VI shows
the difference in relative intensity (ΔI) of the quenched minus
slowly-cooled samples and illustrates the change in spectral
distribution of the Mn emission on quenching. The diffuse reflectance data for the slowly-cooled and quenched samples are

Table I

X-Ray Diffraction Data (Intensity and d Spacing) as a Function of Quenching in Chlorophosphates Compared to Fluorophosphates

$Ca_5(PO_4)_3(F,Cl):Mn,Sb$ Slowly cooled		$Ca_5(PO_4)_3(F,Cl):Mn,Sb$ Quenched		$Ca_5(PO_4)_3(F,Cl):Mn,Sb$ Quenched, reheated, slowly cooled		$Ca_5(PO_4)_3(F):Mn,Sb$		hkl
I	d (Å)	I	d	I	d	I	d	
7	4.08	7	4.07	6	4.08	10	4.06	
5	3.88	6	3.90	6	3.90	6	3.88	
28*	3.44	24	3.45	27	3.45	24	3.45	002*
10	3.17	9	3.17	9	3.17	8	3.17	
17*	3.08	22	3.08	18	3.08	21	3.07	120*
100	2.81	100	2.81	100	2.81	100	2.79	121
38	2.78	37	2.77	38	2.72	38	2.78	112
65*	2.71	82	2.71	68		74	2.70	300*
23	2.63	22	2.63	23	2.63	21	2.62	202
4	2.59	6	2.52	5	2.52	7	2.51	301
6	2.29	5	2.29	5	2.30	4	2.29	122
26*	2.25	29	2.26	27	2.26	32	2.25	130*
4	2.23	4	2.23	5	2.23	5	2.22	131
7	2.14	7	2.14	7	2.14	7	2.13	113
4	2.10	4	2.06	4	2.06	3	2.06	203
4	2.00	4	1.99			3	1.99	222
26	1.94	27	1.94	27	1.94	27	1.93	132
13	1.89	14	1.88	14	1.88	13	1.88	
4	1.87	6	1.86	5	1.86	4	1.86	123
31	1.84	29	1.84	30	1.84	25	1.84	231
18	1.80	18	1.80	16	1.80	17	1.80	140*
16*	1.78	19	1.78	17	1.78	18	1.77	402*
14*	1.75	12	1.75	15	1.75	14	1.74	004
10	1.72	12	1.72	12	1.72	12	1.72	

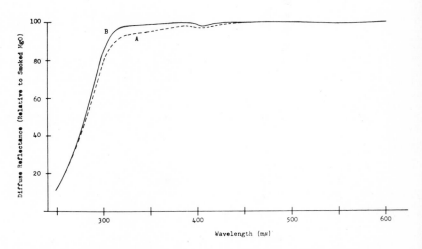

Fig. IV — Diffuse reflectance (vs. MgO) of calcium chlorofluorophosphate with Sb and Mn

A — ------------ Slowly-cooled
B — ———— Quenched

listed in Figure VII. Again the diffuse reflectance of the quenched sample is greater.

Although the X-ray data of the samples containing no Sb were less definitive, the direction of change in line intensities listed in Table I were observed.

To complete the information on the effects of quenching calcium chlorofluorophosphates, the diffuse reflectivities (vs. MgO) of unactivated samples are shown in Figure VIII. Again, the diffuse reflectivity of the quenched sample is greater, especially in the 2500—4000Å region.

c. Calcium Chlorophosphate

The spectral distribution of slowly-cooled calcium chlorophosphate with Mn and Sb is shown in Figure IX. Also included is the plot of the difference in relative emission intensities, ΔI, (quench minus slow-cool) vs. wavelength. Note that the spectral distribution of the Mn emission in slowly-cooled calcium chlorophosphate peaks at about 5860Å. Also the difference in spectral distribution (Mn emission) between the quenched and slowly-cooled samples is greater than in the chlorofluorophosphates. It appears, also, that the ratio of relative intensities, I_{Sb}/I_{Mn},

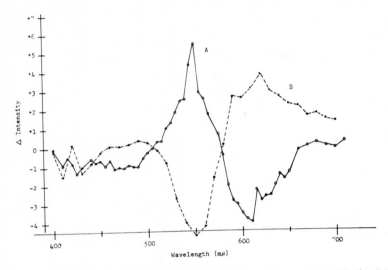

Fig. V — Difference in relative emission intensities (ΔI) vs wavelength of calcium chlorofluorophosphate with Sb and Mn.

A — o-o-o-o- Quench minus slow-cool (1)

B — ⋯⋯⋯ Quench and slow-cool (2) minus quench

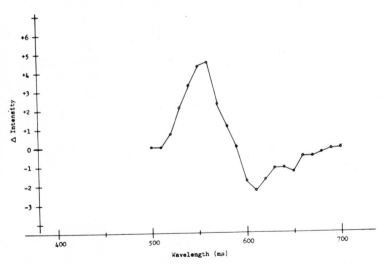

Fig. VI — Difference in relative emission intensity, ΔI, (quench minus slow-cool) vs. wavelength of calcium chlorofluorophosphate with Mn (CR excitation)

may be slightly greater in the quenched sample. Although the data are not presented it should be mentioned that the spectral

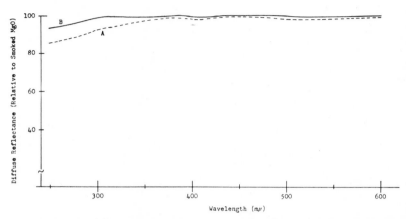

Fig. VII — Diffuse reflectance (vs. MgO) vs. wavelength of calcium chlorofluorophosphate with Mn.

A — ------------ Slowly-cooled
B — —————— Quenched

shifts were reversible in a slow-cool, quench, slow-cool sequence just as in chlorofluorophosphates.

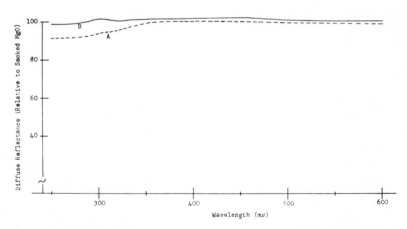

Fig. VIII — Diffuse reflectance (vs. MgO) vs. wavelength of unactivated calcium chlorofluorophosphate

A — ------------ Slowly-cooled
B — —————— Quenched

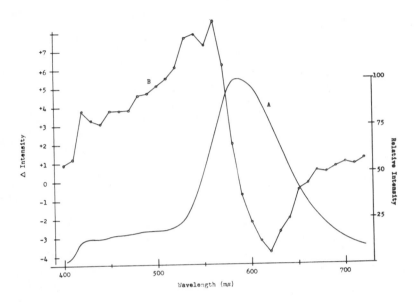

Fig. IX — Spectral properties of calcium chlorophosphate with Mn and Sb
  A — Spectral distribution of emission of slowly-cooled sample
  B — Difference in relative intensity, ΔI, of Mn emission (quench minus slow-cool) vs. wavelength

The X-ray diffraction data for the quenched and slowly-cooled chlorophosphates are listed in Table II. Only the major lines are listed.

d. Radiation Damage

Formation of color centers in activated and unactivated calcium halophosphates by X-ray or 1850Å radiation has been reported by Johnson[7] and Suchow.[8] We have observed the formation of these absorption centers by 1850Å, X-ray, cathode ray radiations, as well as by the discharge from a high frequency coil (Tesla coil) in rough vacuum. Further, we have observed that the damage produced by a given source for a timed exposure is less in the quenched than in the slowly-cooled sample.

Figure X plots the difference in diffuse reflectivities (vs. MgO) of calcium chlorofluorophosphate before and after one minute exposure to the discharge from a high frequency coil in rough vacuum. Unactivated, Mn-activated, and Sb, Mn-activated

Table II

X-Ray Diffraction Data of Chlorophosphates
Effect of Quenching Compared to a Change in the Cl/F
Only Data of Major Lines Shown

$Ca_5(PO_4)_3Cl:Sb,Mn$ Quenched		$Ca_5(PO_4)_3Cl:Sb,Mn$ Slowly cooled	
I	d	I	d
21	3.39Å	23	3.39Å
100	2.85	100	2.85
146	2.77	152	2.78
12	2.63	11	2.63
31	2.30	32	2.31
40	1.96	38	1.96
14	1.91	14	1.91
47	1.83	42	1.84
14	1.81	17	1.81
13	1.69	11	1.69

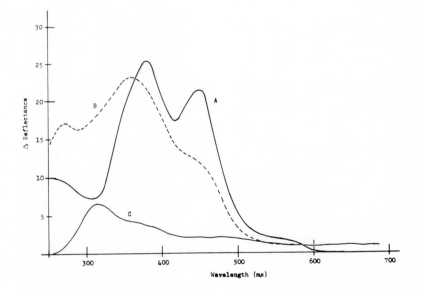

Fig. X — Difference in diffuse reflectivities, ΔI, (before-after one minute irradiation with Tesla coil) vs. wavelength

A — Calcium chlorofluorophosphate
B — Calcium chlorofluorophosphate:Mn
C — Calcium chlorofluorophosphate:Sb,Mn

samples are listed. Although the method of excitation seems crude it was much more expedient than using 1850Å radiation and the results were reproducible to within less than two percent. The plot represents the increase in absorption (ΔR) due to the exposure to the discharge. It is seen that both Mn and particularly Sb change the absorption of the centers. Antimony inhibits the color center formation or shifts the spectral distribution of the centers out of the area of observation.

Figure XI shows the diffuse reflectivities (vs. MgO) for a

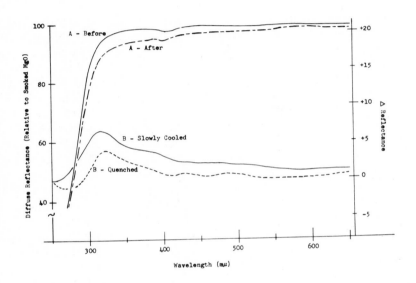

Fig. XI —
    A — Diffuse reflectance spectra of slowly-cooled calcium chlorofluorophosphates showing effect of irradiation
    B — Differences in diffuse reflectivities, ΔR, (before-after one minute irradiation with Tesla coil) vs. wavelength for quenched and slowly-cooled calcium chlorofluorophosphate: Sb,Mn

slowly-cooled calcium chlorofluorophosphate with Mn and Sb activator before and after one minute exposure to the discharge from a Tesla coil and also shows the differences in reflectivities, ΔR, (before minus after irradiation) in the quenched and slowly-cooled samples. It is seen that less absorption, *i. e.* fewer color centers, is introduced by irradiation in the quenched than in the slowly-cooled sample. These results have been confirmed with 1850Å irradiation. It should further be noted

that the decrease in brightness of the quenched samples is
less for a given time of irradiation.

DISCUSSION

As is well known, the spectral distribution of the Mn emission lies in a shorter wavelength region in calcium fluorophosphate than in calcium chlorophosphate. In the present study the
peaks of emission were found at about 5720Å and 5860Å respectively.

The experimental results show that the spectral distribution
of the Mn emission in calcium chlorophosphate and chlorofluorophosphate phosphors with Mn and Sb activators depends on the
rate of cooling from elevated temperatures to room temperature. The Mn emission occurs at shorter wavelengths, *i. e.*
toward that observed in fluorophosphate, in the quenched than
in the slowly-cooled samples. The spectral distribution shifts
are reversible in a slow-cool, quench, slow-cool sequence. In
addition, the X-ray diffraction data, which also indicate a reversibility in the above sequence, also approach those observed
for fluorophosphate in the quenched sample.

The structures of calcium chlorophosphate and fluorophosphate are very similar. A portion of the unit cell of calcium
fluorophosphate, as proposed by Naray-Szabo, showing the Ca
and F atoms, is shown in Figure XII.[4] Note that the fluorine is
in the plane of, and surrounded by, three adjacent Ca II atoms.
Hendricks et al[5] found the same structure for calcium chlorophosphate except because of size restrictions and from line
intensities they suggested that the chlorine atoms are between
instead of in the planes of Ca II atoms. A portion of the structure is shown in Figure XIII.

To explain the results of the quenching experiments we propose that quenching causes a slight change in the structure of
the halophosphate phosphor, specifically in the location of the
halogen in the reflection plane (normal fluorine site) or between
the reflection planes (normal chlorine site). A "change of structure" implies only a rearrangement of the halogen as indicated.
We propose that at high temperatures the lattice is sufficiently
expanded to allow a chlorine to occupy a normal fluorine site
and thus partial randomization of the halogen and reorientation
of O and PO_4 groups may occur. With rapid cooling, this configuration is frozen in with the net result that the structures of

a quenched chlorophosphate or chlorofluorophosphate approach more nearly that of fluorophosphate. Possibly the O atoms around the Ca II or the PO_4 groups rearrange so that on quenching the chlorine is retained in a fluorine site even at room temperature. That this is true is suggested by the change in

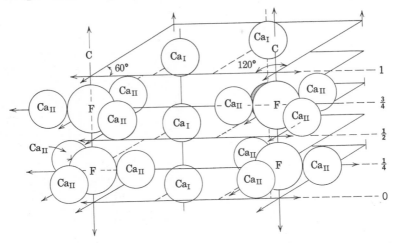

Fig. XII — Representation of unit cell of calcium fluorophosphate showing the positions of fluorine and calcium only

intensity of X-ray diffraction lines in the quenched chlorofluorophosphate having indices hk O which of course are not dependent directly on either position of the halogen. We propose that the spectral distribution of the Mn emission is determined to a large extent by the structures, i.e. whether the halogens are in or between the reflection plane containing the Ca II atoms.

The apparent invariancy of the spectral distribution of Mn emission in fluorophosphate would indicate that the fluorine occupies its normal site in both quenched and slowly-cooled samples. It would be expected that quenching of a chlorophosphate would result in a shift in spectra to shorter wavelengths since chlorine atoms may be quenched in normal fluorine sites. Both a shift in spectral distribution and a change in the X-ray diffraction pattern toward those expected for chlorofluorophosphate phosphors are indeed observed.

It should be pointed out that in calcium chlorofluorophosphate phosphors a chlorine atom in its normal site (between reflection planes) will require adjacent halogens to occupy

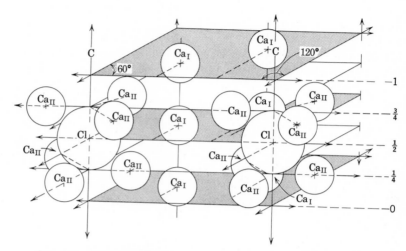

Fig. XIII — Representation of unit cell of calcium chlorophosphate showing the positions of chlorine and calcium only

similar positions. Thus incorporation of a small amount of
chlorine should have an abnormally large effect on both the
crystal structure and on the position of the Mn emission band.
The latter effect has been observed experimentally. Instead
of a linear relationship of percent Cl in halophosphate vs.
wavelength of emission peak, the peak position changes super-
linearly initially with percent Cl. Conversely, a small number
of chlorine atoms quenched in fluorine sites should have the
opposite effect, *i. e.* a larger shift toward the fluorophosphate
structure and emission spectra than would be expected assuming a linear relationship. The foregoing discussion attempts
to correlate the change in structure with the change in luminescence on quenching and suggests that the spectral distribution
of emission depends on the particular structure, *i. e.* position
of halogens, involved.

The results of quenching do not clearly distinguish which of
the models proposed for the Mn center [6,9,10] is the more correct. It does seem difficult to explain the change in spectral
distribution on quenching a chlorophosphate in terms of the
model proposed by Butler [9] since the Mn would be bonded
directly to chlorine in either quenched or slowly-cooled samples and consequently no shift in the spectra would be expected.
The results seem to be more consistent with Johnson's models

which suggest that both structure and Mn distribution are important in luminescent properties.[6,10]

In addition to, and possibly because of, the effect of slightly changing the structure, quenching also may "freeze in" a different configuration of activator atoms than that observed in slowly-cooled samples. Johnson has suggested that luminescent Mn probably occupies the Ca II site in calcium chlorophosphate, both Ca I and II sites in chlorofluorophosphate, and the Ca I site in fluorophosphate.[6] His data, however, are obtained from single crystals containing much less Mn than the phosphor powders. As has been mentioned, the Ca I site is surrounded by six O and away from the halogen while the Ca II site is next to the halogen. See Figures XII and XIII. Obviously the arrangement of atoms around a Ca II site would be different in chloro and fluorophosphate.

It is proposed that quenching a chloro or chlorofluorophosphate from high temperature "freezes in" a more random distribution of Mn over the two Ca sites, whereas on slow-cooling the Mn tends to migrate to and occupy the Ca II site. Since the rate of cooling has no effect on the Mn emission in fluorophosphate, it is proposed that the luminescent Mn in this case occupies only Ca I sites in either case. Continuing in this line of thought, it could be conjectured that Mn is luminescent only when it occupies the Ca I site or the Ca II site in which the halogen is between the reflection planes (a regular chlorophosphate structure). The spectral distribution of the Mn emission would depend on which site it was located since the immediate surroundings of the two sites are different.

It is suggested that the structure affects the distribution of Mn between the two Ca sites, and thus the effects of quenching on structure and luminescence are consistent with the optical and resonance measurements reported by Johnson.

Although many of the ideas presented in this paper are speculative, they do suggest interesting areas for future investigations. The use of quenching and annealing techniques on single crystal samples in conjunction with polarization and resonance measurements would serve to either substantiate or disprove many of the ideas presented here.

It should be mentioned that preliminary measurements of the change of polarization of the antimony emission on quenching in a chlorofluorophosphate single crystal are consistent with the idea that the halogens tend to be quenched into normal fluorine sites.[6] Assuming the model for charge compensation of Sb in which oxygen is incorporated in place of a halogen adjacent to an antimony atom[11,12] and assuming that the polarization arises from the Sb-O configuration, it would be expected that quenching would cause a decrease in the polarization (parallel to C axis) in chlorofluorophosphates. Such a decrease is observed.

In addition to differences in structure and luminescence between slowly-cooled and quenched samples, we have observed that the quenched chloro or chlorofluorophosphates are more resistant to discoloration under 1850Å, CR, or X-ray bombardment. Formation and partial characterization of color centers in calcium halophosphates have been reported by Johnson[7] and Suchow.[8] The latter reported that color center formation under 1850Å is inhibited in fluorophosphates. Our results on quenching are consistent with the above observations in that the quenched samples approach more closely the fluorophosphate structure.

SUMMARY

We have observed that the rate of cooling from elevated temperatures affects the structure and luminescence of calcium chloro or chlorofluorophosphate phosphors with Sb and Mn. The structure and the spectral distribution of the Mn emission of rapidly cooled (quenched) samples more closely approach those found in fluorophosphates. The results suggest that quenching causes a modification in structure and in Mn distribution between the two Ca sites.

REFERENCES

[1] M. R. Lorenz and J. S. Prener, J. Chem. Phys., 25, 1013 (1956).

[2] H. Koelmans, J. Phys. Chem. Solids, 17, 69 (1960).

[3] W. E. Ishler, E. F. Apple, and H. C. Froelich, Conference on Luminescence, Balatonvilagos, Hungary (1961); to be published in Acta Physica (Academiae Scientiarum, HUNGARIAE).

[4] S. Naray-Szabo, Zeit. Krist., 75, 387 (1930).

[5] S. B. Hendricks, M. E. Jefferson, V. M. Mosley, Zeit. Krist., 81, 352 (1931).

[6] P. D. Johnson, this conference'

[7] P. D. Johnson, J. Appl. Phys., 32, 127 (1961).

[8] L. Suchow, J. Electrochem. Soc., 108, 847 (1961).

[9] K. Butler and C. W. Jerome, J. Electrochem. Soc., 97, 265 (1950).

[10] P. D. Johnson, Bull. Am. Phys. Soc., February 1961, p. 30.

[11] J. L. Ouweltjes, Philips Tech. Rev., 13, 346 (1951).

[12] J. S. Prener and F. E. Williams, Electrochem. Soc., Electronics Division Extended Abstracts, May 1955, p. 31.

INFRARED EFFECTS IN ZnS

Karl Luchner*
Technische Hochschule, Munich

I am going to report some results concerning infrared stimulation and quenching in ZnS phosphors.

Stimulation and quenching, as you know, can be observed if one excites the crystal, for instance by UV, and then adds IR radiation. In this way one can observe a transient increase in the luminescence intensity (stimulation); then in most cases the intensity decreases to a value lower than that obtained before the IR was switched on (quenching). As a measure of stimulation we take ΔI, the difference in the intensities of the stimulation peak and the equilibrium fluorescence without IR irradiation. The quenching can be understood with the model of Schön and Klasens: IR releases holes into the valence band, and these holes then have a chance to recombine non-radiatively with trapped electrons. This quenches the luminescence intensity because fewer activators are excited, and because electrons disappear non-radiatively. For the stimulation it would not seem too unreasonable to assume a symmetric process, namely an IR-induced release of electrons into the conductivity band and a subsequent recombination. There are, however, certain findings which do not agree very well with this explanation of the stimulation process. For instance, the photoconductivity (observed together with the luminescence) does not increase when IR is switched on. Instead it drops at once while the luminescence exhibits the transient increase. The question arises: how can the photoconductivity decrease if it is true that electrons are released into the conduction band by IR? In order to clear this up we have tried to establish a correlation between the trap population and the amount of stimulation, ΔI. To express myself as clearly as possible, I will first report the conclusion at which we arrived, and then I will discuss the measurements.

*Work done while on leave at Radiation & Solid State Laboratory, New York University. An extended version will be presented for Habilitation at the Technische Hochschule, Munich.

The conclusion we arrived at is that stimulation does not consist mainly in a release of trapped electrons, but rather in a faster recombination between free electrons and ionized activators induced by IR. What we mean by faster recombination I will say at the end. With this faster recombination the decrease in photoconductivity together with the increase in luminescence can be understood.

The following experiments were performed. First the phosphor sample was excited to equilibrium. Then the UV was switched off and a glow curve taken. Instead of taking a full glow curve, however, the heating was stopped after the first glow maximum had disappeared, and then the phosphor was cooled down again to liquid nitrogen temperature. This means that only the shallowest traps had been emptied. When IR was switched on we no longer got any stimulation. This in itself does not mean very much. It just means that the stimulation either depends on the presence of filled shallowest traps or on a great number of free electrons, because, if the shallowest traps are empty, the number of free electrons also decreases strongly. In order to decide whether the stimulation depends on either a great number of free electrons or on a great number of filled shallowest traps, the following experiments were performed. During the glow curve infrared was switched on for a short period, only long enough to see ΔI. In this case stimulation occurs, even in the later parts of the glow, when the shallowest traps and also some deeper traps have already been emptied. Even more, the height of each stimulation peak is roughly proportional to the corresponding glow intensity. This shows that the stimulation does not depend primarily on the trap population, because we showed earlier that stimulation disappears when the shallowest traps are empty. Now we are left with the possibility mentioned above: stimulation depends on the number of free electrons. The proportionality between ΔI and the glow intensity also indicates this. In order to give the idea a stronger foundation, we studied the behavior of glow curves under continuous IR irradiation.

In this way it was found, among other things, that the second glow maximum appears at a temperature lower than without IR. This must mean that the IR causes a faster recombination between conduction electrons and excited activators, i.e., the conduction electrons disappear faster, the retrapping process decreases, the traps empty earlier, and the glow maximum, therefore, appears at a lower temperature than without IR. One can calculate the increase in recombination probability from the shift of the glow maximum using a theory of Schön, and in our case we find the increase to be fifteen-fold. This is in very good agreement with what we found with IR pulses during the glow. The increase in luminescence then was 14.5-fold, or the increase in the recombination probability was 14.5-fold. [This analysis is successful quantitatively only when quenching plays a negligible role. For phosphors with strong quenching the glow curve under continuous IR is quite distorted. For phosphors with only weak stimulation the shift of the glow maximum is too small to be observed. For details see H. KALLMANN and K. LUCHNER, Phys. Rev. 123, 2013 (1961).]

In order to explain the faster recombination we must assume that an activator has more than one electron level, and that the levels have different cross sections. If the hole is in a level with a small cross section, then we observe a low recombination probability. If the hole is in a level with a large cross section, we observe a high recombination probability. Since we observe a faster recombination under IR, it is safe to assume that the IR is able to shift holes from levels with a lower to those with a higher recombination probability. Depending on the wavelength of the IR, the shift of the hole can go via the valence band (hole into valence band, then capture by the levels of high cross section with short wavelength IR) or directly (either absorption of energy or forced emission with long wavelength IR). On energy considerations this process requires a difference between the emission spectra without IR and with IR (during stimulation and quenching). This spectral change is observed (see H. KALLMANN, K. LUCHNER and J. POWELL, Phys. Rev. Letters, in press).

A striking feature of this spectral change is the fact that in the center of the normal emission spectrum the stimulation is weakest, and the quenching is strongest. This confirms our model. The excitation (holes) of the center activators is shifted away by IR, therefore stimulation occurs at the edges of the normal emission, and quenching occurs in the center.

A comparison between these effects in phosphors activated with Cu, with Ag, and with Cu, Pb as well as differences in the effects caused by long and short wavelength IR on these phosphors fits into our model.

RELATION BETWEEN PHOTOCONDUCTIVITY AND LIGHT EMISSION IN ZnS

P. Wachter

New York University, New York, New York

I should like to discuss some photoconductivity measurements performed with an ac impedance method.[1] I should like to discuss especially some glow curve measurements.

The following measurements were performed on a ZnS:Ag phosphor which was excited with X-rays. In the temperature range between liquid nitrogen and +130°C we can distinguish four glow maxima in conductivity (Fig. 1) but only three maxima in luminescence (dotted curve). We are, of course, interested in the correlation between the luminescence and conductivity maxima. If we excite the phosphor at low temperatures, and, after a considerable dark decay, make a glow curve, the maxima in luminescence and conductivity at about −172 ° C disappear together. Apparently, the corresponding shallowest trap level decays.

To determine the connection between the following conductivity and light peaks, the phosphor was excited at various intermediate temperatures and then heated. With excitation at, for instance, 145°C, the shallow levels cannot be filled with any stability and their glow peaks are therefore missing. Fig. 2 shows such a glow curve. The glow peaks corresponding to the shallow traps are missing, as is the conductivity peak at −145°C. Maxima at higher temperatures are only slightly changed. We can see that the light peak at −120°C did not disappear. If the conductivity peak at −145°C and the light peak at −120°C were due to transitions from the same level, they would vanish together. A further experiment with excitation at −80°C finally leaves only light and conductivity peaks at −40°. The conductivity, σ, peak at −145°C has no corresponding light peak, and is probably due to a process different from that of the other glow maxima which we wish to connect with the emptying of electron traps. We can also see from Figs. 1 or 2 that light and conductivity maxima do not appear at the same temperature. Since we have established the connection between luminescence and

---

1 Described by B. Kramer, this conference

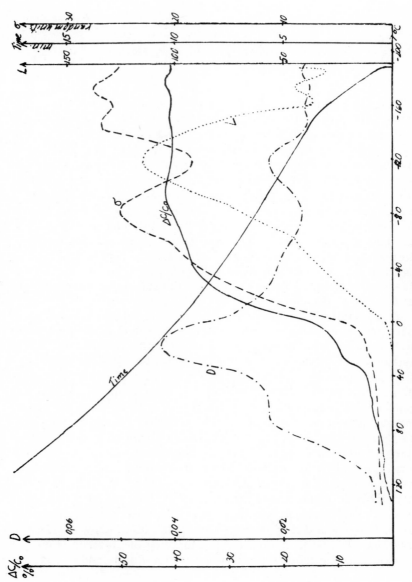

Fig. 1 — Glow curve of ZnS:Ag after X-ray excitation at -188°C. Heating rate 18°/min. (σ = conductivity, L = Luminescence intensity, $\Delta C/C_0$ = relative capacitance change, D = dissipation factor.)

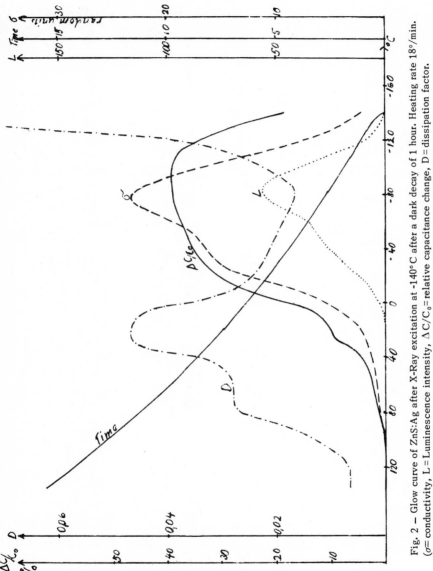

Fig. 2 – Glow curve of ZnS:Ag after X-Ray excitation at -140°C after a dark decay of 1 hour. Heating rate 18°/min. (σ= conductivity, L= Luminescence intensity, $\Delta C/C_0$= relative capacitance change, D= dissipation factor.

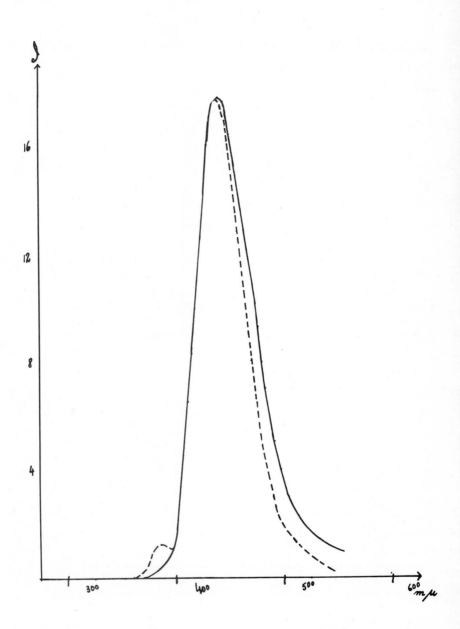

Fig. 3.— Emission spectrum of ZnS:Ag at room temperature ———— and at liquid nitrogen temperature -------- under excitation with X-Rays.

conductivity maxima, we see that the light peaks are shifted to lower temperatures relative to the conductivity peaks. The amount of shift depends on the heating rate. The luminescence is proportional to $\beta n p_t$ (where β is the coefficient of radiative recombination, n the free electron concentration, and p_t the trapped hole concentration); the trapped holes decrease continuously during the glow curve, which means that the luminescence decays earlier than the conductivity. But still we are left with one single conductivity peak for which there is no corresponding luminescence peak. If we assume that this peak is caused by the emptying of another trap level, we would not understand why we have luminescence at lower as well as at higher temperatures from this peak. Our conclusion is that we deal here with the emptying of an activator level where the trapped holes from the activator go into the valence band. We then would have hole conductivity. (The experimental method that we use cannot distinguish between hole and electron conductivity.) This leads to the conclusion that we must have at least two activator levels in this phosphor. In this case we should have, at a temperature below this σ maximum, two activator levels available and consequently two emission bands. At temperatures above this maximum we should have one emission maximum less.

Fig. 3 shows the emission spectrum of this ZnS:Ag phosphor at low temperatures and at room temperatures with X-ray excitation. At low temperatures we have, in fact, two maxima. One is the well known blue emission of this phosphor at 425 mμ, and the second is in the ultraviolet region at 380 mμ. At temperatures above $-145°C$ we can only distinguish the blue maximum. If we calculate the energy depth of this activator level from the glow curves, we get about 0.25 ev. The maximum of the ultraviolet emission yields about 3.2 ev. Considering that a factor of two exists between thermal and optical release of electrons from traps, and applying this to the release of holes, we can add these two energies, which then yields the band gap of ZnS of 3.7 ev.

I should like also to make some remarks concerning the IR effects on this phosphor. We illuminate this phosphor with IR of about 3μ in the dark decay at low temperatures, and after cessation of excitation we make a glow curve. In addition to the normally decaying shallowest traps, the unpaired conductivity maximum disappears at $-145°C$. If we repeat this experiment with 1.2μ, the light and conductivity maxima at $-120°$ and $-80°$, respectively, disappear; the maxima at higher temperatures are only slightly reduced. IR of 1μ apparently empties all levels of this phosphor. This would indicate that the various wavelengths of IR act in about the same way as temperature. This is somehow in contradiction with normal quenching effects, which would show rather that infrared mainly produces holes in the valence band and, therefore, drains off electrons from the traps non-radiatively.

ELECTROLUMINESCENCE OF ZnS EXCITED WITH LINEAR VOLTAGE TRANSIENTS*

G. Bonfiglioli, P. Brovetto, C. Cortese

Instituto Elettrotecnico Nazionale Galileo Ferraris, Torino (Italy)

I. INTRODUCTION

This communication describes a particular technique of excitation of electroluminescence, and the results obtained by its use on ZnS commercial cells of the condenser type.

The justification of this approach resides in the fact that there are still a lot of open questions in electroluminescence, discussions still taking place about rather fundamental aspects of its mechanism, for instance, about the actual role of impact excitation, or about the way charge carriers are supplied to the phosphor. Moreover, the vast and complicated group of phenomena related to the so-called frozen polarization and particularly to its relation to the light output, has been studied only very partially.

Actually, these phenomena can become quite impressive under certain operating conditions; while the technique mentioned above is particularly well suited to their study. These circumstances persuaded us that the waveforms used so far to excite electroluminescence (in condenser type cells) were not the proper ones and that with a wiser choice more significant results could be obtained. Obviously, the wave-form is to be chosen in such a way as to give the maximum information. *A priori* one would guess that periodic waves, like sine waves, are well suited, as are single pips, but this attitude would actually be too arbitrary. In fact, it is obvious that, for exciting an electroluminescent cell it is necessary to apply to it a voltage and to let it change with time. The value of the voltage and its behavior as a function of time, and the value and behavior of its time derivative are in principle completely independent of each other. However, this is not the case with periodic waves, where, on the contrary, the function and its derivative are substantially proportional. They become

*The research reported in this document has been sponsored by the Office of AEROSPACE RESEARCH, of the UNITED STATES AIR FORCE, through its European Office, under Contract No. 61(052)-328.

605

independent if single transients are used, which has actually been done rather seldom.

The most natural approach in this direction is, of course, to excite the samples with single transients (both rising and falling) having a constant derivative with time. This is precisely the technique we made use of.

II. EXPERIMENTAL

The cells used in the experiments reported here* were commercial cells: Westinghouse, Rayscent Panels, of the green type. They consisted of ZnS:Cu,Cl, mostly cubic phase. These cells undergo single voltage transients increasing or decreasing at a strictly constant rate versus time, from zero to a certain value V_{max}, or from V_{max} to zero, respectively.

The value of V in our experiments could be varied from about 120 up to 220 Volts and the rate of variation with time from about 10 V/msec up to 10^3 V/msec. This was accomplished through a conventional electronic circuit, where a bootstrap insured the constancy of slope of the voltage step. The cell was viewed by an R.C.A. photomultiplier model 6810 A (14 dynodes) through an interference filter of about 150 Å band width and a honeycomb collimator to reduce the incident angle spread. Two filters were used alternately in our experiments, a green one centered at 5200 Å and a blue one at 4700 Å. Fig. 1 shows an enlarged view of this set-up. Let us stress that when operating with such high gain phototubes and fairly long light pulses (around 10^{-3} seconds) care must be exercised to avoid saturation. Therefore a calibration of the maximum output admissible was performed with a special device.*

All the measurements referred to here were made at room temperature. Both rising and falling voltages were used and every measurement was performed once with the green filter and then repeated with the blue one.

Fig. 2 reproduces a couple of typical oscillograms showing both the voltage step and the light pulse, recorded at the same time on the two channels of the C.R.T. One oscillogram refers to a rising voltage and the second to a falling voltage, but the voltage step has actually been inverted in the C.R.T. amplifier.

---

*For a more complete description of the experimental details, the reader is referred to Technical Note No. 4, Contract AF 61(052) 328, (ARCD,USAF), by the same authors.

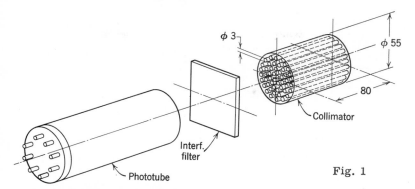

Fig. 1

The quantities which were measured using the rather large series of pictures taken were the following: 1) the height of the light peaks; 2) the time for the half-height; 3) the "phase-time", that is, the difference between the time the voltage step starts and the time the light pulse reaches its maximum.

These three quantities have been plotted against the rate of variation of the voltage, $\dot{V} = V_{max}/\tau$. Fig. 3 shows the results relative to the height of the light pulses for the case of rising voltage. Three different values of V_{max} have been considered and the behaviors of the green and blue components are shown separately.

Fig. 4 shows the same situation for a voltage falling with time. It can be seen that green and blue components behave in the same way, showing an almost constant ratio, green to blue, of roughly 5. This behavior is common both to rising and falling steps, but for each color the pulse height for rising steps is always about twice as great as for falling steps.

Fig. 5 shows the ratio of the half-height time to the duration of the voltage step for rising and for falling voltage together. And Fig. 6 shows the ratios of the phase-time to the step duration.

It can be seen that these two quantities, the half-height time and the phase, behave in a very similar way, while their common behavior is different for rising or for falling voltages, respectively.

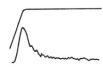

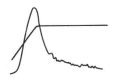

Fig. 2

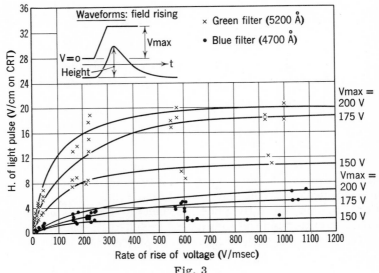

Fig. 3

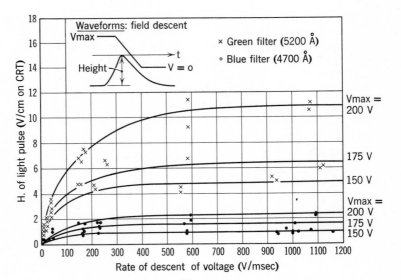

Fig. 4

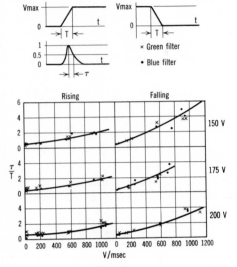

Fig. 5

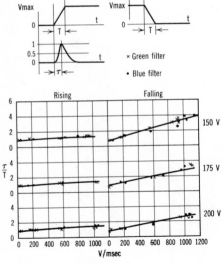

Fig. 6

To these results it can be added that, as was already mentioned, we were able to observe, with this technique, important time dependent phenomena. The light emitted during a certain transient depends in an exceedingly strong way upon the time which has elapsed from the last transient undergone by the cell; if this time is very short, say, at room temperature, less than one second, the light output is bigger by a factor of perhaps several hundred. This factor tends asymptotically to unity when the time elapsed grows longer. At room temperature the value 1 is almost reached in our cells after 10-15 minutes. All the measurements reported here have thus been made after sufficient recovery; in fact, 7 minutes always separate two consecutive pictures. Investigations on these recovery effects at various temperatures have been started in our Laboratory and their correlation with phenomena of "frozen polarization" is currently being investigated.

III. DISCUSSION

It is worthwhile to point out that some striking features of the above experimental results, for example the saturation shown by the curves of Fig. 3 and 4, are no doubt connected with rather trivial aspects of "circuital" character, of the phenomenon investigated. Therefore, some comment is needed to elucidate which "physical" information one may hope to extract from the present data.

It is in fact well known that an electroluminescent condenser-type cell can be represented roughly by a condenser C in series with a resistor R. The non-ohmic behavior of this resistor, or its even more complex nature (potential barrier, with perhaps parallel capacitors) clearly do not substantially affect the qualitative behavior of the current pulse flowing through the cell, when the latter undergoes a transient of the shape used in our experiments. That is, the current pulse consists of the following two parts:

$$\text{for } t \leqslant \tau : i = \dot{V}C\left(1 - e^{-t/RC}\right)$$

$$\text{for } t \geqslant \tau : i = \dot{V}C\left(e^{\tau/RC} - 1\right) e^{-t/RC}$$

Its shape then recalls the aspect of our light pulses, with obvious differences whose character can be easily guessed. The

value of i_{max} [that is $i(\tau)$] as a function of V and V_{max}
turns out to be given by

$$i_{max} = \dot{V}C \left(1 - e^{-V_{max}/\dot{V}RC}\right)$$

which clearly explains the saturation already mentioned. In
this way, several features of our curves can be understood,
in their main aspects. On the other hand, the difference in the
behavior of the measured parameters, when rising or falling
voltages are respectively considered, cannot be accounted for
on these grounds and its origin is to be sought elsewhere.

Very likely the potential barrier which is generally assumed
to exist at the surface of the sulfide grains is modified during
the passage of the current, as frozen polarization indicates.

In conclusion, stressing again that the present paper has
only a preliminary character, it appears that the kind of
measurements presented here, if accompanied by an accurate
analysis of the equivalent circuit, instead of the rough analogy
mentioned above, should be capable of giving valuable information about several aspects of the mechanism through which ac
electroluminescence takes place.

RADIATION INDUCED DC ELECTROLUMINESCENCE IN ZnS:Mn

M. Vogel
International Business Machines Corporation
San Jose, California

I would like to offer these experiments as a contribution to the general knowledge of electroluminescence. I will describe the method by which we have made a non-electroluminescent phosphor dc responsive.

We prepared a ZnS:Mn phosphor by firing it at 1250°C for one hour with flux of between one and two percent potassium sulfate. The atmosphere was air, and a careful attempt was made to remove any halogens from the phosphor. A heavy concentration of the phosphor was embedded in an epoxy resin binder. We used an epoxy 815 with a hexahydro-phthalic anhydride heat curing catalyst. A conductive-glass plate was coated with this mixture and heated at 176°C for one hour to produce a hard film on the surface of the glass. In laboratory experiments, this phosphor showed no electroluminescent response to ac or dc stimulation.

This phosphor has been made electroluminescent by the simultaneous application of ultraviolet and a direct current. The area to be rendered dc electroluminescent is coated with an electrolyte—in this case a 10 pct. solution of potassium chloride in polyvinyl alcohol, which forms a soft plastic film on the surface of the conductive-glass plate. The glass is positive, the electrolyte negative. The same was irradiated with 3660 Å (the radiation required to excite the phosphor to photofluorescence). At the same time, a field of 300 v dc is applied, and the phosphor emits a glow typical of the field-enhanced effect reported by Destriau,[1] Studer, and Cusano. But in this case the area remains dc responsive when the ultraviolet is removed.

By projecting the ultraviolet through a gelatin mask, a permanent electroluminescent image can be stored on the phosphor-

---

[1] D. A. Cusano, Unique Phosphors that Amplify Light, GE Review, September, 1956, Page 2.

G. Destriau, J. Mattler, M. Destriau, H. E. Gemlich, J. Electro-Chem. Soc., 102, 682 (1955).

coated plate. The image stored on one such plate is still visible after three years with no apparent loss of image quality. After the original exposure to ultraviolet, the panel was washed with soap, dried, and baked. As you can see, under field stimulation the panel reproduces the image projected by the ultraviolet with half-tone gradations. The image is a permanent part of the phosphor grains themselves; even when a portion of the upper surface of the film is cut away, the area below still shows the dc electroluminescence. Further, there is no spreading or diffusion of the image; only the portions of the surface exposed to ultraviolet emit radiation.

Chernow: Have you tried this with anything except epoxy resin as a binder?

Vogel: Yes, I have. I have made it also in a silicon resin, instead of epoxy, and it works as well. The important thing is that there must be contact between the phosphor grain and the electrolyte. A minute film, a fraction of one mil thick, using such things as acrylics, completely negates the effect and one sees no electroluminescence. One can do that either on the top surface or on the conductive-glass plate. The phosphor grains must be in contact with the bottom electrode and the top electrolyte.

Kallmann: This is something similar to what was observed by the people at Philco, about two or three years ago, I think. They excited CdS. They could control the luminescence completely by the electric field. By taking out the holes they had no luminescence. By reversing the voltage they had a fluorescence. I think the whole explanation was that if you have an electrolyte electrode you can get the holes out of the sample..

Vogel: In this case one has a permanent change, which is not capable of reversible action. This sample now is completely stable. Once this change has been initiated, you have a stable dc electroluminescence. Looking at the sample under the microscope, one does not see any scintillation effects that one can note in a pulsed dc effect. One sees the steady state emission of the phosphor grains. In the forthcoming publication you will see photomicrographs of some of these phosphor grains. They are brightly glowing, emitting a steady pulse.

Lohmann: What happens when you reverse the voltage? Is it
still dc electroluminescence? Only in the one direction?

Vogel: This is a good question. When one makes the electrolyte
positive and the plate negative, one gets no dc electroluminescence. In the electrolysis of the platinum electrode in the
electrolyte an ionization of the solution takes place. Only
photoconductive phosphors can be made electroluminescent by
this method. One can measure the photoconductivity of the
phosphor film and one can watch, then, the growth process.
It forms a growth curve very similar to a hysteresis curve.
There is initial rapid growth, leveling, and finally stabilization of the electroluminescence at any particular voltage. The
voltage we used was 300 v dc, but we can get down as low as
100 v.

MICROSCOPIC OBSERVATIONS
OF ELECTROLUMINESCENCE IN ZnS

J. L. Gillson, Jr. and F. J. Darnell

E. I. du Pont de Nemours and Company

Wilmington, Delaware

A number of investigators have reported that electroluminescence in ZnS is not homogeneous but originates from spots, streaks, or patches.[1-14] We have carried out detailed microscopic studies of the localization of electroluminescence in ZnS crystals to determine what role physical impurities (other than point defects) may play in the electroluminescent process.

Single crystals of average dimension 0.5 mm. were prepared by sublimation of ZnS powder and growth on a cooler surface. Cu, Cu + Pb, or Ag were used as activators. The usual crystal was a prism with its axis parallel to the [00·1] direction of the hexagonal structure, and consisting of alternating layers of cubic and hexagonal structure. Electroluminescence was excited by sine wave or variable length rectangular pulse voltages. Similar results were obtained for electrodes either attached directly to the crystals or insulated from the crystals.

Observations on many ZnS crystals have shown that electroluminescent activity is generally confined to layers parallel to the basal plane of the wurtzite structure. In these layers the emission originates at tiny glowing lines and spots as shown in Figure 1. The most frequent arrangement consists of straight lines with apparent width of a few microns and lengths up to several hundred microns. The lines form parallel sets which lie at 60° to each other (Figure 2). X-ray orientation showed that the lines lie at 30° to the hexagonal a axis, i.e., along [11·0] directions. Photoluminescence observations on the same crystals showed emission sometimes restricted to definite layers normal to the prism axis, but no discrete localization, as in the electroluminescence, was found.

The lines appear somewhat like tiny comets, being brightest at one end and fading toward the other end. Lines frequently occur in collinear pairs, tail to tail, as in Figure 3. The bright ends are fixed while the length increases with increasing voltage or decreasing frequency of excitation. Each line was found

Fig. 1 – Photograph of localized electroluminescent emission from a ZnS crystal viewed parallel to the prism axis. Area 65 x 100 microns.

to emit only on one half cycle, that in which the voltage at the head of the line became positive. No emission was observed unless a negative voltage was previously applied at the head end of the line. The two ends of a double ended line thus emitted on alternate half cycles.

The observed emission patterns indicate the necessity of specific linear physical defects for electroluminescence in the ZnS crystals studied. A model incorporating such defects, and more detailed descriptions of the voltage, frequency, and temperature dependence of the observed lines, will be published elsewhere.[15]

REFERENCES

[1] W. W. Piper and F. E. Williams, Phys. Rev. 87, 151 (1952)
[2] J. F. Waymouth and F. Bitter, Phys. Rev. 95, 941 (1954)
[3] P. Zalm, G. Diemer, and H. A. Klasens, Philips Res. Rept. 9, 81 (1954); ibid., 10, 205 (1955)

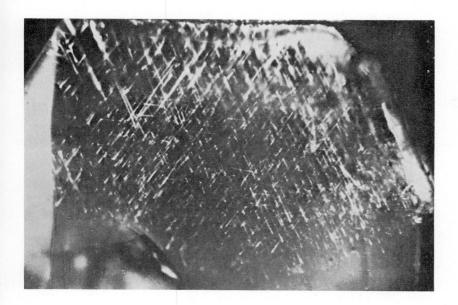

Fig. 2 — View as in Figure 1, for a different crystal. Area 0.8 x 1.2 mm.

Fig. 3 — View as in Figure 1. The double ended line is 100 microns in length.

[4] E. E. Loebner and H. Freund, Phys. Rev. 98, 1545 (1955), Abstract

[5] G. Diemer, Philips Res. Rept. 10, 194 (1955)

[6] M. A. Short, E. G. Steward, and T. B. Tomlinson, Nature 177, 240 (1956)

[7] P. Zalm, Philips Res. Rept. 11, 353 (1956)

[8] W. Lehmann, J. Electrochem. Soc. 104, 45 (1957)

[9] J. Woods, J. Electronics and Control 3, 531 (1957)

[10] D. R. Frankl, Phys. Rev. 111, 1540 (1958)

[11] V. E. Oranovskii and B. A. Khmelinin, Optics and Spectroscopy (USSR) 7, 336 (1959) (English transl.)

[12] A. Kremheller, J. Electrochem. Soc. 107, 8 (1960)

[13] W. Lehmann, J. Electrochem. Soc. 107, 20 (1960)

[14] W. Lehmann, J. Electrochem. Soc. 107, 657 (1960)

[15] J. L. Gillson, Jr. and F. J. Darnell, Phys. Rev. (to be published)

Ivey: Did I understand you to say that silver worked as well as copper for this? That is quite an innovation!

Darnell: I did not grow any of these crystals, so I have to accept the word of those who did. These crystals were grown by adding silver to a phosphor charge and then subliming them by growing them on a cooler surface.

Rump: Have you tried to make a correlation between these light spots and crystal defects like stacking faults?

Darnell: Yes, we used a microbeam X-ray to look at the structure, and we have also done some bi-refringence studies. We find that the emission always occurs at places where the structure is changing rapidly, but we cannot determine whether it occurs in the structure of a given type or at the boundary.

Carlston: Do you think that it is possible that the electroluminescence is a result of the finite impurity trapping at the basal plane rather than of anything physical?

Darnell: Well, I am not sure why they should be localized in lines; they could be localized in planes. But why these fixed lines should exist aside from any additional defects within that plane, I cannot see.

Wachtel: If the crystal is viewed in the microscope without
the application of a field, can anything be noted at the places
where the bright part of the line could be seen during the
electroluminescence, such as inclusions?

Darnell: There is no good correlation. We have some pictures
of surface defects which are apparently little hills, but in
white light you cannot see this structure without an applied
field. The luminescence itself, photoluminescence, may appear in layers, but there is no structure within the layers,
as there is to the electroluminescence.

EXCITATION AND EMISSION SPECTRA
OF DONOR-ACCEPTOR PAIRS IN ZINC SULFIDE

Ferd E. Williams

Physics Department, University of Delaware
Newark, Delaware

In this contribution we are concerned with determining whether the theoretical studies[1] on donor-acceptor pairs are in accord with experimental work reported by Apple and Williams[2] and more recently by Van Gool[3] on the luminescent emission from zinc sulfide containing equivalent concentrations of Group IB activators and Group IIIB coactivators. In addition, we report and interpret experimental measurements of the excitation spectra of these materials.

Two effects of association influence the excitation and emission spectra which can be attributed to donor-acceptor pairs. First, the energy levels of donor and acceptor are perturbed towards their respective band edges as a consequence of association. This effect leads to an increase in transition energy for each transition between a particular donor state and a particular acceptor state as the interimpurity distance is decreased. Second, with donor-acceptor pairs characterized by large interimpurity distances, only transitions between the conduction band edge or excited donor states and the ground acceptor state can occur. However, as the interimpurity distance is decreased, the overlap between the wave function for the ground state of the donor and the ground state of the acceptor becomes sufficient so that this transition which has a smaller transition energy can occur. These effects are illustrated in Fig. 1 for short wavelength emission involving an excited donor state in a less highly associated pair, and for long wavelength emission involving the ground state of the donor in a more highly associated pair. The acceptor state lies lower in the latter pair; however, the transition energy is less because the transition involves the ground rather than the excited state of the associated donor. For very highly associated pairs, such as nearest neighbor pairs, the ground states of the donor and acceptor will be strongly perturbed toward the band edges so that the transition energy will increase.

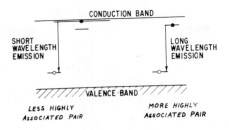

Fig. 1

Apple and Williams[2] proposed that red emission from zinc sulfide containing equivalent concentrations of Group IB activators and Group IIIB coactivators arises from the fourth or slightly greater nearest neighbors ($l \geq 4$). We shall, therefore, consider the magnitude of the two effects of association on the emission and excitation spectra for the fifth nearest neighbor pair. The interimpurity separation for this pair is 8.6 Å. This is almost an order of magnitude smaller than the average interimpurity separation for a random distribution with a concentration of 10^{-4} donors and acceptors. Therefore, the fifth nearest neighbor pair can be properly described as associated.

We shall first consider emission. It has been shown that the transition energy for the radiative annihilation of the electron and hole in particular states of the pair is increased for small overlap[1] as follows:

$$\Delta E_a \approx \frac{e^2}{K_o R}$$

where K_o is the optical dielectric constant. The energy ΔE_a equals 0.3 e.v. for the fifth pair. However, if the transition now involves the ground state of donor, where $E_D \approx 0.5$ e.v. for a typical Group IIIB donor, then emission from the fifth pair should correspond to a transition energy approximately 0.2 e.v. less than the transition energy for less highly associated pairs. This is qualitatively in accord with experiment but is quantitatively too small by a factor of two or three. The quantitative discrepancy probably arises in part from the large central cell and polarization effects characteristic of emission. Typical experimental emission spectra on these materials have been reported by Apple and Williams[2] and by Van Gool.[3]

We now consider excitation spectra. The transition energy for the radiative creation of electron and hole in particular states is increased for small overlap as follows:

$$\Delta E_c \approx \frac{e^2}{R}\left(\frac{2}{K_s} - \frac{1}{K_o}\right),$$

where K_s is the static dielectric constant. This equals 0.1 e.v. for the fifth pair. However, if the transition now involves the ground state of the donor, which for the condition of polarization corresponding to being unoccupied $E_D^1 \approx 0.2$ e.v., then excitation of the fifth pair should correspond to a transition energy approximately 0.1 e.v. less than the transition energy for less highly associated pairs. This is, perhaps fortuitous, quantitative agreement with the data of Fig. 2. At the lower concentration, the less highly associated pairs are involved, whereas at the higher concentration, the pairs responsible for the red emission predominate. More detailed studies at low temperatures of the excitation spectra for the different emission bands confirm the data of Fig. 2.

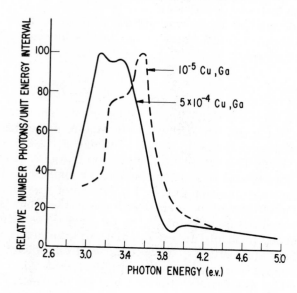

Fig. 2

In general, the experimental data on zinc sulfide containing equivalent concentrations of Group IB activators and Group IIIB coactivators are in accord with the theoretical investigations of donor-acceptor pairs. In the application of the theory, it should be emphasized that the energy level structure and oscillator strength for each transition are characteristic of each pair with a particular interimpurity spacing, the distribution function for the different pairs changes with impurity concentration, and the emission intensity from each pair depends on the occupational probabilities of the states of that pair for both electrons and holes, as well as on the energy level structure, oscillator strengths for particular transitions, and concentration of that pair. At low temperatures specific pairs should be capable of excitation without photoconduction; at high temperatures there will, of course, be approximate equilibrium of the electrons among the donor and conduction band states and of the positive holes among the acceptor and valence band states. The previous considerations suggest that of the order of the fifth nearest neighbors may dominate the emission under suitable conditions because these may have the smallest transition energy combined with a favorable oscillator strength for that transition. This is, of course, the red emission.

REFERENCES

[1] F. E. Williams, J. Phys. Chem. Solids 12, 265 (1960)
[2] E. A. Apple and F. E. Williams, J. Electrochem. Soc. 106, 224 (1959)
[3] W. Van Gool, Philips Research Supplement No. 3 (1961)

Potter: If you speak of the long wavelength center being associated up to the fourth nearest neighbor, then starting at the fifth nearest neighbor, you apparently really ought to speak of long and short wavelength emission rather than of centers, because presumably from the fourth nearest neighbor you may have either type of transition. Is this correct?

Williams: I want to emphasize in answering this question the complexity of the situation, and this is perhaps the most important point I can make. Association of activators and coactivators is now quite generally accepted, therefore, we must appreciate that we do not have a uniform type of center in the ZnS phosphors. Any theory that depends only on a single type of center is unrealistic. Therefore, what we must keep in mind in answering this question is that there is a broad distribution of donor-acceptor pairs, and as the concentration is increased, the distribution function changes. As one increases concentration the fraction of pairs that is more highly associated increases. The fourth, fifth and sixth nearest neighbors will be characterized by a small transition energy for excitation or emission. The reason for this is that these donors and acceptors are now close enough, so that a transition can occur from the ground state of the donor to the ground state of the acceptor because of overlap of the electron and hole wave functions. This will be the dominant emission process at ordinary temperatures because the other transitions require thermal excitation to the excited states of donor or acceptor. As noted by Broser and others, at ordinary temperatures one has equilibrium, to a good approximation, of the electrons among donor states and separately of the holes among acceptor states. Neighbors that are approximately the fourth or fifth nearest have the smallest transition energies; the total energy of the crystal is the lowest when these are excited, therefore, these pairs will be responsible for the dominant emission process, if there are an appreciable number present. With further increase in concentration more of the pairs become more highly associated, and the levels will be perturbed towards the respective band edges, and the transition energy increases. Thus, the transition energy goes through a minimum and that is, I think, what makes it understandable that there are, at most, a few long wavelength emission bands rather close together rather than a continuous spectrum. The specific question, as you may remember, concerned whether one expects a transition from the excited state in addition in a pair in which the ground state transition can occur. This transition does not compete at low temperatures because most pairs will be in the ground state; with increasing temperature, more of the shorter wavelength process occurs because the excited states of all pairs become populated and this emission can occur in pairs less highly associated than those capable of the long wavelength emission.

Shionoya: May I ask your opinion on the so-called copper blue luminescence? What transition is responsible for the copper blue luminescence?

Williams: On the copper blue, I think, the work of Professor Riehl is perhaps more relevant. Both that work and the earlier work of Kröger strongly suggest that one has not only a substitutional copper, but probably also another copper present, such as an interstitial copper, and this center is certainly more complicated than these others we have just described.

Curie: It does not seem that the energy of the transition between the donor and the acceptor is highly sensitive to the distance between them, because, at first sight, one can get to an emission band when they are associated in the nearest neighbor position or also when they are associated as second neighbors, as third neighbors, etc. We do not have as many bands as that. Of course, we can say that perhaps the transition probability is very small when the overlap is poor, and that the bands that we can foresee when the distance between the donor and the acceptor is large, are not sufficiently intense to be observed. Now, the calculation you performed gives, on the contrary, a rather fast dependence of the energy between the donor and the acceptor on the distance between them. What do you think of this?

Williams: I do not believe that any of these bands that we are now referring to, this is not including edge emission, but, say, the copper green band and the long wavelength band, involve the first or the second or the third nearest neighbor pairs. It is in this region where the transition energy between particular states of the donor and acceptor changes rather rapidly with interimpurity separation. Thus, I do not think that there is any conflict in the theory for these bands; that is, the red band we attribute to the fourth to sixth nearest-neighbor pairs and these have interimpurity distances just small enough for overlap of the ground state donor wave function with the ground state acceptor wave function. We look at the theory, the effective mass theory, which should apply for these large distances, and we find that the perturbation of the levels for excitation is of the order of a tenth of a volt; for emission it is of the order of three tenths of a volt. When one considers the less highly associated pairs that must involve an excited state of the donor or possibly the conduction band edge, the transition energy is greater because the depth of the donor is now included. Because these depths are greater than the perturbation energies for pairs such as fifth nearest neighbors, the emission involving excited donor states has greater transition energy than the emission involving the ground state of the donor. There is, therefore, no conflict between experiment and theory.

Luchner: I have a question concerning the consequences of your model with regard to the electronic kinetics which would come out of the close association of donor and acceptor pairs. Is it safe to assume that if you have a close association of donor and acceptor, this would give a monomolecular recombination mechanism, while when donors and acceptors are not very close, this would give a bimolecular recombination mechanism?

Williams: I slightly object in the present context to the term "close association"; if we mean by that the fifth nearest neighbor or pairs less associated, that is all right. As we consider pairs characterized by smaller and smaller interimpurity distances, the levels between which transitions can occur come closer together, because we are concerned with different levels for which transitions are permitted due to increased overlap of the more tightly bound states. And then as the interimpurity distance is reduced further, all levels are pushed towards the band edges. At ordinary temperatures —at this point the argument does not apply to very low temperatures—one should to a good approximation have equilibria of electrons among donor states and holes among acceptor states. If this is a good approximation, then the recombination, in general, will be of second order.

Brandt: Would this apply to all concentrations? I think, the question really was: would it be strictly second order or would there be indications of first-order components?

Williams: If one goes to sufficiently low temperatures and excites specifically in pairs of a certain type, then one could predict from this model that the recombination would become first order.

Luchner: Can one discriminate between the luminescence which arises from close centers and that from centers farther away? For close centers one would have a first order recombination in the phosphorescence and in glow, and, in the other case, there would be a quite different phosphorescence and glow curve.

Williams: Yes, I think that there would be something in experiments of this type, that is, at temperatures below which the equilibrium approximation would not apply, the phosphorescence would be different for the different centers.

Riehl: I wanted only to ask whether we have some experimental evidence for the existence of some pairs? I know the experiments of Apple and Prener on the dependence of the exact shape of the emission bands on the coactivator. This is one indication. Do you know any other indications?

Williams: In this particular context, that is the red emission in these compensated crystals, the overwhelming piece of evidence is that the emission spectrum, in most cases, depends on the chemical identity of both activator and coactivator.

van Gool: According to your opinion, the green emission is also influenced both by activator and coactivator. Should you not expect a continuous transition from green emission to the red emission when the concentrations of activator and coactivator are increased? Experimentally a discontinuous change of green to red is found under these conditions.

Williams: No, the reason is that there is a large energy difference between the ground state of the donor and the first excited state. As one considers pairs characterized by decreasing interimpurity distances, one first considers pairs in which the excited states overlap adequately with the ground state of the acceptors, so that there is a good matrix element for these transitions. Further reduction in interimpurity spacing has essentially no effect until the interimpurity spacing has been reduced to the point at which the overlap of the ground state of the donor with the ground state of the acceptor becomes appreciable. Therefore, the pairs responsible for the two different emission bands will be characterized by markedly different interimpurity distances, as well as by markedly different transition energies.

Luchner: How far apart from each other do you think the donor and acceptor would have to be in order to be able to observe photoconductivity?

Williams: This, of course, depends on the energies of the donor and acceptor states compared to the temperature; that is, if we have the condition that the electrons are in equilibrium among donor states and the holes among the acceptor states, then they are also in equilibrium with their respective band edges. Thus, we should see photoconductivity under the same circumstances in which we see this second order process referred to earlier. If one excites only particular pairs at low enough temperatures, then one does not expect photoconduction.

Luchner: But is it not so that, since we do not have a random distribution, most of these donors and acceptors are pretty close together, so that the largest part would be this first order recombination without photoconductivity?

Williams: If I understand the last comment correctly, there is a misunderstanding. Because in the effective mass approximation and, I think, this applies to the most highly associated pairs, e.g. nearest neighbors, one has a dipole field and the levels are near the band edges. Therefore, these would contribute to the photoconduction. The cases where you should not see the photoconduction are something like the fourth and fifth nearest neighbors. If one specifically excites these at low temperatures, then the electron is frozen in the lowest state of the donor, the hole in the lowest state of the acceptor. Therefore the conduction band edges are not involved at all.

Grillot: Your theory of associated pairs seems interesting in the case of ZnS because it is necessary to have chlorine, for example, or other coactivators. I think that there is a similarity with the semiconductor theory, and there is a possibility to perform some interesting calculations. But I think that there is a great disparity between the luminescence centers in ZnS and in CdS. And it is known that in CdS you can form luminescence powders absolutely without coactivators and you can do the same in the mixtures of ZnS and CdS with only 5% of the latter. I cannot understand how your theory can be taken into consideration in this possibility of transformation of the luminescence centers from the ZnS through the different mixtures to the CdS.

Williams: That is another problem which is, however, relevant. This is the problem of compensation by imperfections. As a consequence of the large band gaps of ZnS and CdS, if one puts in only donor or only acceptor impurities, the crystal will try to create imperfections, such as vacancies, which will thereby compensate for the impurity. These are similar electrically to the impurities and everything I have said about association applies to these defects. This is relevant to the discussion on Shionoya's work, in which clearly he is dealing with these donor-acceptor pairs, but not of the impurity type entirely; but rather one impurity and the other of the defect type. I should point out again that this is a complicated system. One has to get used to the idea that one has this distribution of pairs, each characterized by different energy levels and different probabilities for transitions between particular states.

Kallmann: I just wanted to clear something up. What is the relationship of your associated centers to the traps?

Williams: We talked about this in Paris in 1956. In the case of the more highly associated pairs one does not expect traps. In the case of the pair which is less highly associated and which is characterized by the probability for the transition from the ground state of the donor to the ground state of the acceptor being negligible the ground state of the donor will behave as a trap. This state, which is the emitting state in the more highly associated pair, is a trap in this pair.

THE EFFECT OF Ni ON THE ASSOCIATED DONOR-ACCEPTOR LUMINESCENCE CENTERS IN ZINC SULFIDE PHOSPHORS*

E. F. Apple

General Electric Co.,
Cleveland, Ohio

In a previous investigation, a comprehensive study of ZnS:x(Cu or Ag), y(Ga,In) was made.[1] Two emission bands were observed in each series of samples—the normal short wavelength emission in the blue with Ag and in the green with Cu activators (acceptors), and a long wavelength emission in the yellow with Ag and in the orange red with Cu. Because the spectral distribution of the long wavelength emission depended on the identities of both activator and coactivator (donor) and because the relative intensities of the long and short wavelength emissions depended on concentration of activator and coactivator, it was proposed that the long wavelength emission involved transitions between a highly associated donor-acceptor pair. Specifically, it was suggested that the radiative transition occurred from the ground state of the donor to the ground state of the acceptor. It was later shown that, in addition to the effects of concentration and temperature, the effect of substitution of Cd for Zn in ZnS:(Cu or Ag), (Ga or In) on the ratio of relative intensities of the long to short wavelength emission was consistent with the proposed model.[2]

More recently, van Gool has investigated the systems ZnS:(Cu or Ag or Au), (Ga or Sc or In)[3] and reports results consistent with the original work. He also concludes that the long wavelength emissions arise in associated centers.

Ni is a well-known "killer" for both fluorescence and phosphorescence in ZnS phosphors. It has been observed that gradual addition of Ni to samples of ZnS:(Cu or Ag), In which show both the long and short wavelength emissions causes the ratio of relative intensities of the long to short wavelength emissions (I_l/I_s) to increase. This is shown for ZnS:10^{-5} Ag,In in Figure 1. The ratio I_l/I_s increases from 1.14 to 2.08 on

*This work was done at the General Electric Research Laboratory, Schenectady, N. Y.

increase from 0 to 10^{-5} gram atoms Ni/mol ZnS added. Similar changes are observed in the spectral distribution of ZnS:10^{-4} Ag,In and ZnS:2×10^{-4} Cu,In which are shown in Figures II and III. These results suggest that Ni is a more effective "killer" toward the short wavelength than the long wavelength emission.

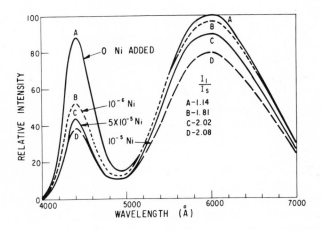

Fig. 1 — Effect of Ni on Emission in Cubic ZnS:10^{-5} Ag,In 3650Å excitation at -196°C

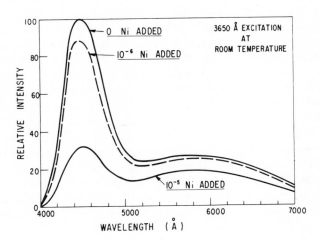

Fig. 2 — Effect of Ni on Emission in Cubic ZnS:10^{-4} Ag,In

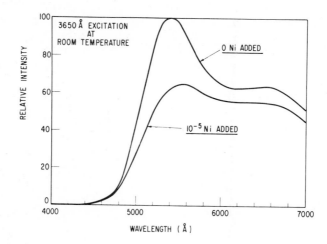

Fig. 3 — Effect of Ni on Emission in Cubic ZnS:2 x 10⁻⁴ Cu,In

The results are consistent with the idea that the long wave-length emission involves transitions between highly associated donor-acceptor pairs. In fact, as suggested in Reference 1, the excitation process at −196°C for the long wavelength center occurs at longer wavelengths than that of the short wavelength center. This would indicate that both excitation and emission of the long wavelength luminescence are highly localized, particularly at low temperatures. Since Ni probably introduces deep traps in ZnS and its killing action is due to electron capture and subsequent radiationless de-excitation,[4] it would be expected that Ni, distributed at random, would have less chance to interfere with the luminescent process in a highly associated (or localized) center than it would in a less associated or non-associated center. In the latter two cases, the chance for electron capture by the Ni center is much greater due to the large spatial extension of the centers and the relatively large distance traversed by the electron involved in the luminescent process. It appears that the effect of Ni on the ratio of relative intensities, I_l/I_s, is consistent with the idea that the long wave-length emission arises in a highly associated center involving both activator and coactivator.

REFERENCES

[1] E. F. Apple and F. E. Williams, J. Electrochem. Soc., _106_, 224 (1959)
[2] E. F. Apple, J. Electrochem. Soc., 107, 418 (1960)
[3] W. van Gool, Philips Research Reports Supplement No. 3, 1961; This Conference
[4] W. Hoogenstraaten, J. Electrochem. Soc., _100_, 356-365 (1953)

Cu BLUE CENTERS

Ralph M. Potter

General Electric Co.,
Cleveland, Ohio

I would like to report an experiment which supports Professor Riehl's interpretation of the nature of the Cu blue centers in ZnS. In this experiment, the absorption spectra as well as the emission spectra were used to qualitatively demonstrate the conversion of Cu green centers into Cu blue centers.

A series of ZnS:xCu, 2% NaCl phosphors was prepared (with $x = 0$, 10^{-5}, 10^{-4}, 3×10^{-4}, and 10^{-3} mole fraction) by firing for one-half hour at 1200°C in telescoping quartz tubes in N_2. (A series fired at 900°C showed analogous results.) The samples were cooled by removing the tubes from the hot furnace. The emission spectra and diffuse reflectance spectra are presented in Figures 1 and 2.

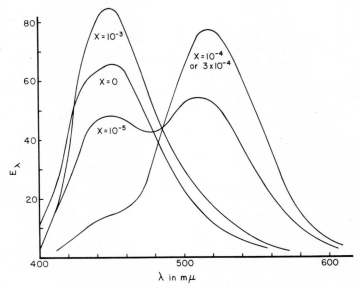

Fig. 1. Luminescence of ZnS:XCu (2%NaCl,1200°C)

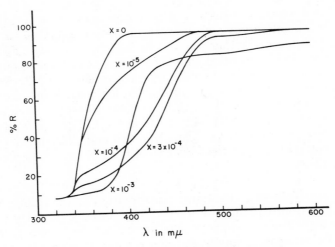

Fig. 2.   Reflectance of ZnS:XCu (2% NaCl, 1200°C)

For $x = 0$, the emission is that of the "self-activated" blue center, and only weak absorption extending to 4000Å is evident. As x is increased from 10^{-5} to 3×10^{-4}, the Cu green band becomes dominant in emission and a strong absorption band extending to 5000Å appears, whose strength increases with Cu content. From evidence of excitation spectra, this new absorption band can be associated with the Cu green emission band. At $x = 10^{-3}$, the Cu blue band becomes dominant, and the absorption increases out to ~4000Å, but decreases from there to ~4600Å. (The increased absorption for $\lambda > 4600$ Å is due to an excess Cu_2S phase which was not removed.) Clearly, the concentration of green centers is lower for $x = 10^{-3}$ than for $x = 10^{-4}$ or 3×10^{-4}. Evidently the green centers (Cu^+ at lattice sites) have become associated with the additional Cu (interstitial Cu^+), presumably with the consequent formation of Cu blue centers.

Melamed: I should like to ask Dr. Apple a question about the orange emission in the ZnS:In. Is it the same as the orange emission in the ZnS:Ag,In and in the ZnS:Cu,In?

Apple: In the In series ZnS:In has an emission spectrum which peaks at about 6200Å; ZnS:Ag,In peaks at about 6100Å. I think ZnS:Cu,In peaks at 6500 or 6600Å.

van Gool: May I add something to what you said? ZnS with In
  alone behaves completely differently; it has nearly no emission, or only a very weak emission. With ZnS:Cu,In and
  ZnS:Cu the emissions are not far apart. ZnS:Au,In and
  ZnS:Ag,In show emission which is different from ZnS:Cu,In.
  Therefore the only question which remains is whether the
  emissions of ZnS:Cu,In and ZnS:Cu have the same cause. We
  have done much work on this problem. We have been able to
  prove that in the case of ZnS:Cu,In the indium is really incorporated in the ZnS. Thus, the two bulks are different, and
  I think that the correspondence of the emissions is merely an
  accident.

Cusano: This is a question on association and perhaps Williams
  or van Gool can answer it. We seem to be frequently stretch-
  ing experiments to prove whether or not we have a given type
  of association or any at all, and the question that comes up in
  my mind is, shouldn't we first find out what happens in the
  substitution of Group V acceptor-like materials such as
  phosphorus, arsenic, or antimony. Perhaps the new experimental findings here could throw light on some of the association ideas and test some of the theories. Very little has been
  done with these impurities by comparison to others. I further
  want to ask, whether in pursuing the finer aspects of association, are we really sure, for example, that indium substitutes
  only for zinc and does not substitute at all for sulphur? In
  other words, could't we imagine some of the species existing
  at different places or are we unambiguously going to have
  copper at zinc sites, aluminum at zinc sites, chlorine at
  sulphur sites, and arsenic at sulphur sites? Could we think,
  for example, of a copper at a zinc site but an indium at a
  sulfur site, and perhaps the two as another associated center
  to be taken into account in ZnS:Cu,In.

Williams: It seems to me that association on theoretical grounds
  alone is rather well established. It is rather fortunate that
  the experimental work is good enough to fit in with the theory.
  It is assumed in applying the theory that the Cu substitutes
  for Zn, Ga for Zn and Cl for S, and then obviously from
  elementary semiconductor theory copper is an acceptor and
  chlorine is a donor. This is plausible on rather simple
  grounds, and the fact that things work out, at least qualitatively, is perhaps the best support that this is the case. Now,
  as to the Group V elements, such as phosphorus, I think that

people who have done experimental work on this could comment better, but certainly, to the extent they do substitute for sulphur, they are clearly acceptors and there will be pairing with the compensating impurity or imperfection at adequate concentrations. One should see these same effects as are observed with the copper. Now, if one does not see these effects, one possible explanation would be that the substitution is not that simple.

Birks: I would just like to make one remark relevant to something Dr. Williams just said. It is a quotation by Leonardo da Vinci, which I do not think is sufficiently familiar to people who work in the field of science. The quotation goes as follows: "Experiments never deceive. It is our judgement that sometimes deceives itself, because it expects results that experiment refuses. We must consult experiment varying the circumstances until we have deduced reliable rules."

LUMINESCENCE IN ALUMINUM NITRIDE AND ALUMINUM OXIDE

I. Adams, Optech Inc., Chatham, N. J.

and

T. R. AuCoin, U. S. Army Signal Research and Development Laboratory
Fort Monmouth, New Jersey

Aluminum nitride may be prepared by the reaction of aluminum powder with nitrogen at 1000°C and 1000 psi pressure. When sufficient Al_2O_3 powder is mixed with aluminum powder, and the mixture is fired under the conditions given above, a spinel with the composition Al_3O_3N is formed.[1] AlN and Al_3O_3N emit a blue phosphorescence without further treatment when excited with 2537 Å Hg radiation. By doping with transition or rare earth elements, this phosphorescence can be changed in color, and electroluminescence is observed when Cl_2 is introduced into the doping atmosphere. In addition, Al_2O_3 can be made electroluminescent when treated in a similar manner.[2] Doping is achieved by firing a mixture of the powder with the proper activator at 600 to 800°C for 30 minutes in a Cl_2 atmosphere. When higher temperatures are required, the activator is mixed with the aluminum powder and this mixture is fired under the same conditions used to prepare the pure undoped product. A subsequent treatment at 600 to 800°C for 30 minutes in a Cl_2 atmosphere without additional activator produces electroluminescence.

An investigation of the fluorescence, phosphorescence and electroluminescence of these materials was made. As reported previously for AlN.[3] The electroluminescent spectra of Al_3O_3N and Al_2O_3 consists only of the first and second positive systems of N_2 when the pure material is subjected to the Cl_2 atmosphere with no activator added. When these powders are doped, however, additional light is emitted which is of higher intensity than the N_2 emission. Attempts to remove the N_2 emission by oil immersion or excitation in high vacuum quenched the electroluminescent emission as well.

The following types of emission are observed:

AlN

1. Red fluorescence, phosphorescence and electroluminescence is found in AlN samples doped with about 2 mole percent Mn at

high temperature. The spectra show a broad band in the 580–650 μ region with a maximum near 610 μ. The activator is probably Mn^{4+}.

2. Green electroluminescence is found in AlN samples doped with Mn at lower temperatures in the presence of Cl_2. No green fluorescence or phosphorescence is observed, and the electroluminescence appears in the 490–570 μ region with the maximum near 520 μ. The activator is probably Mn^{2+}.

3. Blue phosphorescence is seen in AlN powder to which no activator has been added, as well as samples to which Mn has been added at low temperatures. The phosphorescence is a broad band extending from about 350 μ to about 470 μ with a peak at about 430 μ. This phosphorescence is excited by 2537 Å Hg radiation.

Al_3O_3N

1. Red fluorescence and electroluminescence is found in Al_3O_3N doped with Cr. The activator is probably Cr^{3+}.

2. Green electroluminescence is found when Al_3O_3N is doped with Mn at low temperatures in a Cl_2 atmosphere. The activator is probably Mn^{2+}.

3. Blue phosphorescence is seen in pure Al_3O_3N or when it is doped with Cr or Mn at low temperatures.

Al_2O_3

1. Red fluorescence and electroluminescence is found in Al_2O_3 doped with Cr in a Cl_2 atmosphere. The activator is probably Cr^{3+}.

GENERAL OBSERVATIONS

1. All three materials show red electroluminescence when Eu is the activator.

2. The rate of impurity diffusion is substantially increased by the use of a halogen gas atmosphere.

3. Electroluminescence is observed only with transition and rare earth elements as activators, and consists essentially of the fluorescence spectra of these ions.

4. Electroluminescence is observed only when Cl_2 is present in the doping atmosphere. When the surface of the powder is changed in any way after doping, by oil immersion or high vacuum, there is a corresponding change in the electroluminescent intensity. While electroluminescence can be excited by an a.c. field by insulating the electrodes, the light intensity is highest when the electrodes are not insulated from the powder and when a d.c. field is used. In addition, electroluminescence is accompanied by an increase in current over that observed in non-electroluminescent materials.

A possible explanation of these observations is as follows: The Cl_2 gas is believed to create cation vacancies, which results in a more rapid diffusion of the foreign atoms into these materials. This gas also effects the surface of the powder in such a way that electron emission occurs under the influence of an electric field. Carrier injection is increased, and recombination at impurity centers produces fluorescence. Oil immersion or high vacuum, or anything which affects the absorbed Cl_2 surface layer will adversely affect the emission. The N_2 emission is not the source of the electroluminescence because most of these materials are only weakly fluorescent, and the intensity of the electroluminescence is independent of the N_2 intensity. It is possible that the electron emission is the source of the N_2 excitation.

REFERENCES

[1] I. Adams, T. R. AuCoin, and G. A. Wolff, Proc. Conf. Ultra-Purification of Semiconductor Materials, 1961. The Macmillan Co., to be published.
[2] I. Adams, T. R. AuCoin, and J. W. Mellichamp, J. Appl. Phys., to be published.
[3] G. A. Wolff, I. Adams, and J. W. Mellichamp, Phys. Rev. 114, 1262 (1959).

MOBILE AND IMMOBILE EXCITONS IN NaI*

W. J. Van Sciver

University of Puerto Rico and Puerto Rico Nuclear Center
Rio Piedras, Puerto Rico

The concept of the exciton, originally introduced by Frenkel to explain optical absorption phenomena which did not produce photoconductivity, was made more specific by von Hippel[1] in calculating the first maxima in the fundamental absorption spectra of some of the alkali halides. von Hippel's model assumed the transfer of an electron from a halide ion to a neighboring alkali ion. Recently Knox and Inchauspé[2] showed that an equally good model considers the ground and excited states of the halide ion perturbed by its neighbors. A third model, used by Wannier[3] takes into account the periodic potential of a polar crystal lattice and assumes an electron and hole bound together by electrostatic force in a hydrogen-like structure. Wannier's calculations yield exciton states at energy levels below that of the conduction band. It turns out that while the von Hippel model and the Knox-Inchauspé model result in rather good predictions of the first maxima in the alkali halide absorption spectra, the Wannier model does not.

We now turn to some interesting luminescence properties of purified (and unactivated) NaI at low temperatures. In the figure are shown the absorption spectrum and the excitation spectrum for a 4.2 ev emission band of high quantum efficiency (approaching unity at 77°K). We note that at energies of 5.5 ev and above the absorption and excitation spectra are very nearly the inverse of one another. See Fig. 1.

Some other characteristics, not apparent upon examining the figure are as follows:

a) The excitation band centered at 5.3 ev, while apparently weak, is in a spectral region of approximately 80% transparency. Thus it would be stronger in a thicker crystal. (The data were obtained from a crystal of 1 mm thickness.) Below −150°C

---

* Research supported by U.S. Atomic Energy Commission. For a full report of experimental procedures and results see: Phys. Rev. 120, 1193 (1960).

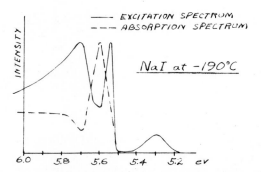

Fig. 1 — Absorption spectrum, dashed line, and the
excitation spectrum for 4.2 ev emission, solid line,
as observed in NaI single crystals at −190°C.

the strength of this band is temperature independent. It is believed to arise from an unknown impurity or defect of very low
density.

b) Quantum efficiency in the region of 5.5 ev to 8.0 ev (the
high energy limit of the experiments) is strongly dependent
upon temperature, rising approximately ten fold between the
temperatures −150°C and −190°C with the maximum at the
lower temperature.

c) With excitation at 5.5 ev the emission appeared to be
slightly strongest in a direction perpendicular to the axis of
illumination and to be maximized when the crystal was illuminated perpendicular to a cleaved face, in the (100) direction.
On the other hand, when excitation energy was 5.7 ev or higher
emission was found to be strongest with the crystal oriented at
45° to the incident illuminating beam, (110) direction. Furthermore, it was observed that as excitation energy was increased
toward 8 ev the emission increasingly preferred the foreward
direction, parallel to the axis of illumination.

d) At 5.3 ev, 5.55 ev, and 5.7 ev the quantum efficiency was
observed to be independent of incident flux density. However at
8 ev the quantum efficiency was found to increase with increasing flux density.

It would appear that the mechanism which accounts for the
fundamental absorption spectrum in NaI is not the same as that
which accounts for the low temperature luminescence spectrum.
It is reasonable to assume that the latter consists of a mobile
exciton of the Wannier type whereby energy is absorbed by the
bulk lattice within a few hundred angstroms of the crystal

surface, is conveyed a moderate distance to the 5.3 ev centers where relaxation and emission occurs. At incident photon energies above 6 or 7 ev it is probable that photoionization occurs, but this is promptly followed by some recombination of electrons and holes to form the mobile excitons. Such a re-combination would be of a bimolecular form and therefore sensitive to flux density, in agreement with d) above.

REFERENCES

[1] A. von Hippel, Z. Physik 101, 680 (1936).
[2] R. S. Knox and N. Inchauspé, Phys. Rev. 116, 1093 (1959).
[3] G. H. Wannier, Phys. Rev. 52, 191 (1937).

Gaulé: I did not quite understand your remark in which you said that the exciton does not hold together any more. The exciton is a bound state; if it is no longer a bound state, then it is no longer an exciton.

Van Sciver: What I mean by saying that it is not holding together is that the illumination by photons of the energy of about approaching 8 ev, which is some volts above the band gap, creates electron-hole pairs rather than excitons. The electron and hole degenerate to minimum energy because of collisions and, if the radiation is sufficiently intense, associate to form excitons.

Gaulé: Now I think that I understand your remark. Did you first form free pairs if the energy is high enough, and they, rather than staying in the two bands, go together and form excitons? And this also requires high intensity of radiation because you must have high numbers so that the partners can find one another.

Van Sciver: Yes, that is right. I think you answered your own question.

Birks: I wish to ask Dr. Van Sciver whether he feels that these very interesting phenomena, this dependence on light flux at higher energies of the quantum efficiency, may be related to the scintillation behavior of these materials, in particular, to the way in which the behavior both with regard to the time components and the efficiency depends on the ionization density produced by the particle. Such a variation in ionization density might provide the equivalent of these increased light fluxes.

Van Sciver: That actually is where this whole investigation started, with an investigation of scintillation phenomena. I think that the same kind of model or concept is applicable in studying the behavior of scintillation phenomena in the alkali halides. I would like to talk to you later about the possible connection with the organics, but I think that this is an applicable concept for understanding sodium iodide phenomena in scintillation.

SOME QUESTIONS ON INORGANIC SCINTILLATORS

J. B. Birks

The University, Manchester

Having an audience of people who are experts in the field of inorganic phosphors, I wish to pose some questions relevant to the scintillation behavior of inorganic materials.

The inorganic phosphors which are used as scintillators fall into the two catagories of materials we have been mainly discussing this afternoon, ZnS activated with Cu or Ag, and sodium iodide activated usually with thallium. The properties which are important for their use as scintillators are as follows: firstly, the scintillation efficiency of conversion of the ionizing radiation energy into luminescence; secondly, the decay time of this luminescence with the possible presence of any slow components in the decay time, which may depend on the nature of the ionizing radiation; and thirdly the scintillation response to the different types of radiation, the fact that the scintillation efficiency may also depend on the nature of the particle.

ZnS is the most efficient of the scintillator materials and, therefore, it would be the ideal material which we would like to use for many purposes in nuclear physics. One restriction on the use of this material is the fact that there are no large crystals available. Hence my first question is, why can't we have large ZnS crystals? Secondly, if we obtained such crystals, would there be a large overlap between the emission and the absorption spectra? We already know of some crystals that are not suitable for use as large scintillators, because of their self absorption. Is there a similar overlap of emission and absorption spectra in ZnS?

A further point about ZnS is that it has a scintillation decay with a tail on it, that is, a long-lived component. ZnS has been improved by the addition of nickel to the material, which apparently quenches the tail emission. I should be interested if anybody could tell me why. The Ni quenching of ZnS (this is not quenching of the main emission but quenching of the slow component only) is an empirical result, but it has resulted in a more useful material for scintillation purposes.

If we now move on to consider sodium iodide, sodium iodide can be used as an efficient scintillator at low temperatures in the pure state, as Dr. Van Sciver has shown. On the other hand, this is rather inconvenient. In the majority of applications people prefer to use the scintillator at room temperature. The material which is almost invariably used as the activator in sodium iodide is thallium, and I would like to know why thallium is chosen for this particular purpose. One answer is the fact that the emission spectrum of sodium iodide activated with thallium happens to fit rather nicely the spectral response (S11) of the glass-windowed photomultipliers that nearly everybody uses. It has been recently* shown, however, that if you don't restrict yourself to a glass-windowed photomultiplier, but use instead a quartz-windowed photomultiplier, the photo-electric quantum efficiency of this tube is practically constant from a wavelength of about 450 mμ down to at least 300 mμ. Therefore, if there are any alternative activators with an emission in this spectral region, which will give us adequate scintillation efficiency and, preferably, a shorter decay time than thallium, there is no reason technically why one should not use them. My question is whether thallium is the only activator for sodium iodide which will provide suitable scintillation properties.

The final question is this. The reason why inorganic scintillators are not used for a number of purposes is because the decay time is in the region of 10^{-6} sec, while those who attended the organic session will have heard us talking in terms of nanoseconds, that is 10^{-9} to 10^{-8} sec. I would like to know why it is that the decay times in inorganic scintillators are a factor of 100 or more longer than they are in organic scintillators. Has this to do with the nature of transition processes? Can the theorists give an answer as to why the decay time of the emission is so much longer than in organic scintillators? If we could have the decay time shorter or if we could have any other such improvements, then we should have a new regime of inorganic scintillators. Since so much work has been going on on the inorganic phosphors, I should be interested if anybody could suggest even partial answers to any of these questions.

---

*Birks and Munro, Brit. J. App. Phys., 12, 519 (1961).

<u>Brandt</u>: I should like to retort to Dr. Birks and ask, why there are no
organic scintillators with lifetimes shorter than nanoseconds,
because in coincidence work limitations are in the scintillator and no longer in the electronics. There are coincidence
phenomena which are shorter than 10^{-10} sec one would like
to measure.

<u>Williams</u>: I would like to point out that the answers to some of
Dr. Birks' questions are available in the recent literature.
For example, on the problem of other activators in the alkali
halides for scintillators there has been a tremendous amount
of work done by the Esthonian group at Tartu, and the annual
reports from there are available. They have put in indium,
lead, gallium, all the elements that as ions have the same
type of energy levels as thallium, and their absorption and
emission spectra are available. In the forthcoming edition
of the American Institute of Physics Handbook these data
are tabulated. On the question of ZnS crystals, both Reynolds
at the Wright Aeronautical Laboratory and Piper at General
Electric have published techniques for growing single crystals of ZnS which are centimeters in dimensions.

<u>Brandt</u>: The last part of the session has been reserved for
free discussion of all the problems, or some of the problems,
that have been left open in the course of the sessions during
the week. Dr. Williams kindly agreed to start up with a
summary of the problems that might have emerged and the
problems we might be working on in the future.

SOME OPEN PROBLEMS
F. Williams
Physics Dept., University of Delaware
Newark, Delaware

This is, as you gathered from the introduction, a solicited
presentation. What I gather I am supposed to do or what, at
least, I plan to do is to talk about some of the more basic prob-

lems that to me seem to remain still unsolved. I will talk a
little bit about alkali halides. I was pleased to see that this
did get into the session already. Then, I will talk a little bit
on ZnS and perhaps on other inorganic materials.

One might get the impression from the tremendous amount
of published works on the alkali halides, particularly on the
thallium activated potassium chloride, that all the problems on
that material have been solved. We may have felt this several
years ago, but we do not feel this way now, even though there
has been progress in the last few years on this subject. In
particular, the matter of the 4750 emission band of thallium in
the alkali halides still remains unsolved. That is, it is not even
settled for certain as to whether that emission arises from the
same center as the 3050 emission, which is pretty unambiguously attributed to isolated thalliums at potassium sites. If the
4750 emission arises from the same center, it is not clear
what modifications have to be made in the theory, for example,
whether the Jahn-Teller effect will be sufficient to account for
that emission band; in particular, what changes in the nuclear
coordinates are required or actually occur leading to that
emission band. Thus, a serious piece of theoretical work
probably coupled with some good experimental work, is needed
to identify the 4750 emission. In the alkali halides, the problem
of the trapping states is not well understood. At one time it was
felt that these could be attributed to the $^3P_0^0$ and the $^3P_2^0$ states
of the Tl^+. The very long lifetimes at low temperatures of these
states suggest that this is probably not the case, that there
actually may be energy transfer involved and that other imperfections in the crystal are responsible for these trapping
states. On this subject one should couple to the tremendous
progress that has been made in recent years on the native
imperfections in the alkali halides, things like H-centers and
F-centers. Still on the alkali halides, another interesting unsolved problem is the high efficiency of the iodides compared
to other halides when excited with nuclear particles. It is my
understanding that the iodides, sodium iodide in particular, are
considerably more efficient as scintillation materials than any
of the other halides activated with thallium or anything else.
Here we have a problem of energy transfer, and why this is so
good for the iodides is a very good question, and a complete
theory of the luminescence of these materials ought to answer
this question.

Let me turn now to the zinc sulfide. It is reassuring on the
zinc sulfides to see the fields of photoconductivity, semi-con-
ductivity and luminescence all merging and merging with mutual
benefits as to the understanding of each of these phenomena.
There is a great deal left to be done on the problems connected
with associated donor-acceptor pairs. One might have gotten
the impression from the way some of the material was presented earlier that here all the basic problems have been
solved, and I want to emphasize that this is not the case. In
particular on the energy level structure of these pairs, in fact,
on the energy structures of separated donors and acceptors in
zinc sulfide, there is a problem as to how one takes account of
the large central cell correction, for the acceptor, in particular. Most of what has been done so far has been in the effective
mass approximation, and this gives states for donors and acceptors of the order of a couple of tenths of a volt from the
respective band edges. Now, we know that copper is of the
order of a volt above the valence band. So clearly, there is a
tremendous central cell correction. Dr. Birman has reported
on some very nice work within the past year using a quite
different approach, using a tight binding approach for the copper
levels in ZnS. It is my feeling that neither approach is the
whole story. In the region of the central cell one must do a
crystal field type calculation, while at larger distances from
the impurity one must do an effective mass type calculation.
The problem of matching these two solutions is not a trivial
one. The matter of the transition probabilities for these dia-
tomic impurity systems is a real problem. One feels intuitively
that the transition probability depends on the overlap of the
donor electron wave function with the acceptor hole wave function. These are envelope functions, and the problem must be
examined rigorously and it must be done including the effect
of the central cell correction. The problem of identifying the
precise pairs responsible for each emission band is a real
problem, that is we speak loosely of the fourth to the sixth
nearest neighbor pairs as being responsible for the long wavelength emission. What is needed is very ingenious experimental
work, that I do not myself see how to do, in which one prepares
crystals having only donor-acceptor pairs of a specific interimpurity spacing; for example, with the vapor deposition
processes just lay down pure ZnS and then put down a monolayer
of a dilute concentration of donors and acceptors in pure ZnS,

and then, at least in one dimension, one will have a definite donor-acceptor pair distribution. I leave it to the full-time experimentalists to figure out how to do this in three dimensions.

On electroluminescence in general, I have been reassured in recent years to see so much fine work done on single crystals, and we must do more of this. We must do this fine work that Dr. Kallmann reported with stored electroluminescence on single crystals. And then, we will perhaps be able to unravel the details of that phenomenon, at least as completely as the early work on single crystal electroluminescence contributed to the general understanding of electroluminescence.

We have today not talked at all about a number of other materials and activators that seem to me remain problems, for instance, tetravalent manganese. There has been work in recent years by a number of people applying crystal field theory to explain the origin of the multiplet structure of the emission of this material. Now, I do not want to go into detail, but there are features of that work that need modification and extension. In particular, there is a basic question which is as follows. Tetravalent manganese is iso-electronic with trivalent chromium, and trivalent chromium in aluminum oxide has sharp lines that are so important for lasers. Why is it that tetravalent manganese does not have these sharp lines, but has this multiplet band structure?

These are some of the problems that should be looked at more seriously.

TRANSITION MODELS FOR ZnS TYPE PHOSPHORS

B. Kramer*

Physics Department, New York University

I wanted to return to an issue that was discussed widely several years ago, but has not come up in the discussions at this meeting, that is, a comparison of the Schön-Klasens model and the Lambe-Klick model. All the people who have reported at this meeting seem to have limited their remarks to the Schön-Klasens model. Now, some of the results that we obtained indicate quite clearly that the very simple relation which one obtains from the Schön-Klasens model relating light to free electrons and ionized activators, $L = \beta n p_t$, does not seem to be correct, if one investigates the light, conductivity, and trapped electrons separately. Because of charge neutrality the number of ionized activators p_t will be equal to the number of electrons in traps n_t as long as the conduction electron density n and the hole density p are low. We can do separate experiments on n, n_t and L, and we find that this relationship does not hold. Of course, one way out is to change the β, and this is one of the proposals that have been made. We can say, however, that perhaps we ought to go to a different model, and the other model that can be considered is the Lambe-Klick model.

Let me briefly point out what they stated. They assumed that, if you have band to band excitation, you create a positive hole and a free electron. The free electron drops to an impurity state somewhat below the conduction band, and then the light recombination is essentially the transition between this trapped electron and a free hole. Remember, with the Schön-Klasens model, if you have band to band excitation, the hole would first have to be trapped at an activator level, and then the transition between a free electron and a trapped hole would give light. What happens if you excite with longer wavelength than the band to band edge in the Schön-Klasens model? There is no difficulty, since there are electron levels somewhat above

---

*Also at Physics Department, Hunter College, New York.

the valence band, and with long wavelength excitation you can excite them to the conduction band and get conductivity and luminescence. What happens with the Lambe-Klick model under such conditions? Well, we went back to the original Lambe-Klick paper, and for long wavelength excitation they also assume activator levels somewhat above the valence band. Thus, if we go to long wavelength excitation in the Lambe-Klick model, there we again free an electron by ionizing an activator but now the question is: how does the hole travel from the ionized activator into the valence band so that light emission occurs? At room temperatures this may be possible. In other words, at room temperatures there may be enough energy for the hole to be liberated from the positive activator and to go into the valence band. But what happens at very low temperatures? At very low temperatures the excitation can get the electron into the conduction band, but how does the hole travel from the positive activator into the valence band? We know from all experimental results that the light emission does not drop drastically as the temperature is reduced. I was wondering if anybody has some comments on this model.

Broser: First I would like to make a remark on the names 'Schön-Klasens' and 'Lambe-Klick' model. If you think about it, Schön did take into account recombination from traps to the valence band which could occur with radiation. I really feel that both possibilities exist, and the only way to find out the difference between the two models is to see whether you create free holes or free electrons and what is the connection between the photoconductivity (p or n type) and the transition associated with these models.

I have another comment. There are lots of transitions known for ZnS where two levels are involved. Take, for instance, the model of Dr. Williams, where you can have a transition without any photoconductivity. It is not the Schön-Klasens model and not the Lambe-Klick model. It is really difficult to say whether there is a great deal of difference between the two models.

Brandt: This illustrates that one should not fall into the trap of mistaking models for theories.

van Gool: I should like to make some general comments on these two models. I think we have to state very clearly what materials we are dealing with. In the case of CdS activated with Cu and CdS activated with Ag, it has really been proved —and I think this is one of the few things that has been proved in the fluorescence of ZnS—that copper and silver behave as acceptors. When gallium is introduced, CdS can become n-conducting and, when an equal amount of copper and silver are added, it becomes an insulator. In that case there is no question about the position of Cu and Ag. Now the position of Cu and Ag in CdS is related to the position of Cu and Ag in ZnS, as can be seen by following the fluorescence and other properties in a series of mixed crystals (Zn,Cd)S. So, in that case, it is my feeling that there are no difficulties, and Cu and Ag in ZnS will behave acceptor-like also.

Now to the work of Lambe and Klick. Lambe has worked with CdS crystals containing only silver. In the case where the activator concentration is larger than the coactivator concentration other possibilities exist, for instance, the blue copper emission. From this emission it has been said in connection with the work of Prof. Riehl that there is some other center, which may be an associated center and which may have two levels. Thus, it is quite possible that the blue copper emission and the corresponding emission in the case of silver behave as has been described by Lambe or behave in the manner of Williams' associate model. Therefore, I think it is necessary to indicate exactly which materials we have in mind, what fluorescence is being studied and whether the things that are measured are really related to each other. Therefore, I do not believe that the Schön-Klasens and the Lambe-Klick model are opposite. They only occur in different situations.

Williams: I am essentially in agreement with Dr. Broser and Dr. van Gool and want to point out that one can expect in different systems just about all the cases that have been considered. That is, if one looks at cadmium sulfide, the acceptors are deep and the donors are shallow. Therefore, a transition which is expected is an electron transition from the conduction band edge to the acceptor, and this is in accord with Schön-Klasens. On the other hand, if one looks at zinc telluride, which has about the same band gap as cadmium sulfide but which has deep donors and shallow acceptors, then a transition which is expected is a hole transition from the valence band edge to the donor, and this is in accord with Lambe-Klick. In general, the recombination process is essentially the annihilation of a hole by an electron. In the first case it is a bound hole by a free electron; in the second case it is a bound electron by a free hole. In the cases in which the donor and acceptor energies are the same magnitude, and in addition if there is sufficient concentration of donor and acceptor so that the donors and acceptors associate into pairs, then neither model is a complete description. What we do have is an annihilation process between a bound hole and a bound electron. In general, I feel that the controversy that raged a few years ago between the Schön-Klasens and the Lambe-Klick models has appropriately largely disappeared. In accord with what Dr. Broser and Dr. van Gool said we can expect suitable systems to show the characteristics of each and, in addition, we can expect other types of radiative annihilation processes to occur.

Kramer: May I make just a short remark. Dr. van Gool stated that in ZnS with Cu and Ag there does not seem to be any question but that the activator level lies somewhat above the valence band. Then he pointed out that from the mixtures between zinc and cadmium sulfide there seems to be a steady transition in all these developments. Therefore, we would certainly expect the silver activated CdS to behave according to what we would call the Schön-Klasens model, which is directly opposite to the Lambe-Klick model.

I would also like to ask Dr. Williams how he knows that in the zinc telluride material this is the transition that occurs.

Wachtel: I think some clue as to what type of transition we are dealing with can be obtained by the behavior of the phosphor when it is excited by UV and IR at the same time. We have prepared some copper red emitting phosphors containing a trace of oxygen or halides that show both the copper red and some green emission. It was found that if, while exciting with UV one also irradiates with IR, the green is quenched and the red is enhanced. This seems to indicate that the green emission is a Schön-Klasens transition and the red may be a Lambe-Klick transition because, if the acceptor centers are being kept filled by the IR, the probability of the red emission occurring will be enhanced. The same thing also occurs during electroluminescence.

Kramer: That is certainly one possible interpretation, but that could also be interpreted in terms of our previous model by saying that the IR has shifted the positive activators from the green centers to the red centers. That might be a simpler explanation.

van Gool: May I first answer your remark about the relation of fluorescence in ZnS and CdS. What we have in ZnS is the blue emission with the peak position at about 4400 Å, and when a continuous transition to CdS is made this emission comes at about 7300 Å. That is an IR emission and it corresponds to the blue emission. However, Lambe has investigated an emission at 6300 Å, and that is an emission which corresponds to an emission in ZnS at about 3900 Å. Both emissions behave in a manner quite similar to the blue copper emission. Thus, when you are speaking about the blue copper emission in ZnS and the emission investigated by Lambe in CdS, you have two different emissions corresponding to different types of centers.

Williams: The following concerns the question on the transitions in zinc telluride. The zinc telluride is p-type; I do not believe that it has been made in an n-type form. This is in contrast to the CdS in which electron conduction is observed. This does not prove, but it does strongly suggest that the transitions are as I indicated. The examples were cited for pedagogical reasons: to illustrate that examples of Schön-Klasens, Lambe-Klick, and associated pair transitions can all be expected in materials with suitable energy levels.

Van Sciver: This is an addition to the list of things that need to be investigated to be appended to Prof. Williams' list. That is the band gap in the alkali halides, and the question of why we do not get photoconductivity in the alkali halides. There was a long investigation by Taylor and Hartman.[1] They published a paper in 1959 which was completely negative with respect to photoconductivity in alkali halides.

---

[1] J. W. Taylor and P. L. Hartman, Phys. Rev. 113, 1421 (1959).

Gaulé: You said that photoconductivity is not observed in alkali
halides. Is this up to very high frequencies or is this only for
dc measurements?

Van Sciver: Frankly, I am not aware that anyone has attempted
the Kallmann type of ac measurement with alkali halides.
Whether that might yield positive results I do not know. I
think that the other work done was all dc. Of course, one of
the difficulties is that the energy is generally high enough that
everything is photoelectric. What do you think, Dr. Kallmann?

Kallmann: I remember a paper by MacDonald in 1958 or 59.
He studied with an ac method the photoconductivity of alkali
halides with insulating layers, mylar I think. It was a relatively small effect, but it had been measured.

Brandt: It would seem to me that one of the things one might
add to this list is the rate dependence of these phenomena.
If one departs from a more or less simple energy level discussion that involves spatial parameters, then the decay behavior should give an indication of the importance of inhomo-
geneities in space.

Broser: I have another problem which might be added to Dr.
Williams' list. If you think about the zinc cadmium sulfides,
you mostly deal with copper. I feel that copper is really a
special activator system. I gives anti-stokes luminescence,
it gives IR emission, which silver does not, and with regard
to electroluminescence copper takes a special place. I am
really not so sure why copper has this special place. Perhaps
I'll get an answer now.

A COMPARISON OF ORGANIC AND INORGANIC PHOSPHORS

H. Kallmann

Physics Department, New York University

Now I am on the spot. I have always spoken about the important correlations between organic and inorganic phosphors and now the time has come when I finally have to describe the strong correlations which exist between these two fields of luminescence research. I feel a little bit like a man who has two very good friends, but these two friends don't talk to one another. I am here to reveal to them and to you their close relationship.

Three different aspects of fluorescence may be discussed: the various states which are excited and emit, the way these states can be excited, and the charge transfer which takes place in organic and inorganic fluorescent materials.

EXCITED STATES

Four types of excited states should be considered
a) exciton states
b) states in the bulk material, belonging to the bulk material which are, however, not actual exciton states, but can be better described as states of single molecules or atoms
c) energy states of impurities
d) states which have highly forbidden transitions.

All of these types of states occur in inorganic as well as organic systems. Let me start with the exciton state. You have just heard from Dr. Van Sciver a description of exciton states in alkali halides. Dr. Sponer spoke about exciton states in naphthalene where certainly such states are observed at liquid helium temperature. In other discussions also, exciton states in organic materials were mentioned. But there are, of course, some differences; the binding forces in organic materials between nearest neighbors are much smaller than those in inorganic materials, as is the energy exchange between an excited atom or molecule and its neighbor. Because these exchanges

657

are small they are more easily disturbed by thermal motion, and, therefore, exciton states in organic materials are detected only at very low temperatures. Another way to state this is that the scattering length of an exciton wave is shorter in organics. Recall that at room temperatures the excited states appear as those of isolated molecules: the well known fluorescence spectrum of solid anthracene is rather similar to the spectrum of the isolated anthracene molecule. But it was reported that in organic crystals, not only in solutions, excited dimers are observed even at room temperature. These may be looked upon as a first step in the formation of excitons in organic crystals at room temperature.

Another consequence of the smaller interaction in organic materials is probably that fluorescence from the bulk material occurs at room temperature much more often than in inorganic materials because quenching is reduced. Only in certain tungstates does one observe an emission from the bulk material at room temperature, which is attributed to the WO_4^{++} ion, strongly distorted by the surrounding atoms, however. You will see a further correlation between the tungstates and organic materials when we look at the way energy is transferred in these systems.

Let us now consider impurities. They occur in organic as well as in inorganic materials, but one finds that they are much more distorted in the latter because of the strong crystalline field to which they are exposed. If one incorporates an organic impurity into an organic host, the impurity states are almost those of the impurity in the vapor phase. Thallium or silver activators in alkali halides or manganese in many host materials are very strongly distorted. These activators are, of course, not atoms, but ions, because atoms would not easily enter the bulk material. That there is also some distortion in organic systems was shown by Dr. Förster, who described certain fluorescent spectra in solutions which were influenced by the solvent.

The correlation can be carried still further, if one looks at forbidden states and their transition probabilities to the ground state. The manganese transition, being a sextet quartet transition, is rather highly forbidden and in the organic field the singlet-triplet state transitions, for example, also are highly forbidden. Both types of states and transitions can be influenced by the surroundings. The triplet state-ground state transition can be made more probable by introducing iodine, for instance, into the organic system. Then the absorption to the triplet state

becomes measurable, and the reverse transition to the ground
state is also enhanced. The same is true in the inorganic field for
the manganese ion, for which the transition probability from the
excited state to the ground state is strongly influenced by the surroundings, as can be seen from the fact that the lifetime of the excited manganese changes tremendously with the surroundings.[1]

There are many more such analogies, if one only keeps in
mind that the forces and their magnitudes are different in organic and inorganic systems.

EXCITATION

The correlations between inorganic and organic phosphors
become still more obvious if one looks at the way their states
are excited. There is direct excitation; this, of course, is
identical in both cases. Or, one can excite a specific state by
energy transfer from another state. This other state is directly
excited, (it may belong to the bulk material or to another impurity) and then from this excited state energy is transferred
to the state in question in three ways; either by radiation, or by
energy exchange transfer over several atomic distances
(Förster mechanism), or by migration of energy terminating in a
transfer when it comes close enough. The excitation of a state
by energy transfer is very important in those cases where the
state cannot be readily reached from the ground state, either
because this transition is highly forbidden or because the concentration of the species having this state is so small that direct
excitation, particularly by high energy, is unlikely, and absorption overwhelmingly takes place in the surroundings. It is observed in organic materials as well as in inorganic materials.

Energy transfer by radiation occurs in organic solutions and
in mixed crystals when the bulk molecule emits light and the
solute absorbs this light, or in solutions which contain two
solutes, one of which absorbs the light emitted by the other. In
inorganic systems it occurs when the phosphor contains two activators. The far more interesting cases, however, are those
where radiative transfer cannot occur, either because the primary
excited system does not emit light because of the high probability
of non-radiative transitions or because the second system absorbs
the light emitted by the first system only weakly. Then the
two other types of energy transfer occur. This situation is
exactly the same for inorganic as for organic systems. A very
good case is that which Dr. Shionoya presented, where one has

lead activated ZnS, and the lead is excited by light and its energy is transferred to the second activator, in his case manganese, which cannot be excited directly because of its small absorption. In the tungstates one often has two activators, lead and samarium. From the activator which absorbs light, energy is transferred by exchange to the non-absorbing one. Similar processes go on in organic systems, when energy is transferred to a triplet state of an impurity; one absorbs in the singlet state which has strong absorption, and then energy is transferred to the triplet state of the same molecule and from there to the triplet state of a neighboring molecule, e.g., benzophenone-naphthalene,[2] in which energy is transferred by exchange to the triplet state of the naphthalene. There are many other examples of this type of energy transfer both for organic and inorganic systems. It only occurs when the interacting systems are not too far from each other, not more than a few atomic distances.

If the interacting systems are not very close together, then another mechanism may set in, namely that of energy migration in the bulk material. The excitation energy migrates through the bulk until it comes close enough to an accepting molecule for transfer. Again, these migration processes occur in organic as well as in inorganic systems. In organic systems when the bulk materials are excited by high energy radiation, these processes are responsible for the excitation of the fluorescence of solute molecules in liquid and plastic solutions, as well as in mixed crystals. Similar migration occurs in the tungstates under bulk excitation, probably of the tungstate ion. Energy migrates through the bulk material to an impurity, for instance manganese.

But the analogy between organic and inorganic materials is still closer. If one excites organic materials with α-particles of 5 mev, a strong decrease in fluorescence efficiency is noted compared to that obtained under excitation with electrons of the same energy. The reason for this decrease is that a mutual quenching of excited molecules takes place due to the migration process and due to the strong density of excited molecules.[3] The same type of quenching, by a factor of about five, occurs in tungstates, in which, as was described above, migration also occurs.

CHARGE TRANSPORT

The last mechanism of excitation we want to consider is that by charge transport. Here the situation is quite different. This mode of excitation is very important in the inorganic field, especially in ZnCdS, but it seemed to be relatively unimportant or non existent in the organic field. This is not quite true. In inorganic phosphors of the ZnCdS type one has activators and, when the bulk material is excited, free electrons and holes are created which move through the system independently until they are trapped. This trapping may occur in special trapping levels, but eventually the positive charges reach the activator and charges it more positively. Finally the electrons may recombine with the positively charged activator, and in this way the energy absorbed in the bulk is transferred to the activator. One has found recently that a very similar energy transfer by charge transport takes place in certain organic systems, for instance, in the system durene-naphthalene, with durene as the bulk material. When durene is excited by high energy radiation the triplet state of naphthalene is strongly excited, much more strongly than when the durene is excited by light in its lower excitation bands. The explanation is the following. Under high energy excitation, not only excitation, but ionization as well, is produced; thus a positive hole and an electron in a high lying conduction band are created. Now, just as in ZnS the positive hole moves through the durene and is eventually trapped in the naphthalene, and will remain thus because the latter has a considerably smaller ionization energy than durene. The electron, which is still in the conduction band or in shallow traps, will finally recombine with the positive hole which is trapped in the naphthalene. This recombination will lead to a strongly increased phosphorescence from the lowest tripet state of naphthalene, since the recombination of an electron and a positive hole will partially end in the lowest triplet state of the molecule. With light excitation of the bulk material, energy also will reach the triplet state of the solute but only by energy migration, and this is apparently not as effective a process as ionization. The strong enhancement of triplet state phosphorescence by high energy excitation is not only observed in the durene-naphthalene system, but in other similar systems, too.[4] This is a strong indication that energy is transferred by charge transport in organic materials.

That charge transport, particularly that of positive holes, takes place readily in certain organic materials is also evidenced by the large photoconductivity observed in some organics. In anthracene, for example, which is something like a test substance in the field of organic photoconductivity, positive holes are injected from the electrode into the crystal under the influence of light and move under the influence of an electric field, jumping from one anthracene molecule to a neighboring one. If one incorporates molecules with a smaller ionization energy into the anthracene, the photoconductivity should be reduced, because the holes should be trapped by the molecules of smaller ionization energy. This has, indeed, been found by Northrup and Simpson.[5] It is in complete analogy to the ZnCdS system, where Ag or Cu activators trap the positive holes and reduce their mobility considerably. There is again an important difference which comes from the energy situation. In the case of the organics, the conducting electron states lie energetically rather high, whereas in the inorganics they are rather low in energy.

This analogy between organic and inorganic materials with respect to charge transport goes still further. I will give you just one example concerning the photovoltaic effect. If one has an anthracene crystal with a suitable electrode--a suitable electrode is important--and if one excites the anthracene crystal by light which is strongly absorbed in a thin layer adjacent to the electrode, then excitons move toward the electrode and produce hole injection from the electrode into the anthracene, as Dr. Pope has described.[6] As a consequence of this, just by illuminating the crystal a voltage is built up, in which the crystal is positively charged because of the positive hole injection. If one takes instead a CdS layer with a cuprous oxide electrode and if one excites the CdS layer strongly by light in a thin layer adjacent to this electrode, again charges are injected into the layer, but this time electrons instead of positive holes, and a negative photovoltage develops since this time the electron moves from the copper layer into the interior.

If one considers the various processes and states I have mentioned, one certainly comes to the conclusion that the same types of states and processes occur in organic as well as in inorganic phosphors. The main difference is that the forces, and thus the location of the energy levels, are quite different in both cases, and thus the quantitative results vary, of course, in these materials.

REFERENCES:

[1] H. W. Leverenz, Colloques Internationaux du Centre National de la Recherche Scientifique LXXII, 4 (1956).

[2] A. H. Terenin and V. L. Ermolaev, Trans. Faraday Soc. 52, 1042 (1956); V. L. Ermolaev and A. H. Terenin, J. Chim. Physique 55, 698 (1958); V. L. Ermolaev, Optics and Spectroscopy, 6, 417 (1959).

[3] M. Furst and H. Kallmann, Phys. Rev. 91, 766 (1953).

[4] A. Adelman and H. Kallman, to be published.

[5] D. C. Northrup and O. Simpson, Proc. Roy. Soc. Lond. A244, 277 (1958).

[6] H. Kallmann and M. Pope, J. Chem. Phys. 30, 585 (1959).

Shionoya: May I add one more example which I believe to be the best system which correlates the luminescence of organic and inorganic materials. In the paper of Prof. Makishima the luminescence of alkali nitrite was discussed. Alkali nitrite is no doubt inorganic, but the transition which is responsible for the blue luminescence of nitrite is an $n \to \pi$ transition and nitrite is the simplest π electron system. Luminescence in organic materials is mostly due to a π electron system. One thing nitrite has is the following: the luminescence emission of nitrite is composed of very sharp lines, and we can know that the frequency of vibration associated with nitrite luminescence is a bending vibration frequency of the nitrite ion. Therefore, if we imbed some nitrite in an organic and in an inorganic material and if we look at how the structure of the emission is changed, then we believe that we can gain some useful information on the influence of the surroundings on the system of π-electrons.

Birks: I wish to mention that there is one rather special kind of electroluminescence known in organic systems; that is, if you allow a liquid organic system as belonging within the class. It has been reported in recent work done at Queen Mary College in London that in high electric fields below breakdown in liquid scintillators one observes fluorescence emission which is characteristic of the solute. This work has been done quantitatively, and what is being observed is an emission which is stimulated by pre-breakdown currents.

Riehl: Let me say a few words. Dr. Kallmann has already
emphasized that the unification of organic and inorganic
solid state physics is a very important thing. It is certainly
necessary to make an attempt in this direction. I believe
the attempt we have made in this direction in the last few
days was not completely unsuccessful because I have observed that while the organic people were sitting here the
inorganic people were sitting in cafeterias not very far
from here.

Now the question arises as to the best method of such a
unification. I was very impressed when Dr. Halperin said
that the investigation of diamond is the best way, since the
diamond belongs to both the organic and the inorganic fields.
I believe that it is an excellent method, especially since it
would be a very good method of getting cheaper diamonds for
our wives. On the other hand, I am not quite sure if this
method is the best one.

My wife is not present; therefore I can tell you my true
opinion. And my true opinion is this. The best method for
such a unification is the method of enthusiasm for science,
love for science. Yes, I speak of you, Dr. Kallmann, and of
your coworkers.

All I have to do now is to express our deep thanks to you,
Dr. Kallmann, to you, Dr. Spruch, and to all your coworkers
for all your trouble and for this very successful and very
enjoyable conference. Thank you very much.

Kallmann: Now I have to thank you for coming here and having
spent such a long week discussing these problems of organic
and inorganic luminescence. If you go home with some new
information, with some new inspiration, some new connections
and friendships, then I am very satisfied and this would be the
best that could happen to me. Thank you all very much.